CREATIVE ARTS THERAPIES MANUAL

ABOUT THE EDITOR

Stephanie L. Brooke, Ph.D., NCC, teaches sociology and psychology online at the University of Phoenix. Dr. Brooke has written three books on art therapy and continues to write and publish in her field. Additionally, she serves as the Vice Chairperson for ARIA (Awareness of Rape and Incest through Art). For more information about Dr. Brooke, workshop information, publications, and presentations at professional conferences, please visit her web site: http://stephanielbrooke.com

CREATIVE ARTS THERAPIES MANUAL

A Guide to the History, Theoretical Approaches,
Assessment, and Work with Special Populations
of Art, Play, Dance, Music, Drama,
and Poetry Therapies

Edited by

STEPHANIE L. BROOKE, Ph.D., NCC

CHARLES C THOMAS • PUBLISHER, LTD.
Springfield • Illinois • U.S.A.

Published and Distributed Throughout the World by

CHARLES C THOMAS • PUBLISHER, LTD.
2600 South First Street
Springfield, Illinois 62704

© 2006 by CHARLES C THOMAS • PUBLISHER, LTD.

ISBN 0-398-07620-0 (hard)
ISBN 0-398-07621-9 (paper)

Library of Congress Catalog Card Number: 2005052930

With THOMAS BOOKS *careful attention is given to all details of manufacturing
and design. It is the Publisher's desire to present books that are satisfactory as to their
physical qualities and artistic possibilities and appropriate for their particular use.*
THOMAS BOOKS *will be true to those laws of quality that assure a good name
and good will.*

Printed in the United States of America
JW-R-3

Library of Congress Cataloging-in-Publication Data

Creative arts therapies manual : a guide to the history, theoretical approaches,
assessment, and work with special populations of art, play, dance, music, dramas,
and poetry therapies / edited by Stephanie L. Brooke.
     p. cm.
  Includes bibliographical references.
  ISBN 0-398-07620-0 (hbk.) — ISBN 0-398-07621-9 (pbk.)
    1. Arts—Therapeutic use. 2. Creation (Literary, artistic, etc.)—
Therapeutic use. I. Brooke, Stephanie L.

RC489.A72C76   2006
616.89'1656—dc22
                                 2005052930

PREFACE

In any given period of history, a culture is to be judged by its dominant philosophy, by the prevalent trend of its intellectual life as expressed in morality, in politics, in economics, in art. Professional intellectuals are the voice of a culture and are, therefore, its leaders, its integrators and its bodyguards. (From *For the New Intellectual* by Ayn Rand, 1961)

In 1993, I became a Nationally Certified Counselor and opened a private practice in Raleigh, North Carolina. I developed an art-based group for survivors of sexual abuse as part of my master's thesis (Brooke, 1996a). In this study, art activities significantly increased the self-esteem scores of a group of adult, female, sexual abuse survivors. In my practice, I began to use art as a means of expression. I found this worked well for my clients, even the ones who were adamant that they could not draw.

My passion for using this type of approach was fueled by attending the seminars of Harriet Wadeson. She did the foreword to the first edition of *Tools of the Trade* (Brooke, 1996b). In the best interests of my clients and my obligation to be ethical in my practice, which Dr. Larson does a wonderful job discussing in the last chapter, I left North Carolina and came to New York to study under Ellen Horovitz, Director of Nazareth's Art Therapy program and one of the contributors to this volume. In 1995, I became a certified art therapist. My interest continues in the creative therapies as I am now studying play therapy and had the good fortune to work directly with Dr. Hilda Glazer during my dissertation and took a seminar from Dr. Kevin O'Connor, both contributors to this book. My intention was to bring together a handbook of all the creative therapies, a collage of art, play, dance, music, drama, and poetry therapies in very specific areas not covered in other creative therapy manuals.

The book is organized to provide first, a history of the field taking a historical, evolutionary approach to the creative therapy. Next, I wanted to cover the field's theoretical orientations and this is the grounding force for anyone in practice. Theory guides our work and influences the types of techniques that we use with clients. And of course, I could not leave out assessments, as I have been so very drawn to writing critical test reviews and reviews of art therapy assessments (Brooke, 2004). Last, I wanted to include some chapters on how the creative therapy is used with special populations.

The authors who contributed to this book are credentialed and well-known in their fields. I commend them for their outstanding work. Most of all, I praise them for their commitment to the use of creative therapies as an avenue to help clients heal and grow.

My artwork on the cover of the book represents the collage of the creative therapies that I had in mind when editing this book. The mask – drama; the cats/butterfly – Jungian art archetype; Pan – music; the Rorschach – assessment; the dancer – dance/movement therapy; the journal – poetry therapy; and the animate animal friends – play therapy. The mask was particularly important and it was an exercise that I learned from Dr. Horovitz. You will find that some of the authors write about the importance of masks for those clients who may be defensive, at first, when talking about their feelings. As the therapeutic alliance grows and the client is ready, they can make a connection between the mask and his or her internal feelings. All of these creative therapy approaches: Art, play, dance, music, drama, and poetry provide acts of meaning for clients by allowing them to tell their stories and work toward a new definition of self (Brunner, 1990).

This book is fascinating because each creative therapy presents the historical development of their field. Many individuals mistakenly believe that these are new therapies; yet, the use of some of these therapies dates back to prehistoric times. The movement toward creating formal organizations is what is recent for these fields.

For each section, theoretical approaches are discussed. I thought this was particularly important since a creative therapist must have a theoretical base in order to justify the activities he or she is using with a client. "Just because" or "I just knew it would work" is not good enough. A clear understanding of the theoretical base is essential in guiding our work with clients and is important in terms of ethics.

One of my favorite sections, to no surprise to people familiar with my work, are the assessment chapters. Whether norm-referenced tests, interviews, case observations, or informal assessments, these tests contribute significantly to the field of the creative therapies as it provides a rationale for the validity of using these approaches with clients. For those therapists who serve as expert witnesses in court proceedings, thorough knowledge of an assessment's norm base, validity, and reliability is critically important. My concern is that we do not have enough research in this area. In other words, we need to make valid and reliable tests and start using them to collect research for the creative fields, which would engender respect for the creative therapies and present the view that creative therapists are committed to using the scientific approach to examine the results of their work. Barry Cohen, who did the foreword to the 2nd edition of *Tools of the Trade,* shares this concern:

> Naturally, the vast majority of American art therapists are less interested in, or comfortable with, assessment or evaluation than clinical work; it stands to reason that art therapists would much rather engage in the activities they are trained to do, such as making art with their clients and otherwise helping them to heal. Moreover, as a gen-

eral rule, artists tend to shy away from anything that smacks of scientific studies, especially those that involve numbers or statistics. (Cohen, in Brooke, 2004, p. vii)

One of the important criteria for my dissertation program was to show how my work could promote social change. This is one of the reasons that I became Vice Chair Person of ARIA (Awareness of Rape and Incest through Art) since it not only allowed the use of creative expression for survivors but provided a forum for the opportunity for consciousness raising on the issue of rape and sexual abuse. I wanted to take my certification to art therapy to a higher level through my writing and through my commitment to ARIA.

Friere (1971) used the term, consciousness raising, as a social change approach that liberates people from the oppressive myths and misunderstandings that surround our work. Friere considered this a transformative process that involves critical thinking and reframing. "Thinking does not separate itself from action, but constantly immerses itself in temporarily without fear of the risks involved" (Friere, 1971, p. 81). As creative art therapists, we liberate our clients through various creative therapies in a safe, therapeutic milieu, so that the client can take risks without fear and ultimately grow and heal.

This text, with the help of many talented, creative art therapists, is my endeavor to engage in consciousness-raising and promoting social change. According to Hocoy (2005), the creative therapies and social action can become interconnected, with the goal breaking myths and unjust events. "Art [creative] therapists should examine their complicity in unjust social arrangement and take a moral stance to work for justice by actively redressing imbalances, within and without the consulting room. It is suggested that art [creative] therapists adopt an action research approach by relinquishing theoretical dogma and cultural assumptions to consider the specific needs and worldview of the individuals being served" (Hocoy, 2005, p. 7).

Golub (2005) describes social action in the creative therapies as a "shared power of the community for the benefits of the community" (p. 17). The authors of this book have engaged in social action and consciousness-raising by providing information about their fields: The historical development, theoretical approaches, strengths and weaknesses of assessments, as well as demonstrating ethical ways that the creative therapies can be used to promote change with special populations.

REFERENCES

Brooke, S.L. (1996a). Art expression: An approach to working with incest survivors. *The Arts in Psychotherapy, 22*(5), p. 447–466.

Brooke, S.L. (1996b). *A therapist's guide to art therapy assessments: Tools of the trade.* Foreword by Dr. Harriet Wadeson, ATR. Springfield, IL: Charles C Thomas, Publisher, Ltd.

Brooke, S.L. (2004). *A therapist's guide to art therapy assessments: Tools of the trade,* (2nd ed.). Foreword by Barry Cohen, ATR. Springfield, IL: Charles C Thomas, Publisher, Ltd.

Brunner, J. (1990). *Acts of meaning.* Cambridge, MA: Harvard University Press.

Friere, P. (1971). *Pedagogy of the oppressed.* New York: Herder and Herder Press.

Golub, D. (2005). Social action and art therapy. *Art Therapy: Journal of the American Art Therapy Association, 22*(1), 17–33.

Hocoy, D. (2005). Art therapy and social action: A transpersonal framework. *Art Therapy: Journal of the American Art Therapy Association, 22*(1), 7–16.

ACKNOWLEDGMENTS

I wish to express my deepest appreciation and admiration for Dr. David Taylor, who is my mentor and my dearest friend, who supported me through the personal and professional journey in creating this book. I am also indebted beyond measure to the knowledge, support, and encouragement generously provided by all the contributing authors to this text. Without their patience and understanding, this endeavor to raise consciousness and hopefully promote social action and change would not have been possible.

I wish to acknowledge Charles Myers for his help assembling my artwork into a collage that was fitting for the cover of this text. Finally, I recognize and appreciate the selfless support, encouragement, and love provided me by my friends through all my professional endeavors and personal struggles, Dr. David Taylor, Gina Kim, Michael Hand, and Charles Myers. They all hold a special place in my heart.

CONTENTS

Page

Preface v
Acknowledgments ix

Chapter 1 A SHORT STORY OF ART THERAPY PRACTICE
           IN THE UNITED STATES
           Patricia St. John 3

Chapter 2 THE THEORY AND PRACTICE OF JUNGIAN
           ART THERAPY
           Hoda Mazloomian 21

Chapter 3 THE ASSESSMENT ATTITUDE
           Anne Mills 31

Chapter 4 INDIVIDUAL ART THERAPY WITH RESISTANT
           ADOLESCENTS
           Susan Boyes 40

Chapter 5 ART THERAPY WITHIN AN INTERDISCIPLINARY
           FRAMEWORK: WORKING WITH APHASIA AND
           COMMUNICATION SCIENCE DISORDERS
           Ellen G. Horovitz 47

Chapter 6 THE HISTORY OF PLAY THERAPY
           Mistie D. Barnes 56

Chapter 7 THEORETICAL PERSPECTIVES OF PLAY THERAPY
           Joshua A. Thomas-Acker and Sally S. Sloan 65

Chapter 8 COMBINING PLAY AND COGNITIVE
           INTERVENTIONS IN THE TREATMENT OF
           ATTACHMENT DISORDERED CHILDREN
           Kevin O'Connor 71

Chapter 9 PLAY THERAPY ASSESSMENTS
           Charles E. Myers 82

Chapter 10 EXPRESSIVE THERAPIES WITH GRIEVING
           CHILDREN
           Hilda R. Glazer 87

Chapter 11   MOVING WITH MEANING: THE HISTORICAL
PROGRESSION OF DANCE/MOVEMENT THERAPY
Laurice D. Nemetz 95

Chapter 12   THEORETICAL PERSPECTIVES IN D/MT:
VISIONS FOR THE FUTURE
Sabine C. Koch 109

Chapter 13   THE KESTENBERG MOVEMENT PROFILE
Suzanne C. Hastie 121

Chapter 14   ASSESSMENT IN DANCE/MOVEMENT THERAPY
Robyn Flaum Cruz 133

Chapter 15   IN-SCHOOL DANCE/MOVEMENT THERAPY
FOR TRAUMATIZED CHILDREN
Rena Kornblum and Robyn Lending Halsten 144

Chapter 16   MEDITATION AND MOVEMENT THERAPY
FOR CHILDREN WITH TRAUMATIC
STRESS REACTIONS
Deborah A. O'Donnell 156

Chapter 17   THE HISTORY OF MUSIC THERAPY
Joke Bradt 168

Chapter 18   MUSIC THERAPY THEORETICAL APPROACHES
E. Magdalena LaVerdiere 175

Chapter 19   A MOSAIC OF MUSIC THERAPY ASSESSMENTS
Eric B. Miller 182

Chapter 20   EMPOWERING WOMEN SURVIVORS OF
CHILDHOOD SEXUAL ABUSE: A COLLABORATIVE
MUSIC THERAPY-SOCIAL WORK APPROACH
Sandra L. Curtis and Gisèle C. T. Harrison 195

Chapter 21   MUSIC THERAPY WITH INNER CITY, AT-RISK
CHILDREN: FROM THE LITERAL TO THE
SYMBOLIC
Vanessa A. Camilleri 205

Chapter 22   ANCIENT AND MODERN ROOTS OF
DRAMA THERAPY
Sally Bailey 214

Chapter 23   DRAMA THERAPY THEORETICAL PERSPECTIVES
Yehudit Silverman 223

Chapter 24   THE USE OF ROLE-PLAY AS AN ASSESSMENT
INSTRUMENT
Ted Rubenstein 232

Chapter 25   DRAMATHERAPY AND REFUGEE YOUTH
Yasmine Rana 244

Chapter 26 PSYCHODRAMA STILL GROWING AND
EVOLVING AFTER ALL THESE YEARS
Karen Carnabucci 248

Chapter 27 POETRY, THE HEALING PEN
Mari Alschuler. 253

Chapter 28 THE THERAPEUTIC VALUE OF POETRY
Norma Leedy 263

Chapter 29 CREATIVE CONNECTIONS
Michael P. Hand 269

Chapter 30 ETHICAL DELIVERY OF CREATIVE THERAPEUTIC
APPROACHES
Kristin Larson 275

Appendix 281

CREATIVE ARTS THERAPIES MANUAL

Chapter 1

A SHORT HISTORY OF ART THERAPY PRACTICE IN THE UNITED STATES

PATRICIA ST. JOHN

INTRODUCTION

Art therapy uses symbols, metaphors, visual images, and the process of art making to heal and restore physical and mental health. Art therapy's roots predate use of the word art to describe the visual, symbolic productions of preliterate societies. Additionally, it predates the formal practice of therapy. Preliterate societies used visual symbols and images in religious ceremonies for healing, to communicate with the gods, and in communication with people. Decorating tools and implements made them "special" (Dissayanake, 1988). The term art evolved into a different meaning, but the power of art and the creative process to tap inner resources and heal remained.

From its earliest days, the field continued to define itself. Students and practitioners of art therapy quickly learned that the definition of art therapy was always evolving. As of this writing, the American Art Therapy Association provided this definition:

Art therapy is the therapeutic use of art making, within a professional relationship, by people who experience illness, trauma, or challenges in living, and by people who seek personal development. Through creating art and reflecting on the art products and processes, people can increase awareness of self and others, cope with symptoms, stress, and traumatic experiences; enhance cognitive abilities; and enjoy the life-affirming pleasures of making art. (*AATA Newsletter*, 2004, p. 4)

This definition emerged from decades of lively and passionate debate among practitioners of art therapy.

The underpinnings of art therapy took form with a fascination with artwork by patients in European insane asylums (MacGregor, 1983; Pickford, 1967; Prinzhorn, 1922). These collections of patient art amassed by psychiatrists raised many questions: Did insanity stimulate creativity? Did art making decrease as patients regained sanity? Did the artwork of patients have particular characteristics, and was it like or different from that of trained artists? Could artwork help to diagnose? Why did patients make art? In his theory of the unconscious, Freud (1900/1955) proposed that creative acts were the result of unresolved, unconscious material. If this were so, one would find evidence of early trauma in the artwork of artists. Was there a link between insanity and creativity? Or, alternatively, was art making a healing process, and could the creative process be useful in treatment of patients? As Jung (1964) personally discovered, painting allowed exploration of his own problematic material. But could this apply to patients, as well?

The two initiators of art therapy in the United States, Margaret Naumburg (1947) and Edith Kramer (1958), subscribed to art's healing potential. Naumburg claimed to have coined the term, art therapy (Junge & Asawa, 1994). Later, Kramer's (1971) work with disturbed children was called art therapy. In case studies, each pioneer demonstrated her distinct approach to treatment: Naumburg's art-in-therapy and Kramer's art-as-therapy (Ulman, 1987/2001).

Innovative treatment approaches did not cease with Naumburg and Kramer. Elinor Ulman created the first journal devoted to art therapy, the *Bulletin of Art Therapy* in 1961. The journal provided a

How can DT present this material?

venue for art therapists to learn about each other's work. By presenting papers and exhibits of patient artwork at psychiatric conferences, early art therapists acquainted the medical community about the benefits of art therapy. At one of these conferences a small group agreed it was time to form a national association. The American Art Therapy Association (AATA), established in 1969, held its first annual conference the next year (Junge & Asawa, 1994).

The next two decades, influenced by new theoretical developments in psychology, marked a period of rapid growth and enormous innovation and diversity as approaches to art therapy proliferated. Junge and Asawa (1994) recalled that art therapists of this period, like many creative people, were passionate about how art therapy should be defined and practiced. They also debated how and who should train the next generation of art therapists and what made art therapy different from other mental professions. AATA's committees developed guidelines for training, ethical standards, and standards of practice as art therapists. As in all professions, change was a constant.

The two most recent decades (1984–2004) demonstrated continuing change in response to state licensing of art therapists. Accountability, short-term treatment, managed care, treatment of a wider range of ethnic and cultural groups, the emptying of large psychiatric hospitals, identification of other treatment groups, such as the sexually abused, traumatic brain injured, HIV-positive and AIDS patients, challenged art therapists to create innovative treatments. Diversity in treatment sites, such as outpatient facilities, nursing homes, cancer units, and shelters for the homeless, required changes in education, training, and standards.

Early art therapists typically treated inpatients in long-term care in psychiatric hospitals (Wadeson, 1980). Eventually, art therapists practiced short-term, group art therapy in a broad range of treatment settings. Despite the presence of art therapy in so many settings, or perhaps because of it, the profession grappled with how to demonstrate art therapy's efficacy and effectiveness and attain national recognition (Kapitan, 2004). This chapter traces art therapy in the United States from its beginnings to present, highlighting the people whose innovations created the field. This is the story of how art therapy grew.

PRECURSORS TO ART THERAPY

Art therapy evolved as a hybrid field. It was generally agreed that art therapy emerged from the confluence of developments from the late 1700s to the early 1900s in several fields. These fields were psychiatry, psychoanalysis, art history, projective techniques, and education.

Psychiatry

During the nineteenth century in Europe, patients in insane asylums used available materials, bread, and bits of paper to create drawings and sculpture. The German psychiatrist, Hans Prinzhorn, (1886–1933), amassed "The Prinzhorn Collection," one of the earliest compilations of such works (Prinzhorn, 1922–1995). In the late 1800s, Cesare Lombroso and Paul-Max Simon raised questions about a possible link between madness or degeneration and creativity, and whether characteristics in patient art were useful for diagnosis and treatment (MacGregor, 1983).

Another psychiatrist, Fritz Mohr (1874–1966), continued these explorations into the twentieth century in *The Drawings of the Mentally Ill and Their Usefulness* (1906) where he tried "to connect certain characteristic types of designs with specific forms of mental illness" (Hogan, 2001, p. 82). His systematic assessment required patients to copy simple figures. This assessment evaluated the patient's current condition based on their perceptual and motor skills rather than on their spontaneous images (Hogan, 2001). Not all psychiatrists employed artwork for assessment purposes. "In both the work of Freud and Lombroso there is an emphasis on primitive mentality being expressed through pictorial symbolism" (Hogan, 2001, p. 87).

Psychoanalysis

Freud's theories of repression, projection, the unconscious, and symbolism in dreams, as well as his seminal book, *The Interpretation of Dreams* (1900/1955), identified the importance of visual images to understanding mental illness. Freud speculated that free association brought the unconscious, repressed material to the conscious level. Further, free association elevated primary process thinking to the secondary process level. Artwork, like dreams, wrote Pickford (1967), explaining Freud, contained symbolic content with its basis in four main processes: "(1) symbolic transformation; (2) condensation; (3) displacement of affect, and

(4) secondary elaboration" (p. 14). Symbolic transformation referred to images that replaced fantasies or impulses, but in some way were like them. For example, the male organ symbolized "spears, guns, snakes, teeth . . ." while female organs took on forms of ". . . containers, such as bowls, cups, bottles and houses" (Pickford, 1967, p. 14). Freud further proposed that projection played an important role in the style and content of artwork. Primary and secondary process fantasy material thus evolved into symbolic imagery, i.e., artwork.

Freud's studies of the life histories of artists, such as Leonardo da Vinci, suggested that unconscious material projected into artwork as well as dreams (Pickford, 1967, p. 14). In *Study of Leonardo da Vinci* (1919 cited in Pickford, 1967), Freud interpreted da Vinci's *Madonna and Child with St. Anne* (Louvre), based on da Vinci's childhood experiences. Freud proposed that an unconsciously painted vulture in the composition demonstrated homosexual tendencies. In an example of the difficulties of symbolic interpretation, Freud's vision was shown to be incomplete. In fact, da Vinci, in his notes, wrote about his fascination with kites, a hawk-like bird. A German who translated da Vinci's notes substituted the word vulture for kite, thereby generating the following Freudian interpretation: the Madonna as vulture. Freud saw da Vinci's early experiences as the basis for the composition, with the phallic tail replacing the mother's breast. In other words, Freud speculated that da Vinci identified with the phallic mother and the early roots of homosexual tendencies were represented unconsciously (Pickford, 1967, p. 278). The da Vinci code remains unbroken.

Furthermore, Freud was incorrect about the story about da Vinci's childhood when he claimed his mother raised da Vinci until age five. Neumann (1959) observed that da Vinci grew up in his father's home, raised by his grandmother and two stepmothers. It is speculative, at best, whether da Vinci's paintings reflected his early experiences. Even though Freud made errors, his psychoanalytic method is worthwhile. Connections between the artist's or client's life and what appears in a painting or drawing gave possible clues to motive and behavior.

Symbolic images not only had meaning for the artist, they also resonated with the viewer whose unconscious is at work. From a psychoanalytic perspective, "Art is . . . in part a process of ego defense, by which phantasies are extruded and exteriorized by projection, and, in part a therapeutic process, by which the ego may find out that its most dangerous phantasies are harmless" (Pickford, 1967, p. 18). Within the process of art making, sublimation, an ego defense, brought about ". . . adjustment of conflicts and stresses, and the constructive use of libido and aggression" (Pickford, 1967, p. 19). Kris (1952), a psychoanalyst trained in art history, explored these ideas from a neo-Freudian position. The field's two early pioneers in art therapy, Margaret Naumburg and Edith Kramer, adapted Freud's ideas in their practice. For a discussion of their work, see below under *Pioneers of Art Therapy.*

Jung's influence on art therapy was important, as well, as will be expanded upon in the next chapter. Jung (1964), a student of Freud, rejected Freud's theory of infantile sexuality and repressed memories. Instead, he conceived a theory of archetypes and universal images that resided in the memory of all humans as the collective unconscious. These symbols survived in various religions, rituals, and artwork of diverse cultures. The mandala related to the wheel and the sun. Naumburg and her sister, Florence Cane, incorporated some of Jung's ideas into their work. Later, several art therapists (e.g., Keyes, 1983; Wallace, 1975) adapted his ideas to art therapy practice calling it active imagination. Psychoanalytic theory afforded a basis for the development of projective techniques in the form of tests that invited the viewer to free associate to ambiguous images.

Projective Techniques

The Rorschach Test (Rorschach, 1921) and the Thematic Apperception Test (TAT) (Murray, (1943) offered an understanding of the personality and unconscious material that influenced behavior. Applications to art therapy turn up in Karen Machover's assessment that she described in *Personality Projection in the Drawing of the Human Figure* (1949), and later in assessments designed by other art therapists (e.g., the Ulman Personality Assessment Procedure, 1975, and Kwiatkowska's *Family Evaluation Procedure*, 1978).

Florence Goodenough (1926), a psychologist, developed the *Draw-A-Person (DAP)* test: ". . . the first published drawing test to assess children's intelligence" (Groth-Marnat, 1984, p. 116). One can calculate the child's intelligence quotient by counting the number of details included in the drawing. This test was reviewed by Brooke (2004). Goodenough assumed that accurate drawing of details related to intelligence. Dale B. Harris' (1963) later revision of the DAP required three drawings: a man, a woman, and a drawing of the self. According to Groth-Marnat (1984), "Goodenough and Harris both maintain that children's figure drawings are largely an intellectual task, and cannot be used as projective techniques to infer personality characteristics or underlying conflicts" (p. 116). Karen Machover criticized the *DAP* because it assessed only intelligence and she proposed assessing "personality variables" (Groth-Marnat, 1984). Just two years after Margaret Naumburg's first book on art therapy, Machover's revised scoring system came out. It was an easy step from testing children's intelligence and personality variables to innovative applications in education.

Movements in Education and Art Education

The Child Study Movement of the late 1800s and early 1900s hypothesized that children progressed through recognizable stages of development. Ebenezer Cooke (1885) proposed that educators take into consideration the child's developmental stage and interests (cited in Harris, 1963). This idea differed radically with the copy-drawing techniques of the time. Corrado Ricci (1887), in his study of drawings by Italian children, suggested that drawings can give clues to the psychology of the child and Cyril Burt (1921) refined the theory of developmental stages (cited in Harris, 1963). Building on this early work, Viktor Lowenfeld, a psychoanalytically oriented art educator, depicted six developmental stages in children's drawings from early scribbles to adolescence in *Creative and Mental Growth* (1947). In a chapter titled "Therapeutic Art" (1957), he suggested that art could and should be taught to children with disabilities. With the passage of federal legislation in the mid-seventies (e.g., Public Law 94-142, 1975) that mandated equal education for all children, including special needs students, art therapists (e.g., Anderson, 1978/1992; Henley, 1992) developed specialized art education. This led to the practice of art therapy in some school systems (Bush, 1997).

John Dewey, a progressive educator and professor at Columbia University, initiated the well-received idea the idea that children learn best by purposeful activity rather than the rote memory

practices that were prevalent in the late 1800s and early 1900s. His graduate student, Margaret Naumburg, an early pioneer of art therapy, applied progressive and psychoanalytic ideas at The Children's School in 1914 (later, the Walden School) in Manhattan (Frank in Detre et al., 1983).

The Walden School took its place within the fertile intellectual setting of New York City, with its groups of visual artists and writers, including Alfred Stieglitz's gallery, *An American Place*. The gallery hosted the first showing in the United States of works of young European artists such as Picasso, Matisse, and Braque (Frank in Detre et al., 1983). Teaching methods at The Children's School derived from progressive and psychoanalytic principles; the faculty, made up of artists and writers known to Naumburg, brought their understanding of the role of the unconscious into their teaching. Not only should children be schooled in the academics, but the school should provide for their emotional education, as well. In line with progressive techniques, the faculty recognized the importance of self-motivated learning. With psychoanalytic principles at the core of her idea of education, Naumburg stressed that children should freely express their ideas, fantasies, hopes, and fears, as a means to counter repression and promote mental health. Naumburg portrayed her years at the school in *The Child and the World* (1928).

Naumburg's sister, Florence Cane, joined the school's faculty around 1920, as their art teacher. Her innovative techniques, expressed in *The Artist in Each of Us* (1951/1983), combined visual art, chanting, and movement to loosen defenses and encouraged children to find their own themes and ideas for visual expression. With a mood or feeling as the topic, the children would develop their own visual interpretations based on their own experiences, rather than relying on adult models. Elinor Ulman and Hanna Yaxa Kwiatkowska designed assessment procedures that incorporated Cane's scribble drawing technique to tap the unconscious (discussed below). Besides setting up her school, Naumburg became the first pioneer of art therapy.

PIONEERS OF ART THERAPY

In the United States, psychoanalytically oriented psychiatrists within the medical community endorsed art therapy (Kramer, 1958; Levick, 1968;

Naumburg, 1973; Ulman, 1975, cited in Junge & Asawa, 1994). The earliest and best-known art therapists in the United States are Margaret Naumburg and Edith Kramer. Elinor Ulman and Hanna Yaxa Kwiatkowska also made valuable contributions in the early years of the field.

Margaret Naumburg

Margaret Naumburg, known as the mother of art therapy, underwent Freudian and Jungian analyses. She subscribed to a psychodynamic orientation. Based on her work with behavior problem children at the New York Psychiatric Institute, she applied "dynamically-oriented art therapy." Based on psychoanalytic theory, ". . . she departed from traditional analytic techniques in that she insisted that the patient sit upright, take an active rather than a dependent role, and analyze and interpret his or her own imagery" (Junge & Asawa, 1994, p. 25).

Naumburg said that art therapy, like psychoanalysis, always occurred within a transference relationship, a form of dependence on the therapist that was gradually overcome through the making of art. The client, empowered to more clearly see the source of his/her problems, developed a narcissistic cathexis to the artwork. Artwork produced spontaneously did not have to be made in the presence of the art therapist; instead, sessions could be devoted to verbal free-association to the artwork. The client arrived at her or his own interpretations (Naumburg, 1958). Naumburg asserted, "The Art Therapy approach offers a specialized additional nonverbal technique for releasing, through symbolic imagery, the unconscious, repressed emotions" (Naumburg, 1973, p. vii). She explained that Freud's patients often said they wished they could paint their dreams. Art allowed them to do just that.

Naumburg, a prolific author, lecturer, and spokesperson for this new field (e.g., 1947, 1950, 1953, 1966), encouraged the spread of art therapy by teaching social work and education students at the New School for Social Research and New York University. Her two chapters in Emanuel Hammer's *The Clinical Application of Projective Drawings* (1958) placed art therapy squarely within the psychoanalytic/psychodynamic group. Her approach, art-in-psychotherapy, signified that the art-making process was less important than free association and client-initiated interpretation of the artwork. The art therapist need not be trained in art, but needed to know psychodynamic theory and practice.

Edith Kramer

In contrast, Edith Kramer argued that healing occurred within the art-making process itself rather than uncovering unconscious material through the process of free association. She defined art therapy in this way: ". . . art therapy is conceived primarily as a means of supporting the ego, fostering the development of a sense of identity, and promoting maturation in general" (Kramer, 1971, p. xiii). She explained that making art was central to the work of the art therapist:

> The basic aim of the art therapist is to make available to disturbed persons the pleasures and satisfaction which creative work can give, and by his insight and therapeutic skill to make such experiences meaningful and valuable to the total personality. (Kramer, 1958, pp. 5–6)

Her ideas about how the art therapist functions also differed from Naumburg.

She emphasized the idea of sublimation within the art therapeutic process. The art therapist promoted the process of sublimation and assisted in this process, she wrote. "Since the artistic quality of the production is an indication of the depth and strength of sublimation, the art therapist will encourage a high artistic level of performance within the limitations of the student's talent" (Kramer, 1958, p. 23).

> The art therapist's main field of action remains the process of sublimation wherein the material undergoes that final transformation by which it is formed into tangible visual images, and the peculiar fusion between reality and fantasy, between the unconscious and the conscious, which we call art is reached. At this point the art therapist assists the process by substituting his skill and insight where the student's own resources fail. (Kramer, 1958, p. 23)

Unlike Naumburg, Kramer proposed that a transference relationship between the art therapist and client should not be relied upon for treatment. Instead, a therapeutic relationship is to be established and transference ". . . centers around the student's work." (Kramer, 1958, p. 22)

> The therapeutic relationship to the student remains less intimate than in psychotherapy. . . . It

does not become the core of the therapeutic situation as in psychotherapy, but remains subordinate to the task of making the student productive. (Kramer, 1958, p. 22)

Her neo-Freudian, ego psychology approach was especially suited to work with children with emotional problems. Because a strong ego was needed to channel and transform this material, and clients often had weak or poorly developed egos, the art therapist assisted the process by becoming a third hand, providing opportunities to strengthen the ego.

Years of college teaching, four books (1958, 1971, 1979, 2001b), and countless articles and lectures disseminated her ideas and practices. Her approach, art-as-therapy, placed art making at the core of treatment. As such, the art therapist must be first an artist who understood human behavior and its underlying principles and processes. Kramer's emphasis on the *art* in art therapy derived from her training in art in her native Austria where she was acquainted with psychoanalytic ideas. Later, she underwent an orthodox Freudian analysis. During the 1930s, Kramer's work with traumatized refugee children in Prague generated therapeutic uses of art. To escape the Nazi invasion, she immigrated to New York City in 1938 and worked at the Little Red Schoolhouse, the Wiltwyck School for Boys, and the Leake and Watts Children's Home, as well as in a tool and die factory. During this time she continued to paint and sculpt, always emphasizing that, "I think of myself as a painter and as an art therapist, not a clinician, an art therapist – which means also understanding something about clinical work but being an art therapist who really uses art as the therapy" (Kramer in McMahan, 1989, p. 107). Kramer's emphasis on the healing potential in the creative process of art making, rather than on free association to the art product, made available a second approach to the practice of art therapy. Junge and Asawa (1994) observed that,

> These two perspectives established warring camps as the profession evolved, with followers who often vociferously argued the merits of their positions. Later training programs tended to attach themselves to one of the two theories. The debates continue to this day and contribute to the liveliness of the field. (p. 31)

The third pioneer, Elinor Ulman, integrated the ideas of Naumburg and Kramer.

Elinor Ulman

Ulman created the *Bulletin of Art Therapy* in 1961, the first journal in the United States dedicated exclusively to art therapy, retitled *American Journal of Art Therapy*, in 1970 (Junge & Asawa, 1994). From 1974 to 1985, it was the official journal of the AATA. As the journal's editor, Ulman endorsed high standards and a continuing dialogue within the profession. Through the journal, the practices and thinking of art therapists became available nationally. Ulman supported a series of lectures by Naumburg and invited Kramer to write the journal's first article (Junge & Asawa, 1994). Like Naumburg and Kramer, she based her approach on psychoanalytic theoretical orientation, but incorporated both art-as-therapy and art-in-psychotherapy approaches (Ulman, 2001). Art therapy was a way to identify the inner world and the outer world, differentiating between the two, and bringing the two together in a new way (Ulman, 1961). Art therapy, she expounded, decreased chaotic feelings, and changes in personality became a permanent part of the client's individual qualities.

Within the context of her art therapy practice, Ulman designed one of the first assessments, later titled the Ulman Personality Assessment Procedure (UPAP; Ulman, 1975), a diagnostic tool to be given in the first session of treatment. Identification of the patient's pathology and strengths established the treatment goals. Interpretation of the four pictures produced during the assessment was psychoanalytically based and depended heavily on the art therapist's interpretative skills. Another psychoanalytically-oriented art therapist was best known for designing treatment for patients with schizophrenia that demanded an approach that included the whole family.

Hanna Yaxa Kwiatkowska

Kwiatkowska began her art therapy career in 1955. Her six-drawing assessment, the Family Art Evaluation (Kwiatkowska, 1967; 1978), incorporated directives by Ulman (UPAP; Ulman Personality Assessment Procedure, 1975) and Cane (1951/1983) and used methods uniquely suited to family and group work. Her innovations were known through her writings, her college teaching, and as AATA's first chair of the Research Committee. The work of these pioneers introduced art therapy to the mental health community and stimulated the professionalization of art therapy.

COMING TOGETHER: FORMING A NATIONAL ASSOCIATION OF ART THERAPISTS

Because of the work of Junge and Asawa (1994), who used original sources in the AATA Archives, we know how the American Association of Art Therapists came about. By the mid-1960s, some art therapists discussed forming a national association (e.g., Don Jones and Robert Ault at the Menninger Clinic in Kansas; Sandra Kagin and Marge Howard in Oklahoma). "Rather than just a measure of pathology," the emphasis was on treatment using art (Junge & Asawa, 1994, p. 87). In 1968, at the annual meeting of the American Psychiatric Association (APA), seven art therapists exhibited patient work (e.g., Naumburg, Kwiatkowska, & Levick). They met with two psychiatrists and the result was a discussion of "the possibility of establishing an American Society of Art Therapists" (Minutes from the meeting of May 14, 1968, cited in Junge & Asawa, 1994, pp. 88–89). In subsequent meetings, they wrote and adopted a constitution, and elected officers, with Myra Levick, Director of the Hahnemann Hospital art therapy program, as president. They held their first annual conference in Warrenton, Virginia, in 1970 and distributed a newsletter to the national membership. With establishment of a national association, art therapists began the ongoing processes of definition of the profession, professional standards, and guidelines for training. Rapid changes in the mental health field, new theoretical orientations and client populations, and a move away from the traditional psychiatric/medical model contributed to passionate discussions on all these topics from 1970 to today.

AN EXPANDING FIELD: 1969–1989

The period from 1969 to 1989 was one of rapid changes. New approaches in art therapy treatment addressed the needs of a rapidly diversifying client population. Although inpatient psychiatric treatment dominated the venues of treatment settings, shorter treatment periods replaced the traditional long-term period. After discharge, patients continued treatment in community settings. Art therapy became an appropriate treatment for the developmentally delayed, families, school children, and with people who wanted to increase their creative potential.

The American Art Therapy Association identified training of art therapists as an important next step in developing the new profession. It established that art therapy training should be at the master's level. The AATA published guidelines for art therapy training and assigned a special committee, the Education and Training Board (ETB), to review applications from programs that apply for AATA Approval.

By 1973, the AATA established training standards for approval by AATA's Education Program Approval Board (EPAB), formerly the Education and Training Board. Several programs initiated formal training at the master's level: The University of Louisville in 1959 and 1973, Hahnemann Hospital in 1967, and Pratt Institute in 1970 (Junge & Asawa, 1994). By 1985, the AATA listed 14 approved training programs; in 1992, 24 programs had approval status, and today (2004), 28 programs appeared on the AATA's approved listing (www.arttherapy.org, accessed 7/28/04). Approved programs complied with Education Standards, a task of the AATA Education Committee that recommended changes to the AATA Board of Directors. Periodically, revised standards addressed changes in client populations and professional standards of practice identified by the mental health community.

NEW APPROACHES TO ART THERAPY

In addition to the formation of the AATA, the period from 1969–1989 marked an expansion of the field from its early ties to the medical/psychiatric community with its psychoanalytic/psychodynamic model to approaches that adapted new psychological theories to art therapy treatment. Although the psychoanalytic/psychodynamic method continued to be taught in some programs and some art therapists continued to use this approach in practice, other approaches gradually expanded the field. Object relations and self-psychology advanced psychoanalytic theory. A Jungian scheme appealed to some art therapists who emphasized centering their work on the created image. Humanistic process emerged during the 1970s, as part of the human potential movement and the writings of Carl Rogers, Abraham Maslow, and others. Around the same time, psychoeducational and developmental approaches emerged to treat children and adults in special educational settings. Because treatment of children affected the whole family, family art therapy made use of a systemic technique. Group art therapy also applied a systemic technique, as well, a format favored in hospital and other institutional settings. With so many modes of treatment, some art therapists preferred to use an integrated approach or selected the appropriate manner depending on the client's changing needs at each phase of treatment. Each method is discussed below, based on Judith Rubin's *Approaches to Art Therapy* (1987/2001).

Psychodynamic Approaches and Neo-Freudian Directions

The pioneering work of Margaret Naumburg and Edith Kramer represented psychodynamic and neo-Freudian methods, as described above. Three art therapists embraced a neo-Freudian process. Arthur Robbins (e.g., 1987a) based his approach on object relations theory (Robbins, 2001) that conjectured that from birth to about two-and-a-half years the child formed an attachment to the mother and then separated and individuated in the process of forming an identity and object constancy. Problems with these tasks resulted in a range of problems, from psychosis to deep neurosis. As a component of the dynamic relationship between client and art therapist, artwork was seen as a ". . . container or organizer that mirrors internal object relations, as well as associated defenses and developmental problems" (Robbins, 2001, p. 58). Through a process of empathy, using transference and counter transference material, the art therapist guided the client through the painful process of loss and separation with the goal being formation of an identity and object constancy.

Mildred Lachman-Chapin (2001) used a self-psychology technique, based on the theories of Kohut (1971). Treatment took the form of mirroring, in which both she and the client drew simultaneously. Using empathy, her drawing reflected and responded to that of the client. A dialogue followed, with the goal to nurture the client and assist the process of a cohesive self. Art and art making helped clients find ". . . ways to express, *without shame*, those grandiose, exhibitionistic wishes which have not been integrated into the personality and sense of self" (Lachman-Chapin, 2001, p. 77).

Judith Rubin (1978), combined ". . . ego psychology, object relations, and self-psychology. However, her theoretical base was fundamentally psychoanalytic (Rubin, 1987, p. 12)" (Junge & Asawa, 1994, p. 203). Naumburg and Kramer influenced her approach. She based treatment on "the integrative

aspects of the creative process itself, as well as the use of art as a tool in the service of discharge, uncovering, defense, or communication" (Rubin, 1987, p. 17). Among her innovations were a nonstructured assessment and methods that decoded symbolic messages. She described the therapeutic process from the "testing" phase to the end of treatment (Rubin, 1978), and she outlined the qualities of a good art therapist (1984). Others used the image and active imagination itself as the basis of art therapy.

Jungian Approaches

Two art therapists represented this Jungian approach. The first was Michael Edwards, a Jungian analyst and art therapist in private practice in Cornwall, England. Edwards noted that around 1917, Jung asked his patients ". . . to make visual representations of their dream and fantasy material" as a way to enter ". . . into a relationship with an unconscious image" (2001, p. 82). With the image providing a "buffer, filter, screen, container" that "mediates between patient and therapist" (Edwards, 2001, p. 84), a dialogue ensued to uncover hidden material and bring it to consciousness.

Edith Wallace, a Jungian analyst and psychiatrist in private practice in Santa Fe, New Mexico, used active imagination and meditation (1975, 1990). At the center of treatment were drawn or painted images that arose ". . . from the depth of the psyche" (Wallace, 2001, p. 95). Rather than dialoguing, Wallace asked clients to write a story about the image. She explained:

> This method presupposes that truth resides in the unconscious, not only on a personal, ego level, but also as a profound historical truth, and is manifested in archetypal images arising from the collective unconscious. The central archetype, which Jung called the "Self," is of special importance in healing. It has a regulating, stabilizing function, compensating for any imbalance that might arise. (Wallace, 2001, p. 95)

In contrast to what might be seen as a deterministic feature of psychoanalytic/psychodynamic approaches, others placed emphasis on personal responsibility and taking an active role in shaping one's life.

Humanistic Approaches

Humanistic approaches to art therapy were more diverse than those in the psychoanalytic/psychodynamic group. Rubin described this as an "optimistic view of human nature and the human condition" (2001, p. 119). Josef Garai (2001) used a "humanistic-holistic" approach that rejected the idea that creativity occurred because of our struggles with life and death to gain immortality (Meerloo, 1968; Rank, 1932, 1973 cited in Garai, 2001). He incorporated Jungian ideas of a collective unconscious, archetypes, and symbols, including dream interpretation. Through creativity the person became individuated. The client used drawing to take charge of his/her own life (Garai, 2001, p. 151).

Mala Betensky described her work as phenomenological art therapy (1973; 2001), or a free, expressive process in which clients chose their own materials to make images. Color and line in the images had expressive features. Using the Gestalt idea of isophomorphism, and borrowing from the Rorschach interpretation of identifying relationships between lines, shapes, and colors, she encouraged clients to make and later talk about their images in a structured dialogue termed *"What do you see?"* (Betensky, 1995). The art therapist, a careful listener, guided the client to deeper levels of engagement with the depicted object. The goal was phenomenological integration or self-discovery and the client took personal responsibility for him/herself (Betensky, 2001).

Janie Rhyne also emphasized that the client must take responsibility in Gestalt art experience (1973/1996; 2001). This approach, based on her training under Fritz Perls (1969), addressed cut-off emotions and supports feeling in the here-and-now. Interpretation was not encouraged. Clients gave images a voice to better understand themselves. The art therapist and client were equal partners, working as a team. Clients who developed awareness could even "direct what they need in therapy" (Rhyne, cited in Jordan, 1989, p. 9).

Rubin (2001) identified Natalie Rogers' (1993) expressive arts therapy approach as a humanistic model. Like Garai, Betensky, and Rhyne, emphasis was on "the ability of individuals to find appropriate self-direction" within a therapeutic relationship that was "empathic, honest, and caring" (Rogers, 2001, p. 164). Where her approach differed is that she integrated "dance, art, and music therapies . . . journal writing, poetry, imagery, meditation, and improvisational drama" to "express . . . feelings in visible forms . . . [by] . . . using art as a language to communicate our inner truths" (2001, p. 163).

Pat B. Allen (1995) endorsed an open studio process, and she saw art therapy as a spiritual path. Mentored by Naumburg, Allen became inspired by Jung and Cane (2001, p. 181). Participants identified and were responsible for setting their own goals. Art making refined one's awareness. Talking to the artwork confronted difficulties and enhanced trust. The art therapist became a witness to "record all that we experience" (Allen, 2001, p. 184). The ultimate goal was personality transformation. A goal of other art therapists became treatment of special needs children.

Mastery & control

Psychoeducational Approaches

Psychoeducational approaches gained popularity during the 1970s when Public Law 94-142, the Education for All Handicapped Children Act (July 1, 1975), guaranteed that special needs children be placed in the least restrictive environment. As a result, more special needs children were mainstreamed into public school art classrooms. Behavioral, cognitive-behavioral, developmental art therapy, and assessments for cognition and emotions became mainstream methods. Their common link was emphasis on learning new skills and behaviors to replace maladaptive behaviors. Changing behavior altered the client's view of the world.

Ellen Roth's (1978) method of reality shaping was an adaptation of behavioral theory to art therapy. This means people learned from their environment and the environment sustained that learning. Undesirable or problematic behavior could be identified, unlearned, relearned, or modified. Roth's method came from two psychologists, Pavlov (1927) who focused on emotional learning, and Skinner (1953) who emphasized behavior modification (Roth, 2001, p. 195). Reality shaping used standard behavior modification techniques (identifying a target behavior, taking a history, developing a therapeutic relationship, stating treatment goals, assessing the frequency of the target/undesirable behavior) to establish a baseline against which treatment effects could be measured. After establishing a baseline, one could begin treatment.

Marcia Rosal (2001) applied cognitive-behavior theory to art therapy for special needs children. Aaron T. Beck (1976) pioneered a cognitive-behavioral approach based on cognitive theory. Its popularity increased during the 1970s. The assumption was that thoughts, feelings, and behaviors were

CBT & Rythec

integrally bound up with one another. What the client projects into the artwork, whether a positive or negative image, revealed important consequences of future behavior and the client's feelings and behavior.

Mary Wood (1975) preferred a developmentally based treatment for handicapped children. She described it as ". . . a psychoeducational approach to therapeutic intervention with young children who have serious emotional and behavioral disorders" (Wood, 1975, p. 3). The purpose was to ". . . facilitate the social and emotional growth of the child" (Wood, 1975, p. 3). The therapist provided a pleasurable environment where successful learning experiences were at the child's developmental level. Normal developmental stages guided therapy with periodic evaluation of progress (Wood, 1975, p. 3). Geraldine Williams, an art therapist, worked with Wood to develop a structured, developmentally based treatment program, described in their book *Developmental Art Therapy* (1979).

Carole Aach-Feldman and Susan Kunkle-Miller (2001) created an art therapy method for seriously disturbed handicapped children who were in Piaget's (1951) sensorimotor and preoperational stages, the zero to seven years age range. Relying on a formal assessment, goals included fostering attachment and supporting separation, developing simple motor routines, and promoting discovery of cause-and-effect relationships, and sequential ordering (Aach-Feldman & Kunkle-Miller, 2001). The preoperational child progressed toward representation, developed language to label thoughts and feelings, understood concepts, and became more autonomous (Aach-Feldman & Kunkle-Miller, 2001, p. 234).

Writings of Piaget (1951; Piaget & Inhelder, 1967) also guided Rawley Silver, best known for her three art-based assessments published between 1982 and 1996. In *Three Art Assessments: The Silver Drawing Test of Cognition and Emotion; Draw a Story: Screening for Depression; and Stimulus Drawings and Techniques* (2002), she created tools to evaluate cognitive and emotional levels in children, adolescents, and adults. An updated review of the Silver Drawing technique is available in *Tools of the Trade*, 2nd edition (Brooke, 2004). Numerous quantitative and qualitative studies tested the validity and reliability of these assessments with a wide range of populations and age groups. Silver's work and that of her colleagues gained international attention

and acceptance as tools that evaluate treatment progress and outcomes. Other art therapists thought that a psychoeducational approach for special needs children was worthy, but treatment of the whole family merited consideration.

Systemic Approaches

Judith Rubin brought attention to systemic techniques for families and groups in the second edition of her book, *Approaches to Art Therapy*. Systemic approaches referred to practices designed especially for treatment of families or groups. The process viewed clients as part of a system (Rubin, 2001). Barbara Sobol (2001) worked with families and Katherine Williams (2001) specialized in in-group work. Shirley Riley (1994; 2001a; 2001b) worked from this perspective, as did Landgarten (1981; 1987).

Sobol and Williams (2001) identified Kwiatkowska as providing a foundation for family systems art therapy and cited her *Family Art Evaluation (FAE;* Kwiatkowska, 1978) as a valuable assessment tool to identify problem areas, and used Kwiatkowska's 18-month treatment program to "explore feelings and relationships and [make] analytically based interpretations to the family" (1978, pp. 137–175, cited in Sobol & Williams, 2001, p. 264).

Sobol described her approach in 1982. Patients' problems were interpersonal, rather than solely intrapsychic (Rubin, 2001, p. 259), whether in a family or other groups. The individual adapted to the environment; sometimes the environment was unhealthy, and required unhealthy adaptations. As the individual in treatment became healthier, the environment/system/family or group faced pressure to change. Treatment of whole families created conditions to "disrupt, interrupt, amplify, or otherwise disturb the ongoing operations or organization of a family system as first steps toward introducing new and healthier patterns of interaction" (Sobol & Williams, 2001, p. 262.

In-group treatment art therapy individuals with problematic histories and experiences interacted with each other. Problems, particularly with relationships, typically emerged within a group context. To Sobol and Williams (2001), art making "may at times help participants to avoid relating, but it can also titrate relationships, allowing some families or groups members to tolerate being together in uncustomary ways" (p. 278). This method facilitated communication and group members made connections with each other, and relationship problems were worked through via the artwork. Several art therapists whose work is presented next described their efforts either as eclectic or integrative.

Eclectic and Integrative Approaches

An eclectic approach was the model preferred by most AATA members (Elkins & Stovall, 2000), suggesting that today's art therapists do not select one approach, but choose and select based on client needs. *The Random House College Dictionary* defined eclectic as "not following any one system, as of philosophy, medicine, etc., but selecting and using what are considered the best elements of all systems" (Stein, 1975, p. 418). Described earlier, Elinor Ulman's work integrated an art-as-therapy with an art-in-psychotherapy approach, based on psychoanalytic principles. Integrate referred to making up, combining, or completing "to produce a whole or larger unit" (Stein, 1975, p. 692).

Eclectic art therapist, Harriet Wadeson (1980; 1987), initially influenced by Kwiatkowska, used a variety of approaches, depending on the needs of her treatment population. She was clear about which approach she used and when and why. Many years of practice resulted in an "Eclectic Layer Cake" (2001, p. 307). She used Freudian, humanistic, existential, Gestalt, developmental, and even behavioral approaches, as well as group dynamic theory. Wadeson wrote that theory was "an essential foundation of our work" (Wadeson, 2001, p. 317). Knowing which theory to select for treatment became key to her methodology.

Shaun McNiff preferred using all arts therapies in his work, an approach termed by Paolo Knill as "intermodal expressive therapy" (McNiff, 2001, p. 319). McNiff asserted that "the practice of art therapy is enhanced by – indeed, requires – a more comprehensive understanding of expression through all of the senses" (2001, p. 320). For example, McNiff beat on drums while participants painted, effecting a ". . . flow of imagery," that resulted in " bolder and more expressive gestures," and "sustain[ing] expression" (McNiff, 2001, pp. 320 & 321). Sound, movement, and performance were combined with visual work within an environment that McNiff kept "safe and creative," similar, he said, to Winnicott's holding environment (McNiff, 2001, p. 322).

Finally, David Henley (1992), who studied with Kramer, used art therapy treatment in educational settings by designing a therapeutic curriculum that was structured into five one-hour components. The integration of reading, artwork, and writing to motivate, focus, express ideas, and address educational goals set out by the student's individualized educational plan (IEP) became Henley's *modus operandi*. The goal was to engage the student in academic processes and promoting "healthy coping capacities that will endure into adulthood" (Henley, 2001, p. 338). The above synthesis profiled the evolving practice of art therapy to the end of the twentieth century.

SUMMARY AND CONCLUSIONS

Visual symbols were a key component in preliterate societies to communicate and heal. During the nineteenth century, forward-thinking European psychiatrists encouraged patients in asylums to draw, paint, and sculpt. Their productions, sometimes referred to as degenerate art, garnered attention as a possible means of diagnosis (Hogan, 2001). Lombroso (1835–1901) and Nordeau (1849–1943) linked madness and genius together (Hogan, 2001). Toward the end of the nineteenth century, the Child Study Movement brought attention to the drawings of children, and the Scientific Movement, in the early 1900s, embraced the idea that children's drawings could be used to measure intelligence.

Art therapy began to take shape under the influence of Freud's method of free association as a means to tap the unconscious, and Jung's theories about universal archetypes and a collective unconscious. Both relied on the client's visual images in dreams. These ideas became important in an approach to art therapy devised by Margaret Naumburg during the 1930s. Within a transference relationship, she encouraged clients to free associate to their artwork as a means to uncover the unconscious and interpret their images, a practice termed art in psychotherapy.

Alternatively, art as therapy, developed by Edith Kramer during the 1950s, introduced another way to use the art-making process in treatment. Kramer proposed that within a therapeutic alliance the art therapist took an active part in supporting the patient's ego and encouraging sublimation. Art as therapy offered another practice method, and, as

Junge and Asawa (1994) observed, the lines were drawn. Elinor Ulman integrated both methods and Hanna Yaxa Kwiatkowska devised techniques for working with families in her efforts with patients with schizophrenia.

In 1961, Ulman initiated the first journal devoted entirely to art therapy, and, in 1969, art therapists throughout the United States formed the American Art Therapy Association (AATA). Members of the AATA formulated standards of education, ethical practices, and registration requirements. Training programs adopted education standards to prepare students to work in a variety of settings. Innovations in treatment proliferated during the 1970s and 1980s, closely matched to recent psychological theories. Art therapists utilized a broad range of theories, including neo-Freudian, humanistic, psychoeducational, and systemic. They practiced in schools, outpatient clinics, day treatment, in medical settings, with trauma survivors, in homeless shelters, nursing homes, hospice, and many other venues.

This diversity of practice settings with their new complexities necessitated increased attention to educational training for art therapists. State licensing of art therapists created pressure to standardize training. The notion of accountability demanded that art therapy treatment demonstrate its effectiveness.

Note

An abbreviated history of art history could not do justice to the nuances and complexities of this field. The earliest account of the formation of the field was by three of its pioneers: Elinor Ulman, Edith Kramer, and Hanna Yaxa Kwiatkowska. In *Art Therapy in the United States* (1978), they defined art therapy and discussed how it was practiced. Diane Waller (1991) described the formation of art therapy in England in *Becoming a Profession: The History of Art Therapy in Britain 1940–1982*. In *Healing Arts: The History of Art Therapy*, Susan Hogan traced the beginnings of art therapy in England, from 1790 to 1966. Basing their history on archives of the American Art Therapy Association, published interviews, letters, memos, and personal accounts, Maxine B. Junge and Paige P. Asawa (1994), in *A History of Art Therapy in the United States*, provided a chronological account of the people and events that led to the formation of the American Art Therapy Association (AATA) and major movements in the field. In her chronological, edited volume, *Approaches to Art Therapy*, Judith A. Rubin (1987/2001) presented chapters written by practitioners of the dominant approaches to art therapy, from psychoanalytic approaches to systemic and integrative approaches. These books gave an in-depth presentation of the history of art therapy. Also, note that the history of art therapy assessment was not covered in this chapter because it appears later in this book.

A Short History of Art Therapy Selected Timeline

Date	Event
1914	Margaret Naumburg opened The Children's School, later called The Walden School, in New York City.
1921	Rorschach test published.
1922/ 1995	Hans Prinzhorn's *Artistry of the Mentally Ill* published.
1925	Nolan D. C. Lewis, mentor to Margaret Naumburg, encouraged "free" painting with adult patients in New York City.
1926	Florence Goodenough's *Draw-A-Man* test published.
1928	Margaret Naumburg's *The Child & the World* published.
Late 1930s	Mary Huntoon practiced dynamically-oriented art therapy at the Menninger Sanitarium in Topeka, Kansas.
Mid to later 1930s	Edith Kramer worked with traumatized refugee children in Prague.
1930s through 1940s	Margaret Naumburg traveled, met Nolan D. C. Lewis at the New York Psychiatric Institute, where he encouraged her to develop techniques using art with children, adolescent, and adult patients.
1938	Edith Kramer emigrated from Austria to New York City.
1942	Don Jones worked at Marlboro State Hospital in New Jersey and wrote about art therapy.
1947	Naumburg's *Studies of the "Free" Expression of Behavior Problem Children and Adolescents as a Means of Diagnosis and Therapy* published.
1947	Viktor Lowenfeld's *Creative & Mental Growth* published. Thereafter, eight editions were published.
1949	Karen Machover's *Personality Projection in the Drawing of the Human Figure* published.
1950	Naumburg's *Schizophrenic Art* published.
	Don Jones used art therapy at the Menninger

Clinic. Kramer practices art therapy at the Wiltwyck School for Boys in upstate New York. Felice Cohen was art therapist at Houston State Psychiatric Hospital.

1950s   Naumburg conducted training in art therapy in the Northeast; in attendance were Elinor Ulman and Hanna Yaxa Kwiatkowska. Ulman joined Bernard Levy at District of Columbia General Hospital and practiced art therapy in Washington, DC.

1951   Florence Cane's *The Artist in Each of Us* published.

1952   Florence Cane died.

1953   Naumburg's *Psychoneurotic Art* published.

1955   Kwiatkowska practiced art therapy at St. Elizabeth's Hospital in Washington, DC.

1957   Ulman taught art therapy in Washington, DC.

1957   University of Louisville initiated the first master's degree training in art therapy. The program folded within two years.

1958   Kramer's *Art Therapy in a Children's Community*, based on her work at the Wiltwyck School for Boys, published. Introduced the art-as-therapy approach.

1958   Hammer's *The Clinical Application of Projective Drawings* published. It included Naumburg's two chapters about art therapy.

1960   Robert Ault practiced art therapy at the Menninger Clinic in Kansas.

1961   Ulman and Kramer initiated the first journal devoted to art therapy: *Bulletin of Art Therapy*, later titled *American Journal of Art Therapy (AJAT)*.

Early 1960s   Harriet Wadeson trained with Kwiatkowska.

Ault and Jones discussed forming a professional organization of art therapists.

1964   Kramer practiced art therapy in New York City at the Jewish Guild for the Blind.

1964   Janie Rhyne combined Gestalt psychology with art in gestalt art experience.

Tarmo Pasto received a grant to categorize graphic imagery of atypical populations.

1965   Ulman's *Ulman Personality Assessment Procedure (UPAP)* published.

1966   Naumburg's *Dynamically Oriented Art Therapy* published.

1967   Myra Levick named director of graduate art therapy training at Hahnemann Hospital in Philadelphia, PA. Art therapists who exhibited patient artwork in Boston, MA, at the American Psychiatric Association conference decided to form a national organization of art therapists.

Helen Landgarten began to practice art therapy in Los Angeles, CA.

1969   The American Art Therapy Association (AATA) formed with Myra Levick as president.

1970   First annual conference of the AATA held in Warrenton, VA.

Josef Garai initiated a humanistically oriented art therapy master's degree program at Pratt Institute in New York City.

1971   Kramer's *Art as Therapy with Children* published, later translated into several foreign languages. AATA held its second conference. Levy and Ulman initiated master's level art therapy program at George Washington University, Washington, DC.

1973   The AATA published guidelines for art therapy education and training.

The Arts in Psychotherapy, a journal dedicated to creative/expressive arts therapies, published. Rhyne's *Gestalt Art Experience* published. Mala Betensky proposed humanistic, phenomenological approach to art therapy in *Self-Discovery through Self-Expression*. The University of Louisville initiated the first master's level program in expressive therapies.

1974   Immaculate Heart College in Los Angeles was first west coast art therapy master's program; it trained art therapists to practice as primary clinicians, rather than adjunctively.

The *American Journal of Art Therapy* became AATA's official journal.

1975   Meeting of the first International Convocation of Art Therapy Educators; they discussed educational guidelines.

1978   Rawley Silver's *Developing Cognitive & Creative Skills through Art* published.

Kwiatkowska's *Family Therapy & Evaluation through Art (FEC)* published.

Frances Anderson's *Art for All the Children* published.

Judith Rubin's *Child Art Therapy* published.

Later 1970s   Arthur Robbins directed art therapy program at Pratt Institute based on an object relations approach.

1979   Kramer's *Childhood & Art Therapy* published.

1980   Kwiatkowska died.

Wadeson's *Art Psychotherapy* published.

1981   Helen Landgarten's *Clinical Art Therapy* published.

Laurie Wilson's *Louise Nevelson: Iconography and Sources* published.

Shaun McNiff's *The Arts in Psychotherapy* published.

1983   Margaret Naumburg died at the age of 93.

The *American Journal of Art Therapy* ceased to be official journal of the AATA. Gary Barlow named the editor of AATA's new journal *Art Therapy: Journal of the American Art Therapy Association.*

Silver's *Silver Drawing Test of Cognition & Emotion* published, revised in 1996.

Kramer & Schehr's *Art Therapy Evaluation Session* published.

1984   Rubin's *The Art of Art Therapy* published.

1985   The AATA listed 14 master's degree programs approved by the Education Training Board (ETB).

Cohen's *The Diagnostic Drawing Series Handbook* published.

1987   Oster & Gould's *Using Drawings in Assessment & Therapy: A Guide for Mental Health Professionals* published.

Robbins' *The Artist as Therapist* published.

Wadeson's *The Dynamics of Art Psychotherapy* published.

Rubin's *Approaches to Art Therapy* published.

1988   Cohen, Hammer, & Singer's *Diagnostic Drawing Series* published.

1989   Silver's S*timulus Drawings & Techniques* published.

Wadeson's edited book, *Advances in Art Therapy* published.

The Levick Emotional & Cognitive Art Therapy Assessment (LECATA) distributed at training workshops.

1990   The AATA begins to survey its membership.

Bruce Moon's *Existential Art Therapy* published.

Edith Wallace's *A Queen's Quest* published.

Cathy Malchiodi became second editor of AATA's journal, *Art Therapy.*

Malchiodi's *Breaking the Silence: Art Therapy with Children from Violent Homes* published.

1991   The AATA collaborated with the American Dance Therapy Association to support legislation for the Older American's Act.

1992   Public Law 102-375 passed, specifically naming art therapy.

AATA membership reached 4,018; 24 master's art therapy programs listed as "Approved" by the AATA.

Publication of AATA's first monograph, *A Guide to Conducting Art Therapy Research* edited by Harriet Wadeson.

David Henley's *Exceptional Children, Exceptional Art* published.

1993   Silver's *Draw a Story* published.

Landgarten's *Magazine Photo Collage* published.

AATA identified master's level training as entry level for the profession.

New Mexico was first state to license art therapists.

1994   Robbins' *A Multi-Modal Approach to Creative Art Therapy* published.

A History of Art Therapy in the United States by M.B. Junge & P.P. Asawa published by the AATA.

Frances Anderson's *Art-Centered Education & Therapy for Children with Disabilities* published.

1995   Mala Betensky's *What Do You See?* published.

1996   Stephanie Brooke's *A Therapist's Guide to Art Therapy Assessments* published.

Marcia Rosal's *Approaches to Art Therapy with Children* published.

1997   Janet Bush's *A Handbook for School Art Therapy: Introducing Art Therapy into a Public School System* published.

Bruce Moon's *Art & Soul* published (2nd edition published in 2004).

1998   Linda Gantt & Carmello Tabone's *Formal Elements Art Therapy Scales* published; used Lowenfeld's "Person picking an apple from a tree" drawing directive.

McNiff's *Trust the Process* published.

Rubin's *Art Therapy: An Introduction* published.

1999   McNiff's *Art-Based Research* published.

Malchiodi's *Medical Art Therapy with Adults and Medical Art Therapy with Children* published.

Frances Anderson became third editor of AATA's journal, *Art Therapy.*

2000   Frances Kaplan's *Art, Science and Art Therapy* published.

Wadeson's edited book, *Art Therapy Practice* published.

Measuring the effects of creating art on physiological changes in the brain has an impact on the field and fuels brain-based research by art therapists.

2001   Frances Kaplan became fourth editor of *Art Therapy.*

Kramer's *Art As Therapy: Collected Papers* published.

Shirley Riley's *Art in Group Therapy* published.

Rubin's *Approaches to Art Therapy*, 2nd edition published.

Silver's *Art As Language* published.

Laurie Wilson's *Alberto Giacometti: Myth, Magic, and the Man* published.

2003   Matt Dunne, legislative consultant to the AATA, speaks at AATA's annual conference in Chicago; stressed the need for art therapy research, outcome studies, clinical trials, grant monies, and demonstrating efficacy and efficiency of art therapy with veterans and children with Post-traumatic Stress Disorder. Malchiodi's summary of his remarks printed in the AATA *Newsletter*, Winter 2004.

Donna Bett's *Face Stimulus Assessment (FSE)* published.

Maury Rabin's *Art Therapy & Eating Disorders* published.

2004   Stephanie L. Brooke second edition of *Tools of the Trade*

AATA President Lynne Kapitan wrote in the AATA *Newsletter* about the importance of "cross-training;" suggested that art therapy education include training in counseling. The AATA Education Committee revised Education Standards in accordance with CACREP and NBCC standards for training.

REFERENCES

Aach-Feldman, S., & Kunkle-Miller, C. (1987/2001). Developmental art therapy. In J. A. Rubin (Ed.). *Approaches to art therapy* (pp. 226–240). Philadelphia: Brunner-Routlege.

Allen, P. B. (1995). *Art as a way of knowing.* Boston, Shambhala.

Allen, P. B. (2001). *Art making as spiritual path: The open studio.* In J. A. Rubin (Ed.). *Approaches to art therapy* (pp. 178–188). Philadelphia: Brunner-Routledge.

American Art Therapy Association. (2004). Art therapy: Definition of the profession. *AATA Newsletter, 35* (2), 4.

Anderson, F. E. (1978/1992). *Art for all the children: Approaches to art therapy for children with disabilities.* Springfield, IL: Charles C Thomas, Publisher, Ltd.

Anderson, F. E. (1994). *Art-centered education and therapy for children with disabilities.* Springfield, IL: Charles C Thomas, Publisher, Ltd.

Beck, A. T. (1976). *Cognitive therapy and the emotional disorders.* New York: International Universities Press.

Betensky, M. (1973). *Self-discovery through self-expression.* Springfield, IL: Charles C Thomas, Publisher, Ltd.

Betensky, M. (1995). *What do you see?* London: Jessica Kingsley.

Betensky, M. (2001). Phenomenological art therapy. In J. A. Rubin (Ed.). *Approaches to art therapy* (pp. 121–133). Philadelphia: Brunner-Routledge.

Betts, D. (2003). Developing a projective drawing test: Experiences with the Face Stimulus Assessment (FSA). *Art Therapy: Journal of the American Art Therapy Association, 20* (2), 77–82.

Brooke, S.L. (1996). *Tools of the trade: A therapist's guide to art therapy assessments.* Springfield, IL: Charles C Thomas, Publisher, Ltd.

Brooke, S.L. (2004). *Tools of the trade: A therapist's guide to art therapy assessments: Tools of the trade,* (2nd ed.). Springfield, IL: Charles C Thomas, Publisher, Ltd.

Bush, J. (1997). *A handbook for school-art therapy: Introducing art therapy into a public school system.* Springfield, IL: Charles C Thomas, Publisher, Ltd.

Cane, F. (1951/1983). *The artist in each of us.* New York: Pantheon Books.

Cohen, B. M. (1985). *The Diagnostic Drawing Series handbook.* Alexandria, VA: Barry Cohen.

Cohen, B. M., Hammer, J. S., & Singer, S. (1988). The Diagnostic Drawing Series: A systematic approach to art therapy evaluation and research. *The Arts in Psychotherapy, 15,* 11–21.

Dissayanake, E. (1988). *What is art for?* Seattle and London: Washington University Press. Edwards, M. (2001). Jungian analytic art therapy. In J. A. Rubin (Ed.). *Approaches to art therapy* (pp. 81–94). Philadelphia: Brunner-Routledge.

Elkins, D. E., & Stovall, K. (2000). American Art Therapy Association, Inc.: 1998–1999. Membership survey report. *Art Therapy: Journal of the American Art Therapy Association, 17,* 41–46.

Frank, T. (1983). Margaret Naumburg, Pioneer art therapist: A son's perspective. In K. C. Detre, T. Frank, C. R. Kniazzeh, M. C. Robinson, J. A. Rubin, & E. Ulman, Roots of art therapy: Margaret Naumburg (1890–1983) and Florence Cane (1882–1952). *American Journal of Art Therapy, 22,* 111–123.

Freud, S. (1900/1955). *Interpretation of dreams,* Standard (ed.). Vols. 4–5. London: Hogarth Press.

Gantt, L., & Tabone, C. (1998). *Rating manual for the Formal Elements Art Therapy Scale.* Morgantown, WV: Gargoyle Press.

Garai, J. (2001). Humanistic art therapy. In J. A. Rubin (Ed.). *Approaches to art therapy* (pp. 149–162). Philadelphia: Brunner-Routledge.

Goodenough, F. (1926). *Measurement of intelligence by drawings.* New York: Harcourt, Brace, & World.

Groth-Marnat, G. (1984). *Handbook of psychological assessment.* New York: Van Nostrand Reinhold Company.

Hammer, E. F. (Ed.). (1958). *The clinical application of projective drawings.* Springfield, IL: Charles C Thomas, Publisher, Ltd.

Harris, D. (1963). *Children's drawings as measures of intellectual maturity.* New York: Harcourt, Brace, & World.

Henley, D. (1992). *Exceptional art, exceptional children.* Worcester, MA: Davis Publications.

Henley, D. (2001). Art therapy in creative education. In J. A. Rubin (Ed.). *Approaches to art therapy* (pp. 326–339). Philadelphia: Brunner-Routledge.

Hogan, S. (2001). *Healing arts: The history of art therapy.* London & Philadelphia: Jessica Kingsley, Publishers.

Jordan, H. (1989). An interview with Janie Rhyne. *American Journal of Art Therapy, 27*, 107–112.

Jung, C. G. (1964). *Man and his symbols.* Garden City, NY: Doubleday.

Junge, M. B., & Asawa, P. P. (1994). *A history of art in the United States.* Mundelein, IL: The American Art Therapy Association.

Kapitan, L. (2004). Cross-training: The case for creating the next generation of art therapy credentials. *AATA Newsletter, 37* (2), 1–2.

Kaplan, F. F. (2000). *Art, science and art therapy: Repainting the picture.* London and Philadelphia: Jessica Kingsley, Publishers.

Keyes, M. F. (1983). *Inward journey: Art as therapy.* LaSalle, IL: Open Court Publishing Company.

Kohut, H. (1971). *The analysis of the self.* New York: International Universities Press.

Kramer, E. (1958). *Art therapy in a children's community.* New York: Schocken Books.

Kramer, E. (1971). *Art as therapy with children.* New York: Schocken Books.

Kramer, E. (1979). *Childhood and art therapy.* New York: Schocken Books.

Kramer, E. (2001a). Sublimation and art therapy. In J. A. Rubin (Ed.), *Approaches to art therapy* (pp. 28–39). Philadelphia: Brunner-Routledge.

Kramer, E. (2001b). *Art as therapy: Collected papers.* London & Philadelphia: Jessica Kingsley, Publishers.

Kramer, E., & Schehr, J. (1983). An art therapy evaluation session for children. *American Journal of Art Therapy, 23,* 3–12.

Kris, E. (1952). *Psychoanalytic explorations in art.* New York: Schocken Books.

Kwiatkowska, H. Y. (1967). The use of families' art productions for psychiatric evaluation. *Bulletin of Art Therapy, 6,* 52–69.

Kwiatkowska, H. Y. (1978). *Family therapy and evaluation through art.* Springfield, IL: Charles C Thomas, Publisher, Ltd.

Lachman-Chapin, M. (2001). Self psychology and art therapy. In J. A. Rubin (Ed.), *Approaches to art therapy* (pp. 66–78). Philadelphia: Brunner-Routledge.

Landgarten, H. B. (1981). *Clinical art therapy.* New York: Brunner/Mazel.

Landgarten, H. B. (1987). *Family art psychotherapy.* New York: Brunner/Mazel.

Landgarten, H. B. (1993). *Magazine photocollage: A multicultural assessment and treatment technique.* Springfield, IL: Charles C Thomas, Publisher, Ltd.

Levick, M. (1998). *The Levick Emotional and Cognitive Art Therapy Assessment (LECATA).* Unpublished manuscript, received April 24, 1998.

Lowenfeld, V. (1947). *Creative & mental growth.* New York: Macmillan.

Lowenfeld, V. (1957). *Creative & mental growth,* (3rd ed.). New York: Macmillan.

MacGregor, J. (1983). Paul-Max Simon: The father of art and psychiatry. *Art Therapy: Journal of the American Art Therapy Association, 1,* 8–20.

Machover, K. (1949). *Personality projection in the drawing of the human figure.* Springfield, IL: Charles C Thomas, Publisher, Ltd.

Malchiodi, C. (1990). *Breaking the silence: Art therapy with children from violent homes.* New York: Brunner/Mazel.

Malchiodi, C. (Ed.). (1999a). *Medical art therapy with adults.* London & Philadelphia: Jessica Kingsley Publishers.

Malchiodi, C. (Ed.). (1999b). *Medical art therapy with children.* London & Philadelphia: Jessica Kingsley, Publishers.

Malchiodi, C. (2004). Increasing art therapists' income opportunities: A summary of the strategic planning report by Matt Dunne, legislative consultant. *American Art Therapy Association Newsletter, 37* (1), 1–3.

McMahan, J. (1989). An interview with Edith Kramer. *American Journal of Art Therapy, 27,* 107–114.

McNiff, S. (1981). *The arts in psychotherapy.* Springfield, IL: Charles C Thomas, Publisher, Ltd.

McNiff, S. (1998). *Trust the process.* Boston: Shambhala.

McNiff, S. (1999). *Art-based research.* London & Philadelphia: Jessica Kingsley, Publishers.

McNiff, S. (2001). Pandora's gifts: The use of the imagination and all of the arts. In J. A. Rubin (Ed.). *Approaches to art therapy,* (2nd ed.) (pp. 318–325). Philadelphia: Brunner-Routledge.

Moon, B. (1990/1995). *Existential art therapy.* Springfield, IL: Charles C Thomas, Publisher, Ltd.

Moon, B. (1997/2004). *Art & soul.* Springfield, IL: Charles C Thomas, Publisher, Ltd.

Moon, B. (2000). *Ethical issues in art therapy.* Springfield, IL: Charles C Thomas, Publisher, Ltd.

Murray, H. A. (1943). *Thematic-Apperception-Test.* Cambridge, MA: Harvard University Press.

Naumburg, M. (1928). *The child and the world.* New York: Harcourt, Brace.

Naumburg, M. (1947). *Studies in the "free" art expression of behavior problem children and adolescents as a means of diagnosis and therapy.* New York: Teachers College Press.

Naumburg, M. (1950). *Schizophrenic art.* New York: Grune & Stratton.

Naumburg, M. (1953). *Psychoneurotic art.* New York: Grune & Stratton.

Naumburg, M. (1958). Art therapy: Its scope and function. In E. G. Hammer (Ed.), *The clinical application of projective drawings* (pp. 511–517). Springfield, IL: Charles C Thomas, Publisher, Ltd.

Naumburg, M. (1966). *Dynamically oriented art therapy: Its principles and practice.* New York: Grune & Stratton.

Naumburg, M. (1973). *Studies in the "free" art expression of behavior problem children and adolescents as a means of diagnosis and therapy.* (Rev. ed.). New York: Teachers College Press.

Neuman, E. (1959). *Art and the creative unconscious: Four essays.* London: Routledge & Kegan Paul.

Oster, G., & Gould, P. (1987). *Using drawings in assessment & therapy: A guide for mental health professionals.* London: Brunner-Routledge.

Pavlov, I. P. (1927). *Conditioned reflexes.* (G. V. Anrep, Trans.). London: Oxford University Press.

Perls, F. (1969). *Gestalt therapy verbatim.* Moab, UT: Real People Press.

Piaget, J. (1951). *Play, dreams and imitation in childhood.* New York: W. W. Norton.

Piaget, J., & Inhelder, B. (1967). *The child's conception of space.* New York: W. W. Norton.

Pickford, R. W. (1967). *Studies in psychiatric art: Its psychodynamics, therapeutic value, and relationship to modern art.* Springfield, IL: Charles C Thomas, Publisher, Ltd.

Prinzhorn, H. (1922/1995). *Artistry of the mentally ill (revised).* New York: Springer-Verlag.

Rabin, M. (2003). *Art therapy & eating disorders: The self as significant form.* New York: Columbia University Press.

Rhyne, J. (1973/1996). *The Gestalt art experience.* Monterey, CA: Brooks/Cole Publishing Company.

Rhyne, J. (2001). Gestalt art therapy. In J. A. Rubin (Ed.). *Approaches to art therapy* (pp. 134–148). Philadelphia: Brunner-Routledge.

Riley, S. (1994). *Integrative approaches to family art psychotherapy.* Chicago, IL: Magnolia Street Publishers.

Riley, S. (2001a). Art in group therapy. In J. A. Rubin (Ed.). *Approaches to art therapy.* Philadelphia: Brunner-Routledge.

Riley, S. (2001b). Commentary. In J. A. Rubin (Ed.). *Approaches to art therapy* (pp. 281–284). Philadelphia: Brunner-Routledge.

Robbins, A. (1987a). *The artist as therapist.* New York: Human Sciences Press.

Robbins, A. (1994). *A multi-modal approach to creative art therapy.* New York: Taylor & Francis, Inc.

Robbins, A. (2001). Object relations and art therapy. In J. A. Rubin (Ed.). *Approaches to art therapy* (pp. 54–65). Philadelphia: Brunner-Routledge.

Rogers, N. (1993). *The creative connection: Expressive arts as healing.* Palo Alto, CA: Science and Behavior Books.

Rogers, N. (2001). Person-centered expressive arts therapy. In J. A. Rubin (Ed.). *Approaches to art therapy* (pp. 163–177). Philadelphia: Brunner-Routledge.

Rorschach, H. (1921). *Psychodiagnostics.* Bern: Bircher.

Rosal, M. L. (1996). *Approaches to child art therapy.* Burlingame, CA: Abbeygate.

Rosal, M. L. (2001). Cognitive-behavioral art therapy. In J. A. Rubin (Ed.). *Approaches to art therapy* (pp. 210–225). Philadelphia: Brunner-Routledge.

Roth, E. (1978). Art therapy with emotionally disturbed-mentally retarded children: A technique of reality shaping. In B. K. Mandel, et al. (Eds.). *The dynamics of creativity* (pp. 168–172). Baltimore: American Art Therapy Association.

Roth, E. (2001). Behavioral art therapy. In J. A. Rubin (Ed.). *Approaches to art therapy* (pp. 195–209). Philadelphia: Brunner-Routledge.

Rubin, J. A. (1978). *Child art therapy.* New York: Van Nostrand Reinhold.

Rubin, J. A. (1984). *The art of art therapy.* New York: Brunner/Mazel.

Rubin, J. A. (Ed.). (1987/2001). *Approaches to art therapy.* Philadelphia: Brunner-Routledge.

Rubin, J. A. (1998). *Art therapy: An introduction.* Philadelphia: Brunner-Routledge.

Silver, R. (1978). *Developing cognitive and creative skills through art: Programs for children with communication disorders.* Baltimore: University Park Press. Author's Guild Backinprint.com Edition.

Silver, R. (1983/1996). *Silver Drawing Test of cognition & emotion.* Sarasota, FL: Albin Press.

Silver, R. (1989/1991). *Stimulus drawing and techniques.* Sarasota, FL: Albin Press Distributors.

Silver, R. (1993). *Draw-A-Story.* Mamaroneck, NY: Albin Press.

Silver, R. (2001a). *Art as language.* Philadelphia: Brunner-Routledge.

Silver, R. (2001b). Assessing and developing cognitive skills through art. In J. A. Rubin (Ed.). *Approaches to art therapy* (pp. 241–253). Philadelphia: Brunner-Routledge.

Silver, R. (2002). *Three art assessments: The Silver Drawing Test of cognition and emotion; Draw a story: Screening for depression; and Stimulus drawings and techniques.* New York: Brunner-Routledge.

Skinner, B. F. (1953). *Science and human behavior.* New York: The Free Press.

Sobol, B., & Williams, K. (2001). Family and group art therapy. In J. A. Rubin (Ed.). *Approaches to art therapy* (pp. 261–280). Philadelphia: Brunner-Routledge.

Stein, J. (Ed.). (1975). *The Random House College Dictionary* (Revised ed.). New York: Random House, Inc.

Ulman, E. (1961). Art therapy: Problems of definition. *Bulletin of Art Therapy, 1* (2), 10–20.

Ulman, E. (1975). A new use of art in psychiatric diagnosis. In E. Ulman, & P. Dachinger (Eds.). *Art therapy in theory and practice* (pp. 361–386). New York: Schocken Books.

Ulman, E. (2001). Variations on a Freudian theme. In J. A. Rubin (Ed.). *Approaches to art therapy* (pp. 289–305). Philadelphia: Brunner-Routledge.

Ulman, E., Kramer, E., & Kwiatkowska, H. Y. (1978). *Art therapy in the United States.* Craftsbury Common, VT: Art Therapy Publications.

Wadeson, H. (1980). *Art psychotherapy.* New York: John Wiley.

Wadeson, H. (1987). *The dynamics of art psychotherapy.* New York: John Wiley.

Wadeson, H. (Ed.). (1989). *Advances in art therapy.* New York: John Wiley & Sons, Inc.

Wadeson, H. (Ed.). (1992). *A guide to conducting art therapy research.* Mundelein, IL: The American Art Therapy Association.

Wadeson, H. (Ed.). (2000). *Art therapy practice.* New York: John Wiley & Sons, Inc.

Wadeson, H. (2001). An eclectic approach to art therapy. In J. A. Rubin (Ed.). *Approaches to art therapy* (pp. 306–317). Philadelphia: Brunner-Routledge.

Wallace, E. (1975). Creativity and Jungian thought. *Art Psychotherapy, 2,* 181–187.

Wallace, E. (1990). *A queen's quest.* Velarde, NM: Moon Bear Press.

Wallace, E. (2001). Healing through the visual arts. In J. A. Rubin (Ed.). *Approaches to art therapy* (pp. 95–108). Philadelphia: Brunner-Routledge.

Waller, D. (1991). *Becoming a profession: The history of art therapy in Britain 1940–1982.* London: Tavistock/Routledge.

Williams, G., & Wood, M. (1979). *Developmental art therapy.* Baltimore: University Park Press.

Wilson, L. (1981). *Louise Nevelson: Iconography & sources.* New York: Garland Publishing, Inc.

Wilson, L. (2001). *Alberto Giacometti: Myth, magic, and the man.* New Haven and London: Yale University Press.

Wood, M. M. (1975). *Developmental therapy.* Baltimore: University Park Press.

Biographical Statement

Patricia St. John, Ed.D., ATR-BC, is Program Coordinator of the Graduate Art Therapy program at The College of New Rochelle and Associate Professor of Graduate Art Therapy and Art Education. She held elected offices as president of the New England Association of Art Therapists (NEAAT), served on the Board of Directors of the American Art Therapy Association (AATA), and as Associate Editor and, currently, Book Review Editor of *Art Therapy: Journal of the American Art Therapy Association.* She serves on AATA's Research Committee, Education Committee, Conference Program Committee, and is past chair of the Strategic Planning Committee. She has taught the history of art therapy for the past two decades.

Chapter 2

THE THEORY AND PRACTICE OF JUNGIAN ART THERAPY

HODA MAZLOOMIAN

INTRODUCTION

The contributions C.G Jung to the development and practice of art therapy are the core objective of this chapter. The seminal conflict between Freud and Jung precipitated their break in 1913 and led to Jung's formulation of a theory of psychology, which transcended the individual and linked all to a collective unconscious. This chapter contains concepts such as the centrality of the archetypes common to all humanity, and active imagination – the process through which everyone can reach her own inner images, at once unique and universal. Attention is paid to the development of Jungian ideas regarding creativity, art making, and the way they have influenced the theoretical orientation and the practice of art therapy.

THE THEORETICAL AND PHILOSOPHICAL CONFLICT BETWEEN FREUD AND JUNG AS CATALYST FOR ART THERAPY

There is no doubt that the initial impulse, stirring to generate the modern practice of art therapy, germinated from a statement made by Freud that dreamers dream in imagery and often say, "I could draw it but I don't know how to say it" (Freud, 1963, p. 90). As Rubin explains, Margaret Naumburg believed that Freud, in spite of this important discovery, "did not peruse this notion by including drawing as a part of the classical technique" (Rubin, 1987, p. 8). The mantel of including art therapy and a host of other creative modalities fell to Freud's one-time heir Carl Gustav Jung. It was the multifaceted ideological and theo-

retical conflict between Freud and Jung which led to their infamous break in 1913.

Cornett (1998) states that the fracture between psychology and spirituality to a large extent are ascribed to Freud's discomfort at the thought that psychoanalysis would be viewed as a Jewish phenomenon and subsequently marginalized. Jung's radical ideas of including spiritual concerns into his psychoanalytical model, Cornett asserts, were to a large extent tolerated by Freud because of Jung's father's position as a Protestant minister. Freud's undeviating attachment to rationalism and scientific positivism has led to the illusion that "human behavior is explainable, predictable, and ultimately controllable with accurate knowledge and the application of that knowledge" (p. 12).

The overemphasis of sexual drives seems to be a major concern for Jung when considering Freudian theories. Jung (1933) wrote, "Freud began by taking sexuality as the only psychic driving power, and only after my break with him did he grant an equal status to other psychic activities as well. For my part, I have subsumed the various psychic drives and forces under the concept of energy in order to avoid the arbitrariness of psychology that deals with the drives and impulses alone" (p. 120).

The idea of a complex, or a constellation of emotionally charged feelings, ideas, and archetypal images, was another main point of difference between Freud and Jung. According to Jacobi (1959), Freud regarded the complex, merely, as a symptom of pathology. In contrast, Jung viewed the complex as also relating to psychological health. Philipson (1994) quoted Jung criticizing both Freud and Adler for "overemphasizing the pathological aspect of life and for interpreting man too exclusively in the light of his defect. . . ." "For my part, I prefer to look at a man in the light of what is healthy and sound" (p. 39).

Edwards (1987) highlights the important distinction between Freud and Jung towards their very diverse approaches to the imagery generated in dreams and fantasy. He states "Freud treated the dream, the fantasy, or the unconscious factor in a picture as a puzzle to be solved and explained in terms of psychoanalytical theory, whereas Jung attempted to relate to the unconscious image as an entity in its own right" (Edwards, 1987, p. 94).

ARCHETYPES AND THE COLLECTIVE UNCONSCIOUS

Hopcke (1999) explains that Jung saw the unconscious as more than the one-dimensional repository of forgotten and repressed personal memories. Jung re-christened the Freudian notion of the unconscious as personal, the second and deeper layer of the unconscious, he labeled the collective unconscious, a repository of "the patterns of psychic perception common to all mankind" (Hopcke, 1999, p. 14). These patterns included the archetypes which are "the inherited, unconscious, ideas and images" common to all cultures in their essential forms (Reber, 1995, p. 52).

Two of the most central archetypes in Jungian theory are the anima and the animus. Both words denote soul in Latin. The anima can be described as the feminine part of the male psyche and the animus is the masculine aspect of the female psyche. Fryrear and Corbit (1992) state that "Men identify their egos, or consciousness with masculinity and the corresponding feminine side is unconscious, while woman identify themselves consciously as feminine while the masculine side is unconscious"(p. 14). According to Hopcke (1999) Jung referred to theses archetypes as inferior, meaning that it both existed below the level of conscious awareness and that they are functioning imperfectly. This narcissistic projection of such imperfectly formed inner manifestations of the opposite sex is often seen in such acts as men holding their wives or girlfriends to be Madonna figures, and women waiting for their knights in shining armor. This is to say, we see in perfection some aspect of the opposite sex that is imperfectly manifested in our own inner selves.

The shadow can be described as an archetype that encapsulates all that an individual does not like about him or herself, including unacceptable thoughts, feelings, desires, and impulses he or she wishes to conceal. It is also a source of human vitality, creativity, and knowledge. This aspect of the psyche is often denied, repressed, or projected. Edwards (1987) states that the images that originate from the shadow in therapy have a quality of "otherness" and are "feared and rejected "by the client (p. 105). Jung (1966) noted the importance of learning about our shadow and integrating it within our consciousness. "The shadow is a living part of the personality and therefore wants to live within it in some form. It cannot be argued out of existence or rationalized into harmlessness" (p. 20). Jung also asserted that, "Seen from the one-sided point of view of the conscious attitude, the shadow is an inferior component of the personality and is consequently repressed through intensive resistance. But the repressed content must be made conscious so far as to produce a union of opposites, without which no movement is possible" (Keyes, 1976, p. 77). Hopcke (1999) argues that according to Jung ". . . the individuation process almost always begins with this humbling integration of the shadow into the conscious sense of self, the first and most important task on the road to psychic health" (p. 84).

The self is the archetype of wholeness. Jung defines the self as ". . . a quantity that is superordinate to the conscious ego" embracing both the conscious and the unconscious psyche (p. 175). Hopcke (1999) states that Jung was fascinated by the appearance of this symbol in many of the world's religious systems symbolizing both "completion and integration" (p. 96). Wallace (1987) asserts, ". . . the self is of special importance as a healing factor. It has a regulating, stabilizing function, compensating for any imbalance that may arise" which she prefers to call "the creative source" (p. 114).

The mandala, which in Sanskrit represents the sacred circle, denotes prehistoric and ancient symbols repeated throughout nature. In addition, it is a recurring motif echoed in the world's diverse cultures. The mandala is an archetype, which has become of particular interest to the art therapists as a graphic presentation of the continuously shifting nature of the self and the pictorial symbol of its wholeness. Jung in McGuire and Hull (1977) stated that "The mandala is . . . the archetype of inner order. . . . It is the symbol of wholeness . . . , bringing order, showing the possibility of order" (pp. 327–328). Jung (1973) notes that the mandala archetype seems to surface when the psyche is a state of chaos and bewilderment. The mandala, he contends, can transform this state of disorientation and tension to organization and calm (pp. 76–77). Jung drew his first mandala in 1916 during his own period of psychic disturbance following his traumatic break with Freud. He realized later that the nature of the mandalas changed and tended to correspond to his inner condition at any given time.

In ancient Greek plays, the persona was referred to the mask the actor wore to represent a particular character. Jung borrowed this term to refer to our tendency to wear a social mask in order to project a public image of ourselves and to protect our more vulnerable inner reality. According to Hopcke (1999), Jung, preoccupied as he was with the inner life of the individual, often tended to talk about the persona in derogatory terms. He asserts, however, that Jung also valued the persona as a necessary mediator between the ego and the outer world. Hopcke contends that the overdevelopment of the persona can cause one's overidentification with social position or occupational role. On the other hand, an inadequately developed persona can leave a person insufficiently protected and much more vulnerable to psychic injury (p. 89).

There are numerous other important archetypes such as the wise old man, the mother, the father, the divine child, the maiden, the hero, and the trickster, not explored here, as their mere perusal is beyond the scope of this chapter. The reader should refer to other sources such as Jung's collected works for further study. It is in the careful study of the archetypes and their universal resonance, that we awake to the glimpses of the collective unconscious, at once their container and conduit.

Jung developed his notion of the universal human experience as manifested in the collective unconscious by traveling to many countries around the first decade of the twentieth century. His destinations included a visit to the United States followed by his travels "to North Africa, to the Pueblo Indians of New Mexico, to East Africa and finally to India" (Jafé, 1979, p. 149). He was struck by the similarities of the myths current amongst different cultures and understood that they are deeper connections that join the diverse peoples of the world

through dreams, religion, and mythology. Such myths he found in the sacred art forms such as Native American sand painting, Indian sculpture, and African ceremonial artifacts. Jung's endeavors unearthed the images that are the thread connecting all humanity (Jafé, 1979). His approach to art and therapy is then rooted in the multicultural commonalities that are universal.

McConeghey (1986) suggests that Jungian analytical art therapy is synonymous with multiculturalism. He postulates:

> The image goes beyond the merely personal layer of the unconscious. The patient's problem is not then merely a personal matter, but something which crosses individual boundaries of those of any single culture, to touch upon the problems of mankind in general. (p. 111)

McConeghey (1986) expresses the view that it is the archetypal material that is the source of the mythical images, which then become "constellated by the disease" (p. 111). He believes that the function of the therapist is to assist the patient to relate to the archetypal connotation of his/her images. According to him, the contextual associations of an image can only be provided by the client. In Jungian terms, the process of inviting the patient's own elaboration of the subjective meaning of their images is called amplification. Amplification can lead to the discovery of the patient's complexes and particular attention must be paid to how the patient operates within the context of his or her complexes. In brief, McConeghey (1986) is saying that the personal image and its associated complexes can be best understood in the context of their archetypal meaning and the clients own associations. Since the archetypal art therapy is based on universal symbolism that resonates in all cultures then, its practice is necessarily multicultural.

JUNG'S BREAKDOWN AND THE DISCOVERY OF ACTIVE IMAGINATION

It was both the public and personal irreconcilable differences that led to the acrimonious professional divorce between Freud and Jung that became the catalyst for Jung's systematic use of art in the process of his work with his patients. Joan Chodorow (1990, 1997) describes vividly how Jung experienced a great psychic turmoil after his separation from Freud. Haunted by intrusive and disturbing imagery, he quit his post as the professor of psychiatry at the University of Zurich. It was during this turbulent time that Jung reviewed his entire life in order to get to the roots of his psychological pain. This inner turbulence convinced Jung that he needed to return to an infantile state of play and in this manner discovered the process of active imagination, a pivotal methodology used in his analytical approach, to give concrete form to the often unconscious archetypal imagery. In spite of his great inner resistance and feelings of humiliation, Jung remained faithful to his strong conviction and spent much time at a lakeside, building miniature cities which eventually led to the retrieval of a childhood fantasy which allowed his recovery from the psychological crisis within which he had fallen.

McGregor (1989) also examines this period in Jung's life describing Jung's mental state as "approximating psychosis" (p. 247). He explains a process by which Jung wrote his fantasies in a black book and then transferred them into a red book, where they were given pictorial form through sketches and drawings of mandalas. The two-step process then became the core methodology for the application of the active imagination.

Wallace (1987) quotes Jung defining active imagination as "a method, devised by myself, of introspection for the observing of the stream of interior images (p. 117)." She refers to a letter that Jung wrote to Hermann Keyserling, in which he described its process step-by-step. Jung advised Keyserling to:

- Ask, who or what has come alive . . . who or what has entered my psychic life and created disturbances and wants to be heard.
- Switch off your noisy consciousness and listen quietly inward and look at the images that appear before your inner eye.
- Write down what then comes without criticism. Images should be drawn and painted assiduously no matter whether you can do it or not.
- Wait a day to ask the unconscious any emerging questions.
- Disregard his own rationalizations no matter how apt they may seem.

Jungian theory focuses on the emergence of imagery from the unconscious which includes shouldering the moral and ethical responsibility to try and understand the meaning of the emerging images and integrating them into the psyche. According to Wallace (1987), Marie-Louise Von Franz systematized the process of active imagination and broke it down into four steps:

1. Empty the mind from ego's distracting thought patterns.
2. Allow the image to come into the sphere of awareness, achieving a balance between letting the images pass unseen and concentrating so hard the process is hampered.
3. Express the encounter with the images in concrete form by writing, painting, sculpting, dancing or playing music.
4. Contemplate the meaning of the messages received. (pp. 117–118).

THE PRIMACY OF THE IMAGE

Watkins (1981) delineates six different fundamental perspectives in relating to the images brought forth from the unconscious in the process of art therapy. These include diagnostic, perceived as dangerous, for the sake of treatment, interpretive, expression as curative, and respecting the image as it is. First, in the diagnostic approach the patient is encouraged to produce images for the benefit of the clinical practitioner at the start or the end of the sessions, which are not seen as a part of his or her treatment. There is precious little involvement by the patient and the artwork is sequestered by the art therapist for analytical scrutiny.

The second approach is the perspective that envisages the unconscious and its manifestations as dangerous. Responsible clinicians are to avoid colluding with the client's propensity to dredge up disturbing images from their psyche. To do so is seen as tantamount to encouraging delusions and other positive schizophrenic symptoms. "Crafts and representational art may be emphasized but not art that reaches towards fantasy" (Watkins, 1981, pp. 109–110).

Third, the image itself is seen as the patient. "The image does not heal, we heal the image" (p. 111). The art therapist makes value judgments and encourages the creation of what he or she considers positive or ego-enhancing imagery. Attention is deliberately withdrawn from the artwork with unsettling imagery.

The fourth is what Watkins labels as "interpretive" (p. 115). The image is given lesser priority than the hidden messages sought by the interpreter as manifestations of "traumatic events and psychosexual issues" arising from the clients personal history (p. 115). The causes of such images are symbols that are assumed to be unsatiated desires, and would evaporate if a more satisfying reality were to be experienced by the patient.

Within the fifth approach, the image itself is assumed to be the curative agent. The therapeutic relationship between patient and therapist and their interactive interpretation of the image are not seen as influencing healing. "There is virtually no attempt to form an insightful integration of the imaginal and the daily" (p. 116).

Watkins advocates for the sixth approach where the image is afforded respect regardless of the apprehension it may evoke. Active imagination is encouraged and there is no attempt made to manipulate the image or the manner in which it is manifested. The image is seen as the "eye" through which one experiences reality. The art therapist's role is seen as the vital interventions of a trained helper who assists the patient to stay with the unadulterated image and understand the metaphorical meanings it has to bestow (Watkins, 1981). In order for art therapists to remain faithful to the integrity of their patient's images, they should maintain a dialogue with their own images.

Greg Furth (2002) was attracted to the work of theorists using projective techniques such as the House Tree Person Test (Buck, 1973) and found them to be ". . . insightful indicators of both psychological and somatic information about the person drawing" (p. viii). This assessment was reviewed by Brooke (2004). Furth describes his book, *The Secret World of Drawings*, as a tool to decipher and understand client's drawings and getting insight to their psyche. He felt frustrated that Jung had underscored the primacy of symbols but had not devised any formal device for ". . . analyzing drawings for their unconscious content" and so he devised a system of his own (p. 1). His presumption is that the therapist is the active agent that can uncover the curative factors in the relationship, relegating the role of the client to that of the passive patient whose imagination is systematically mined for images that surface from the psyche.

All this seems to belie the spirit of Jung's theoretical convictions. As Philipson (1994) proposes "it is

not the consequence of Jung's thought that the work of art should be treated as if expressing a Neurosis, which then could be analyzed " (p. 4). He goes on to suggest that this kind of analysis seems to be less valuable than the synthetic method of analysis, which Jung developed to delve deeply in to the bizarre fantasies of his clients.

Joy Schaverien (1992) focused mainly on the wide-ranging implications of transference in the process of art therapy. She postulates that images are elemental parts of the transference process and not merely their graphic externalization by the client. She draws distinctions between images that embody symbolic meaning and those that illustrate an object/concept. The former type of image, she asserts, is richer in deep symbolism arising from the psyche, which can be analyzed within the therapeutic relationship with the full participation and involvement of the client. Pat B. Allen (in press) refers to being influenced by Jung's "revolutionary psychological ideas" of making a deep commitment to respond to the spontaneous images revealed by his psyche by painting, meditating, and writing about them.

McNiff sees Jung's work as the ". . . unacknowledged foundation of art therapy practice..." (Fryrear & Corbit, 1992, p. v). He gives credit to Jung for anticipating the process of active imagination, which he names "image dialogue" (McNiff, 1992, p. 145). McNiff (1998), states that his method of inquiry into the image is similar to Jung's active imagination. McNiff's methodology also entails questioning the very framework of art-based research, joining Jung in his "voyage of discovery" which "involves an immersion in the creative imagination and its 'uncertain path'" (McNiff, 1998, p. 13).

THE JUNGIAN APPROACH TO ART THERAPY IN ACTION

The work of several practitioners is examined below, in order to attempt to create a consensus in developing a theoretical framework that can be called Jungian. This section will address the flexibility and diversity inherent in the conceptual approach Jung applied to all his investigations, which is the notion of the union of opposites. Jung postulated that "in nature the resolution of the opposites is always an energetic process: she acts symbolically, in the truest sense of the word, doing something that expressed both sides, just as the waterfall mediates between above and below" (Chodorow, 1997, pp. 166–67).

Dougherty (1974) described co-leading an art therapy group with "five women between the ages of 18 and 55" all sharing a diagnosis of schizophrenia (p. 230). In the beginning, the therapists chose to instruct the group to "draw the group" and processed the resultant artwork for the second half of the session. This approach produced a feeling of alienation between the members, as they drew representations of themselves and rotated to embellish one another's work. Processing led to stereotypical and pointless conversations. When they changed the focus of the activity to art-centered, there was a move towards the expression of the fears and dangers intrinsic to the group process. Next, there was a chaotic response to the theme of landscapes. There was no agreement on the orientation of sky, land, or water and participants began to work on top of each other's areas "in an aggressive manner" (p. 232). At this point the axis of leadership changed from the therapists to the group, when a member suggested that they should work with geometrical shapes. There followed discernable group cohesiveness with resultant mandala-type joint mural. Dougherty concluded that Jung's theory that mandalas promoted psychic unity was therefore upheld. She concluded that Jungian approach to art therapy is effective in allowing the patient to see that the archetype of the shadow manifested as "the monster that threatens to devour is the other side of the wish to love and be loved," i.e., a classical Jungian notion of the union of opposites was detected within the art therapy process (p. 236).

Wilmer (1976) also dealt with a similar population but detailed his work with the clients in the context of a therapeutic community in the Veteran's Administration hospital in San Antonio in 1974. He described this community as "Jungian-orientated" wherein the clients were motivated to remain within the program and deal with their inner realities. Medications were reduced to the absolute minimum necessary to insure the control of violent or severely disruptive behaviors but were not given for control of delusions, hallucinations, and other psychotic symptoms. Clients were encouraged to make art at any time of day and night instead of using medication. Wilmer further asserts, "There is clinical evidence that antipsychotic drugs interfere with cognitive learning, with perception and communication and with sponta-

neous creativity" (p. 339). He advocates the acceptance of the chaotic inner life of patients "as meaningful and symbolic and a necessary state to be passed through, not to be reasoned or drugged away" (p. 339). This, he believes, will lead to instillation of hope and the reintegration of the fractured psyche.

Finely (1975) describes the fundamentals of the technique of dialogue drawing or a type of nonverbal and spontaneous visual communication between the analyst and analysand. She believes that the shared artwork gives graphic form to the relationship between her and the analysand, and thus makes it visible. In her words:

> The technique has two basic aspects, the image and the dialogue. The dialogue takes place as a graphic speaking and responding. (p. 87)

Finely noticed two polarities when working with people. On one extreme there are people who do not trust spoken interactions and would be instead inundated with images. On the other polarity, there are individuals who hide behind the words and need some help in accessing their inner images. The former, Finely helps to control the flood and the latter she catalyzes to find their images. She believes that this process puts the therapist in a more vulnerable position; therefore, increases the possibility of empathy and trust being established. In the context of Jungian principle of the union of opposites she asserts, ". . . the process in which we are involved goes with *and* against nature, requires the experience of both hubris and humility, alienation and communication, rejection and acceptance . . ."(p. 88). It is within these paradoxical "betweenness" where the "transforming images" come to the surface and are made visible (p. 88). In addition, Finely expresses the awareness that, during this process, the images usually seen as negative and aggressive can become fully engaged with those that are normally seen as positive and inspirational and be experienced simultaneously. She warns that the practitioner must realize that his own personal unconscious may be resisting his/her analysand's expression of the collective unconscious. If the analyst learns how to get out of the way quickly, it is possible for the analysand to be healed "at the nonego level where the wounds accrued in the first place, between the child's and the parent's archetypal constellations" (p. 97).

Keyes (1976) discusses the process of evoking and integrating the shadow archetype. Her methodology includes the use of writing, meditative amplification, and art making. It seeks to identify and depict the various aspects of the shadow that is most intensely projected on to the members of the same sex, who possess similar traits. This culminates in an invitation for each individual to Gestalt the aspects of the shadow by giving them a voice and in present tense and acting out their energies (p. 77). Another method entailed clients choosing several diverse photographs that included "every conceivable human emotion and behavior" (p. 78). The participants were asked to pick five or six images they interpreted as positive, and five or six they perceived as negative, and to make a collage with them, paying particular attention to their arrangement in a personally meaningful manner. Keyes found that clients had a tendency to place images that represented important issues currently occurring in their lives in the center of the picture. The images they were consciously concerned with were placed at the right of the central theme and the projected or denied aspect of the shadow to the left of it.

Selegelis (1987) sought to empirically explore the theory and clinical application of the mandala in the context of a Jungian approach to "art psychotherapy" (p. 301). Particularly, she examined any discernable differences between artwork produced within a circle as opposed to a square. She contends that is evidence to relate fearful and hostile feelings with angular lines. To test her hypothesis, she selected a group of 32 college students between the ages of 17 and 25 and randomly divided them in two groups. One group was asked to draw within circles and the other within squares. Selegelis found that there was statistically significant data in the resultant drawings to support her hypothesis that fewer angles were drawn within circles, supporting Jung's contention that mandalas had a calming and soothing effect on both the client-artist and the viewer.

Fryrear and Corbit (1992) made extensive use of instant photographs in their practice of art therapy with their clients. Therapy participants were encouraged to pose for the photographs in response to their inner feeling states and then to confront their self-image by allowing the integration of other media such as drawing, painting, collage, and sculptural elements. If such personal tales were found to be ego distonic, these clients were then encouraged to change their own personal mythic stories. They see photo art therapy not as a new discipline but as a different medium within the spectrum of media used by art therapists, expanding the pool of possible approaches to suit the diverse needs of various clients. Jung is quoted as stating ". . . the multi dimensionality of human nature requires the greatest variety of standpoints and methods in order to satisfy the variety of psychic dispositions" (Fryrear & Corbit, 1992, p. xiv). In other words, people who may find it too intimidating to draw are more willing to consider instant photography. One of their stated goals, in using photo art therapy, is the Jungian notion of "giving emotional disturbance visible shape" (p. xiii). In this way the image becomes a tangible focal point to be confronted, discussed, and changed as needed. They provide their clients with cameras, film, a variety of art media, crafts tools, and materials, to encourage a union of differing art therapy processes. Art is seen as the catalyst for the manifestation of sublimated but unconscious materials from psyche depth, making it more accessible to the self. On the other hand, "Photography begins with an image outside the self" which is then "generalized and integrated with the internal self" (p. xv). Jung asserted that self-understanding requires increased self-knowledge. One of the methods used in increasing self-knowledge is the self-portrait box, which enables each participant to pose record and examine different aspects of their persona, i.e., the masks they present to the outside world. These images are then compared with their true and hidden selves and will allow them to abandon the persona and to be ready to reveal their authentic selves to others.

Jung's theoretical perspective has also been a prominent source of development in the field of art-based assessment procedures. Doris Arrington (1992) lists as "Jungian" Arrington's Visual Preference Test, Mari Card Test, Old Masters Series, and Shoemaker's Rainbow Phenomenon. The first two are dealt with in this chapter as the interested practitioner is referred to the above-mentioned text.

Arrington's Visual Preference Test includes 56 graphic signs selected by art therapists from a much greater pool of images that appeared frequently in the artwork of their clients. "The cards represent four Jungian categories: Feminine, masculine, self (sense of self), and transformation (change) concepts" (p. 153). Participants are asked to rank a set number of images from most to least preferred. This test is said to have been "emperially tested with 128" mainly Caucasian women with children (p. 153).

The MARI Card Test was developed by Kellogg and has been used for more than a quarter of a century and involves the use of mandalas. During the test, the participants are asked to use oil pastels to draw and color inside a circle of 10.5 inches in diameter. The resultant mandala was then interpreted on "the basis of color, movement and symbols" (p. 153). The 26 cards were subsequently developed to correspond to 13 stages of life and 38 colored papers. The participants are requested to choose five cards and a corresponding color for each card. This test is only conducted by trained instructors. Tayer (2003) elaborates in detail regarding the Mari assessment test with its emphasis on the relationship between the participant's choices in accepting, rejecting cards, and assigning color schemes to both types of cards.

CONCLUSION

We can be sure with a strong degree of certainty that it is Jung who has the distinction of being the first art therapist. Jung (1960) stated as early as 1916 that "emotional disturbance can also be dealt with . . . not by clarifying it instinctually but by going by its visible shape" (p. 78). He went on to say that the patient can paint and draw such affective turbulence and that technical and aesthetic proficiency is not significant, but the aim is to approach the activity with playful fantasy that will make tangible the unconscious images. It is also important to know that, as Junge and Asawa (1994) recall, both Margaret Naumburg and her sister Florence Cane were analyzed by Beatrice Hinkle, who in 1916, had just translated Jung's *Psychology of the Unconscious* ". . . indicating a decidedly Jungian attraction and influence"(p. 13). Perhaps due to what Edwards (1987) refers to as "transference context" excising between the followers and Freud and Jung following their acrimonious break, Naumburg was lead to choose between Freud and Jung (p. 97). She increasingly identified herself with the writings and theories of Freud after this time.

Malchiodi (1999) agrees that the increasing liberal appropriation of concepts and practices from

psychology by art therapists can be mainly attributed to ". . . the prominent and lasting influence of Naumburg on art therapy education" (p. 2). It is clear that Naumburg, a strong and charismatic personality, heavily influenced and continues to affect generations of art therapists. Her adaptation of a seemingly empirical style which downplays the principal Jungian notions of the collective unconscious, the primordial influence of archetypes, the process of active imagination, and the essentially spiritual nature of man, has become a trend that has polarized the art therapy community.

Linda Gant (1998) can be seen as an exponent of the scientific pole questioning the veracity of almost every other mythology. Frustrated with many colleagues who resist or reject the scientific inquiry, she advocates the objective measurement of the client's images with the mythology developed by psychologists, anthologists, and statisticians. She contends that artworks are concrete objects, ideal for scientific inquiry, and denies that such mythologies applied to clients are reductionistic.

Wadeson (2002), on the other hand, exclaims that "we want outcome studies to prove that art therapy works, even though there are few studies demonstrating that psychotherapy works" (p. 170). She advocates that we "open our eyes to see that the artwork of our clients before us is the real magic in the art therapy process . . ." (p. 170). If we do, she promises that our clients ". . . will tell us about their lives, and open our hearts to reach out to them in a caring way" (p. 170).

Allen (1995) also sees art making as her "spiritual path" and states that the art therapies development into a profession modeled after the field of mental health has making art to become ". . . co-opted as just another treatment modality with prescribed goals and outcomes requiring predetermined meaning assigned to images" (p. xvi). She warns us that "this sort of professionalism robs art of one of its most potent properties, the ability to dissolve boundaries and reveal our interconnectedness with one another and reveal the dignity of our uniqueness"(p. xvi).

Ironically no one would enjoy such controversy more than Jung. In his characteristic fashion, he may well have argued both extremes for their merits and reached a golden mean by the union of such opposites. He taught us to tolerate and stay with such divergent thoughts and attitudes because he believed that "the extraordinary diversity of individual life necessitates the constant modifications of theory which are often applied quite unconsciously by the doctor himself, although in essence they may not accord with his theoretical credo" (Chodorow, 1997, p. 87).

The Jungian approach to art therapy is therefore not a fixed and inflexible system of ideological dictates which hampers the therapist to respond to the needs of his or her clients. Regarding his basic objective, Jung declared "My aim is to bring about a psychic state in which my patient begins to experiment with his own nature – a state of fluidity, change and growth where nothing is eternally fixed and hopelessly petrified" (Chodorow, 1997, p. 87).

Art therapists may do well to apply the same solutions to our field and bring about a state of fluidity. It is the conviction of the present writer that we must listen to the exponents of scientific approach to see what we can learn from a systematic approach of various images. In some ways archetypes are such psychically ingrained codifications. Their dilemma for them is how to avoid feeling as the superior active agents in the curative process and not to alienate the very clients they purport to assist. At the same time we must respect the gate keepers of the mysterious in the art therapy process, and understand that science can not have all the answers to the subtle inner workings of the human psyche. McNiff (1992) quotes Jung as warning that if we attempt to explain such mystery, "the bird is flown" (p. 65).

REFERENCES

Allen, P.B. (in Press). Eye of the soul. In Rubinov-Jacobson, P. (Ed.) *Eye of the soul.* Manuscript submitted for publication.

Allen, P.B. (1995). *Art is a way of knowing.* Boston, MA: Shambhala Publications.

Arrington, D. (1992). Art-based assessment procedures and instruments used in research. In *A guide to conducting art therapy research.* Mundelein, IL: The American Art Therapy Association, Inc.

Brooke, S.L. (2004). *A therapist's guide to art therapy assessments: Tools of the trade* (2nd ed.). Springfield, IL: Charles C Thomas, Publisher, Ltd.

Buck, J. N. (1973). *The house – tree – person technique/ revised manual.* Los Angeles, CA: Western Psychological Services.

Chodorow, J. (Speaker). (1990). *Active imagination* (Cassette Recording No. 415). Evanston, IL: C. G. Jung Institute of Chicago.

Chodorow, J. (Ed.). (1997). *Jung on active imagination.* Princeton, NJ: Princeton University Press.

Cornett, C. (1998). *The soul of psychotherapy: Recapturing the spiritual dimension in the therapeutic encounter.* New York: Free Press.

Dougherty, C.A. (1974). Group art therapy: A Jungian approach. *American Journal of Art Therapy, 13*(3), 229–236.

Edwards, M. (1987). Jungian analytic art therapy. In Ruben, J. A. (Ed.). *Approaches to art therapy* (pp. 92–113). New York: Brunner/Mazel, Inc.

Finely. (1975). Dialogue drawing: An image-evoking communication between analyst and analysand. *Art Psychotherapy, 2*(1), 87–99.

Freud, S. (1963). Dreams. In J Strachey (Ed. and Trans.). *New introductory lectures on psychoanalysis.* (Vol. XV, Part II). London: Hogarth Press.

Fryrear J, & Corbit I. (1992), *Photo art therapy: A Jungian perspective.* Springfield, IL: Charles C Thomas, Publisher, Ltd.

Furth, G.M. (2002). *The secret world of drawings: A Jungian approach to healing through art.* Toronto, Canada: Inner City Books.

Gant, L.M. (1998) A discussion of art therapy as a science. *Art Therapy: Journal of The American Art Therapy Association, 15*(1), 3–12.

Hopcke, R. R. (1999). *A guided tour of the collected works of C.G. Jung.* Boston, MA: Shambhala Publications Inc.

Jacobi, J. (1959). *Complex, archetype, symbol in the psychology of C.G. Jung.* NY: Bollingen Foundation Inc.

Jafé, A. (1979). *C.G Jung: Word and image.* Princeton, NJ: Princeton University Press.

Jung, C. G. (1933). *Modern man in search of a soul.* Orlando, FL: Harcourt Brace Jovanovich, Publishers.

Jung, C. G. (1960). *The structure and the dynamics of the psyche.* Collected Works, Vol. 8. Bollingen Series XX. Princeton, NJ: Pantheon Books, Princeton University Press.

Jung, C.G. (1966). *The practice of psychotherapy,* (2nd ed.). Collected works, Vol. 16. Bollingen Series XX. Princeton, NJ: Pantheon Books, Princeton University Press.

Jung, C.G. (1973). *Mandala symbolism,* (3rd ed.). (RFC Hull, Trans.) Bollingen Series. Princeton, NJ: Princeton University Press.

Junge, M.B & Asawa, P.P. (1994). *A history of art therapy in the United States.* Mundelein, IL: American Art Therapy Association.

Keyes, M. F. (1976). Art processes evoking awareness of the shadow archetype. *Art Psychotherapy, 3*(2), 77–80.

Malchiodi, C. A. (1999). The artist's way: Is it the art therapist's way. *Art Therapy: Journal of The American Art Therapy Association, 16*(1), 2–3.

McConeghey, H. (1986). Archetypal art therapy is multicultural art therapy. *Art Therapy: Journal of The American Art Therapy Association, 3,*111–114.

McGregor, J. M. (1989). *The discovery of the art of the insane.* Princeton, NJ: Princeton University Press.

McGuire, W., & Hull, R. (1977). *C.G Jung Speaking.* Princeton, NJ: Princeton University Press.

McNiff, S. (1992). *Art as medicine: Creating a therapy of the imagination.* Boston, MA: Shambhala Publications Inc.

McNiff, S. (1998). *Art based research.* London, England: Jessica Kingsley, Publishers Ltd.

Philipson, M. (1994). *An outline of Jungian aesthetics.* Boston, MA: Sigo Press.

Reber, A. S. (1995). *The Penguin dictionary of psychology.* (2nd ed.). New York: Penguin Books.

Rubin, J. A. (Ed.). (1987). *Approaches to art therapy.* New York: Brunner/Mazel.

Schaverien, J. (1992). *The revealing image.* London: Routledge.

Slegelis, M. H. (1987). A study of Jung's mandala and its relationship to art psychotherapy. *Arts in Psychotherapy, 14*(4), 301–311.

Tayer, Cox, C. (2003). The Mari assessment. In *Handbook of art therapy* (pp. 428–434). New York: The Guilford Press.

Wadeson, Harriet, (2002). The anti assessment devil's advocate. *Art Therapy: Journal of The American Art Therapy Association, 9* (4) 168–170.

Wallace, E. (1987). Healing through the visual arts: *Approaches to art therapy* (pp. 114–134). New York: Brunner/Mazel Inc.

Watkins, M.M. (1981). Six approaches to the image in art therapy. *Spring,* 107–125. Dallas, TX: Spring Publications.

Wilmer, H.A. (1976). Origins of a Jungian-oriented therapeutic community for schizophrenic patients. *Hospital and Community Psychiatry, 27*(5), 338–342.

Biographical Statement

Hoda Mazloomian MAAT, ATR-BC, LCPC, has worked for the last 18 years as an artist, art educator, art therapist, and consultant. He graduated in 1999 from the Masters program at the Art Institute of Chicago. For the last five years, he has been working at the Alternative Behavior Treatment Centers, Mundelein, Illinois, as their full-time art therapist where he initiated and developed an art therapy program. There, he has been working with adolescents with severe emotional and behavioral difficulties. For the last two years he has operated the art therapy program he initiated for Visions Network in Des Plaines, Illinois, working with adults with severe autism. He supervises several interns and has a small private practice in Evanston Illinois, where he currently resides.

Chapter 3

THE ASSESSMENT ATTITUDE*

ANNE MILLS

INTRODUCTION

Before a person becomes an expressive therapist, he or she must have already developed an artist's familiarity with a selected modality, whether it is visual art, dance, poetry, or music. We all remember the discipline inherent in learning skills in the arts, which might be exemplified by a Western visual artist who begins to learn the proper way to hold, load, use, and clean a Japanese sumi-e brush. The skill set is broken down, and practiced carefully (if clumsily) until it is second nature. Eventually, through a process of integration and transformation, the skills become part of the artist. Using the Japanese brush in a way that is in keeping with his or her own style, the artist also uses the tool correctly, with attention to issues of quality and dignity (Ivey & Ivey, 2003).

Learning to administer assessments skillfully also requires discipline, not in the sense of harshness but rather, as "an expression of caring for ourselves and the quality of our lives" (Welwood, 1983, p. 49) that helps make issues simple and "more straightforward" (Podvoll, 1983, p. 187). Once competence in assessment administration is achieved, it is followed by a time of transformation when the new knowledge is integrated, and becomes part of the clinician's therapeutic style. The behavior of an art therapist administering an assessment can be free, authentic, and also correct. This complex developmental sequence from discipline to freedom is little discussed, and often not achieved, in my observation.

Some art therapists have not developed the skill of administering assessments because they are "not comfortable with the notion of evaluation" (Feder & Feder, 1998, p. 3), diagnosis (Farmer, McGuffin, & Williams, 2002; Mills, 1986), or the perceived rigidity of the testing situation (Cohen, 2004). I would venture that sometimes art therapists rebel against the discipline of the standardized art interview, seeing it only as a restriction or punishment, rather than as a structure that frees one to focus attention on the other person. As a result, many art therapists do not use the correct wording or art materials for standardized drawing assessments (Mills & Goodwin, 1991). Sometimes art therapists feel the best of what they have to give is blocked from the session if they must follow certain guidelines. One hopes this is not so. While it is important to relax and use one's own style as a therapist, mastery of the discipline of the protocol should come first. An assessment interview is not merely a conversation, after all. It will be sequential, well organized, the interviewer will tend to control the interaction, and the client may be asked to dwell on uncomfortable feelings or memories (Benjamin, 1974). To be ambivalent about following a protocol could be self-indulgent or unfair to the client.

At the other end of the spectrum are those clinicians, particularly students, who tend to be stuck in the discipline stage. So focused are they on administering an assessment correctly, that they lose sight of the point of doing it, and forget to use the clinical skills they already possess when administering assessments. The core value of an assessment interview is to be willing to engage the person (Groth-Marnat, 1997, p. ix), or, as Kwiatkowska emphasized in her teaching, to interact with another person

* Much of this material was presented at the 2003 AATA conference as part of a panel of Barry M. Cohen, Kathryn Johnson, and Anne Mills entitled "A Twentieth Anniversary Assessment of the Diagnostic Drawing Series."

31

using art materials (J.K. Williams, personal communication, July 21, 2004). All else is "incidental" (Benjamin, 1974, p. xi). If one is there to merely "get the information" or "do an assessment for class," the client is reduced to being a tool (that is, an object and not a person). That is poor methodology, and even worse morality.

Recently, I began asking research participants (volunteers participating in research on the drawings of normal adults) if an art therapy student could observe me administering an art therapy assessment. Since then, a number of students have been allowed to sit in, individually. When the students subsequently expressed surprise at the warmth and "humaneness" of the art interview, and the richness of the discussion of the drawings, I was a little dismayed. I inferred that they had misconceptions about art interviews for assessment purposes, and that they had become so caught up in the procedure that they did not consider the attention they should be giving to the art and the person.

Teaching people how to administer assessments in a competent way – meaning, neither too narrowly nor too loosely – has not been addressed in the literature. In this chapter, I will often speak in terms of art therapy graduate students at the beginning of the learning curve, but my remarks could apply equally to trainees in other mental health professions, as well as seasoned clinicians. My aim is to help students and others become competent assessors by explicating what I call the assessment attitude.

SCIENTIST-PRACTITIONER

In the field of psychology, the term "scientist-practitioner" describes someone whose clinical work informs her research, and for whom research informs her clinical work. The field of art therapy has the term "artist as therapist" (W. Miller, personal communication, July 9, 2001), which I am using to describe someone who works in a studio environment, and who regards creativity as healing. The personal art making of the artist-therapist informs his or her work with others, and vice versa. These two ways of approaching clinical work might be dichotomized simplistically as systematic vs. spontaneous, objective vs. subjective, psychometric vs. impressionistic, or actuarial vs. intuitive.

The former approach might be considered a technical style that focuses on the integrity of the test and the information that can be quantified. Practitioners of the latter approach might say they do not assess but they "perform a similar function in a different or more informal manner" (Mills & Goodwin, 1991, p. 12). In such a case, the art interview would focus on the unique quality of the art-based interaction between two people. The challenge is to find a balance between these identities and world views in how we assess, as well as within our profession and ourselves (Kaplan, 2000). For discussion purposes, I have separated the two paradigms, but in theory, education, and practice, they need to be aligned.

ASSESSMENT

Now I will begin to use the term "assessment" to refer to "the more formal procedure in which an assessment instrument is used to produce a specific result, often a diagnosis," as Wadeson defined it (2002, p. 169). A related term, protocol, means the written directions for the administration of a standardized art therapy assessment. Admittedly, these definitions favor the scientist-practitioner part of our identity.

Assessment procedures themselves seem to fall more into either the psychometric camp or the impressionistic camp, depending on whether the tool is perceived as being related to research (such as the Person Picking an Apple from a Tree, or PPAT; Gantt & Tabone, 1998), which was reviewed by Brooke (2004), or diagnosis, or whether the art materials are the same as those that artists use (such as the Ulman procedure; Ulman, 1992). The attitude that the practitioner brings to the art interview, however, has greater influence over the quality of the interaction than the protocol of the assessment. For instance, the protocol may set time limits on art making, which could be helpful in busy settings. But it would be the prerogative of the clinician, not the protocol, to set the time limits on the verbal processing of the images. In practice, this could mean that sometimes discussion of the art might take longer than the administration of the assessment itself. An entire art interview could range from 10 minutes (inpatient) to 1 hour and 15 minutes (outpatient private practice). The sensitivity of the response to the person and the art product is where the art of the assessment process comes in, as will be discussed below.

LEARNING THE DISCIPLINE OF THE ASSESSMENT PROCEDURE

Many art therapy students feel like they have entered a foreign land when they begin to learn about assessment and tend not to see the administration of assessments as an aspect of their work as clinicians. Instead, assessment is sometimes perceived as different, inferior, boring, or frightening. Some view the discipline of the assessment (the materials, time limits, or precision of wording) as oppressive, or become overly anxious about their own performance. While a small amount of anxiety can improve one's performance, too much can impede performance, and even interfere with one's ability to concentrate on what the subject has said. It is important for assessment administrators to understand that mistakes happen. Benjamin (1974) noted it is completely acceptable to make statements like "I'm sorry; I missed that last part. What did you say?"

The administration of an assessment must be correctly done in order to be a competent and responsible practitioner. But mere correctness will not give the best possible results when we are trying to learn about a person's emotional state, personality traits, and his or her estimation of the circumstances at hand.

> The objective psychometric approach is most appropriately applicable to ability tests such as those measuring intelligence or mechanical skills. Its usefulness decreases, however, when users attempt to assess personality traits such as dependence, authoritarianism, or anxiety. Personality variables are far more complex and therefore need to be validated within the context of history, behavioral observations, and interpersonal relationships. (Groth-Marnat, 1997, p. 4)

Therefore the objective approach is less useful in most art therapy assessment situations (Groth-Marnat, 1997). The subjective approach supports the interviewer's ability to make observations of the person's behavior and how he or she relates to the interviewer and the art task. This yields complex and valuable information that can be used by the art therapist to test his or her emerging hypotheses about the client's diagnosis and strengths (Groth-Marnat, 1997).

In fields related to mental health, such as criminology and medicine, tests of the accuracy of clinical prediction show that a subjective or intuitive approach is less accurate than an actuarial approach. That is, an approach that uses research-based statistical models to predict diagnosis or recidivism outperforms clinical interviews (Dawes, Faust, & Meehl, 1989). Furthermore, the accuracy of clinical prediction may not even improve with experience. These findings cannot be generalized to art therapy but they may have some implications for how to train art therapists to serve clients well. It adds weight to the assumption that understanding the research on assessments may be essential to clinicians. They will need to know the strengths and weaknesses of various art therapy assessment procedures and, statistically, how people respond to them.

Many art therapists have the mistaken impression that merely administering an assessment procedure that is linked to analytical research, like the Diagnostic Drawing Series (DDS; Cohen, Mills, & Kijak, 1994), will result in diagnostic information. In fact, one needs to understand thoroughly the concept of psychopathology as well as the diagnostic manual (the DSM or ICD), their limitations, the idea of the interaction of various diagnoses, the notion of multiple causation of psychopathology, an understanding of the importance of the social context of the patient, and so on. One must also understand the rating terms of the art assessment accurately, and the research results and their strengths and weaknesses. Of course, the more research results that exist, the more complicated or daunting the task of familiarizing oneself may be. Needless to say, administering the DDS once will not suffice for a clinician to feel confident with this tool.

The student art therapist is not to blame if the objective point of view seems paramount when learning about assessments. After all, most introductory writing about administering art therapy assessments focuses on what materials to use, what to say, how much time to allow, and how to rate the pictures. To the student, the client must seem like an imaginary figure that will exist only to enter the room, pick up the materials, and use them according to the instructions. Normative studies of a given art therapy assessment tend to neglect the individual subject in favor of what has been observed in cumulative responses to this assessment protocol (e.g., Silver, 1990; Silver, 1997). Nor is the subjective response of the clinician addressed. A recent book aimed at psychiatrists and others that address how to measure psychopathology in clinical practice; yet, it does not mention the characteristics of the clinician (Farmer, McGuffin, & Williams, 2002). However:

> Depending upon the tester's own personality and emotional state, his reaction to the patient, his usual method of the administering tests, his talents and sensitivities and articulateness, and other trends and circumstances, the tester will contribute more or less . . . he will never be an nonentity in the situation. (Schafer as cited in Hammer, 1980, p. 607)

The mental health literature contains some books on helping interviews that do not mention diagnoses and some books on diagnostic interviews that do not mention empathy or closure. This dichotomy might reinforce the clinician's tendency to forget everything one has learned when one studies assessments.

ART THERAPY LITERATURE PRESENTS A DICHOTOMY

Some art therapists may be uncomfortable following the protocol of an art therapy assessment because the power difference between therapist and client is particularly visible at this juncture (Davis, 1971). This differential is especially noticeable if the assessment is taking place in the first or only session with the client – that is, in the absence of a preexisting relationship that may include mutual influence. Just as therapists may have "strategies for maintaining this [power] advantage" (Davis, 1971, p. 149) and clients may have gambits for competing for power, so may both parties prefer less competitive power structures, depending on their world views. An art therapist who doubts the legitimacy of this power structure (perhaps due to not accepting the culturally sanctioned role of therapist or due to not feeling like an expert) may present directions for drawings in an equivocal or apologetic way that encourages the client to regard the directions as merely a suggestion. This is why it is important to examine the art therapist's motivation, both to be a therapist and to administer assessments.

In Watkins's classic 1981 paper, she began by defining the diagnostic approach as one in which the image is evoked by the clinician for his or her own understanding. She said the image is not considered to be part of the treatment nor is its purpose to help the patient gain insight. Projective

tests would certainly exemplify this approach. She noted "there is little interaction with the patient around the drawings. The paintings are confiscated by the art therapist for analysis" (Watkins, 1981, p. 108).

Watkins, for the purposes of advancing an idea, was presenting a pure type. She articulated the most negative and, if you will, shadowy, manifestations of the objective approach. This includes the widespread assumption that therapy cannot happen when one is working with a standardized tool. I would disagree with that, which is not to say that this sort of behavior does not occur. The dim view that Watkins took is still shared by many art therapists toward any form of standardized art interview. One manifestation of this is the tendency to think of assessments as research tools only, or, conversely, tending to think that all research must incorporate assessments.

Robbins and Sibley (1976) differentiated between the techniques used for diagnosis of the patient, techniques used to gather objective information, and techniques used to enhance communication in the therapeutic session. They called these, respectively, projective techniques, research techniques, and therapeutic techniques. Although Robbins and Sibley noted that there was some overlap, the fact of separate categories implied that the means as well as the ends of these techniques might be dissimilar. The fact that an atmosphere of trust and curiosity which promotes open interaction with the therapist is desirable in situations where the goal is diagnosis or research, no less than those in which the goal is therapeutic, was not addressed. Art therapists' work is better when the objective and the subjective aspects are integrated, even though our literature has not drawn attention to this.

The motto of the Tavistock Institute in London is "no research without therapy; no therapy without research" – an admirable, achievable, and ethical position (M. Edwards, personal communication, March 8, 1985). Rigid divisions between styles or classes of techniques may be superficially correct but somewhat misleading. When I describe a clinician as kind, questioning, interested, and nonjudgmental, does the reader think of this person as doing an assessment or doing therapy? The description should fit both, even though there may be additional and different actions in a therapy session (e.g., in a psychoanalytically-oriented art therapy session, the clinician may also make interpretations). In general, the qualitative distinctions between an assessment session and a therapy session may be overemphasized (MacKinnon & Michels, 1971).

IMPORTANCE OF CLOSURE

To put it another way, collecting an art therapy assessment for research purposes needs to follow the protocol and be conducted as if the participant were in one's professional care. And collecting an art assessment for clinical purposes needs to follow the protocol and be conducted in the therapist's usual style. The only difference between these two situations should be that if something occurs beyond one's control that breaks the guidelines of the protocol. This might include a fire drill during the session, or the artist producing and drawing with a hidden pencil that is not part of the prescribed materials before he or she could be stopped. In such cases, the art and the session may still yield useful clinical information, but the art products could not be used as part of a research sample.

One assumes that all competent mental health professionals should be able to discuss a piece of art with a patient (Hammond & Gantt, 1998), and certainly this is true of art therapists. Yet, art therapists are often uncertain of their skills in bringing language into the session. Perhaps because of this, the need to provide proper closure at the end of the art assessment has not been emphasized enough. I recall being appalled when I first saw a list of optional questions that one might ask after administering a Diagnostic Drawing Series, and being even more horrified to learn from Barry Cohen (1994), co-author of the DDS, that some art therapists found the list helpful because they did not know what to say once the pictures had been drawn. The questions are inoffensive (e.g., "is this tree you know, or is it imaginary?"), and the answers have been of great interest to some researchers (e.g., Kress, 1992). However, could a person who needs help talking about art be competent to administer an art assessment?

With the Levick Emotional and Cognitive Art Therapy Assessment (LECATA; Levick, Bush, Blackmore, Burchett, Dachinger, Earwood, Garber, Knuth, Ochipa, Pfeiffer, Platz, & Taulbee, 1989), also reviewed in Brooke (2004), as one exception,

art therapy assessments do not provide a structured post-art-making interview. Instead, we often say we process the art, which is a vague, jargon term, the kind of language that art therapy pioneer, Elinor Ulman might have deplored (Ulman, 1992).

What do we mean by this overused expression? Here is a part of my definition. When researchers/student art therapists indicate that art making will be followed by verbal processing, they mean that they will conduct an interactive conversation in the style of psychotherapy, rather than that of a semi-structured research interview or a social situation. The goals of processing are to: be as gentle and unthreatening as possible; avoid dominating or disturbing the person who made the art; listening very closely; remembering the content and also reading between the lines; eliciting in-depth responses from the person who made the art; and letting the emotions, behaviors, memories, or stories of the participant emerge in his or her own language.

The process is nonrestrictive and unstructured. Questions are not set in advance or asked in a particular order. It is a topical interview in that the intention is to learn more about the art product (and possibly the process of art making, as experienced by the participant), to the end of learning more about the patient. Open-ended questions are asked and the participant answers in whatever way he or she wants. Examples are: "Tell me about [this aspect of the picture]." "How did it feel to make this picture?" "Is there anything else you would like to let me know?" Clarification probes ("I want to make sure I understand . . .") and minimal encouragers (nodding, "uh-huh") may also be used.

Meeting with someone to administer an art therapy assessment for research purposes and failing to provide adequate closure – the time in which the participant returns to his or her normal, relatively well-defended homeostasis – would arguably be unethical. Similarly, we may have an ethical obligation to give information to the interviewee on his or her performance during the art interview. The AATA codes of ethics, as well as those of the American Counseling Association, refer to reporting the results of assessments. Usually, we think of that as a report to a referring mental health professional. It is clear, however, in the ethics of psychology that the results of testing or other forms of assessment are shared with the person who is being assessed. Pope and Vasquez (1998) noted that this can place an unrealistic demand on the clinician since payment may not cover this time. They also recommended that clinician and client may both expect very little time to be spent on the assessment process. What is more important, they note that therapists may be uncomfortable discussing assessment results with a client. It is certainly intimidating when one is still learning about the test, as well as about art and psychopathology. Dealing with the wish to give only good news, using plain English instead of technical language, or making sense of conflicting or incomplete interpretations are also very difficult. These and other factors may encourage clinicians to forget that feedback is a dynamic, interactive process that is an aspect of the larger process of assessment, and either dump the results on the client or withhold feedback (Pope & Vasquez, p. 156).

SPECIAL CONDITIONS

Someone who does not yet have confidence in his or her abilities can tend to focus too much on trying to do it right. Novice interviewers might instead bear in mind that they are giving of their time, empathy, interest, and understanding, all of which should preexist any knowledge of art therapy or a particular assessment procedure, and that this may be a unique opportunity for the client.

The optimal conditions are those in which the interviewer is confident that he or she knows the protocol and has the appropriate materials ready. This also includes the option of having a cheat sheet or cue cards so that one can give the verbal directions accurately. One could say, "So that I can be sure that I'm giving you the best possible interview today, I'm going to read the next words from this card." As the possibly apocryphal advice has it, you can say anything to a patient, what matters is how you say it. The goal here is not to be perfect but to be prepared and confident. If the administrator is uneasy, the interviewee will be uneasy as well (Benjamin, 1974).

It is important to provide privacy for the interviewee. More than once I have seen art therapy assessments being administered in rooms through which others needed to walk. If appropriate private space is not available, an attempt should be made to divert traffic or to shield the participant from distraction. This would include putting away any art by others, and turning off one's cell phone. Drawing tools that are not part of the protocol (pencils or tissues, perhaps) should be placed out of sight.

When I introduce an art assessment procedure, sometimes participants will ask, "What are you going to be doing?" and are a little nervous when I say that I plan to observe. They may want me to draw also, but this would not serve the purpose of the session well. I have found that, for me, having a small (walnut-sized) piece of clay readily accessible is helpful. I say that I am going to be working with this piece of clay and I may glance at them from time to time. Clients seem to understand that I am still observing but in a way that feels more natural to them, and this subtle change in focus can make the procedure more comfortable.

Some of the most challenging advice I got in my art therapy training was, of course, the most vital. When I asked what I should do in my first session, the director of my program, Michael Edwards, advised me to "Be quiet, sit on your hands, and don't do something." In other words, watch and listen and provide a space for the client to make something happen. Being overly concerned about what you are going to say or do next gets in the way of hearing and observing, being curious, and following the client's lead. This is by no means a passive stance. It is helpful to remember that "we hear with our ears but we listen with our eyes and mind and heart and skin and guts as well" (Ekman as cited in Benjamin, 1974, p. 44).

THE NOVICE'S GOALS

Barry Cohen sometimes jokingly refers to "art therapy voodoo" – those instances where the art therapist demonstrates but cannot explain his or her knowledge about the maker of the art, based on the art alone (B. M. Cohen, personal communication, November 19, 1984). We have all heard of such moments, some of us have witnessed them, and some of us have been the art therapist who has exhibited these unique powers. An example might be the ability of an art therapist familiar with the Rainbow drawing assessment to speak accurately of the medical condition of a client, based on seeing one rainbow drawing (Shoemaker, 1982). Explaining in words how one arrived almost instantaneously at this special knowledge is a teachable skill (not a mystical gift) that can be understood by carefully studying the observational and pattern-matching process (Mills, 2003). Bringing words to this ability to read the art is invaluable, as attested to by competent art therapists who explicate their judgment in a way that fellow mental health professionals can follow and trust. I mention this to point out that many lay people spontaneously express fear that the art therapist will be able to read more in their art than they wish to disclose, or will challenge the art therapist to demonstrate his or her powers (usually, on a defiantly produced scribble). The client's fear of or longing for "art therapy voodoo" may have to be addressed, even simply by saying "I can't do a magic show; I need you to be a sincere and honest participant here." Sometimes the art therapist in training, having witnessed "art therapy voodoo" by his or her supervisor, thinks this is the goal. The person who is learning to administer an assessment competently should not hold him or herself to this standard. Art therapists should not be expected to supply certainty in cases that may even be baffling to our colleagues in other disciplines. Rather, having modest goals for the assessment session can help keep us acting in a responsible and professional manner.

The novice should focus on questions he may be able to answer without specialized knowledge of the research findings behind the tool he is using. Here are examples of such questions, predominantly inspired by Benjamin's (1974) work. What does the art say about how the client thinks and feels about himself? His or her body? What does the art say about how the client thinks and feels about others, particularly significant relationships? What does the art say about how, in the client's eyes, others think and feel about him or her? What does the art say about what he or she thinks and feels about what he or she wants to work on? What does the art say about his or her goals? What does the art say about what coping mechanisms he or she uses or might be able to use? What does the art say about his or her values or philosophy of life?

Here are further questions, largely derived from the work of Watkins (1981). How can the image be reflected upon so that it is not simply marks on a page but leads to an awareness of patterns and similar moments in the client's life? What is alive in the client's life that is also alive in the artwork? Have the many details of the picture been seen not only as something that can be rated, but also as a necessary part of this particular image as a whole? How can the image be deepened or extended? In what way is the image working out its own solutions to the problems at hand?

An art therapist, generally, is not regarded as having valued expertise on the scale of a physician, or even other mental health workers. Because art, which is marginalized and not subject to the same assumptions as linear communications, is involved, the use of art in assessment can be considered novel, silly, or even too threatening to use with a client. Due to these points, special care must be taken in communicating observations and even tentative conclusions. Having the tangible record of the art interview may help in presenting the clinician's findings to the treatment team, but it is also disturbingly open to the projections of colleagues who lack similar training. The necessity of keeping the art flat so that it can be easily presented, having it covered when not actively presenting, rehearsing the presentation, and being ready to substantiate one's work should be well known to all art therapists. The following "As an art therapist, I . . ." statements may be of some use; for example, "I am trained to recognize developmental markers in art," or, "I see X number of examples of psychiatric art in a year." Our profession requires an advanced degree but its pay and prestige are relatively low, which can arouse conscious or unconscious feelings of resentment, entitlement, the wish to be omniscient, shame, and guilt. In the spirit of keeping in balance, we must resist acting on these and instead value the professional responsibility to use solid, if less dramatic, statements that can be substantiated.

CONCLUSION

The ability to integrate knowledge of the assessment, knowledge of art, and knowledge of the complexity of human behavior takes a great deal of practice and systematic study (Brooke, 2004; Kinget, 1980). Much time is required to achieve expertise – a drawback of a large number of assessments in psychology as well as art therapy. My expectation is that art therapists will approach the discipline of administering assessments with a seriousness of purpose, understanding that mastery and the full value of the assessment will be revealed after a sojourn of feeling unskilled. Modest goals are the touchstone. There is a need for internal balance between the discipline stage of learning and the freedom of successful integration with one's style, and a need for external balance in the field between art and science, always keeping in mind that humans are not machines. We have the curiosity of an artist and the rigor of a scientist when we employ the assessment attitude.

REFERENCES

Barthell, B. (2001). Personal communication, August 18th.

Benjamin, A. (1974). *The helping interview* (2nd ed.). Atlanta, GA: Houghton Mifflin.

Brooke, S.L. (2004). *A therapist's guide to art therapy assessments: Tools of the trade.* (2nd ed.). Springfield, IL: Charles C Thomas, Publisher, Ltd.

Cohen, B. M., Mills, A., & Kijak, A. K. (1994). An introduction to the Diagnostic Drawing Series: A standardized tool for diagnostic and clinical use. *Art Therapy, 11*(2), 105–110.

Cohen, B.M. (1984). Personal communication, November 19th.

Cohen, B. M. (2004). Foreword. In S. L. Brooke (Ed.). *A therapist's guide to art therapy assessments: Tools of the trade* (2nd ed.). Springfield, IL: Charles C Thomas, Publisher, Ltd.

Davis, J. D. (1971). *The interview as arena: Strategies in standardized interviews and psychotherapy.* Stanford, CA: Stanford University Press.

Dawes, R. M., Faust, D., & Meehl, P. E. (1989). Clinical versus actuarial judgment. *Science, 243,* 1668–1674.

Edwards, M. (1985). Personal communication, March 8th.

Farmer, A., McGuffin, P., & Williams, J. (2002). *Measuring psychopathology.* Oxford: Oxford University Press.

Feder, B., & Feder, E. (1998). *The art and science of evaluation in the arts therapies: How do you know what's working?* Springfield, IL: Charles C Thomas, Publisher, Ltd.

Gantt, L., & Tabone, C. (1998). *Formal Elements Art Therapy Scale: The rating manual.* Morgantown, WV: Gargoyle Press.

Gantt, L. (2004). The case for formal art therapy assessments. *Art Therapy, 21*(1), 18–29.

Groth-Marnat, G. (1997). *Handbook of psychological assessment* (3rd ed.). New York: John Wiley & Sons.

Hammer, E. F. (Ed.). (1980). *The clinical application of projective drawings.* Springfield, IL: Charles C Thomas, Publisher, Ltd.

Hammond, L. C., & Gantt, L. (1998). Using art in counseling: Ethical considerations. *Journal of Counseling and Development, 76,* 271–276.

Ivey, A. E., & Ivey, M. B. (2003). *Intentional interviewing and counseling: Facilitating client development in a multicultural society* (5th ed.). Pacific Grove, CA: Brooks/Cole.

Kaplan, F. (2000). *Art, science and art therapy: Repainting the picture.* London: Jessica Kingsley.

Kinget, G. M. (1980). The Drawing Completion Test. In E. F. Hammer (Ed.), *The clinical application of projective drawings* (pp. 344–364). Springfield, IL: Charles C Thomas, Publisher, Ltd.

Kress, T. (Speaker). (1992). *The Diagnostic Drawing Series and multiple personality disorder: A validation study* (Cassette No. 55). Denver, CO: National Audio Video.

Kwiatkowska, H. Y. (1978). *Family therapy and evaluation through art.* Springfield, IL: Charles C Thomas, Publisher, Ltd.

Levick, M. F., Bush, J., Blackmore, J., Burchett, L., Dachinger, P., Earwood, C., Garber, E. S., Knuth, K., Ochipa, D. T., Pfeiffer, L. J., Platz, I., & Taulbee, R. S. (1989). The Levick Emotional and Cognitive Art Therapy Assessment (LECATA). Unpublished manuscript.

MacKinnon, R. A., & Michels, R. (1971). *The psychiatric interview in clinical practice.* Philadelphia: W. B. Saunders.

Mills, A. (Speaker). (1986). *The art therapist and the antipsychiatry movement* (Cassette Recording No. S303-22). Garden Grove, CA: Infomedix.

Mills, A. (2003). The Diagnostic Drawing Series. In C. Malchiodi (Ed.). *Handbook of art therapy* (pp. 401–409). New York: W.W. Norton.

Mills, A., & Goodwin, R. (1991). An informal survey of assessment use in child art therapy. *Art Therapy,* 10–13.

Miller, W. (2001). Personal communication, July 9th.

Podvoll, E. (1983). Uncovering a patient's history of sanity. In J. Welwood (Ed.). *Awakening the heart: East/ West approaches to psychotherapy and the healing relationship* (pp. 43–54). Boston: New Science Library.

Pope, K. S., & Vasquez, M. J. T. (1998). *Ethics in psychotherapy and counseling* (2nd ed.). San Francisco: Jossey-Bass.

Robbins, A, & Sibley, L. (1976). *Creative art therapy.* New York: Grune & Stratton.

Shoemaker, R. J. H. (1982). *The Rainbow booklet.* Unpublished manuscript.

Silver, R. A. (1990). *Silver drawing test of cognitive skills and adjustment.* New York: Ablin Press.

Silver, R. A. (1997). Sex and age differences in attitude toward the opposite sex. *Art Therapy, 14*(4), 268–272.

Ulman, E. (1962; 1992). The war between therapese and English, II. *Bulletin of Art Therapy, 2,* 127–128. Reprinted 1992 in *American Journal of Art Therapy, 30*(3), p. 75.

Ulman, E. (1992). A new use of art in psychiatric diagnosis. *American Journal of Art Therapy, 30*(3), 78–88.

Wadeson, H. (2002). The anti-assessment devil's advocate. *Art Therapy, 19*(4), 168–170.

Watkins, M. (1981). Six approaches to the image in art therapy. *Spring,* 107–125.

Welwood, J. (1983). On psychotherapy and meditation. In J. Welwood (Ed.), *Awakening the heart: East/West approaches to psychotherapy and the healing relationship* (pp. 43–54). Boston: New Science Library.

Biographical Statement

Anne Mills, MA, ATR-BC, LPC, is Director of the Graduate Program in Art Therapy at The George Washington University in Washington, DC, and chair of the AATA Research Committee. She is also in private practice with Art Therapy Services of Washington, DC. Her areas of specialization are supervision, trauma, bereavement, and dissociation.

Professional member of the AATA
Director, Art Therapy Program
The George Washington University,
Washington, DC
Private Practitioner, Art Therapy Services,
Washington, DC

Address for correspondence: Anne Mills, Director, Art Therapy Program, The George Washington University, 2129 G St. NW (Bldg. L, rear), Washington, DC, 20052 USA

Chapter 4

INDIVIDUAL ART THERAPY WITH RESISTANT ADOLESCENTS

Susan Boyes

INTRODUCTION

In this chapter, I will discuss working in art therapy with resistant teen-aged clients. Like all therapies and counseling arrangements, the participation of the client is crucial to the success of developing a therapeutic alliance. While it is not uncommon to meet with clients who are wary or protected emotionally, this is more often the norm than the exception when it comes to working with adolescents. Adolescents can give new and deeper meaning to the word "guarded."

Working with adolescents was not a choice I made consciously. As one of my favorite teachers, Debbie Good, Ph.D., ATR-BC, once informed me, "Whatever you need to work on will walk right in your door." (D. Good, personal communication, November, 1995). During a student internship placement at a psychiatric hospital, I was confronted by teen gangsters, prostitutes, and addicts whose level of hostility and aggression were shocking to me. Although I was never personally harmed, I came away with the distinct impression that adolescents in need of mental health care would never be my dream population. Many years later, I found myself employed in a community mental health agency serving all ages. Among my census were elderly clients, very young children, and yes, adolescents. To my surprise, my experience with adolescents in the agency was completely different. The teens I came to know and love through this agency work were engaged in the therapeutic process. They were curious, resilient, and challenging, but never threatening. Perhaps, as my former teacher suggested, it was time to work on the issues of adolescence from a perspective of healing. I was no longer afraid.

Art therapy engages a client in nonverbal ways. This is particularly useful for clients who may have limited verbal skills. By that I mean for a very young child or for an adult who has had a stroke and suffers some aphasia, art therapy offers an alternate means of communication (Robbins, et al., 1986, p. 129). At the same time, art therapy can support people that have excellent verbal skills. Those who tend to overintellectualize may erect a wall of words so that more typical talk therapy becomes challenging (K. Sly-Linton, personal communication, 1997). Art making can be employed to cut through the chatter and get to the important themes. Art can also be employed with people who speak another language and may have difficulty finding the appropriate words to express a particular issue, feeling, or situation. When it comes to adolescents, however, art provides a safe mode of expression due to the opportunity it provides to open a conversation. Having art in the room is like inviting a third party into the conversation. Discussion about the art product takes direct focus off the client and gives both the therapist and client something to attend to other than each other.

Art is used to externalize and formalize a story, fear, or experience. There is much to be said for getting it out on paper or in clay. It takes a weight off to put the image outside of oneself. Creating an art product is a safe way to express feelings. Nobody gets hurt in making a picture. It can be used to tell about the past, explore the present, and discover the future. Art has a narrative component and provides a record of where I came from, where I am, and where I am going. At the same time, it can be great fun. Clients who come into our offices often have harsh and painful lives in the outside world. A brief hour of fun once or twice a month might provide just enough support to get them through their stressful daily lives.

Sometimes, too, our clients are frozen from years of unrelenting stress and feelings of being overwhelmed. Feelings may be so long dormant that when they do begin to reawaken they are unfamiliar, even threatening. Identifying emotions and normalizing the physical sensation of feelings can all be supported in the creation of an art product. Stimulating the creative flow of images and ideas very often stimulates the flow of creation within the person. The very same creative force that invigorates the world also supports individual physical and mental vigor. Waking that up can be done within a safe therapeutic milieu under the guidance of a knowledgeable and well-trained art therapist.

In this chapter, I will present three case studies that address the objectives listed above. Externalization, narrative, safety, reinvigoration, and fun. All names have been changed. The art therapy methods will include the use of fortune cookie fortunes as a motif, drawing, collage, symbolic containment of affect in a box, and worry beads made out of polymer clay.

FORTUNE COOKIE

This young woman appeared in my office of the community mental health agency where I worked when she was sixteen years old. She was born in another country into a family of seven children to a mother who made her living as a prostitute. This young woman's first memories are of living in an orphanage with her siblings. Her first memories of abuse, other than her abandonment to an orphanage, involved an older sister who took advantage of her when she was sick. This young girl, Alicia, (not her real name) was later adopted and brought to the United States at about age 10. By the age of 12, she was returned to the custody of the state, after the adoptive family rejected her. By the time we met, she had been in another orphanage and several foster placements that had also failed. She had been in and out of therapy for years. At times, she had been on various medications to help her moderate her moods and behaviors.

When we met, she appeared several years younger than her age. She seemed well groomed, articulate, attractive, focused, intelligent and very, very guarded. As I got to know her, I learned she

was an excellent student. She was recently placed in a new foster home that provided two younger sisters, biological daughters to the young parents who were her new foster mother and father. She was coming to me to work on issues of trust and adapting to her new environment. Alicia sat as far away from me as she could in the room, diagonally in the far corner of the office. She crossed her arms and made eye contact with me. She spoke in a matter of fact manner style. Alicia did not want to talk about any of her past. Historically, she had difficulty keeping safe boundaries. She might tell someone she barely knew all about her family background, not realizing that a fellow student could be fickle or unreliable as a keeper of confidences. Here, in a therapy session, she was the complete opposite. Her history was none of my business.

She seemed to be adjusting fairly well to her new foster family, except the parents did not want her to come into their room and the other children were allowed to do so. She thought they must not trust her and she was trying hard to be worthy of their trust. She also did not trust her foster parents. She had been discarded by adults so many times in the past, she could not afford to place her trust in them, either. Alicia did not want to talk and she did not want to draw. It was going to be challenging to cultivate some kind of communication with her.

One of my art therapist colleagues, Jeff Brody, had given me the useful tool of collecting fortune cookie fortunes to use as a stimulus for engaging clients to create art. Stimulus drawing utilizes any type of motif as a theme for the art product. It can consist of simple images for inspiration, or, as in this case, words on a fortune cookie slip. The stimulus then triggers a relational concept in the participant and a unique and personalized image can be developed that serves as an opening to therapeutic discussion (J. Brody, personal communication, 2003). The fortune cookie slip could be picked blindly, with eyes closed, or each could be read and then one chosen purposefully. I asked Alicia to pick out one of the fortune cookie fortunes that I saved in a small bowl in my office. She looked through them all and chose one that said, "You will never be last, but always first."

I suggested she draw a picture of how that fortune applies to her life. She declined to draw and met my gaze with steady, dark eyes, arms again folded across her chest. I sat quietly with her for a few minutes. Then I asked her if she could show me some other way what that might mean to her. Maybe she could create a scene using some of the other objects in my office. She picked out some small plastic animals and lined them up. The one in front was a lioness that was looking back over its shoulder, the next one was an alligator with its mouth open, then a pig, then a coyote, then a skunk. She told me she was the lion in front and behind her were her friends. They were following her. She kept looking back at them, and she was not sure which way to go. She was afraid she might go backwards, back toward some friends that she could get in trouble with. She was not at all sure which way she was able to go forward.

Alicia's courage in setting up the plastic animal figures opened up an opportunity to dialog with me about her inner thoughts and fears. We then could discuss the alligator's open, threatening mouth. She could tell me about the friend she thought was a pig and the coyote, and the one she thought was a skunk. Without naming any names, she was able to identify the personalities around her and what they represented to her. I kept being drawn back to the animal she chose for herself. The lioness (queen of the jungle?) was striding forward, even while it was looking back. With Alicia's permission, I took the animal and turned it around, so that it was now looking over its shoulder toward the future, while striding in the direction of the line of friends. We were able to discuss the difference in feeling and meaning of that position. Then I replaced it the way Alicia had originally done. Within the course of our meeting, Alicia was able to evaluate her life's course and possible choices that she was facing. I got to see how dangerous her past was. Without directly discussing how her life was changing and what her previous life was like, we were able to touch on several major choice points in her adolescent world. She left after that session feeling safe, heard, and according to her caseworker, eager to return. I was left wondering about the threatening alligator mouth behind her. The lioness appeared to be moving away from those past dangers and looking behind her to see what was following her and how closely, possibly indicating Post Traumatic Stress Disorder (PTSD)

PTSD NIGHTMARES

Knowing of Alicia's history by reading her previous treatment records, I knew Alicia had a diagnosis of PTSD. Realizing that recurrent nightmares could be a symptom of PTSD, I researched therapeutic approaches to treating nightmares. Among the most exciting studies I came across was the work done by Dr. Barry Krakow, Principal Investigator of the University of New Mexico Sleep Research program through UNM School of Medicine. (Krakow, et al., 1995) The treatment steps in their controlled studies involved imagery rehearsal in a three-step process.

The patient writes down or recalls a nightmare, then changes the nightmare to a "new dream," then mentally rehearses the changed images during the waking state for several minutes each day. Of the 100 patients treated in their early studies, 70% responded with significant reductions or elimination of the disturbing dreams. At long-term follow up, these results were sustained at 18 and 30 months.

Alicia continued to visit me on alternate weeks for several months. As our therapeutic relationship began to deepen she was somewhat less guarded in speaking with me. I asked her if she ever had the same scary, dream more than once. She told me of a dream she had frequently. In her dream, her sister was trapped in the backyard, being chased by something evil that was going to kill her. Then, she was killed and Alicia could not save her. I asked her to draw a different ending she would like to have for that dream. Alicia remained resistant to creating art, but she was willing to continue to talk. When asked to describe in words what other ending could happen, she insisted, "Nothing else could happen." No matter how much encouragement was offered, she continued to resist and refuse any alternate ending. "That's the only way it can end."

Not willing to take no for an answer, I suggested it did not have to be real. Could Alicia think of something completely new? I suggested she stretch her imagination. Again, she folded her arms across her chest, sitting in the farthest chair away from me, safely out of reach of the art table and any art materials. I sat in silence with her for awhile. When I became convinced she was not going to respond, I found myself leaping out of my chair with my arms raised. "What if Superman came down and picked her up? Can you imagine that?" "What if Superman swooped down and picked her up and flew away with her to a safe place?"

Alicia leaned back and smiled at my antics. "You're crazy," she chuckled. Alicia refused to join in creating the fantasy rescue operation, but she allowed me to continue the demonstration. I asked her to review the new dream ending every day for a few minutes and to add any new safety features she can think of as they come to her. Ideally, a new dream ending should have been created by the client, rather than the therapist. Although the client did not join me in creating a new ending, follow-up interviews in subsequent visits revealed she had no nightmares to report.

TRAUMA DRAWING SERIES

One of my teenaged clients, Janey, was 14 years old. She was living with her father and stepmother because her biological mother was chronically drunk and could no longer care for her. When we first met, Janey looked older than her 14 years. She had a casual comfort in conversing with adults brought on by years of being in adult company and from parenting her mother due to her mother's alcoholism. She and her stepmother appeared to be very good friends, as they joked back and forth with each other in my office. As we got to know each other their relationship became clearer – and more muddied. Much of their jocularity was a put-on show to make themselves and me feel more at ease. In truth, Janey had attempted suicide at least two times in the past and her stepmother was afraid to leave her alone. Having Janey in the household added a financial burden and she took up a lot of physical space with her clothes and personal items. Additionally, she held center stage with all the psychic space in the family as the most injured party.

In addition to her father, who was always working and rarely home, the household also included a stepsister of the same age as Janey and a younger brother. Janey's biological mother had a series of live-in abusive, drunk boyfriends. Janey had been raped by the son of one of her mother's friends. There were so many hard stories in her world I did not know where to start. Leaving that decision up to Janey, I chose to use an approach developed by Gantt and Tinnin, (2003) of the Trauma Recovery Institute in Morgantown, WV. The essential tasks of art therapy to treat trauma include the narrative processing and externalizing of the story (White, 1997).

The series of trauma treatment imagery developed by Gantt and Tinnin (2003) includes at least eight subsequent art projects. Prior to this drawing

series an image of a safe place is created to serve as a grounding and as a reference point. The eight pictures used in the graphic narrative processing include: (1) before; (2) startle; (3) thwarted intention; (4) freeze; (5) body sensations; (6) automatic obedience; (7) self-repair; (8) after.

In this chapter I will touch on three of Janey's images and their significance.

Trauma work requires the patient to recover all of the details and images of the traumatic experience and to construct a narrative that unites the memory fragments and brings closure to the experience. This must be done at both conscious and unconscious levels. Trauma work converts the unfinished experiential memory fragments into a coherent memory of the past event. To accomplish this, it is necessary to reach the nonverbal mind, despite verbal resistance and prepare the narrative for verbal presentation to the person. The patient can then assimilate and avow the experience (Gantt & Tinnin, 2003).

Drawing out images around the traumatic event supports the parts of the experience for which there may be no words. In effect, this can clarify and unfreeze the altered mental state caused by the trauma and help to fill in gaps in memory. Having the image separate from the person, on a piece of paper, can make it easier to create emotional distance from it and maintain an objective viewpoint (Gantt & Tinnin, 2003).

The first task I asked of Janey was to draw herself in a safe place. This safe place was to provide a grounding experience for the demanding work to come. Her second task was to think of a hard time she had and to draw a picture of what was happening just before the event. Janey chose to work on the story of leaving her mother's apartment and moving in with her father and stepmother.

Janey's safe place turned out to be an image of six overlapping mountain peaks. These were large pointed triangles, thrusting up from the bottom of the page, outlined in blue pencil and left white. The summits of the mountains were colored green, in a reversal of the more clichéd snow-capped mountains often depicted. Janey added three blue clouds, a smiling sun in the upper right-hand corner, and five "V" shaped stylized birds in the sky. I then asked her where she would be if she were in that picture. Using a black pencil, she drew herself walking downhill on one of the center, rear, mountains. She was descending from the live, green, peaks to the barren, snow-covered valley. Janey explained she would feel safe all alone. It is not uncommon for adolescent teens in my practice to report their safe places as places where they would be left alone, self-sufficient, and not needing or wanting anything from others. She seemed very small and isolated in the picture.

In Janey's next image, what was happening just before the trauma, she used only black pencil. There was no color added, and the drawing was equally sparse. A large television faced the viewer from the center of the paper, the back of a head rested on the back of a sofa, facing away from the viewer, and a stick figure of her stepmother stood at the doorway in the middle right-hand side. Another stick figure, one of her step-siblings, sprawled on another piece of furniture at the lower right, watching TV with her. Janey was the head facing the television. The size of the head was very small, despite it being in the foreground. Hammer (1980) correlates small size of self-images with feelings of inadequacy or withdrawal. The head poking up over the back of the couch was tiny. The fact that it was turned away from the viewer supports the idea of inadequacy (Drachnik, 1995). Often, a paucity of detail, and/or lack of color, can indicate depression (Hammer, 1980). With Janey, I thought both the lack of color, lack of detail, and the small size of her head offered a true reflection of her state of mind. It was impressive to note how much she was willing to share. Her story of how she came to know she would be staying at her father's house, and not just visiting, was enormous. It needed to be told.

Rather than describe every image she drew in the series, there is just one more that will be included here. Janey's "after" picture had a ground line about one-fourth inch from the bottom of the paper. Three large rectangles with labels on them, "games," "collectables," and "trolls" represented boxes of her things that she had to pack and move. Beside the boxes is a stick figure of herself kneeling near the box of trolls. Beside her is a tilted table and a chair with uneven legs not quite reaching the ground. Although images here were outlined and not filled in with color, Janey did use colored pencil to draw the images. For a depressed and withdrawn client, this was a slightly more hopeful sign. The most striking image in the picture, however, remained her relative size to the objects around her. She was barely as tall as the box and just about as high as the seat of the chair beside her. Janey drew herself the size of a toddler. The sense of powerlessness she felt over her life was evident in her image.

Interesting

WORRY BEADS

Janey bounced into the office one afternoon and picked up a small box that had beads in it. "What are these?" she asked me. I had been working with a group of younger children and we had made worry beads together. I left mine on the shelf when I was finished with them. I explained to her what the process was. Using at least two colors of polymer clay, they were asked to roll the clays together into a bead. The suggestion was to whisper your worries into the bead and then when the beads are baked (polymer clay can be hardened in a conventional oven at low temperature) the worries can no longer escape. I explained this idea to Janey.

"I can believe that," she said to me. I was thrilled that a fourteen year old, worldly-wise as she seemed to be, would consider using this metaphor for containment. I produced the clay for her and let her work. She made several beads, all of them different. She took them outside into the hall to whisper into them without being overheard, and then she came back in. She was a little bit concerned that if she made a hole in the bead the worries could leak out, but I reassured her they would be in the clay, and the clay is solid. I took the beads home to bake them for her and returned them to her at the following visit. We strung them on elastic and Janey could wear the beads as a bracelet.

The need for symbolic containment of our difficult feelings knows no age barrier. However, in teens, especially, there is a search for boundaries (D. Good, personal communication, March, 1996). Containment can be created using a box, a collage project that involves pulling disparate images together and glued on one piece, or a medium such as clay (R. Botkin, personal communication, 1995). The grounding nature of clay that comes from the earth is obvious. Less obvious is that clay is a substance that changes in character from moist and flexible, to brittle and fragile as it dries, and then to stone when it is fired. The metaphorical parallel of going through the fire and coming out changed is not lost on our clients.

Working with clay, even polymer clay, can serve as a grounding project. If a client is struggling with containment of affect, often the medium of choice is one that will bring the client back to earth. Clay involves the kinesthetic, tactile experiences of arm and hand muscle movement (Malchiodi, 1990). This is useful as a way to increase sensory input and help to organize the client's feelings and thought processes. It is important to assess whether a client needs containment of or expansion of affect, and to choose materials accordingly. In general, wetter media, such as watercolors, serve to heighten affect and dryer media, such as pencils or chalk, serve to contain affect. The wetter media are more difficult to control, and may lead to the client becoming frustrated, thus displaying increased affect (R. Botkin, personal communication, 1995). The more familiar pencil is much easier to control and it may be much more comfortable to the client than watercolor may be. There is a whole spectrum of dry-to-wet media along a continuum that the therapist may choose from depending on the nature of the therapeutic work being done.

COLLAGE

I kept a stack of magazines in my office to be used for collage. Another client of mine, a sixteen-year-old girl, appeared always in control of her feelings, her foster family, and her life. Veronica had her future planned out in minute detail. Months would pass before it became clear to us both that she was bulimic, using laxatives and exercise to attempt to control her weight. She was so guarded and careful in disclosing anything to me that it was difficult to assess what she worked so hard to control. The control part was obvious, but what was it that so concerned her?

In this case, I suggested she decorate a box with a lid. I provided a stationery box and asked her to collage the exterior and the interior. The outside was to represent the self that she shows to the world and the interior was to hold the secret self she shares with no one. The box could be used to contain her difficult feelings, other art images that would be created later in our work together. A box can be used to keep secrets (worries, fears, or the past) safely inside.

Over the course of several visits, Veronica worked on covering the top of the box with magazine images of scenery. While working on the box, she chatted with me about her boyfriend, school choir, and feeling fat. She used animals and pastures, waterfalls, and flowers. She layered on multiple pictures. Some images overlapped and covered

other images completely. Despite many suggestions to approach the inside of the box, Veronica never did. At first, I was frustrated at her lack of response. Later, it occurred to me that Veronica may have felt empty inside. She never was able to look inside the box or inside herself, and it could be this was the flip side of having so very much control in the outside world. Perhaps the fear was of what she would find, or that she would find nothing there. Perhaps the empty box was a metaphor for the emptiness she felt inside herself.

PRE-CUT IMAGES FOR COLLAGE

For younger clients, or for those with cognitive or certain physical imitations, I also provided pre-cut magazine images. These were kept sorted into separate boxes for words, people, and things. For all of us it is important to find images that reflect who we really are. As an experiment, try finding images in common publications that show positive reflections of elders and for people of color. It is not so easy! Our marketing culture does not reflect most of the population. Quite the contrary, almost all images are of young, fair skinned people. I worked hard to include in my pre-cut boxes images to reflect a truer diversity than the journalistic norm.

Briana, age eight, lived with her white mother and she was the child of a Cape Verdean father. Her father was incarcerated and unreliable. Her mother had health problems. Briana appeared anxious and confused.

Using pre-cut images, I had her make a collage. Using collage materials, especially pre-cut and ready to glue, takes all the pressure and judgment off creativity. Collage has a freeing quality in the art therapy setting. It can bring up joy and playfulness. In Briana's case, she was able to choose pictures of a birthday party, dolls, clouds, sky, faces, and even a big happy dog. Looking at the words and images chosen, it was interesting to note that the picture of the little white girl in a birthday hat was placed center top on the paper and the phrase "a better life" was just below it. At the bottom of the page was the face of an African-American woman and a volcano, and the phrase, "I know how it feels to get here with no clothes, no shoes, no hope." She placed the dog image on the back of the paper, with the phrase below, "No sign of the enemies."

Without a word, Briana had shown me her sense of being an outsider and being in need of protection from enemies, such as the dog image. No further discussion was needed. I did, however, ask her what picture she thought was most important and she chose the birthday girl.

For some clients more discussion is warranted. I may encourage clients to tell about the picture. I may have them choose a favorite image, or ask them what it might say if it could speak. For a higher functioning client I may ask which image makes her the most uncomfortable and why. We could explore further themes, and find out if this were a story, what it would tell. Collage offers a multitude of options.

CONCLUSION

Art offers a process to aid in articulating a situation that may not be expressible in words. Whether it is the story itself, or the effect on the client of an event, art can provide a safe means to explore and express feelings. Often the client enjoys coming in just to see what new materials are available. While working with adolescents can be challenging, it is thrilling to witness their resilience in facing sometimes daunting life tasks. Rarely was I unimpressed with a client's ability to conceal or reveal his or her thoughts and feelings in therapeutic sessions. The rewards of accompanying a client to navigate through a difficult patch of life and to make meaning of it are well worth the efforts.

REFERENCES

Botkin, R. (1995). Personal communication.

Brody, J. (2003). Personal communication.

Drachnik, C. (1995). *Interpreting metaphors in children's drawings.* Burlingame, CA: Abbeygate Press.

Gantt, L. & Tinnin, L. (2003). Hope, treatment and recovery. Trauma Recovery Institute. Morgantown, WV. Article retrieved on February 15, 2005 from www.traumarecoveryinstitute.org.

Good, D. (1995, November). Personal communication.

Hammer, E. (1980). *Clinical application of projective drawings.* Springfield, IL: Charles C Thomas, Publisher, Ltd.

Krawkow, B., Melendrez, D., Ferreira, E., Clark, J., Warner, T.D., Sisley, B., & Sklar, D. (2001). Prevalence of insomnia symptoms in patients with sleep-disordered breathing. *American College of Chest Physicians, 120*(6), 1923–1929.

Malchiodi, C. (1990). *Breaking the silence: Art therapy with children from violent homes.* New York: Brunner/Mazel.

Marsan, J., & Krakow, B. (Eds.). (1995). The treatment of nightmares in rape victims with PTSD. *UNM Sleep Research Quarterly Newsletter, 1*, 1.

Robbins, A. et al. (1986). *Expressive therapies: A creative arts approach to depth-oriented treatment.* New York: Human Sciences Press.

Sly-Linton, K. (1997). Personal communication.

White, M. (1997). *Narratives of therapists' lives.* Adelaide: Dulwich Centre Publications.

Biographical Statement

Susan Boyes, MA, LMHC, ATR, is trained as an artist, with a specialty in clay and porcelain objects, both functional and decorative. In the middle 1990s she returned to school and earned a Master's Degree in Art Therapy from Southwestern College in Santa Fe, New Mexico. Although thoroughly grounded in the theory and practice of art therapy techniques, Susan has a strong interest in the spiritual aspects of creativity. Susan is also a shamanic practitioner, with education and training from The Foundation for Shamanic Studies in Mill Valley, California. She believes that the source of creativity is the source of all creation, and tapping in to that reservoir can contribute to a healing experience. Susan's art has been published in *Bridging time and space, essays on layered art*, 1998, Maui: Markowitz Press, and also in *The art of layering*, Mary Carroll Nelson and Nancy Dunaway, (Eds.). 2004, Albuquerque: Society of Layerists in Multi-Media. Since moving to Rhode Island in 2000, Susan has become a state licensed mental health counselor [LMHC] in both Rhode Island and Massachusetts. Susan is also a nationally registered art therapist through the Art Therapy Credentialing Board. She is a credentialed member of the American Art Therapy Association. Susan has experience working in a state women's penitentiary, a psychiatric hospital, community mental health agencies, in a public school as a special educator, and as a private practitioner. She provides trainings for community mental health agencies and schools, as well as at national and regional art therapy conferences. Most recently, Susan presented a training at the national conference for United Cerebral Palsy (Boston, 2004). Susan also co-presented a workshop at the National Association of Drama Therapy conference (Newport, RI, 2004). Susan co-teaches a graduate level course at the University of Rhode Island, titled "Exploring Loss Through Creative Arts Therapy." Susan is currently employed as a clinical supervisor for United Cerebral Palsy of Rhode Island in the Children and Family Services division. She maintains a growing private practice and creates ceramic art as well as collage and painted art.

Chapter 5

ART THERAPY WITHIN AN INTERDISCIPLINARY FRAMEWORK: WORKING WITH APHASIA AND COMMUNICATION SCIENCE DISORDERS*

ELLEN G. HOROVITZ

In the year 2000, Dr. Shirley Szekeres, Chair of Communication Science Disorders Department at Nazareth College, and I (then Program Director of Graduate Art Therapy) created an experiment: we intermingled speech/language therapists and art therapists in the same clinic and worked simultaneously with the same clients. It was the inception of our interdisciplinary clinic, which today sports speech/language therapy, art therapy, music therapy, physical therapy, nursing, and social work. The gains from this interdisciplinary stance have been astounding. It was also a challenge and a learning curve for me.

For starters, I had to acquaint myself with the language of speech/language therapists, accept their behavior modification ways, and somehow dovetail that sphere into my eclectic approach, which continues to evolve and defy even my hallmark definition of spiritual art therapy (Horovitz, 2002). In the constant learning state that I am in as therapist/learner to the human condition, I am ever changing. And this I believe is a good idea. It keeps me fresh and while admired as a full Professor (e.g., conveyor of knowledge), it firmly places me where I truly belong: constant apprentice, endless inquirer, challenged ad infinitum by life's conditions and foibles.

So in order to understand the complexity of this new population, I had to indeed acquaint myself with the verbiage of speech/language therapy and have a working knowledge of aphasia, a medical condition with which I had no previous experience.

It was necessary to educate myself. In turn, I hope to enlighten you, the reader, but first, one must be acquainted with the variety of types of aphasia that impact stroke victims. Below are some definitions.

Definitions in understanding the complexities of aphasia and stroke:

Aphasia a•pha•sia (uh-fay'-zhuh) n. An impairment of the ability to use or comprehend words, usually acquired as a result of a stroke or other brain injury. *Webster's International Dictionary*, 6th edition.

The following definitions come from a variety of sources which will be referenced at the end of this chapter (Brookshire, 1997; Gresham and Weiss, 1993; Johnson and Becker, 1999; Lynch, 2001; Ylvisaker and Szekeres, 1981; and a variety of internet sites including apasia.org).

Broca's Aphasia

This is a form of aphasia in which speech output is severely reduced and is limited mainly to short utterances, of less than four words. Vocabulary access is limited in persons with Broca's aphasia, and their formation of sounds is often laborious and clumsy. The person may understand speech relatively well and be able to read, but be limited in writing. Broca's aphasia is often referred to as a "nonfluent aphasia" because of the halting and effortful quality of speech.

Global Aphasia

This is the most severe form of aphasia; patients produce few recognizable words and understand little or no spoken language. Global aphasics can neither read nor write. Global aphasia may often be

*Author's note: This is a condensed version from sections in Chapter 8 of *Art Therapy As Witness: A Sacred Guide* by Horovitz (2005).

seen immediately after the patient has suffered a stroke and it may rapidly improve if the damage has not been too extensive. However, with greater brain damage, severe and lasting disability may result. Often their utterances sound like gibberish and make little sense to the listener.

Mixed Nonfluent Aphasia

This term is applied to patients who have sparse and effortful speech, resembling severe Broca's aphasia. However, unlike persons with Broca's aphasia, they remain limited in their comprehension of speech and do not read or write beyond an elementary level.

Wernicke's Aphasia

In this form of aphasia, the ability to comprehend the meaning of spoken words is fundamentally impaired, while the production of connected speech is verily not affected. Therefore Wernicke's aphasia is referred to as a "fluent aphasia." However, speech is far from normal. The client with this kind of aphasia experiences garbled sentences, irrelevant words intrude, or in severe cases neologisms enter speech and resemble jargon. Reading and writing are often severely impaired.

Anomic Aphasia

This term is applied to persons who are left with a persistent inability to supply the words for the very things they want to talk about – particularly significant nouns and verbs. As a result, the client is frustrated by expressions of vague circumlocutions in grammatical form and output. They understand speech well and, in most cases, read adequately. Difficulty finding words is as evident in writing as in speech. (I often jest with my colleagues that I am having an anomic moment (as opposed to a senior one) as I continually lose sight of a word that I can visualize yet cannot retrieve. In essence, this is what it feels like 24/7 to have the condition of anomic aphasia.)

Other Varieties of Aphasia

In addition to the foregoing disorders that are seen repeatedly by speech clinicians, there are many other possible combinations of deficits that do not precisely fit into the aforementioned categories. Some of the characteristics of a complex aphasia syndrome may also occur in isolation. Following a stroke, this may result in disorders of reading (alexia) or disorders affecting both reading and writing (alexia and agraphia). Severe impairments of computation often accompany aphasia, yet in some instances patients retain excellent calculation in spite of the loss of language.

DISORDERS THAT MAY ACCOMPANY OR BE CONFUSED WITH APHASIA

Various communication syndromes may be due to paralysis, weakness, involuntary speech musculature, or cognitive impairment. Such impairment may accompany aphasia or occur independently and be confused with aphasia. Distinguishing these disorders from aphasia is paramount since the treatment(s) and prognosis of each disorder may vary.

Apraxia

Apraxia is a collective term used to describe impairment in succeeding at purposeful kinesthetic movements. People with severe aphasia are usually limited to pantomime or gesture, except for emotive expression. For example, they might lead you to what they want, or show you their wallets to get their point across, but this is the extent of their ability to communicate nonverbally. Specific examination displays an inability to perform common expressive gestures on request such as waving goodbye, pantomiming drinking, or brushing teeth (*limb apraxia*). Apraxia may also affect oral nonspeech movement like pretending to cough or blowing out a candle (*facial apraxia*). It may even preclude an ability to manipulate objects. Apraxia is often not apparent unless one *asks* a patient to perform or pretend a specific action. For this reason, it is almost never presented as a problem or complaint by the patient or family members. Yet it may underlie the very limited ability of people with aphasia to compensate for the speech impairment by using informative gestures.

Apraxia of Speech

This term is frequently used by speech pathologists to designate a deficit in the voluntary production of articulation and prosody (the rhythm and timing) of speech. It is characterized by highly inconsistent errors.

Dysarthria

Dysarthria refers to a group of speech disorders resulting from weakness, slowness, or clumsiness of the speech mechanism due to damage to any of a variety of points in the nervous system. Dysarthria may involve disorders to some or all of the basic speech processes: respiration phonation, resonance, articulation, and prosody. Dysarthria is a disorder of speech production not language (e.g., use of vocabulary and/or grammar). Unlike apraxia of speech, the speech errors that occur in dysarthria are highly consistent from one occasion to the next.

Dementia

Dementia is often confused with aphasia, thus it warrants a brief discussion herein. Dementia is a condition of impairment of memory, intellect, personality, and insight resulting from brain injury or disease. Some forms of dementia are progressive, such as Pick's disease, Alzheimer's disease, or some forms of Parkinson's disease. Language impairments are more or less prominent in different forms of dementia, but these are usually overshadowed by more widespread intellectual loss. Since dementia is so often a progressive disorder, the prognosis is quite different from aphasia.

INTERDISCIPLINARY TENETS: WHY THEY WORK

So now that the reader has had a brief overview of aphasia and its various hallmarks, I will continue. Beyond understanding the various definitions of aphasia, I scoured the art therapy literature for others who had worked with this population. Paucity doesn't even begin to describe the results: other than an unpublished master's thesis and one article, I was in new territory. As always, I forged ahead cheerfully. But shortly into this work alongside my first graduate intern, Colleen Lynch, it became very clear that educating oneself about not only aphasia but also the methods of the speech/language therapists was pinnacle for success.

After working for four years in this area, I finally felt grounded enough to publish something of this work (Horovitz, 2005). Yet after formalizing written reports in measurable terms, my work with these clients has remained wedded in what I firmly believe. While artistic cognitive gain contributed to improvement of speech and communication, it was matters of the heart that spoke to the client. While I knew this all along, it took years to prove it.

After reading the works of David Hawkins, MD, Ph.D., it became unmistakable what was happening. While I hypothesized certain tenets, reading Hawkins' work, which scientifically calibrated attractor fields, resulted in theoretical notions understood. In his book, *Power vs. Force, The Hidden Determinants of Human Behavior*, Hawkins (2002) discusses consciousness and actually maps it out from the process of elimination (the lowest calibrated field) to pure consciousness (the highest calibrated field). Calibrations were deciphered on everything from people to books. (Everything vibrates at a certain energy level.) In turn, this aided my understanding of the human brain and how wedded cognitive functioning is to emotional repertoire. While I had witnessed cognitive and developmental gain as the result of unlocked emotional triggers, other than performing pre and post tests like the Silver Drawing Test (Silver, 1996) and the Bender Gestalt II (Brannigan & Decker (2003), I was unable to understand my academic paradigm. Then I read Hawkins' work and it *finally* made sense. Regarding consciousness Hawkins stated:

> Consciousness automatically chooses what it deems best from moment to moment because that ultimately is the only function of which it is capable. The relative weight and merit given to certain data are determined by a predominant attractor pattern operating in the individual or in a collective group of minds. These patterns can be identified, described, and calibrated; out of that information arises a totally new understanding of human behavior, history, and the destiny of mankind. And as we explore the nature of man's problems, it becomes clear that there never has been a reliable experimental yardstick with which to measure and interpret man's motivations and experiments over the course of history. (p. 29)

But through the theories of kinesiology as predicated by Goodheart (1976), Diamond (1979), and Hawkins (2002), it became clear that this information could indeed be scientifically and reliably charted. I never *completely* understood what willed the mind (and body) to overcome the most advanced traumatic insult or adversity (Horovitz, 2002). But when I read about the Hawkins' (2002) attractor level of Willingness (log calibration at 310) with emotive hallmarks of "optimism" and process characteristics of "intention" (pp. 68–69), I understood the energy level descriptors explained:

> At this level, self-esteem is high and is reinforced by positive feedback from society in the forms of

recognition, appreciation, and reward. . . . With their capacity to bounce back from adversity and learn from experience, they tend to become self-correcting . . . they're easily trainable. (Hawkins, 2002, pp. 86–87)

Hence, a scientific calibration explicated why some people face adversity and overcome these obstacles while others simply cannot. While Hawkins' theory mirrored previous ideologies such as that of logotherapy (Frankl, 1984), his concept hailed from a reliable and scientific platform.

Plaiting the Brain

Long ago, I hypothesized that marrying speech/language therapy and art therapy worked in concert with the brain: it made great sense that forging a partnership between the left and right hemispheres simultaneously would in turn inform the brain to replait (Horovitz, 1999). And when those strands interwove in such fashion, the brain recreated – synapses and all – and rewiring was achieved. Thus cognitive functioning arose; but figuring out what motivated a person to achieve this end was less clear. After reading Hawkins' theories, I understood what motivated the brain to dip into uncharted waters and emerge victorious. As Hawkins (2002) stated:

> So it's clear that spirit refers to an unseen essence which never changes, even though its expression varies from one situation to another. This essence is vital; when we lose our spirit, we die – we expire from lack of that which *in*spires – The power of high energy attractor patterns is anabolic, sustaining life; their opposites are catabolic, eventually leading to death. (p. 180)

While I have worked with clients who modeled global aphasia to high functioning aphasia, all have made significant cognitive and emotional gains in art therapy with or without being paired with speech/language therapy. Yet, somehow, the pairing of the two disciplines yielded the most progress. The stories are varied yet somehow parallel the outcome – improvement in the following arenas: quality of life, self-esteem, motor functioning, cognitive and emotive repair, communication, socialization, and right/left hemisphere gains. Below is the progress of one client, Bob.

INDIVIDUAL ART THERAPY SESSION: BOB

Background Information

At intake, Bob was a seventy-one-year-old man who sustained massive damage to his left-middle hemisphere (CVA – cerebral vascular accident) in September of 1997, resulting in Broca's aphasia, severe apraxia, and right side hemiparesis. His language was compromised by severe word retrieval. He had been attending the clinic since September 1998. His wife referred him to the aphasia clinic due to concerns about swallowing safety (dysphagia). Bob had pneumonia on three separate occasions between January and May, 2001. He was treated with antibiotics and hospitalized once. (Generally, Bob contracts pneumonia yearly since his stroke. He has also been treated for acid reflux and examined by an otolaryngologist.)

Status at Beginning

Since his stroke, Bob's primary mode of communication was speech – yet it was emitted slowly, of low volume and produced with great effort. His speech production was often inaccurate due to apraxia. His strengths were good auditory comprehension and a wry sense of humor. As well, he attended to detail and had an able, working memory. He also displayed the ability to write if presented with a word to copy.

Speech/Language Therapy Procedures and Objectives

Production of nouns with fill-in the blanks presented verbally accompanied a Boardmaker© picture book. This aided Bob in his speech/language therapy sessions and he responded well to phonetic cueing, repetition, and reading. Missing pictures assisted him as well. Appropriate level of volume was observed when cueing or laughing. *Take Me Out to the Ballgame* was sung during the summer of 2000 and was followed by speech/language therapy games such as *Gesture Bingo, Vocabulary Bingo*, or identifying the correct item (household items and popular restaurants). Bob also liked playing *Rochester Monopoly* and *Poker*.

Speech/Language Objectives at Inception of Treatment

a. Increase sound/symbol recognition for /s/ and /dz/ 8/10 times with minimum cues.

b. Improve functional word production of a set of ten nouns.
c. Increase functional communication using any modality (use of communication book, gestures, or words).
d. Introduce a program of deep breathing exercises to be practiced during therapy and at home.

Because of Bob's history and objectives, Dr. Szekeres referred Bob for group art therapy. While initially he was seen for four months in a men's group by my graduate intern, Colleen Lynch, it was decided that he would benefit from individual art therapy after a chance session occurred without the two other men the following semester. (This was due to one's illness and another's inability to be transported on that day.) I then worked with him individually for a year before he entered dyadic art therapy with another client and Lori Higgins, my current graduate art therapy intern, the following year. All told, Bob has been in art therapy for three and one-half years.

Objectives for Individual and Group Art Therapy

a. Increase processing of auditory information.
b. Augment expressive language through gesture, word retrieval, and graphic materials.
c. Enhance cognitive skills.
d. Amplify self-esteem and ego maturation.
e. Explore affective/emotional issues related to the CVA.

Group Art Therapy with Bob

During the men's group, socialization was key to amplifying communication skills. Copious sessions occurred where the men nonverbally expressed their feelings related to their respective conditions post CVA. On one occasion, Bob rendered how he felt about his stroke. His cognitive level of functioning (working with his nondominant hand) clearly placed him at the lower end of the schematic stage of development (age 7–9 years) according to Lowenfeld and Brittain (1985).

Despite the developmental delay, obvious indices abounded: the lack of hands and feet pointed to Bob's feelings about his inability to both communicate to others and/or locomote. (At this time, Bob ambulated via a walker.) His missing ears suggested his difficulty with auditory processing and

Figure 5.1. Man with a stroke.

hinted at the damage left by Broca's aphasia (Hammer, 1995; Oster & Gould, 1987). These initial works were markers for the therapy to come.

The men's camaraderie contributed to an exchange of feelings about stroke's debilitation and aftermath. After three months, while simultaneously doing art therapy and speech/language therapy, I suggested that perhaps we introduce some music and movement therapy. Colleen, a very creative and able art therapy intern, selected music that spoke to the men's early adulthood years: Perry Como, Bing Crosby, and one day for fun, she presented a song by Muddy Waters called *Walk Like a Man*. The men really responded to the bravado behind those lyrics and we had each of them take turns "strutting their stuff" as we pushed aside the tables and created a space for movement. Much to our surprise, Bob shuffled across the room to the beat of the music unassisted by his walker. The power of music had instilled an inner strength in each of the men and after they "walked like men," the room was rearranged and we next suggested that they draw their feelings from the "walking activity." Below is Bob's illustration of himself feeling (once again) like a man:

Naturally, this led to discussion of their respective feelings of loss: each of them witnessed each other's stories as they communicated through their artwork the pervasive sense of incapacity exacted by their stroke. While Bob's illustration lacked facial features, it was a vast improvement from his first drawing. While the men were encapsulated in the above image, the larger man (whom he identified as himself) at least had hands and feet. It was

Figure 5.2.   Bob as a "man."

unclear who the smaller man was. Below was the next image that Bob created when he communicated that the "dancing" reminded him of what it was like to be with a woman:

While both the man and the woman sport hats (perhaps to keep a lid on their feelings), Bob depicted the man reaching out to his partner, yet she lacked lower arms and hands. As well, he drafted no features below her waistline and Bob represented himself as cut off at the area of genitalia. (While sexual relations are possible post stroke, it is quite possible that this picture may have represented Bob's feelings of being incomplete.) Nonetheless, his attempt to label the artwork "mam, woman" (sic) suggested cognitive repair since the

words were added without prompting by the art therapist or the speech/language therapist. I videotaped the session and the following week showed the dancing part of the session. As the men witnessed their dancing, they laughed and immediately engaged in the session, exactly where they had closed. Continuity between sessions had been firmly established.

Individual Art Therapy with Bob

The following semester on October 8, 2001, the two other men failed to show for the group. So I saw Bob alone. That was a very propitious day: we revisited some of the artwork from the previous last six months. Bob seemed perfectly content to have all of my time. We listened to music and then worked on several gestures drawings. I also signed with Bob and he was able to string an entire phrase "cup of milk" by himself. Remarkably he was able to do this repeatedly and with ease. Later, I gave him a homework assignment: paint anything you want and bring it back in.

Figure 5.3.   Mam woman.

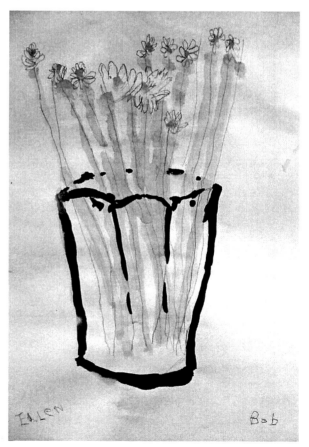

Figure 5.4.   Bob's flowers for Ellen.

The following week he produced his assignment, a lovely watercolor of the desert, which he painted from a magazine picture. It was quite impressive and so I suggested painting a still life of yellow daisies (which I had brought in). He doubted his ability to paint the flowers. I decided to encourage him by painting alongside him but I strung my right hand with a makeshift arm bandage. Allowing for a rare mixture of empathy, I joined him and painted left-handed so that we would be on somewhat equal footing. Since I knew he liked poker and took risks, I bargain chipped and upped the ante: I traded him his work for mine – he agreed to let his go up on the wall (but only in our art room). Below is his trade:

I realized that Bob was much more capable of artistic expression than I had gauged. And so the work began. I brought in an arrangement of Indian corn, mums, small squash and grapes and after several weeks of labor and concomitant increased self-esteem, Bob produced the water color below.

Indeed, Bob relented: he let me hang his artworks in the waiting area of the clinic and one by one, they all danced in frames, a testament to his growth and talent. By March of 2002, he was firmly entrenched in painting. I gave him a table easel, some acrylic paint, brushes, and canvas to take home with him. After months of painting, I still used only my left hand (nondominant) even as I instructed him. He completed a beautiful acrylic painting, which currently is framed in the waiting area of the speech/ language therapy clinic. Below are three pictures, one referencing the still life

Figure 5.6.   Still life referenced.

being painted, one of Bob in the throes of its creation, and the final of the still life prior to framing.

Working with Bob continues to be a rare gift. While his case has been transferred to my current graduate intern, Lori Higgins, he continues to

Figure 5.5.   Bob's watercolor still life.

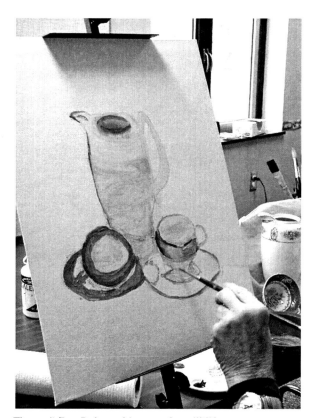

Figure 5.7.   Bob working on the still life.

Figure 5.8.   Still life, finished.

make great progress. Currently, he is being seen in a dyadic group with Mary, a lovely Italian grandmother. Only at the last fifteen minutes of the session do I appear: the art material is quickly ushered away. The flasks of water appear (a mock salute to pub-like behavior gone by and Bob's current dysphargia). The poker chips and cards are dealt. Mary, Bob, Lori, and I ante up and the real game begins. We laugh, we *talk*, we bet against the odds and in the end, despite the bluffing, everyone's a winner.

REFERENCES

Brannigan, G. & Decker, S. (2003). *Bender Visual-Motor Gestalt Test*. Itasca, IL: The Riverside Publishing Company.

Brookshire, R. H. (1997). *Introduction to neurogenic communication disorders*. St. Louis, MO: Mosby-Year Book Inc.

Diamond, J. (1979). *Behavioral kinesiology*. New York: Harper & Row.

Frankl, V. E. (1984). *Man's search for meaning*. New York: Washington Square Press/Pocket Books.

Goodheart, G. (1976). *Applied kinesiology* (12th ed.) Detroit, MI: Privately published.

Gresham, G. E., Duncan, P. W., & Stason. W. B. et al. (1995). *Post-Stroke Rehabilitation. Clinical Practice Guideline*, No. 16. Rockville, MD: U.S. Department of Health and Human Services. Public Health Service, Agency for Health Care Policy and Research. AHCPR Publication No. 95-0662.

Gresham, G.E., & Weiss, C.J. (1993). Heart disease and stroke. A journal for primary care physicians. *Heart Disorders and Stroke, 1* (1), 49–52.

Hammer, E. (1975). *The Clinical Application of Projective Drawing Techniques*, 4th ed. Springfield, IL: Charles C Thomas, Publisher, Ltd.

Hawkins, D.R. (2002). *Power vs. force, the hidden determinants of human behavior*. Carlsbad, CA: Hay House, Inc.

Higgins, L. H. & Horovitz, E.G. (2004). *Invoking industry to support art therapy*. Mundelein, IL: Creative Fire. 35th American Art Therapy Association proceedings.

Horovitz, E.G. (2002). *Spiritual art therapy: An alternate path*. (2nd ed.). Springfield, IL: Charles C Thomas, Publisher, Ltd.

Horovitz, E.G. (2005). *Art therapy as witness: A sacred guide*. Springfield, IL: Charles C Thomas, Publisher, Ltd.

Horovitz, E. (2002). *Belief art therapy assessment*. Springfield, IL: Charles C Thomas, Publisher, Ltd.

Johnson, K. A. & Becker, J.A. (1999). *The Whole Brain Atlas*. Retrieved on April 4, 2001 from http://www.med.harvard.edu./AANLIB/home.html.

Lowenfeld, V. & Brittain, W.L. (1985) *Creative & mental growth*. (6th ed.). New York: Macmillan.

Lynch, C. (2001). *Art therapy: An interdisciplinary collaboration at the Nazareth College speech-language clinic (aphasia) chronic aphasia: A focus on a men's group*. Unpublished thesis, Nazareth College. Rochester: New York.

Maclay, K. (1999). *A painter reinvents herself, art professor Katherine Sherwood's stroke forced her to paint left-handed*. Berkeley, CA: The Berkeleyan: Public Affairs, posted October 13, 1999.

Oster, G.D.. & Gould, P. (1987). *Using drawings in assessment and therapy*. New York: Brunner/Mazel Publishers.

Pink, L. (2004). Personal communication.

Silver, R.A. (1996) *The Silver Drawing Test of cognition and emotion*. Sarasota, FL: Ablin Press.

Ylvisaker, M. & Szekeres, S. F. (1981). Communication disorders. In Chapey, R. (Ed.). *Language intervention strategies in adult aphasia* (3rd ed.) (pp. 547–568). Baltimore, MD: Williams & Wilkins.

Waldman, P. (2000). Master stroke: A tragedy transforms a right-handed artist into a lefty – and a star. *The Wall Street Journal*. Vol. CXII No. 94, May 12, 2000.

HELPFUL WEBSITES

http://www.aphasia.org

http://www.naz.edu/dept/art_therapy/website.html

http://www.wroctv.com/features/story.asp?id=1806&f=Health-Smart

Biographical Statement

Ellen G. Horovitz, Ph.D., ATR-BC, is Professor and Director of Graduate Art Therapy and the Art Therapy Clinic at Nazareth College of Rochester. She has had over thirty years of experience with myriad patient populations and specializes in family art therapy with the deaf. Dr. Horovitz currently is in private practice. She is the author of numerous articles, book chapters, and the following books: *Spiritual Art Therapy: An Alternate Path, A Leap of Faith: The Call to Art and Art Therapy As Witness: A Sacred Guide.* Dr. Horovitz has directed and produced ten films available in DVD format. (Dr. Horovitz's films are available through www.arttxfilms.com) Dr. Horovitz is past President Elect of the American Art Therapy Association (AATA). For additional information contact:

Dr. Ellen G. Horovitz, ATR-BC/Director of Graduate Art Therapy/Nazareth College
4245 East Avenue
Rochester, N.Y. 14618
E-mail: ehorovi4@naz.edu

Chapter 6

THE HISTORY OF PLAY THERAPY

MISTIE D. BARNES

INTRODUCTION

Play therapy is a treatment method that has exploded in popularity. It has been used in the United States and around the world for the last 20 years, and shows an increase in the use of play therapy and play techniques, as well as the growing membership in professional play therapy organizations (The Association for Play Therapy, Inc., 2004). Although play therapy is generally thought of as a relatively new treatment modality, play therapy methods and techniques have been around for generations, slowly emerging and taking its place as a viable treatment modality.

To understand play therapy, it is important to recognize why play therapy emerged and begin to understand its popularity gain as an effective method for treating children. In this chapter, I will address the need for and development of play therapy, from its earliest underpinnings to current practice, discussing its birth in psychoanalytic therapy, and its growth into structured and unstructured/nondirective play therapies.

As a part of this very brief history of play therapy, I will review the development of professional organizations supporting play therapy, such as the Association of Play Therapy, Inc. and the British Association of Play Therapy. This chapter will take a historical and evolutionary approach to play therapy. No history is complete without addressing current, ongoing development, so I will cover the growth of play therapy and its organizations over the years. It is important to note here that while the theoretical underpinnings and ideas associated with each philosophy is extremely important to know and understand as a part of the history and application of each play therapy system, they will not be addressed in this chapter due to their inclusion in other chapters of this book.

HISTORICAL PERSPECTIVES OF PLAY

Early in our history, the prevailing Puritan attitudes of the time often viewed the play of children as a waste of time, resources, and of no particular benefit (Schaefer & Kaduson, 1994). Today, there is still an emphasis on children being productive and a stressing of academics, while de-emphasizing the need for play and social activity when compared to productivity (Schaefer & Kaduson, 1994). While most of our ancestors may have seen play as simply a pastime of children with no productive benefits, great minds in our history, as noted below, began to slowly awaken to the power of play with children (Appendix).

The author of the literary classic *Little Women*, Emily Dickinson, stated "Blessed be they who play for theirs is the Kingdom of Heaven" (Schaefer & Kaduson, 1994, p. 17). Author Ralph Waldo Emerson said, "It is a happy talent to know how to play" (Schaefer & Kaduson, 1994, p. 21). Even earlier, the great philosopher Plato was quoted as saying, "Our children from their earliest years must take part in all the more lawful forms of play, for if they are not surrounded with such an atmosphere they can never grow up to be well-conducted and virtuous citizens. . . . You can discover more about a person in an hour of play than in a year of conversation" (cited in Schaefer & Kaduson, 1994, pp. 60–61). The *Bible* as well points out the value and use of play as a means of rejoicing and expression: " . . . the streets of the city shall be full of boys and girls playing . . ." Zechariah 8:5 (King James Version).

As society began to realize that play was more than just a whimsical activity for children, rather, it provided a means of expression and growth. Those specializing in working with children began to also recognize the merits of utilizing play. As all traditional means of therapy failed to show dramatic results in helping children, child therapists began to explore and implement play and play therapy techniques to work with children in a variety of settings and situations.

HISTORY OF PLAY THERAPY

Play therapy originally developed within an educational setting (Landreth, 1991) and only decades later was it applied to the therapeutic treatment of children (Kottman, 2001). As early as the late 1700s, the necessity of using play to interact with children in an educational manner was addressed (Rousseau, 1979), along with the idea that children are not just small adults, rather, they are unique individuals with a unique set of needs. The introduction of these ideas resulted in those working with children reevaluating their methods of interacting with children. Combating the traditional idea of children needing to be productive members of society and function at an adult level, Rousseau (1979) emphasized the need to observe and learn from the free-spirited and naturalness of a child's expressive play.

Early in the twentieth century, psychotherapists began to realize that children could not process information in the same ways as adults. Children also could not, nor did they desire to, use free association or explore their subconscious or past as adults commonly did when receiving treatment (Axline, 1964, 1969) at that period in time. However, they could play.

Sigmund Freud first documented an application of play in child therapy in 1909 in the case of *Little Hans* (Kottman, 2001; Landreth, 1991; Purdy, 2004). This was the first acknowledged case of a child suffering from an emotional disturbance, specifically a phobia. Freud met only briefly with the child. Treatment was conducted by advising the father on how to respond to and intervene with the child based on the father's reports of the child's play and Freud's subsequent interpretations of the catalyst to the disturbance. Although Freud did not use play directly with the child, he gathered information about the case, then gave the father instructions and direction on how to work with his son based on and using the child's play behavior. This method of assisting parents in working with their children would later be developed into Filial Therapy (O'Conner, 2000).

With this critical and groundbreaking foundation for the use of play in therapy being formed, play techniques began to develop along a variety of paths, resulting in no single continuum for the development of play therapy. Additionally, play began to be used by a number of therapists in a range of settings with varying goals and beliefs, all arising from a need to understand, form a relationship with, and productively work with children, as well as assist children in working through and managing their life situations. Therapists from many backgrounds and theoretical orientations began using play techniques with their young clients (Landreth, 1991).

Psychoanalytic Play Therapy

There are three main contributors to the development of Psychoanalytic Play Therapy, Hermine Hug-Hellmuth, Anna Freud, and Melanie Klein (Gill, 1994; Landreth, 1991; O'Conner, 2000; Purdy, 2004). The use of play in psychoanalytic theory was considered the first attempt to apply play to any type of therapeutic treatment with children (Landreth, 1991). In 1919, Hermine Hug-Hellmuth began incorporating play into her work with children. The late 1920s to early 1930s fostered the incorporation of play into the practice of Melanie Klein and Anna Freud; thus, the birth of psychoanalytic play therapy (Gill, 1994; O'Conner, 2000).

Hermine Hug-Hellmuth

After Freud's groundbreaking work of indirectly using play in his work with children, Hermine Hug-Hellmuth was the second person commonly recognized as having incorporated play and toys into their therapeutic work with children (Gill, 1994; Kottman, 2001; Landreth, 1991; O'Conner, 2000); the first to use these techniques one-on-one directly with a child. Hug-Hellmuth believed that children were unable to participate fully in psychoanalysis as adults did, and often did not care to do so, which resulted in many therapists of the time collecting data on the behavior of children in their attempts to better understand them

(Landreth, 1991). Hug-Hellmuth felt that by using play, a therapist could understand the child (Kottman, 2001). Although Hug-Hellmuth studied play with children extensively and incorporated this into her ongoing treatment with children, she sparsely wrote on the subject and did not develop a separate theory; this was a job for Anna Freud and Melanie Klein.

Anna Freud

Anna Freud held the traditional psychoanalytic belief of the need to strengthen the ego and explore the past as crucial to the treatment of children (Landreth, 1991). In addition, Anna Freud chose to use limited interpretation and to use play to develop a strong emotional (Landreth, 1991) relationship with her child clients before moving on to a more adult-oriented treatment, incorporating more traditional psychoanalytic methods (Drewes, Carey, & Schaefer, 2001; Gill, 1994; Kottman, 2001; O'Conner, 2000). Freud believed that although play was beneficial in establishing a relationship, it could not be used for interpretation or exact symbolism of the unconscious or past (Kottman, 2001). Freud also indicated that play had only limited use as an emotional release, and some deeper, more intense work was necessary to help the children verbalize their thoughts and feelings, and to gain insight into their history and unconscious (Kottman, 2001; Landreth, 1991).

Melanie Klein

Melanie Klein and Anna Freud took very different approaches to their use of psychoanalytic techniques of play in their treatment of children (O'Conner, 2000), although Klein also held the traditional psychoanalytic belief of the need to strengthen the ego and explore the past as crucial to the treatment of children (Landreth, 1991). In contrast to Anna Freud, who used only limited interpretation, Klein was confident that the play exhibited by the child in the playroom completely symbolized the child's' experience, was equivalent to adult-free association and verbalizations (Kottman, 2001; O'Conner, 2000), and could be used for interpretation of the child/therapist relationship. Klein began using play techniques with children under six years of age, believing their play provided a direct connection to their unconscious. Klein used play to explore past issues buried in the unconscious and to encourage insight and under-

standing. To accomplish these goals, Klein used simplistic toys, (Landreth, 1991), allowing each child to have their own set of toys tucked away for their use only, specific to their needs and reflecting their presenting problems (Drewes, Carey, & Schaefer, 2001; Landreth, 1991). Interestingly, Klein exhibited the first documented usage of limits in the play therapy room, allowing verbal though not physical attacks on her person in the playroom (Landreth, 1991).

Development of Structured Play Therapy

Structured Play Therapy, with a basis in psychoanalytic theory (LeBlanc & Ritchie, 2001), was encouraged by the work of play therapists such as David Levy, Joseph Solomon, and Gove Hambridge, in the late 1930s (Gill, 1994; Kottman, 2001). Levy was the originator of release play therapy. Hambridge believed in the benefits of recreating events (O'Conner, 2000; Purdy, 2004). Solomon created active play therapy (O'Conner, 2000). All theorists believed that directing and taking an active role in play sessions was a major responsibility of the therapist and crucial to the outcome of therapy (Kottman, 2001; LeBlanc & Ritchie, 2001).

David Levy

In the 1930s, release play therapy was introduced by David Levy as a way for children under 10 (Kottman, 2001) to release and assimilate the emotions related to a specific traumatic or anxiety provoking situation. Levy felt there was no need for an emphasis on interpretation, only the pure benefit of using play to recreate and work through their problematic situations (Landreth, 1991; Purdy, 2004). The directives in release therapy, as were the toys, were limited. Incorporating Sigmund Freud's theory of repetition compulsion, Levy believed that by providing a child with limited toys specific to the traumatic or anxiety provoking event, a child would replay the traumatic event repetitively until the event had been assimilated and was no longer detrimental or distressing to the child (Gill, 1994; Kottman, 2001; O'Conner, 2000).

Joseph C. Solomon

Joseph Solomon developed a form of play therapy known as active play therapy. Through the use of this structured play (LeBlanc & Ritchie, 2001), a child could express emotions and behaviors openly in a playroom without social consequences, whereas those same emotions and behaviors may be considered inappropriate in other environments. He believed that by having these experiences in the playroom, children were able to learn to behave in a more socially appropriate manner (Gill, 1994; Kottman, 2001; O'Conner, 2000). Solomon also emphasized a differentiation between past traumas/future consequences from current situations to reduce anxiety (Gill, 1994; O'Conner, 2000).

Gove Hambridge

Gove Hambridge followed roughly the same course of implementing play in therapy as did David Levy, by recreating traumatic events in play (Purdy, 2004). However, Hambridge chose to establish a strong therapeutic relationship with a child before addressing the anxiety/traumatic situation. Upon having developed a therapeutic relationship, Hambridge would directly recreate the traumatic event or situation, which created anxiety in the child (Gill, 1994; Kottman, 2001; O'Conner, 2000). When the event or situation had been recreated, the child was encouraged to engage in re-enactment. After completing the re-enactment, the child was allowed free-play to assist in the transition out of the playroom (O'Conner, 2000).

Development of Nonstructured Play Therapy

Nonstructured play therapy techniques developed along a similar path to structured play therapy, evolving from the work of a great many therapists. There are several major contributors and advocates of nondirective or child-centered play therapy, including Virginia Axline, Garry Landreth, and Bernard and Louise Guerney (Kottman, 2001). However, before these play therapists began developing nondirective play therapy, the groundwork was provided by the relationship play therapists.

Development of Relationship Play Therapy

Based on the work of Otto Rank (Gill, 1994), which emphasized the importance of the therapeutic relationship over the clients' history and the unconscious, Frederic Allen, Jesse Taft (Landreth, 1991), and Clark Moustakas (Drewes, Carey, & Schaefer, 2001; Gill, 1994; Kottman, 2001; O'Conner, 2000) introduced relationship play therapy in the 1930s. Relationship therapists focused on the here and now of the child's experiences,

acknowledging children's innate ability to heal themselves, being able to direct their own activities, and being responsible for their own behaviors, qualities, and growth. The relationship between the therapist and the child was also strongly emphasized (Kottman, 2001). Combined, the works of Rank, Allen, Taft, and Moustakas formed the basis for the development of Nondirective Play Therapy (Landreth, 1991).

Nondirective Play Therapy

Based upon the work of the relationship play therapists and by Carl Rogers, nondirective play therapy was first introduced by Virgina Axline in the 1940s (Axline, 1964, 1969; Landreth, 1991; Kottman, 2001; LeBlanc & Ritchie, 2001; O'Conner, 2000). Although relationship play therapy emphasized and encouraged the relationship between therapist and child, Virginia Axline more fully explored and expanded upon the belief that children will strive towards healing, growth, and self-actualization when provided with an appropriate atmosphere of acceptance, understanding, and noninterference. With this atmosphere provided by the therapist, children will be free to more fully explore their feelings, beliefs, and behaviors, working through and accepting them in their own way. The belief is that with adult reflection and acceptance, not interference, children will enter the playroom and eventually begin to work on issues which are pressing to them. In this manner, children may re-enact a situation, recreate an environment, or process an event or situation which has caused their disturbance. By doing this in a safe, accepting environment, children will be able to internally resolve their conflict (Axline, 1964, 1969; Drewes, Carey, & Schaefer, 2001; Kottman, 2001; O'Conner, 2000).

Child-Centered Play Therapy

Following the work of Virginia Axline, Garry Landreth of Texas built upon the concept of nondirective play therapy to develop child-centered play therapy. In child-centered play therapy, the setting in the playroom and the relationship between the child and therapist in play therapy must be different from any other experience the child may have. According to child-centered play therapy, the therapist's main goal is to reflect the child's feelings and experiences, taking noninteractive and nondirective approaches to the play sessions, allowing the child to completely direct the course of activity and the session (Kottman, 2001).

Filial Therapy

Finally, Bernard and Louise Guerney worked to incorporate many of the ideas and techniques on which child-centered play therapy is comprised to assist parents in working with their children in filial therapy (Gill, 1994; Kottman, 2001). In filial therapy, the therapist works directly with the parents, individually or in groups, teaching the skills inherent in child-centered play therapy for the parent to use on a daily basis in their interactions with their children (Kottman, 2001). As well, the parents are encouraged to regularly set aside time to work with the child in a child-centered play therapy session at home, allowing the parent to work as the therapeutic agent (Landreth, 1991; VanFleet, 1994).

DEVELOPMENT OF ASSOCIATIONS

Over the last several decades, associations for the promotion of education and advocacy of play therapy and play techniques have arisen across the globe. Associations have formed in many countries around the world, with mental health professionals in almost every country employing play therapy techniques, beliefs, and ideas. Three such organizations are the Association for Play Therapy, Inc. (APT), the British Association of Play Therapists (BCAP), and the International Society for Child and Play Therapy/Play Therapy International (PTI).

The Association for Play Therapy, Inc.

In 1982, the Association for Play Therapy, Inc. was founded (Purdy, 2004) in New York by Charles Schaefer and Kevin O'Conner for professionals interested in developing a modality of treatment specifically to meet the needs of children (The Association for Play Therapy, Inc., 2004). As Schaefer and O'Conner began to develop the organization, Gary Landreth, Louise Guerney, and John Allan joined the board of the new organization to assist in its development.

In 1984, the first conference of the Association for Play Therapy was held in New York City, and in 1987, in Texas, with the first membership drive being initiated in 1988. In 1992, the *International Journal of Play Therapy* was first published, while 1993 introduced the credentialing process for

Registered Play Therapist and Registered Play Therapist-Supervisor (The Association for Play Therapy, Inc., 2004). The last decade has shown remarkable growth and development in this organization, with the organization moving to an independent status, forming committees, award programs, grant programs, regulations for branch performance, a yearly conference, newsletters, journals, opportunities for continuing education and leadership development, as well as providing networking opportunities and access to the most up-to-date in technology, techniques, and resources.

The British Association of Play Therapists

Just as play therapy developed in the United States, the course of play therapy followed a similar line in the United Kingdom. The 1980s brought about the emergence of new play techniques and growing popularity of the use of play in the United Kingdom. In 1992, the British Association of Play Therapists was created. Currently, the British Association of Play Therapists endorses four training programs throughout England (The British Association of Play Therapists, 2003).

The International Society for Child and Play Therapy/Play Therapy International

The Canadian Play Therapy Institute was established in the 1980s at the Children's Mental Health Center in Canada. Soon after, the faculty members were bombarded with requests for training assistance from around the globe. To meet these growing needs, in 1995–1996 the International Society for Child and Play Therapy/Play Therapy International was founded (International Society for Child and Play Therapy/Play Therapy International (PTI), 2002).

Current Trends in Play Therapy

Membership in professional play therapy associations in the United States, such as the Association for Play Therapy, Inc., has exploded in the last two decades. At its inception, the Association for Play Therapy had a membership of approximately 50 individuals (O'Conner, 2000). Membership in the Association for Play Therapy was approximately 450 in 1988, it jumped to almost 2,000 in 1990 (Landreth, 1991), and continued to increase to 3,346 by December of 1998 (The Association for Play Therapy, Inc., 2004). In 2000, the Association for Play Therapy, Inc., had a membership of over 3,600 individuals (O'Conner, 2000), and in December of 2002, the Association for Play Therapy, Inc., had a still growing membership of 4,369 individuals (The Association for Play Therapy, Inc., 2004). Due to the diligent work on the part of the Association for Play Therapy leadership, member participation and involvement, and ongoing strivings for growth and excellence as an organization, the Association for Play Therapy, Inc. has grown by leaps and bounds and shows no signs of slowing down.

Branch Development – The Association for Play Therapy, Inc.

Branch development and participation has steadily grown in the last several years. In December of 1998, there were 31 branches in the United States, Canada, and South Africa (The Association for Play Therapy, Inc., 2004). In 2000, that number had grown to 33 branches (O'Conner, 2000), and by December of 2002 the number of branches, local and international, had made a leap to 45 chartered branches (The Association for Play Therapy, Inc., 2004).

Registered Play Therapists/Supervisors – The Association for Play Therapy, Inc.

The number of professionals practicing with the credentials administered by the Association for Play Therapy, Inc. has grown along with the membership and popularity of play therapy. In December of 1998, there were 706 Registered Play Therapists and Registered Play Therapists-Supervisors. By December of 2002, there were 1,032 Registered Play Therapists/Supervisors, a growth of 47% (The Association for Play Therapy, Inc., 2004), supporting the fact that not only are the numbers of people interested in play therapy growing, but so is the number of individuals receiving training and becoming credentialed in play therapy.

Currently, the field of play therapy is growing by leaps and bounds. As the field grows, play therapists are exploring, implementing, and developing new techniques and methods in new settings on a regular basis. Some current trends in play therapy include play techniques within the family setting, the ongoing development and use of filial therapy, adult play therapy, Theraplay, group play therapy, and developmental play therapy (Gill, 1994; Landreth, 2001). Play therapy is also being used in

a variety of settings; including hospitals, child care centers, schools, residential placement, and wherever children are located!

Play Techniques in the Family Setting

Due to the frequent inability of young children to adequately articulate their feelings, perceptions, and situations, the entire family may be at a disadvantage in family therapy sessions. Without being able to fully participate in family therapy sessions, young children may at times be left to watch, feel inhibited, or altogether ignore a traditional family therapy session while the rest of the family attempts to operate with one or more members uninvolved. By using play techniques in the family sessions, the therapist is able to bring the younger children into the session, ensuring their viewpoints, opinions, and feelings are incorporated, as well as encouraging understanding and awareness of older family members (Gill, 1994; Kottman, 2001; Landreth, 2001).

Filial Therapy

Filial therapy, developed in the 1960s by Bernard and Louise Guerney, works to remedy childhood problems, as well as promote healthy social and emotional development of the child with the help of the parents. Filial therapy uses parents as the agents of change with their children. By teaching the parent basic helping and play skills, the therapist incorporates the parent in treating the child and improving the parent-child relationship by engaging in weekly play therapy sessions with their child (Kottman, 2001; Landreth, 1991; VanFleet, 1994).

Adult Play Therapy

The newly developing field of adult play therapy is one with remarkable potential. Using play therapy and play activities with adults, the play therapy is the focus of the session, rather than the person and the task of being able to verbalize thoughts and feelings. With the adult becoming immersed in the play, the individual is able to reach a level of self-awareness which otherwise may not be likely to emerge using talk therapy (Landreth, 2001).

Theraplay

Theraplay, originally developed to address attachment issues, consists of a generally set number of sessions to improve parent-child relationships. Sessions may include several dimensions, such as nurturing, play, challenge, structure, and intrusive behavior. Under optimal conditions, at least two therapists are present during a Theraplay session: one or more working with the child while another assists the parent in understanding what is happening (Kottman, 2001).

Group Play Therapy

Group play therapy is yet another trend in the play therapy movement which is gaining momentum. Group play therapy, as in other group therapies, has several benefits over other methods, such as cost-effectiveness and an opportunity to try out new, more appropriate skills with peers. In using group play therapy, children also have the additional benefits of learning to incorporate peers into their interactions with an adult, practice appropriate relationships, which can be generalized into their everyday lives, and learning from the children with whom they are interacting (Gill, 1994; Landreth, 2001; Packman & Bratton, 2003).

Developmental Play Therapy

To address the effect of a stunted developmental level of clients, developmental play therapy was created. In developmental play therapy, the developmental level of the child is assessed, and the developmental play therapist attempts to assist the child in progressing in their developmental growth. The developmental play therapist does this by providing nurturing and attempting to fulfill the developmental needs which were missed at the stunted developmental stage (Kottman, 2001).

CONCLUSION

The development of today's concept of play therapy has followed a long, convoluted pathway to finding the most appropriate, effective, and meaningful methods of assisting children more efficiently and effectively. This pathway has been filled with ruts and bumps as lack of understanding and acceptance of the power of play has at times hindered the development and application of play therapy. However, the overwhelming evidence and simple common sense behind the power of play therapy has smoothed even the roughest patches.

The initial reason for the development of play therapy, finding an appropriate and effective way to treat children, still holds true today. Children do not have the same cognitive and language abilities as adults, and therefore cannot receive the same benefits from adult-oriented therapies. Should one ever question whether play therapy is still needed, one need only look back through the history of its development to see that the history is only beginning.

A PLAY THERAPY TIMELINE

1903	Sigmund Freud outlines the stages of childhood instinctual development – oral, anal, genital (Drisko, 2001).
1909	Sigmund Freud first applies psychotherapy to children indirectly with Little Hans (Landreth, 1991; Kottman, 2001).
1913	Hug-Hellmuth interprets play in terms of Freud's drive theory (Drisko, 2001).
1919	The first documented use of play by Hug-Hellmuth with a child (O'Conner, 2000).
1929	Melanie Klein visits the United States and finds only limited use of play in therapy with children in the United States (Landreth, 1991).
1920s–1930	Psychoanalytic Play Therapy is developed by Hermine Hug-Hellmuth, Anna Freud, and Melanie Klein (Gill, 1994; Kottman, 2001; Landreth, 1991; O'Conner, 2000).
1937	Melanie Klein uses interpretations in play therapy (Drisko, 2001).
1938	There is strong advocacy for the use of play in the growing Child Guidance Movement (Drisko, 2001).
1939	Levy introduces "Release Therapy" (Landreth, 1991).
1930s	Relationship Play Therapy is introduced by Allen, Taft, and Moustakas (Landreth, 1991).
1941	Ghetto Theresienstadt was established during World War II – a concentration camp where artist, political activist, and intellectual Friedl Dicker-Brandeis used play to work with children residing in this camp, with astonishing results (Glazier, 1999).
1944	Sandplay (Sandtable) therapy is introduced (Drisko, 2001).
1947	Virgina Axline publishes her book *Play Therapy*, explaining nondirective play therapy (Axline, 1969).
1949	Buck's "House-Tree-Person" technique is introduced (Drisko, 2001).
1949	*Limits Are Therapy* was written by Bixler, which introduced the benefits of limits to play therapy (Kottman, 2001; O'Conner, 2000).

1962   Piaget differentiates cognitive differences by age grouping (Drisko, 2001).

1982   The Association for Play Therapy, Inc. is established in New York (The Association for Play Therapy, Inc., 2004).

1980s   Trauma is treated using structured storytelling in play (Drisko, 2001).

1990s   Growth in tools and techniques of play therapy and assistance to parents in understanding their young children (Drisko, 2001).

1992   Regulated training of play therapy begins (Drisko, 2001).

1993   The Association for Play Therapy, Inc. begins to offer the credentials of Registered Play Therapist and Registered Play Therapist-Supervisor (The Association for Play Therapy, Inc., 2004).

1995   First continuing education 'Approved Providers' designated through the Association for Play Therapy, Inc. (The Association for Play Therapy, Inc., 2004).

2002   Stricter guidelines on branch activities initiated through the Association for Play Therapy, Inc. (The Association for Play Therapy, Inc., 2004).

2004   The Association for Play Therapy, Inc. initiates the "Leadership Academy" to encourage the growth and development of leadership skills among mental health professionals (The Association for Play Therapy, Inc., 2004).

REFERENCES

Axline, V.M. (1969). *Play therapy* (Rev. ed.). New York: Ballantine Books, Inc.

Axline, V.M. (1964). *Dibs in search of self* (Rev. ed.). New York: Ballantine Books, Inc.

Drisko, J.W. (2001). *A short history of play therapy*. Retrieved July 4, 2004 from http://sophia.smith.edu/~jdrisko/playtimeline.htm.

Drewes, A.A., Carey, L.J., & Schaefer, C.E. (Eds.). (2001). *School-based play therapy*. New York: John Wiley & Sons, Inc.

Gill, E. (1994). *Play in family therapy*. New York: The Guilford Press.

Glazer, H.R. (1999). Children and play in the holocaust: Friedl Dicker-Brandeis – Heroic child therapist. *Journal of Humanistic Counseling, Education, & Development, 37*(4), 194–200.

International Society for Child and Play Therapy/Play Therapy International (PTI). (2002) *International Society for Child and Play Therapy/Play Therapy International*. Retrieved July 27, 2004 from http://www.playtherapy.org.

Kottman, T. (2001). *Play therapy: Basics and beyond*. Alexandria, VA: American Counseling Association.

Landreth, G.L. (1991). *Play therapy: The art of the relationship*. Florence, KY: Accelerated Development, Inc.

LeBlanc, M., & Ritchie, M. (2001). A meta-analysis of play therapy outcomes. *Counseling Psychology Quarterly, 14*.

O'Conner, K.J. (2000). *The play therapy primer* (2nd ed.). New York: John Wiley & Sons, Inc.

Packman, J., & Bratton, S.C. (2003). A school-based group play/activity therapy intervention with learning disabled preadolescents exhibiting behavior problems. *International Journal of Play Therapy, 12*(2), 7–29.

Purdy, C. (2004). *The history of play therapy: Discovering our heritage, a Kid Power Home Study Course*. Retrieved July 4, 2004 from http://www.playtherapycentral.com/home.html

Rousseau, J.J. (1979). *EMILE or on education*. New York: Basic Books, Inc.

Schaefer, C., & Kaduson, H. (Eds.). (1994). *The quotable play therapist: 238 of the all-time best quotes on play and play therapy*. Northvale, NJ: Jason Aronson, Inc.

The British Association of Play Therapists. (2003). *A history of play therapy*. Retrieved March 28, 2004 from http://www.bapt.info/historyofpt.htm

The Association for Play Therapy, Inc. (2004). *About APT – Association for Play Therapy, Inc.* Retrieved May 21, 2004 from http://www.a4pt.org

VanFleet, R. (1994). *Filial therapy: Strengthening parent-child relationships through play*. Sarasota, FL: Professional Resource Press.

Biographical Statement

Mistie D. Barnes, M.Ed., NCC, RPT, LPC, is a Child and Adolescent Support Therapist with Region IV Mental Health/Mental Retardation Commission in North Mississippi. She received her Bachelor of Arts degree in Psychology and English, as well as a Masters Degree in Counselor Education, both from the University of Mississippi. Miss Barnes holds the credentials of National Certified Counselor (NCC) from the National Board for Certified Counselors, Registered Play Therapist (RPT) from the Association for Play Therapy, Inc., and she is a Licensed Professional Counselor (LPC) in the state of Mississippi. Mistie Barnes is on the Board of Directors of the Mississippi Association for Play Therapy. Miss Barnes is serving as President of the Association for the 2005 term. She has previously served on the Executive Board as Secretary/Treasurer, as well as chairing the Promotions and Support committee. Miss Barnes is a board member of the Oxford Play

Therapy Training Institute in Oxford, MS and serves as Secretary of the Board. Miss Barnes is currently engaged in doctoral studies (Ph.D.) at the University of Mississippi in Counselor Education with a specialization in play therapy.

Mistie D. Barnes, M.Ed., NCC, RPT, LPC
171 CR 411, Ripley, MS 38663
Home: 662-837-9168 / Cell: 662-871-8650 /
Work: 662-837-8154
mistiebarnes@yahoo.com

Chapter 7

THEORETICAL PERSPECTIVES OF PLAY THERAPY

Joshua A. Thomas-Acker and Sally S. Sloan

INTRODUCTION

Psychotherapy with children can be traced back to Sigmund Freud and his work with psychoanalysis and children (Leblanc & Ritchie, 2001). Freud's daughter, Anna Freud, developed play theories and techniques for work with children based on psychoanalytic theory (Leblanc & Ritchie, 2001). As art therapy, this is one of the early foundations of play therapy. Psychoanalytic theory focuses on helping individuals discover why they think and behave as they do (Schaefer, 2003). This early theory also emphasized that therapists confront individuals when there are inconsistencies in cognition and behavior. This was applied to assisting children in self-discovery through the use of play. Parents were involved in assessing the home and school environments and behavior outside of therapy sessions. Psychoanalytic theorists applied their perspective to play therapy, and play therapy has evolved over the years branching out into several different theoretical perspectives and treatment options (Leblanc & Ritchie, 2001; Schaefer, 2003).

Play therapy is a treatment modality that is a viable option for working with clients, especially children. It provides safety, empowerment, freedom, and a supportive environment for self-expression. Play therapy provides children with an environment that capitalizes on their skills, is safe, and hopefully fun! This chapter will explore the more common theoretical perspectives in play therapy. Although there are many theoretical approaches to counseling and psychology, this chapter will concentrate primarily on three applications. Play therapy is a technique that requires specialized training (Gladding, 1996). Clinicians need to develop the necessary skill and training before engaging in play therapy treatment options.

Child-Centered Play Therapy

The first theoretical perspective of play therapy examined in this chapter is child-centered play therapy. Much attention will be given to this approach because this theoretical perspective is one of the most common and widely used modalities in play therapy (Gladding, 1996; Peery, 2002). Child-Centered Play Therapy, developed by Virginia Axline, is based on the theoretical model of Carl Rogers' Client or Person-Centered counseling approach (Leblanc & Ritchie, 2001). Rogers believed that a skilled therapist could work to "release and strengthen" individuals without interfering in his or her life in the therapeutic process (Rogers, 1992, p. 163). Rogers' theory is based on his belief that counselors need to have a genuine interest in their client's well-being. He believed the therapist could create a needed atmosphere of warmth to develop a therapeutic relationship with the client. Deceptive techniques used to obtain needed information are unnecessary according to Rogers (1992). Genuineness and warmth are more important factors in Rogers' method for obtaining a rapport that allows for the critical processes of therapy to take place. He believed that the release of feelings was beneficial to the therapeutic process and the therapist can aid by helping to verbalize the feelings for the client. Such an approach advocates helping clients make responsible choices (Rogers, 1992). The therapist does not take responsibility for the choices. Instead, the client is supported and encouraged to take responsibility for his or her own choices. Reflection from the thera-

65

pist helps the client gain insight into their emotional patterns by observations from the therapist. Listening empathically is crucial to the reflective process.

Virginia Axline was a student and colleague of Carl Rogers (Landreth, 1993). She used a nondirective technique and philosophy to create the child-centered approach to play therapy (Landreth, 1993). According to Landreth, play is children's form of expression and a way to demonstrate their experiences and feelings. Self-directed play is a safe modality for children to take an active role in therapy and be candid while experiencing a sense of power and control over the situation. Children can discover alternate outcomes to real world situations; rehearse desired outcomes in family, school, or social situations; and practice interpersonal skills. Landreth points out that the Rogers method applied to play therapy provides an accepting and caring environment for children to communicate their needs and personalities. Children do not always have the linguistic skills necessary to communicate their ideas as required by traditional talk therapy methods. The child's developmental stage influences their ability to communicate in an adult world.

Axline (1947) identified eight basic principles of the child-centered approach. She believed therapists first must be genuinely interested in their child client, and develop a friendly environment of warmth and caring. Such an environment facilitates the establishment of a good rapport between the therapist and child. Additionally, the therapist must unconditionally accept the child as the child presents himself or herself. Permissiveness and a safe therapeutic environment allow children to completely explore and express themselves. Axline (1947) included a component of the relationship that involves the therapist reflecting back the child's observations to promote increased understanding. This method, according to Axline, requires the understanding that each child has the capacity to problem solve and act responsibly. This means trusting the child to move in a forward direction naturally. This type of therapy is gradual and not something that should be rushed. Limits are set only to facilitate the child's development of personal and relationship responsibility (Axline, 1947, pp. 73–74).

Santrock (2002) expresses the need for safe, accepting environmental conditions to insure the best potential for human development. Therapists may have the best of intentions, but cannot force a child to grow faster in development, emotionally, or otherwise. In the child-centered approach, children are offered the opportunity to grow in an accepting, caring, and safe environment where responsible choices are encouraged (Landreth, 1993). In addition, Landreth (1993) believes that therapists are not playing a role where they must make progress happen; instead, they facilitate the client's existing growth potential. The nondirective approach in client-centered therapy allows the child to realize self-control and understand they have choices (Griffith, 1997; Ryan & Needham, 2001).

Axline (1947) pointed out that play therapy is a good form of stress relief for children. Griffith (1997) adds that interventions such as play therapy can be very valuable for sexual abuse victims. Glazer (1999) profiled the use of play therapy in extreme circumstances. She examined the use of this approach with children during the Holocaust. Glazer demonstrated the utility of play therapy by how it was used during the atrocities that occurred in concentration camps.

Cochran (1996) points out that the American population is rapidly becoming more ethnically, culturally, and religiously diverse. He writes that child-centered play therapy allows for self-exploring and self-expression in self-esteem enhancing ways that are free of judgment and barriers to acceptance. This allows for the acceptance of diverse ideas, characteristics, and personal traits that are related to ethnic, racial, cultural, and religious backgrounds. The therapist's nondirective approach allows for freedom for the child, and the ability to apply their own background and experience to their exploration and problem-solving.

Children who are verbally inhibited can benefit from expressing emotions through play therapy (Cochran, 1996). Children can develop confidence in verbalizing through nondirective, supportive expression, and play in a safe environment. For basic actions and explorations in play, verbalization from the child/client is not necessary in play therapy.

To summarize the child-centered play therapy perspective as discussed in this section, it allows children to grow and develop in a safe environment where they can express themselves through a natural and effective medium (Axline, 1947;

Griffith, 1997; Landreth, 1993; Santrock, 2002). This medium distances the child from frightful situations through the use of toys rather than real-life events (Griffith, 1997; Landreth, 2002). It also permits the child to react and gain a sense for the consequences of different reactions and ultimately be better able to cope with his or her life situation. Child-centered therapy recognizes individuals' abilities and positive natural attributes (Axline, 1947; Landreth, 1993). The therapeutic techniques allow children to communicate in a safe and comfortable way while being encouraged to explore with limits in place for safety and security (Axline, 1947). These techniques are not for directing their play and interaction. Limits are designed to define the child's responsibility in the relationship and frame the therapy within the boundaries of reality (Landreth, 2002). The nondirective approach is adaptable to a variety of circumstances including use in diverse cultural populations, with traumatized children, in stress relief, family therapy, schools, and when language barriers are present (Cochran, 1996).

Adlerian Play Therapy

A second theoretical option available in the play therapy creative treatment modality is Adlerian Play Therapy. Understanding the Adlerian approach to counseling and psychology is important in understanding this approach to play therapy. Kottman and Johnson (1993) identify three important aspects of Adlerian Theory. They indicate that this theory assumes that people are inherently in need of social contact and have a need to belong. The theory also assumes that "people are creative, decision-making beings who seek experiences that enhance their own lifestyles" (p. 42). Lifestyles are unique to the individual and are based on the individual's belief systems and values. This theory also assumes that peoples' behavior is intentional and with purpose. The purpose of misbehavior in children could be to gain attention or power, seek revenge, or express feelings of inadequacy (Daigneault, 1999). Yura and Galassi (1974) cite Alfred Adler's belief that children reveal not only their present perceptions and relationships in play, but also their future.

Because Adlerian Theory emphasizes relationships, it is important for the counselor or therapist to develop a good relationship with the child in the first phase of the therapy (Kottman, 1999; Kottman

& Johnson, 1993). Kottman and Warlick (1989) describe this as establishing a democratic relationship. Utilizing a method of expression comfortable to the child is paramount in establishing this important aspect of Adlerian Play Therapy (Daigneault, 1999). A therapist's assessments and observations, encouragement of the child, and limit setting are the first part of the Adlerian approach to play therapy (Kottman & Johnson, 1993). Kottman and Johnson recommend that therapists achieve this egalitarian relationship through tracking what the child exhibits in play therapy, restating the content of the child's play, and reflecting the feelings evidenced by the child's behavior and content of play. The therapist's role is to keep track of the child's play during the process and to verbalize it to the child. Next, the therapist brings significant aspects of play to the child's attention by restating them. The therapist then reflects the feelings associated with these aspects to the child in order to build a connection and understanding of the behavior manifested through play.

Tracking, restating, and reflecting as described in the previous paragraph can be illustrated through a hypothetical example. A therapist watching a child play with dolls may track by stating to the child, "Jennifer, it looks like you are playing with four dolls." The therapist can then restate the behavior by saying something like, "You have four members of your family and you are playing with four dolls and you put the daddy doll in the cupboard." With this information, the therapist can reflect back the feeling that the therapist's judgment is being expressed through the play. The therapist could say something like, "You are sad because your daddy went away and doesn't live with your family anymore." From this example of the use of these techniques, it becomes clear that therapists need to be trained and skilled in the use of play therapy techniques. This is especially crucial in reflecting the feeling associated with the play by the child. Extra care should be taken so that the therapist is not leading the child to a feeling that does not accurately reflect the child's emotions or intentions. Through the establishment of an egalitarian relationship with the child, there is freedom to dialog if the therapist does not accurately reflect the child's emotions or thoughts.

Encouragement is also an important part of developing relationships in Adlerian Play Therapy. Encouraging children in play therapy to accomplish tasks that they have the ability to achieve is central to them developing a positive sense of accomplishment (Kottman & Johnson, 1993). The development of recognition of ability through support from the therapist can help foster a sense of belonging and acceptance.

Kottman and Johnson (1993) emphasize the importance of limit setting consistent with the Adlerian approach. This furthers establishes a healthy relationship with the child. Kottman and Johnson believe that it is through setting limits on damaging play therapy objects or harming self or others that the relationship is furthered with the child. They cautioned that therapists should refrain from setting limits on information provided by the child in therapy whenever possible. This is attributed to the need for the child to have freedom of self-expression that is not hampered by judgmental attitudes or comments from the therapist. Teaching a child how to establish healthy limits through the therapist modeling the behavior and at times negotiating limits with the child have applications outside the therapeutic environment (Kottman & Johnson, 1993).

The first phase includes the opportunity for the child and therapist to interact verbally (Kottman, 1999). Open communication is critical in the development of the relationship and should continue throughout the phases of the Adlerian Play Therapy process (Kottman & Warlick, 1989). It is important that the child and therapist interact and get to know one another. The child and therapist work together to clean up the play therapy room after each session (Kottman, 1999). The connections are very important by allowing significant interaction and trust building between the therapist and child. It also allows for demonstration of limit setting and developing connection.

The second phase in the process of Adlerian Play Therapy is exploring the child's lifestyle (Kottman, 1999; Kottman & Johnson, 1993). This is accomplished by determining the goals of the child's behavior. In other words, what is the child trying to accomplish through play? Part of Adlerian theory is that children seek attention and belongingness. Therefore, children will seek attention through good behavior, and if necessary will use bad behavior or acting out to gain needed attention (Kottman & Johnson, 1993). When children feel inadequate, powerless, or perceive injustice, they may act out in negative ways. Therapists can

further assess lifestyle by determining parenting techniques, family constellation, and the child's perception of the family and its interaction. Having the child address early recollections can also be useful in establishing lifestyle during play therapy (Kottman & Johnson, 1993). This gives the therapist an idea of how the child thinks and perceives interactions and surroundings.

At each phase of the Adlerian process of play therapy, it is important for the therapist to develop hypotheses regarding the child's feelings, relationships, and lifestyle as an insight into behavior (Kottman & Johnson, 1993). This process can be used in the therapeutic relationship to guide children and educate them on their behavior, providing insight for the therapist, the child, and the child's family. The therapist can identify metaphors or symbolic behaviors in the child's play (Kottman & Johnson, 1993). Professional judgment is then used in interpreting the behaviors and deciding on which interpretations to bring to the child's attention. Metaphors are significant in Adlerian Theory (Kottman & Johnson, 1993). Kottman and Johnson (1993) recommend the therapist and child engage in mutual storytelling as a way of identifying metaphors useful in therapy. They indicate this type of storytelling, which includes a beginning, middle, and end to the story, can involve the child using toys and objects to help tell the story. Once the child finishes the story, the therapist can then repeat the story, modifying the ending to help encourage healthier conclusions about self and others and to broaden the self-concept.

The third phase of Adlerian play therapy involves helping the child gain insight into his or her lifestyle (Kottman, 1999; Kottman & Johnson, 1993). In this phase, the therapist shares perceptions of the child's views, feelings, and perceptions of himself or herself, family relationships, and the world. This allows family members and the child to better understand behaviors and dynamics in the family. This phase is based on the integrity of the first two phases. Establishing a solid relationship and understanding of the child's lifestyle allows the therapist the foundation by which he or she can share these insights.

In the fourth phase, the therapist helps use the insights developed through play therapy to help reeducate and reorient the child on new behaviors and perceptions (Kottman, 1999; Kottman & Johnson, 1993). This is the opportunity for the child and family members to partner with the therapist in developing new strategies for how to think about situations and relationships, developing new behaviors, and building new attitudes (Kottman, 1999). When the therapist engages the family in this process through collaborative efforts, each member of the family helps redefine behaviors and relationships in healthier ways. Parents can improve their skills and children can develop new understandings of the family and relationships with others.

Kottman (1999) provides a good summary of the goals of the Adlerian process by citing the concepts of Lew and Bettner. According to Kottman, Adlerian therapists can help children learn to connect with others, develop feelings of being capable, feel like they count, and have courage. Courage is important in such areas as having the bravery to be different or try new ideas. She indicated that these "Crucial Cs" (p. 290) are consistent with the Adlerian principles.

The process of Adlerian Play Therapy allows children to learn in a safe and nonjudgmental environment about issues such as their relationship with others. This learning can also place emphasis on developing an understanding of belongingness (Kottman & Johnson, 1993). Children have this emphasized by the therapist helping to offer alternative solutions to behaviors (Kottman & Johnson, 1993). Children become a part of a team of participants and become engaged in the process of developing resolutions to conflict and problems (Daigneault, 1999).

Filial Therapy

Play therapy is beneficial in empowering clients. This is evident especially in Filial therapy (Ray, Bratton, & Brandt, 2000). Filial therapy, developed by Bernard Guerney, is a psychoeducational tool to train parents in therapeutic interventions with their children (Ray, Bratton, & Brandt, 2000). It combines Play Therapy with Family Therapy. Children can be empowered through this process to communicate their perspective and how they fit into the family dynamics during family therapy. Filial therapy pairs parent and child in the therapeutic process presenting a unique milieu in which they interact to reach a common goal. The parent is taught to recognize play as the child's mode of communication and becomes an ally in achieving the goals of therapy. Parent and child are better equipped to communicate and express their needs.

By facilitating communications, Filial therapy opens options not before understood. Rotter and Bush (2000) indicated that families could benefit from this type of therapy.

Play and Filial therapy are seen as a complement to family therapy or in place of family therapy. Freud is credited with developing the concept of training parents to carry on therapeutic interactions with their children (Ray, Bratton, & Brandt, 2000). When conducting family therapy, play therapy can be helpful with establishing a mode of communications and understanding where the child can contribute to the understanding of the family dynamics, and allows for the entire family to be empowered and express their feelings and view of the family interactions.

CONCLUSION

There are many theoretical perspectives that have adapted forms of play therapy to methods consistent with the various theoretical points of view. Listed in this chapter are three of the major theoretical applications utilized in play therapy. Those applications have been used successfully with individuals, groups, and special populations in both short- and long-term therapy. Play therapy can be applied to both personal and social issues. It is a nondirective approach used within the client's current environment and developmental stage and based on the client's motivation to change given new understanding through awareness. These perspectives offer an opportunity to see ways play therapy is put into practice. Play therapy is an evolving intervention. As practitioners and researchers from various theoretical backgrounds become involved in play therapy, new techniques and viewpoints are developed. Play therapy is a much researched topic. There is quite a bit of support for use of play therapy with children. Providing this natural form of self-expression for children to convey their feelings and perceptions is a valuable tool for use by therapists. Parents and clinicians may want to consider the use of appropriate and competently practiced play therapy for children when exploring treatment options.

REFERENCES

Axline, V. (1947). *Play therapy*. New York: Ballantine Books.

Cochran, J. (1996). Using play and art therapy to help culturally diverse students overcome barriers to school success. *School Counselor, 43,* 287–299.

Daigneault, S. (1999). Narrative means to Adlerian ends: An illustrated comparison of narrative therapy and Adlerian Play Therapy. *The Journal of Individual Psychology, 55,* 298–315.

Fall, M. (1999). A play therapy intervention and its relationship to self-efficacy and learning behaviors. *Professional School Counseling, 2,* 194–205.

Gladding, S. (1996). *Counseling: A comprehensive profession.* (3rd ed). Englewood Cliffs, NJ: Prentice Hall.

Glazer, H. (1999). Children and play in the Holocaust: Friedl Dicers-Brandeis – Heroic child therapist. *Journal of Humanistic Counseling, Education, & Development, 37,* 194–201.

Griffith, M. (1997). Empowering techniques of play therapy: A method for working with sexually abused children. *Journal of Mental Health Counseling, 19,* 130–143.

Guerney, L. (2001). Child-centered play therapy. *International Journal of Play Therapy, 10,* 13–31.

Kottman, T. (1999). Integrating the crucial Cs into Adlerian Play Therapy. *The Journal of Individual Psychology, 55,* 290–297.

Kottman, T., & Johnson, V. (1993). Adlerian play therapy: A tool for school counselors. *Elementary School Guidance & Counseling, 28,* 42–52.

Kottman, T., & Warlick, J. (1989). Adlerian Play Therapy: Practical considerations. *Journal of Individual Psychology, 45,* 433–446.

Landreth, G. (2002). Therapeutic limit setting in the play therapy relationship. *Professional Psychology: Research and Practice, 33,* 529–535.

Landreth, G. (1993). Child-centered play therapy. *Elementary School Guidance and Counseling, 28,* 17–30.

Leblanc, M., & Ritchie, M. (2001). A meta-analysis of play therapy outcomes. *Counseling Psychology Quarterly, 14,* 149.

Peery, J. (2002). Archetype and object: Primary deintegration and primary love in analytical play therapy with young children. *Journal of Analytical Psychology, 47,* 407–420.

Ray, D. , Bratton, S., & Brandt, M. (2000). Filial/family play therapy for single parents of young children attending community colleges. *Community College Journal of Research and Practice, 24,* 469–487.

Rogers, C. (1992). The processes of therapy. *Journal of Consulting and Clinical Psychology, 60,* 163–164.

Rotter, J., & Bush, M. (2000). Play and family therapy. *Family Journal, 8,* 172–177.

Ryan, V. & Needham, C. (2001). Non-directive play therapy with children experiencing psychic trauma. *Clinical Child Psychology and Psychiatry, 6,* 437–453.

Santrock, J. (2002). *Life-span development,* (8th ed.). Boston, MA: McGraw-Hill.

Schaefer, C. (2003). *Foundations of play therapy.* Hoboken, NJ: John Wiley & Sons.

Yura, M,. & Galassi, M. (1974). Adlerian usage of children's play. *Journal of Individual Psychology, 30,* 194–202.

Biographical Statement

Joshua Thomas-Acker, MS, LMHC, LPC, is a veteran law enforcement officer, clinician, and educator. His police background includes patrol and detective experience. His clinical practice includes work with children and adults in grief, working with emergency service workers, inpatient psychiatric treatment, and private practice. He has experience in adult education with a large school district and has experience as an adjunct faculty member for Springfield College (Massachusetts). He is licensed as a Professional Counselor in Illinois.

Sally S. Sloan, M.A., has extensive experience as an educator and as an auxiliary police officer. She has worked with children and adults with various learning and emotional needs. Her school experience includes professional involvement in the classroom, school counseling, anwd testing. In Florida, she has been a certified auxiliary police officer for over 20 years. Sally has worked with children and families as a social worker for the State of Florida. She also has volunteer experience working with emergency service professionals and stress management. Sally is certified in Florida as a school psychologist, school social worker, and in guidance and counseling.

Chapter 8

COMBINING PLAY AND COGNITIVE INTERVENTIONS IN THE TREATMENT OF ATTACHMENT DISORDERED CHILDREN

KEVIN O'CONNOR

INTRODUCTION

In recent years, mental health practitioners have shown a dramatically increased interest in attachment disorders and attachment-related problems in their child clients as partially evidenced by the fact the majority of this article first appeared in the Summer, 2004 *Theraplay® Newsletter*. Problems that were once seen as the result of dramatic neglect akin to that experienced by the babies in Spitz's (1946) study are now known to occur in much more subtle circumstances. Especially at risk are children who are adopted and those who spend time in the foster care system (Hughes, 1997, 1999). Subtle disturbances in attachment range from excessively clingy to excessively distancing behavior on the part of the child toward the caretaker. At the severe end of the continuum are those children whose behavior meets criteria for Reactive Attachment Disorder (DSM-IV, APA, 1994). While even subtle attachment problems have the potential to interfere with children's ability to develop healthy and satisfying interpersonal relationships later in life, the more severe symptoms most assuredly will.

Studies of attachment behavior have proliferated, yielding some findings that have significantly altered the way we think about the process and the long-term effects of children's early attachment experiences. Some of the initial conceptualizations of the attachment process roughly equated it with imprinting behavior in birds failing to capture its very important role in determining the quality of children's relationships later in life. The psychobiological nature of children's attachment to their caretakers is now seen as a very complex process nicely summarized by Polan and Hofer (1999). The role of the caretaker's voice, facial features, scent, and touch is seen as essential building blocks in creating the child's initial bond. The degree to which infants come to see the interactions with their caretakers as both reliable and pleasurable, in turn, becomes the core of children's ability to view their caretaker as a secure base. For the very young child, it is the caretaker him- or herself who serves as the concrete, secure base that allows for successful individuation and exploration of the world and other interpersonal relationships (Mahler, 1967, 1972). Later in life, children's early secure base experiences allow them to use relationships with other adults and peers as secure bases outside the home. This is easily observed in nursery school children who will seek out their teacher when they become hurt or frightened.

Children whose early experience deprives them of a secure attachment to their caretaker later tends to generalize that deprivation to their interactions with other adults, thereby making it difficult for them to establish any sort of secure base to serve as an anchor in the course of their development. Because of this, those children with more severe attachment problems can be very difficult to treat using traditional play therapy methods. Child-centered play therapy (Landreth, 1991), the most prevalent model used by practitioners in the United States, is based on the premise children can resolve their own problems by playing them out within the context of a protective and supportive relationship with a therapist who does not interfere in the child's process of growth. The difficulty in applying that model to this population lies in the fact that the very nature of these children's problems makes it nearly impossible for them to experience relationships, even those with a very caring therapist, as either protective or supportive.

Theraplay

Theraplay is another play therapy model that emphasizes the importance of the relationship between the child and the therapist. The primary difference between it and child-centered play therapy is the degree of responsibility placed on the therapist for quickly establishing a growth-promoting relationship with the child. Theraplay therapists constantly interact with their child clients, refusing to let the child withdraw from the relationship. They strive to make every moment of the session meet the child's needs in fun and playful ways. Through the use of *structuring, challenging, engaging* and *nurturing* activities, the Theraplay therapist provides children with experiences that build their sense of trust and pleasure in interpersonal interactions. These, in turn, help repair or even create the internalized secure base these children need. This base then allows children to be successful in their interactions with their environment and the people in it.

While Theraplay seems to provide excellent interpersonal experiences capable of reversing some of these children's attachment-related symptoms, recent research suggests adding a cognitive component to the therapy to make it even more effective. This research has focused less on the individual's actual bonding/attachment experience and more on the ways in which they come to understand and make sense of those experiences (Siegel, 1999; Siegel & Hartzell, 2003). For one of the most stunning evolutionary capacities humans have developed is their ability to cognitively override and reorganize experiences. Good experiences can be reframed as disastrous and disastrous experiences reframed as good. The capacity to do the latter seems to be a key element in predicting a person's ability to withstand stress and trauma, or resiliency. Similarly, this reframing is the basis of solution-focused and constructivist techniques that emphasize helping people change the meanings they attribute to their experiences (e.g., Anderson & Goolishian, 1992; Eron & Lund, 1996). Thus, for older children and adults, it is not necessarily their actual caretaker and their experience with that person that serves as a secure base but the internalized model of the caretaker and their reframed and recalled view of their attachment to him or her. For older children it is this internalized model that serves as the foundation for their peer relationships. For adults, their model is not only the foundation of their peer relationships but the frame for the relationship they create with their own children. In all cases, the coherence of the person's recalled attachment history, as well as his or her ability to integrate the emotions associated with that history, are excellent predictors of the quality of their current attachments (Fonagy, Steele, Steele, Moran, & Higgitt, 1991; Hesse, 1999).

The focus of this chapter is on the potential for increasing the effectiveness of Theraplay and other play interventions by combining the experiential components with cognitive-verbal interventions. The former foster pleasure and trust in others while the latter help the child develop a coherent and emotionally integrated attachment history. This integrated experiential and cognitive model is consistent with Ecosystemic Play Therapy as described by O'Connor (2000) and O'Connor and Ammen (1997).

This integration will begin by reviewing the ways in which Theraplay can serve as a remarkable strategy for providing clients, both children and adults, with corrective attachment experiences. Sue Ammen (personal communication, 2003) introduced a framework in which structuring, challenging, engaging, and nurturing are subdivided according to the overall functions they serve. Sructuring and challenging activities serve an organizational function within the therapist-child or caretaker-child interaction. Structuring focuses on behavior helping provide children with ways of successfully approaching and interacting with their environment while remaining safe. Challenging focuses on cognition, providing children with a frame for successfully approaching and solving tasks and problems. Engaging and nurturing activities tend to play more of a regulatory function. Like structuring, engaging is more behavioral. Children learn how to regulate interactions so as to make them pleasurable and gratifying. Nurturing is more emotional as children get a sense of how the joy of having a positive connection with another person actually feels. The younger the child the more successful intervention relies on the interactive and experiential nature of Theraplay. With some older clients, this nature allows them to bypass their negative cognitive frame and actually experience an interaction. After completing a single Theraplay session and homework assignment with his father, one incredibly bright 19-year-old in treatment for depression, secondary to disappointment in his relationship with his father, said, grinning, "Our relationship is so much better suddenly. It is not like any of our history changed . . . but it just doesn't seem as important anymore."

Effectiveness of Theraplay

While the experiential nature of Theraplay is incredibly powerful, adding a cognitive-verbal component may increase its effectiveness in three ways. First, the power of a specific intervention may increase if children actually understand how it is supposed to address their current distress. For example, just think how much more eagerly children do schoolwork whose relevance they can see as opposed to work they see as "stupid, pointless, and a waste of time." Second, using cognitive strategies can help children understand the reactions and feelings they are having in response to various Theraplay activities. This can be especially true when the therapist helps children separate their emotional reactions toward the therapist and therapy from the events in those in their past. In psychoanalytic terms, the purpose is to separate transference reactions from reality. Lastly, helping children develop a cognitive-verbal understanding of their therapy experience can greatly facilitate generalization of therapy gains to their lives outside the playroom. Children who can see the connection between how a power struggle with the therapist was resolved in session and how they might resolve the same sort of struggle with their parents or teachers are likely to use that knowledge sooner and more effectively.

Interpretation Strategies

The remainder of this article will focus primarily on how traditional interpretation strategies can be used to facilitate children's understanding (integration) of their emotions in Theraplay sessions and their use of what they learn in session in their daily lives. This chapter is a slight modification of the value and use of interpretation in play therapy (O'Connor, 2002). Although interpretation is used primarily within sessions, it is important to note that interpretation is only one part of the overall treatment process. Maximum treatment effectiveness depends on a multi- or ecosystemic approach.

Within such an approach, the therapist works with the child, the family, and other systems impinging on the child's development and well - social system, the school, medical, legal, social service, community and cultural systems, as well as any other system in which the child is embedded. Usually therapists approach assisting child clients from two directions. One is to help the child learn to function well within these various systems, as they currently exist. This is the primary function of individual Theraplay and other play therapies. The other is to change the systems so that it is easier for the child to function well. The knowledge gained by the child and therapist through the interpretive process usually impacts both. That is, better understanding helps children make necessary changes and may be used by the therapist to guide systemic changes.

Following the six steps delineated here may facilitate therapists' formulation and delivery of optimally effective interpretations.

1. Develop an initial, comprehensive case formulation that includes hypotheses about the underlying causes of the presenting problem and those factors maintaining the child's symptoms and/or behavior.
2. Develop a phenomenologically based treatment contract with the child specifying the way(s) in which the child's life will improve over the course of treatment. Simultaneously, therapists need to be clear with the child that such improvement will take work, including sometimes talking about issues that make the child uncomfortable, sad, scared, etc. Therapists should stress their belief that the long-term gains the child will make will far outweigh the short-term discomfort.
3. Develop a series of interpretations that will be used to guide the child to a new understanding of his or her problems. This new understanding will be based on the hypotheses the therapist developed in Step 1.
4. Begin delivering the planned interpretations to the child as opportunities arise in the play while observing the child's response so as to evaluate the accuracy of the hypotheses. If the child continually rejects the interpretations or does not begin to make behavioral changes, the therapist

should revisit the original case formulation and rethink the hypotheses.

5. As the child gains insight, the therapist moves on to help the child use this new information to problem solve, developing alternative responses and behaviors.

6. Lastly, therapists repeat interpretive material as it applies to a variety of ongoing and new situations so the children are able to use their new knowledge and skills outside the therapy session. This facilitates generalization.

Through this process, a Theraplay therapist can take events or emotions conveyed in the sessions and make meaning out of them so that the conflicts or problems they engendered can be addressed and resolved (Slade, 1994). However, therapists do not impose their a priori thoughts on the child. Rather, much as happens in traditional Theraplay, therapy becomes a delicate dance between the therapist and child. Therapists continuously offer their knowledge to the child, gauge the child's receptivity and response, adjust their thinking as needed, and re-offer these alternatives to the child. When all goes well, the play therapists' years of life and clinical experience are combined with the child's drive to grow and rapid progress is made.

If interpretation is to help the child make meaning and gain knowledge to be used in problem solving, it must be delivered in a way the child can use. This requires the therapist to do two procedures. One is to translate the sometimes complex thoughts and emotions behind the child's verbal and nonverbal responses to the Theraplay activities into language the child can actually understand. Language that is developmentally appropriate. The other is to deliver interpretations in a stepwise and systematic way so the child is not overwhelmed. To facilitate this, the author has developed the following model derived from the work of Lowenstein (1951, 1957); Devereaux, (1951); Bibring, (1945); and Lewis, (1974).

Reflections

Since first developing this model of interpretation (O'Connor, 1991), this first category of interpretation has been split into two subcategories, content and motive. Content reflections are those statements therapists make to identify the thoughts or feelings behind what their child clients do or say.

When the child looks or acts angry or yells, the therapist simply says, "You seem very angry." When the child tells a story, the therapist makes the underlying fantasy explicit. Content reflections are not restatements. They add new material. The therapist does not say, "You seem nervous" when the child has just said, "That made me nervous." Rather, the therapist would say, "You seem very nervous" should the child try to pull away from an interaction without saying anything. Motive reflections are explicit statements of the child's reason(s) for saying or doing a particular behavior. "I think you just threw your M&Ms® on the floor to let me know you don't want me to feed you. You can feed yourself!" Because motive reflections involve a greater level of attribution on the part of the therapist, they are considered somewhat more intense than content reflections and, as such, should be used more carefully.

Reflections serve several purposes. First, they demonstrate for the child the therapist's interest in the "thoughts and feelings behind the action." As such, they help educate the child as to how the Theraplay process will unfold. Second, they help expand the child's affective vocabulary. By using reflections, therapists provide children with the words they need to express their innermost thoughts and feelings more accurately and effectively. Third, by replacing some of the child's behavior with words, the therapist helps reduce the child's tendency to act out both in session and in the real world. Lastly, they give therapists the opportunity to validate their perceptions of the child's emotional state. When a therapist reflects incorrectly, children tend not only to negate what the therapist has said, but to spontaneously correct it. This provides the therapist with information the child might not have otherwise volunteered.

Present Pattern

At this level, the therapist is simply identifying overt or covert repetitions in the child's verbal and non-verbal reactions to the Theraplay activities. The therapist should operationalize the repetition as clearly as possible and give examples of how these have been manifested. The patterns may be very concrete: "This is the third time you started to cry when we were playing peek-a-boo." "The last few sessions you have started out by telling me how stupid our sessions are." Alternatively, the patterns may be thematic "Just today, you wanted to quit hide and seek, moved away when we were using the lotion and threw the M&Ms on the floor when we were feeding each other." The primary purpose of such statements is to help children see their behavior as meaningful and psychologically significant as well as being consistent over time rather than as just a series of random events. Once these consistencies are labeled, then solutions generated to resolve one of the problems in a cluster can be more easily generalized to the other, similar behaviors. This lays the groundwork for subsequent interpretations. Initially, the therapist would label repetitions of behavior within sessions and later patterns across sessions would be identified.

Simple Dynamic

At this level, therapists draw connections between (1) the child's thoughts, affects, and motives as previously reflected; and, (2) previously identified patterns of behavior. For example, the therapist might suggest that the child who withdrew from each of the activities as previously described did so because being nurtured or taken care of felt scary or dangerous. "I think you get really scared when I am being sort of 'mushy-nice' to you and so you try to pull away. That way you go back to being the boss. You can show me you don't need me to take care of you." Once the child has become accustomed to the therapist making simple dynamic interpretations for in-session behavior, he or she can proceed to making simple dynamic interpretations of behavior observed across sessions. At this point, the therapist is moving toward more traditional types of interpretation by helping the child understand the dynamics of his or her behavior in the recent past. Through simple dynamic interpretation, the child is encouraged to see the continuity of affects and meanings across behaviors. Children are sensitized to the internal feelings, processes, and motivations that guide their behavior. Because simple dynamic interpretations are built off of the two previous levels of interpretation, each of which the child has come to accept independently, acceptance of the interaction of the two is less likely to be resisted (O'Connor, 2000).

Generalized Dynamic

These interpretations connect children's in-session behavior to their out-of-session behavior. The therapist points out the similarities between the child's pattern of thinking, feeling, and behaving across contexts. For example, the therapist might point out how the child's tendency to withdraw from "mushy-nice" interactions stems from a fear that dependency will leave him or her vulnerable to neglect or abuse. "It seems like you worry people will only be nice for a little while and then they will stop and hurt your feelings. If you stop first you can't be disappointed and that makes you feel a lot safer."

Genetic

In the original model (O'Connor, 1991), only interpretations of the origins of the child's current problems were included in this category. These are the most traditional form of interpretation as they are structured and delivered so as to provide children with insight into the root of their problems. Since developing the original model, interpretation of the child's significant organizing beliefs have been to this category. These are core beliefs the child holds that are rooted in early, usually repetitive experience. As examples, consider the abused child who now believes the world is a dangerous place and all adults are potential abusers or the neglected child who believes he or she is unlovable and worthless. These beliefs derive from the child's genetic experience and are often the primary reason the child cannot or will not change his or her behavior. To change would engender intolerable cognitive dissonance. To the child with a fear of being nurtured, the therapist might suggest that the fear is connected to the belief that he or she is truly, fundamentally unlovable. That fundamental belief might, in turn, be linked to the child having been constantly disappointed by his or her mother during their early interactions when she was abusing substances. The therapist then goes on to help the child accurately evaluate the reality of his or her cognitive capacities versus the overwhelming negative effect of the mother's behavior.

Interpretations are usually offered in the sequence just listed; however, in formulating them, the therapist usually works backwards. That is, the therapist will first develop hypotheses about the etiology of the child's problems and the child's core beliefs (genetic). The therapist will validate these with examples of the child's behavior as reported in the intake (generalized dynamic). Next, the therapist will develop ideas of how these behaviors and feelings may manifest in session (simple dynamic, pattern, and reflection). Having developed these hypotheses, the therapist will watch for those issues that either confirm or negate the original hypotheses and interpret accordingly. As previously stated, the hypotheses are continuously reevaluated and refined as the therapy progresses. The levels of interpretation are also listed in accordance with the frequency with which they will be used in session. Therapists will reflect on a nearly continuous basis while they may make only a few genetic interpretations over the course of the child's entire therapy.

One other issue to be considered in the delivery of interpretations is the various ways in which the impact of the interpretation can be modulated so that the child is able to make use of the information without becoming overwhelmed. The impact can be modulated by adjusting the "distance" between the child and the content by interpreting within the play, making an "as if" interpretation or interpreting in the context of the therapeutic relationship before interpreting historical material directly to the child.

Interpreting within the play simply involves framing the interpretive material so that it applies to characters in the child's play, stories, drawings, or other fantasy material. It is the figure in the drawing who is sad, or the person riding in the careening toy car who is frightened, not the child. When such interpretations are on target, children often exaggerate them. The figures in the drawing are not just sad, they are overwhelmed like the figures in a Greek tragedy. The superhero is not just strong, he is invincible. This type of interpretation offers the child a good measure of distance from which to examine the content before internalizing it.

"As if" interpretations are those where the therapist applies the interpretive material to other children who share similar characteristics with the client rather than to the client directly. It is other 7-year-olds, or other boys, who are scared at the doctor's office or who feel jealous when a new sibling is born. This strategy provides a great deal less distance and children often see through the pretext if the therapist overuses it. In spite of this, it is a way of transitioning from interpreting the content of the play to discussing the child's real life issues.

Interpretations in the context of the relationship are those that involve the therapist identifying feelings the child is having towards the therapist, him- or herself. When the therapist offers such interpretations, there is very little distance between the child and the content but the power of the content is often tempered. That is, it may be much easier for children to admit being angry with the therapist

than to admit being angry with their mothers. These interpretations are particularly effective in managing resistance and transference. Finally, the therapist will be offering interpretations directly to the child in the context of his or her real life experience. These interpretations are as simple as, "You seem angry" and as complex as, "You feel unlovable because your mother hurt you many, many times from the time you were very little." Applying interpretive content directly to the child's experience is critical if generalization of the gains made in therapy is to occur. (This model of interpretation formulation and delivery is presented in great detail and illustrated with case examples in O'Connor (2000) and O'Connor and Ammen (1997)).

When used effectively and consistently, the combination of the experiential nature of Theraplay and the cognitive work of interpretation support the majority of the essential psychotherapy processes identified by Shirk and Russell (1996). Based on an extensive review of the existing child psychotherapy literature and research, they proposed a list of 11 processes that seemed to account for most of the change that occurs in effective child psychotherapy. While their work was not play therapy or Theraplay, the specific findings certainly apply.

Case Example: Tony

The elements of this combined approach are well illustrated in the following case example (which is actually an amalgam of several different cases). Tony was 5 years old when brought to therapy. He and his younger brother had been adopted 6 months earlier by a couple with no other children. The boys had been freed for adoption by the courts when it became clear their birth mother would not be able to provide them with adequate care. Prior to being freed for adoption, the boys had been in and out of the child welfare system a number of times subsequent to episodes of severe neglect by their birth mother. At the time of referral, Tony's adoptive parents were very concerned about his apparent failure to develop any connection with them since coming into their home. They described him as incredibly independent, distant, and controlling. He did what he wanted, when he wanted. He was rarely difficult or significantly oppositional, rather he seemed to go about his business as if the parents were not there. He took excellent care of his younger brother but seemed to resent how close his brother was becoming to

Shirk & Russell (1996) Processes	Equivalent Theraplay, Play Therapy, and Cognitive Activities
Cognitive Processes	
Schema transformation is the process of changing the child's implicit assumptions or expectations (core beliefs). "Just because your mother abused you does not mean ALL adults will abuse you."	Helping a child differentiate between protective, healthy limit setting and abuse. This can be particularly difficult in children whose abusers hurt them while telling them it was 'for their own good.' Simple dynamic interpretation of limits set in the playroom. Generalized interpretation of current caretaker's behavior. Genetic interpretation of abuser's behavior and child's reaction to it.
Cognitive Processes	
Symbolic exchange is the process whereby a problem becomes clearer through discussion. The process of putting your experience into words and the process of hearing the other person's reaction gradually modifies your understanding of the experience.	Engaging children in telling stories, imaginary play, role-plays, and talking about their life experiences. Creating the Life-Events Timeline. The entire interpretation process.
Insight is simply the reorganization of the meaning of one's experience.	Most often achieved through the interpretation process.
Skill development is the process by which one learns adaptive or compensatory skills.	May be achieved through direct teaching, bibliotherapy, role-playing, and cognitive problem solving done directly or through games and play.
Affective Processes	
Abreaction/release involves the discharge of feelings resulting in a sense of mastery.	Play encouraging exaggerated emotional expression. Enacting a truly grand pretend 'funeral' to mourn abandonment by a birth parent. Beating a Bobo representing a family court judge to vent anger at having to wait for an adoption to be finalized. With aggressive activities it is important for the therapist to help the child separate aggressive fantasies (permissible) from aggressive actions (not permissible).
Through the process of emotional experiencing children come to integrate their emotions into their overall sense of their experience. They come to understand why they feel a certain way in a specific situation	Helping a child see a thematic connection between events that trigger similar feelings, e.g., seeing fear of the dark, avoidance of bedtime, and school phobia as manifestations of separation anxiety. A child might be encouraged to build clay monsters representing different things he or she fears. Pattern and Simple Dynamic interpretation.
Therapists use affective education to help the child identify, label, and express their emotions.	Reflection. Color-Your-Life Technique (O'Connor, 1983). Bibliotherapy.
As children learn new coping strategies and develop new defenses, they become capable of better emotional regulation.	Playing a tickling game where the child is encouraged to laugh very loudly and then suddenly shift to being very quiet and calm and then back to laughing. Simple and Generalized Dynamic interpretations.

(continued on next page)

Table 8.1.
continued

Shirk & Russell (1996) Processes	Equivalent Theraplay, Play Therapy, and Cognitive Activities
Interpersonal Processes	
In play therapy, the therapist provides (1) validation and support which foster the child's emotional, cognitive, behavioral, and social growth and development.	All Nurturing Theraplay activities. All reinforcement strategies. Most Challenging Theraplay activities that build the child's sense of mastery and self-esteem.
Therapists also provide (2) supportive scaffolding when they help children face problems or engage in behaviors that currently exceed the child's capacity.	This occurs when a therapist helps a child face a bully or make a difficult request of a parent. Can also be accomplished through role-plays or pretend play enactment of difficult situations. Generalized dynamic interpretation.
Therapists provide children with a corrective relationship in that they respond to children differently than have persons in the children's past and thus provide them with experiences that disrupt their core beliefs. While schema transformation may be a cognitive experience, this is an interpersonal experience.	Engaging children in experiences inconsistent with their beliefs, e.g., nurturing a child who believes all adults to be neglectful.

their new parents. In spite of his pseudomature behavior, Tony showed signs of being in great distress. He often seemed anxious and regularly wet the bed. He also became quite upset if he could not direct a particular interaction or if events did not proceed as he expected them to.

A brief intervention specifically designed to facilitate Tony's rapid development of an attachment to his adoptive mother was initiated. The eight sessions combined many Theraplay elements with an art/story project and considerable interpretation. The sessions are briefly described here.

The first three sessions consisted of a great deal of very physical interaction between Tony and the therapist with the mother present in the room. The mother was told she could join the play or observe it, as she felt comfortable. Initially, Tony seemed enormously pleased with these interactions. The therapist held Tony, tickled him, tossed him playfully in the air, and wrestled with him. These simple physical activities incorporated all of the Theraplay dimensions. They were highly structured and controlled by the therapist. They were challenging in the sense they pushed Tony to engage in behaviors outside his comfort zone. They were very engaging as Tony was continuously interacting directly with the therapist. And, finally, they were nurturing through the therapist's use of verbal reinforcement and playfulness.

In spite of the fact he was having fun during these interactions, Tony struggled to control every moment of the sessions. As the therapist lovingly, yet firmly, maintained control of the interactions, Tony became more and more aggressive. Interestingly, he never tried to withdraw from interacting with the therapist. Tony's mother reported that no matter how enraged Tony had been during the sessions, he never complained about them, seemed happy afterwards, and looked forward to the next session. Tony's aggression peaked in the third session. The therapist opened the door to let Tony and his mother into the playroom. Tony, who had been playing quietly in the waiting area, launched a full-out physical attack on the therapist. The therapist immediately moved to contain Tony and to provide support and reassurance as Tony raged. Through all of this, Tony's mother sat motionless, stunned by the intensity of Tony's anger.

Before discussing the resolution of this very difficult session, the interpretive material the therapist was delivering along with the activities will be presented. Throughout these first three sessions, the therapist tried to help Tony connect the feelings he was experiencing in the therapy to the thoughts and fears related to his very problematic early attachment experiences. The interpretive material was delivered in two formats. The majority was conveyed directly to Tony as the sessions progressed. At the same time, the therapist built a metaphor that integrated the issues Tony was facing into a coherent fantasy tale.

Reflections (Sessions 1–8): (1) You know you are very smart. (2) You like feeling powerful. (3) You like to be the boss. (4) Wow, you are so angry. (5) Behind all that anger, you seem pretty scared. (6) You sure do seem to worry a lot.

Pattern Interpretations (Sessions 1–2): (1) You hardly ever let your mom do anything on her own without giving her directions. (2) You hardly ever let anyone play with you in a fun way. You only want to play-fight. (3) Every time you come to session you want to be the boss. This pattern was also conveyed through a metaphor: "It is like there is an angry dragon that lives inside you and wants to be the boss all the time so he can protect you and keep you safe."

Simple Dynamic (Sessions 1–5): (1) I think you believe mom won't do a good job if you don't tell her what to do. (2) It seems like it is hard for you to be the boss if you are having fun so you don't let yourself have fun. (3) Play-fighting is one way of playing and still feeling powerful. (4) But being the boss seems like an even better way of feeling powerful and safe. Metaphor: "The problem is the dragon has become too strong so he doesn't just protect you he even keeps people from getting close enough to love you. And, you really want to be loved."

Generalized Dynamic (Sessions 1–2): (1) That is why you hardly ever want your new mom and dad to take care of you or be nice to you. It would mean you weren't the boss any more and then you wouldn't be safe. (2) It is the same reason you don't like to let your teacher be the boss. (3) It is even the reason you never let any other kids be the boss when you play. Metaphor: "That is why the dragon doesn't want your new mom and dad to be nice to you. He would lose his power and he is worried if that happens you won't be safe. But that dragon is part right and part wrong. He is right about losing his power but he is wrong about you being able to be safe. You will be safe now because you have a new mom and dad to protect you. So if all the grown-ups are really nice to you then the dragon won't have any more power and he won't be able to stop people from loving you. So mom, dad, and you and I are going to keep being nice no matter how hard the dragon fights. We'll all prove you don't need him to keep you safe anymore."

Genetic Interpretation (Session 3): Because your birth mom and dad never took very good care of

you and your brother, you decided you needed to be the grown- because it helped make sure you got some of the things you needed but it also was bad because it made you tired and mad. So mad, you never wanted grown-ups to come near you ever again. Metaphor: "The dragon was made out of all the bad things that happened to you. He was there to protect you and make you strong. But now you have a mom and dad who love you and the dragon is losing his power. He still thinks he needs to fight to keep you safe but now his fighting just makes it hard for you to enjoy the love mom and dad have to give. It is time for you to thank the dragon and let him know you want your new mom and dad to love you and protect you now."

After this genetic interpretation was delivered in the third session, Tony completely stopped fighting and began to cry. He sobbed as if he was in agony and the therapist immediately placed him in his mother's lap. The therapist encouraged Tony's mother to nurture and kiss him and tell him he was safe and loved. Mother and child snuggled together for about 20 minutes as Tony slowly stopped crying and molded against his mother.

Immediately upon entering the playroom for the fourth session Tony announced that the dragon was gone. The therapist playfully asked him, "Vacation or gone for good?" Tony replied, "Packed his bags and left for good." Tony's mother reported an amazing change in Tony's behavior since the last session. She said he was constantly affectionate and physical with her and his father. He seemed happy and relaxed. He had even begun to join the rest of the family in their activities.

While Tony and the therapist continued to engage in many highly interactive activities, in the subsequent session, they began work on an art project designed to help Tony flesh out the beginnings of a coherent attachment history. The project was a Life Events Timeline. Dr. Cynthia Bromberg first developed this activity when she was a graduate student at the California School of Professional Psychology specifically to help two boys build a coherent history of their separation and subsequent reunion with their mother. It is done on a roll of old-fashioned fax machine paper, 8 inches wide and many yards long. During each session, Tony, his mother, and the therapist would add elements to a timeline that began with Tony's birth. At the very beginning of the roll, Tony drew pictures of his birth parents before he and his brother were born. Next he drew a picture of his birth mother pregnant with him. Along the bottom edge of the paper, the therapist added in a timeline with the approximate dates of the events Tony drew. When they encountered events about which Tony had very little recall, the therapist or Tony's mother drew these based on either information in Tony's placement history or on supposition. The reality of his neglect and placement in various foster homes were presented as simple facts with as little negative evaluation of his birth parents as possible. The feelings that went with those pictures and their intensity were left for Tony to describe and fill in. Pictures of Tony taking care of his brother were included with the words, "love" and "pride" written in above. Drawings representing the various foster homes and families were included. These were followed by a series of parallel drawings. Tony did drawings along the bottom of the roll representing his and his brother's final foster home stay. Above these, his mother drew pictures depicting the sequence of the adoption proceedings that resulted in Tony coming to live with her and her husband. Together they joined these lines back into one by drawing a picture of the first time they met. Towards the end of the roll, Tony and the therapist drew in pictures representing each of the therapy sessions and between them and pictures reflecting how life at home was changing. This activity took up about 15–20 minutes of each session and towards the end, Tony and his mother began taking the roll home to work on it between sessions. During the final session, the roll was unfurled and taped to the wall around the playroom. During the termination party, Tony, his mother, and the therapist reviewed Tony's life history, their work in therapy, and their new lives together. The end of the roll was taken down and given to Tony. He and his mother were given several yards of blank paper and encouraged to add to the roll with pictures of their lives from this point forward. In this way, it was hoped Tony could continue to settle into his new family without having to deny either the good or bad events about his early attachment history.

CONCLUSION

In summary, the effectiveness of the experiential aspects of Theraplay and other play techniques can be greatly enhanced for any child through the use of systematic interpretation. Such interpretations facilitate the essential therapeutic processes described by Shirk and Russell (1996). Interpretation facilitates the child's use of language and greatly enhances the generalization of the gains children make in session to their day-to-day lives. At this point the model presented herein has solid theoretical support but little hard research backup. There is a great need for clinical research to verify the existence of the underlying therapeutic processes in play therapy in general and Theraplay in particular, the ability of interpretation to support those processes, and the effectiveness of a combined experiential-cognitive-verbal approach in helping children develop a coherent, internal working model of their attachment history to serve as the secure base on which to build their future relationships.

REFERENCES

American Psychiatric Association. (1994). *Diagnostic and statistical manual of mental disorders*, Fourth Edition. Washington, DC: American Psychiatric Association.

Ammen, S. (2003). Personal communication.

Anderson, H., & Goolishian, M. A. (1992). The client is the expert: A not knowing approach to therapy. In K. J. Gergen & S. McNamee (Eds.). *Therapy as a social construction* (pp. 25–39). Newbury Park, CA: Sage.

Bibring, E. (1945). Psychoanalysis and the dynamic psychotherapies. *Journal of the American Psychiatric Association*, II, 745–770.

Devereaux, G. (1951). Some criteria for the timing of confrontations and interpretations. *International Journal of Psychoanalysis, 32*, 19–24.

Eron, J. B., & Lund, T. W. (1996). *Narrative solutions in brief therapy*. New York: Guilford.

Fonagy, P., Steele, M., Steele, H., Moran, G., & Higgitt, A. (1991). The capacity for understanding mental states: The reflective self in parent and child and its significance for security of attachment. *Infant Mental Health Journal, 12*(3), pp. 201–218.

Hesse, E. (1999). The Adult Attachment Interview: Historical and current perspectives. In J. Cassidy & P. Shaver (Eds.). *Handbook of attachment: Theory, research & clinical implications*. New York: Guilford.

Hughes, D. (1997). *Facilitating developmental attachment: The road to emotional recovery and behavioral change in foster and adopted children*. New York: Jason Aronson.

Hughes, D. (1999). *Building the bonds of attachment: Awakening love in deeply troubled children*. New York: Jason Aronson.

Landreth, G. (1991) *Play therapy: The art of the relationship*. Muncie, IN: Accelerated Development.

Lewis, M. (1974). Interpretation in child analysis: Developmental considerations. *Journal of the American Academy of Child Psychiatry, 13,* 32–53.

Lowenstein, R. (1951). The problem of interpretation. *Psychoanalytic Quarterly, 20,* 1–14.

Lowenstein, R. (1957). Some thoughts on interpretation in the theory and practice of psychoanalysis. *The Psychoanalytic Study of the child, 12,* 127–150.

Mahler, M. (1967). On human symbiosis and the vicissitudes of individuation. *Journal of the American Psychoanalytic Association, 25,* 740–763.

Mahler, M. (1972). On the first three subphases of the separation-individuation process. *International Journal of Psycho-Analysis, 53,* 333–338.

O'Connor, K. (1983). The color-your-life technique. In C. Schaefer & K. O'Connor (Eds.). *Handbook of play therapy.* New York: Wiley.

O'Connor, K. (1991). *The play therapy primer: An integration of theories and techniques.* New York:Wiley.

O'Connor, K. (2000). *The play therapy primer,* second edition. New York: Wiley.

O'Connor, K. (2002). The value and use of interpretation in play therapy. *Professional Psychology: Research and Practice, 33*(6), 523–528.

O'Connor, K. (2004). Creating a coherent attachment history: Combining Theraplay and cognitive-verbal interventions. *The Theraplay Institute Newsletter.* Summer, 5–9.

O'Connor, K., & Ammen, S. (1997) *Play therapy treatment planning and interventions: The ecosystemic model and workbook.* San Diego: Academic Press.

Polan, H.J., & Hofer, M. (1999). Psychobiological origins of infant attachment and separation responses. In J. Cassidy & P. Shaver (Eds.). *Handbook of Attachment: Theory, research & clinical implications.* New York: Guilford.

Shirk, S. & Russell, R. (1996). *Change processes in child psychotherapy: Revitalizing treatment and research.* New York: Guilford.

Siegel, D., & Hartzell, M. (2003). *Parenting from the inside out.* New York: Penguin Putnam.

Siegel, D. (1999). *The developing mind: How relationships and the brain interact to shape who we are.* New York: Guilford.

Slade, A. (1994). Making meaning and making believe: Their role in the clinical process. In A. Slade and D. Wolf. *Children at play: Clinical and developmental approaches to meaning and representation.* New York: Oxford University Press.

Spitz, R. (1946). Anaclitic depression. *Psychoanalytic Study of the Child, 2,* 313–342.

Biographical Statement

Kevin O'Connor, PhD, RPT-S, is a Clinical Psychologist and Professor. He is the Director of the Clinical PsyD and PhD Programs and the Coordinator of the Ecosystemic Clinical Child Psychology Emphasis at the California School of Professional Psychology – Fresno of Alliant International University. He is the cofounder and now Director Emeritus of the Association for Play Therapy. He is the author of the *Play Therapy Primer, Second Edition* and numerous articles on child psychotherapy and professional practice. He is the co-author of *Play Therapy Treatment Planning and Interventions.* He is the co-editor of the *Handbook of Play Therapy, Volumes I & II* and *Play Therapy Theory and Practice.* He regularly presents workshops across the United States and abroad including workshops conducted in the Netherlands, Canada, Japan, Korea, Singapore, Kuwait, and South Africa. His areas of specialization include: (1) Ecosystemic Play Therapy, (2) treatment planning, (3) Attachment Disorders, (4) the use of interpretation, (5) conducting structured groups, and (6) the treatment of medically ill children. He also maintains a small private practice treating children and adults.

Kevin O'Connor, PhD, RPT-S
Professor
Director, Clinical PsyD Program
Fresno-Sacramento
Director, Clinical PhD Program
Director, Play Therapy Institute
Coordinator, Ecosystemic Clinical Child
Psychology Emphasis

Chapter 9

PLAY THERAPY ASSESSEMENTS

CHARLES E. MYERS

INTRODUCTION

The importance of play in the lives of children is evident in its pervasiveness in childhood (Lifter, 2000). Play is the child's symbolic language of self-expression. Children play out their experiences and feelings in the most natural, dynamic, and self-healing process in which children can engage (Landreth, 1993). It is generally recognized that a child's play can be a window to understanding a child's experiential and psychological world (Perry & Landreth, 2001). Play can provide the therapist with an insight into how the child applies innate abilities to the world around them from a developmental point of view. Play shows how a child interacts with their environment, with other children, and with adults (Schmidt, 2001). In addition, play offers the therapist a unique psychological tool for viewing the world through the eyes of the child (Perry & Landreth, 2001).

As part of the creative modalities, play therapy offers a therapeutic mode for diagnosis, assessment, and treatment interventions. This chapter will review a number of play assessments. It will look at developmental and diagnostic assessments, measurements of parent-child interaction, as well as instruments for specific concerns.

Transdisciplinary Play-Based Assessment

The Transdisciplinary Play-Based Assessment (TPBA; Linder, 1990, 1993) was developed in response to the need for a more functional and holistic approach to determining a child's level of development, skills, learning style, and interaction patterns. The TPBA evaluates the structured and unstructured play of a child from infancy up through the age of six via systematic observation. Four developmental domains are explored: Cognitive, social-emotional, communication and language, and sensorimotor. The purpose of this instrument is to assist professionals in the development of a program plan for specific interventions for children in early childhood programs.

The assessment is completed in six phases. During Phase I, the child participates in unstructured play, in which the child leads or initiates play with the examiner. Phase II is a structured play facilitation. Phase III provides the opportunity for the child to interact with a peer. During Phase IV, the child and parent participate in structured and unstructured play. Phase IV also includes situations in which the parent is asked to leave so that separation and reunion behaviors may be observed. Phase V involves structured and unstructured motor play. Phase VI, the final phase, screens for oral motor difficulties and other developmental observations (Linder, 1993).

The TPBA is both a useful observation tool and a dynamic process that can be used to assess a child's various levels of development, determine strengths and weaknesses, identify areas needing intervention, and distinguish learning styles and interaction patterns. The outcomes can assist educators and therapists in ascertaining appropriate targets for interventions and in discovering strategies that are likely to enhance developmental progress. The guidelines may also serve as an observational tool for the purpose on ongoing evaluation of developmental progress (Linder, 2000). While the TPBA identifies areas in need of interventions, it provides little information with regard to intervention suggestions for home and school.

DEVELOPMENTAL PLAY ASSESSMENT

The Developmental Play Assessment Instrument (DPA; Lifter et al., 1988) was developed to evaluate the play activities of children with developmental delays and disabilities to assess what the child knows, where he/she is in the process of learning, and what developmental limits the child currently faces. The DPA is an assessment tool designed to identify developmentally relevant play activities. The play actions that are identified and quantified in the DPA are conceptualized from a cognitive/developmental perspective. It allows for interventions that may facilitate progress in development (Lifter, 2000). A useful tool in the planning of educational and therapeutic interventions, the DPA can also be used for screening and diagnostic purposes. Data gleaned from the DPA may be utilized to foster a play therapy treatment program (Brooke, 2004).

There are three steps in the coding of the child's behavior. First, the play actions of the child are recorded in raw frequencies counts. Second, the play actions are reorganized into categories of activities. From this, the scorer can determine the frequency and types of activities. Finally, the scorer summarizes the actions according the developmental sequence outlined by the test authors. The results are categorized as follows: Mastery of learning, emerging learning patterns, and absence of play categories. Mastery was operationally defined as the occurrence of at least 10 instances of the categories with at least four different types represented within the 30-minute time period. Emergence was defined as the occurrence of at least four instances of the category with a minimum of two different types presented (Lifter, 2000).

The DPA is useful in the assessment of developmental disabilities, in particular language delays and language disorders. The normative samples consisted of primarily autistic children. Greater research is needed to explore standardization when working with diverse groups. Further, the normative sample size was small. Methods for teaching and implementing interventions are still under research. Additional validity and reliability research is needed on the DPA (Brooke, 2004).

MARSHAK INTERACTION METHOD

The Marshak Interaction Method (MIM; Lindaman, Booth, & Chambers, 2000) is a structured technique for observing and evaluating the nature of the relationship between two individuals. The MIM measures the relationship between an adult and a child to help determine the parent's capacity to protect and care for the child, the child's capacity for forming relationships, and the quality of the adult-child relationship. The MIM has been used in consideration for placement with foster and adoptive parents, as well as reunification with biological parents.

The MIM is made up of a series of simple tasks designed to elicit a range of behaviors in four dimensions (Lindaman, Booth, & Chambers, 2000). The MIM evaluates a parent's capacity for: (1) *Structure*, setting limits, and providing an appropriately ordered environment; (2) *Engagement*, engaging the child in interaction while being attuned to the child's state and reactions; (3) *Nurture*, meeting the child's need for attention, soothing, and care; and (4) *Challenge*, supporting and encouraging the child's efforts to achieve at a developmentally appropriate level.

Concurrently, the MIM assesses the child's ability to respond to the parent's effort within the four dimensions. The MIM generally includes the following four dimensions: Promoting attachment, alerting to environment, guiding purposive behavior, and assisting in overcoming tension. In addition, tasks are divided according to whether they were to be done together or by each person alone and/or whether they are inviting regressive or striving behaviors (Brooke, 2004). The MIM provides the opportunity for observing the strengths of both the adult and the child and their relationship. The MIM can be used as an intervention tool to strengthen familial relationships and to design interventions to meet those needs (Lindaman, Booth, & Chambers, 2000).

The MIM was designed to assess the nature and quality of the adult-child relationship and its strength lies in its detailed procedures for observing the nature and quality of that interaction. Although it has potential as a research tool, the assessment has not been standardized on a normative sample. Research using the MIM has utilized very small, nondiverse samples. Further research is needed to determine the usefulness of the MIM with other populations (Brooke, 2004).

FAMILY PUPPET INTERVIEW

Puppets have long been recognized as a valuable technique in helping children cope with events in their lives. Woltman (1940) found that puppets were helpful in working with children because they are easy to manipulate, offer richness in symbolism, and provide opportunities for spontaneity. Children project their feelings and displace their conflicts onto puppets (Webb, 1991), thereby allowing clinicians and children to talk about feeling or thoughts that belong to the puppet. As a projective media, puppets offer the universality and ambiguity of many possible identifications. The fantasy material from the child's puppet story can help reveal the child's preoccupations and his or her ways of dealing with them (Irwin, 2000).

Irwin and Shapiro (1975) developed a semistructured puppet interview for assessments purposes, which includes a rating form to assess the content and dimension of story date with a variety of populations. Irwin (1993) outlines the Puppet Interview Assessment as consisting of a warm-up stage in which the therapist brings out the puppets and observes the child's reactions, invites the child to select characters for their story; a puppet show, which the child develops without the therapist's participation; and an interview with the puppets in which the therapist asks what and why questions within the realm of the story; and a post interview with the child, in which the child is invited to discuss the story. From the interview, the therapist can derive diagnostic data regarding the child's defense and coping styles, as well as the child's preoccupations and conflicts (Gil, 1994).

The Family Puppet Interview is a diagnostic technique found to be effective in assessing parent-child and intrafamily relationships as well as reciprocal patterns interaction in therapy cases involving a young child (Ross, 2000). The usefulness in using puppets is in its ability to elicit with remarkable facility some of the critical parent and child interactions. A disadvantage to this assessment is that some family members may be resistant to the use of puppets. In addition, the Family Puppet Interview is a projective assessment, and caution is needed in deciphering the literalness of the play.

PLAY THERAPY OBSERVATION INSTRUMENT

The Play Therapy Observation Instrument (PTOI), developed by Howe and Silvern (1981) and adopted by Perry (1988–1989), is a rating scale of play therapy behavior. The PTOI provides therapists with a useful and readily usable instrument for codifying behavior during a play therapy session. The PTOI consists of 13 play therapy behaviors indicative of important clinical concepts. These scores form three theoretically meaningful subscales, which are social inadequacy, emotional discomfort, and use of fantasy (Perry & Landreth, 2001).

The PTOI uses 12-minute segments of videotaped play therapy sessions. The rater reviews a 12-minute segment and then rates the frequency and/or intensity of the child's play behaviors as represented on each subscale. An examination of the ratings of the child's play behaviors provides information for detailed assessment of the child, planning of therapeutic treatment, and prognosis (Perry & Landreth, 2001).

Research has established support for the use of the PTOI as a measure of children's emotional well-being. There are significant differences between well-adjusted children and maladjusted children in areas of emotional discomfort, social inadequacy, and fantasy play. Greater research is needed to establish the usefulness of the PTOI with diverse populations. Standardization is also needed in the role of the therapist and the physical setting of the playroom. A child-centered approach should be used to minimize intrusion into the child's play and to permit the child to communicate themselves with as little psychodynamic influences as possible.

Play Therapy Screening Instrument for Child Sexual Abuse

Play presents children with a mode of communicating occurrences in their life that are too difficult or scary for them to face. Sexual abuse is one of the most difficult areas for children to communicate. The Play Therapy Screening Instrument for Child Sexual Abuse (PTSI-CSA), based on Homeyer's (1995) research, identifies children who are at high risk of being sexually abused. The PTSI-CSA consists of 15 sexual play behaviors consistent with and highly correlated (Homeyer & Landreth, 1998) with children who have been sexually abused. Each item in the instrument is a specific, spontaneous behavior exhibited by a child in a play therapy session. The PTSI-CSA is to be used when the play therapist begins to question whether the child's play therapy behaviors may reflect sexual abuse.

Primarily designed for use in nondirective play therapy, the PTSI-CSA can also be used to assess spontaneous behaviors that are expressed by the child in a more directive play therapy session (Homeyer, 2001). The PTSI-CSA is an empirically researched screening instrument and is an easy tool for the trained play therapist to utilize in discriminating between sexually abused children and non-sexually abused children in the play therapy setting. Caution does need to be used when interpreting the results to avoid false positive and negative. Additional research is needed to develop norm groups and its usefulness with diverse populations.

Trauma Play Scale

Young children are at a greater risk for traumatic effects because they do not yet have an established sense of self and their coping behaviors are limited. The younger the child, the greater the risk of limiting the child's potential to cope. The recently developed Trauma Play Scale (TPS) measures five areas of a child's play: (1) intense play – extremely focused and absorbed in play that seems to holds specific meaning; (2) repetitive play – returning to specific play behaviors, play sequences, or themes that seem to hold specific meaning (often has literal quality); (3) play disruption – sudden shift in play in response to the child's anxiety/discomfort; (4) avoidant play behavior – avoidance of contact with the therapist and apparent lack of capacity to form a trusting relationship; and (5) expression of negative affect – degree to which the child expresses negative affect during segment (Bratton, 2004a). Sessions are videotaped and evaluated by the degree the play behaviors are present during the play sessions.

The research supported four of the subscales of the TPS with the strongest correlation within the expression of negative affect. There was little discrimination between the repetitive play of traumatized children and nontraumatized children. However, the evaluators were blind to the details of the children and their history. The researchers noted while both groups of children engaged in repetitive play, the traumatized children's play had a literal quality (Bratton, 2004b). The TPS is new; therefore, additional research is needed to establish norm groups and its adaptability to diverse populations.

CONCLUSION

Play is believed to reflect a child's inner life, developmental level of functioning, and competence abilities (O'Conner & Ammen, 1997).

Creative therapists are finding play therapy assessments useful tools for working with children. The assessments reviewed in this chapter represent only a few of the play therapy assessments available today. Some assessments have provided evidence that they are useful tools when working with specific populations, such as survivors of trauma and sexual abuse.

Instruments like the Transdisciplinary Play-Based Assessment and the Developmental Play Assessment Instrument are well-established indicators of a children's developmental level and needs. The Marshak Interaction Method is a structured technique in evaluating parent-child interaction (reviewed in Brooke 2004), while the Family Puppet Interview uses a projective approach. The Play Therapy Observation Instrument looks at the overall emotional well-being of a child. The Play Therapy Screening Instrument for Child Sexual the Abuse and the newly developed Play Trauma Scale measure and evaluate for the specific concerns within their titles. The assessments of a child's play open the window and allow the therapist to see the inner child.

REFERENCES

Brooke, S. L. (2004). Critical review of play therapy assessments. *International Journal of Play Therapy*, 13(2), 119–142.

Bratton, S. C. (2004a). The healing process of young traumatized children in play therapy. *Session presented to the Association for Play Therapy* Conference, Broomfield, CO, October, 2004.

Bratton, S. C. (2004b, October 9). Personal communication.

Gill, E. (1994). *Play in family therapy*. New York: Guilford Press.

Homeyer, L. (1995). *Play therapy behaviors of sexually abused children*. Unpublished doctoral dissertation. University of North Texas, Denton, TX.

Homeyer, L. E. (2001). Identifying sexually abused children in play therapy. In G. L. Landreth (Ed.). *Innovations in play therapy: Issues, process, and special populations* (pp. 131–154). Philadelphia, PA: Brunner- Routledge.

Homeyer, L. E., & Landreth, G. L. (1998). Play therapy behaviors of sexually abused children. *International Journal of Play Therapy*, 7(1), 49–71.

Howe, P. A., & Silvern, L. E. (1981). Behavioral observation during play therapy: Preliminary development of a research instrument. *Journal of Personality Assessment*, 45, (168–182).

Irwin, E. C. (1993). Using puppets for assessments. In C. E. Schaefer & D. M. Cangelosi (Eds.), *Play therapy techniques* (pp. 69–81). Northvale, NJ: Jason Aronson.

Irwin, E. C. (2000). The use of a puppet interview to understand children. In K. Gitlin-Wiener, A. Sangrund, & C. Schaefer (Eds.). *Play diagnosis and assessment* (pp. 682–703). New York: John Wiley & Sons, Inc.

Irwin, E., & Shapiro, M. (1975). Puppetry as a diagnostic and therapeutic technique. In I. Jakab (Ed.). *Psychiatry and art* (Vol. 4). Basel, Switzerland: Karger.

Landreth, G. L. (1993). Child-centered play therapy. *Elementary School Guidance & Counseling, 28,* 17–29.

Lifter, K. (2000). Linking assessment to intervention for children with developmental disabilities or at-risk for developmental delay: The Developmental Play Assessment (DPA) instrument. In K. Gitlin-Wiener, A. Sangrund, & C. Schaefer (Eds.). *Play diagnosis and assessment* (pp. 228–261). New York: John Wiley & Sons, Inc.

Lifter, K., Edwards, G., Avery, D., Anderson, S. R., & Sulzer-Azaroff, B. (1988). The Developmental Play Assessment (DPA) Instrument. Mini-seminar presented to the Annual Convention of the American Speech Language Hearing Association, Boston, MA, November 1988. Developmental assessment of young children's play: Implications for interventions. Revised, July, 1994.

Lindaman, A. L., Booth, P. B., Chambers, C. L. (2000). Assessing parent-child interactions with the Marshak Interaction (MIM). ·In K. Gitlin-Wiener, A. Sangrund, & C. Schaefer (Eds.). *Play diagnosis and assessment* (pp. 371–400). New York: John Wiley & Sons, Inc.

Linder, T. W. (1990). *Transdisciplinary play-based assessment: A functional approach to working with young children.* Baltimore: Paul H. Brookes Publishing Co.

Linder, T. W. (1993). *Transdisciplinary play-based assessment: A functional approach to working with young children* (Rev. ed.). Baltimore: Paul H. Brookes Publishing Co.

Linder, T. (2000). Transdisciplinary play-based assessment. In K. Gitlin-Wiener, A. Sangrund, & C. Schaefer (Eds.). *Play diagnosis and assessment* (pp. 139–166). New York: John Wiley & Sons, Inc.

O'Conner, K., & Ammen, S. (1997). *Play therapy treatment planning and interventions: The ecosystematic model and workbook.* San Diego, CA: Academic Press.

Perry, L. H. (1988–1989). Play therapy behavior of maladjusted and adjusted children. (Doctoral dissertation, University of North Texas, 1988) *Dissertation Abstracts International, 49,* 2937A.

Perry, L. H., & Landreth, G. L. (2001). Diagnostic assessment of children's play therapy behaviors. In G. L. Landreth (Ed.), *Innovations in play therapy: Issues, process, and special populations* (pp. 155–178). Philadelphia, PA: Brunner- Routledge.

Ross, P. (2000). The family puppet technique for assessing parent-child and family interaction patterns. In K. Gitlin-Wiener, A. Sangrund, & C. Schaefer (Eds.). *Play diagnosis and assessment* (pp. 672–681). New York: John Wiley & Sons, Inc.

Schmidt, M. M. (2001). Using play therapy assessment in an elementary and intermediate school setting. In A. A. Drewes, L. J. Carey, &C. E. Schaefer (Eds.). *School-based play therapy* (pp. 3–15). New York: John Wiley & Sons, Inc.

Webb, N. B. (Ed.). (1991). *Playing for their lives: Helping troubled children through play therapy.* New York: Free Press.

Woltmann, A. G. (1940). The use of puppetry in understanding children. *Mental Hhygiene, 24,* 445–458.

Biographical Statement

Charles E. Myers, M.A., RMHCI, NCC, NCSC, RPT, is a Certified School Counselor and Registered Mental Health Counselor Intern in the State of Florida, a National Certified Counselor, a National Certified School Counselor, and a Registered Play Therapist. Mr. Myers has served as school counselor at Cleveland Elementary Academy, an intercity, title I public school in Tampa, Florida. Charles has presented at state conferences, local workshops, and at the University of South Florida on play therapy, filial therapy, sandplay, and elementary counseling. Additionally, he has provided play therapy and filial therapy at Metropolitan Ministries, a homeless shelter in Tampa. Charles has also served in leadership roles for a number of professional organizations, currently as the Vice President of the Florida School Counselor Association, president of the Tampa Bay Chapter of the Florida Play Therapy Association, and Member at Large for the Hillsborough County Counselor Association.

Chapter 10

EXPRESSIVE THERAPIES WITH GRIEVING CHILDREN

Hilda Glazer

INTRODUCTION

Dibs had come to terms with himself. In his symbolic play he had poured out his hurt, bruised feelings, and had emerged with feelings of strength and security. (Axline, 1964, p. 200)

Virginia Axline developed what she called nondirective play therapy. Today it is often called child-centered play therapy, thus acknowledging the focus on the child rather than his or her problems (Guerney, 2001). Play therapy is based on the view of play as a medium of expression for the child which has meaning and is purposeful (Brems, 2002). Further, play is often the attempt by the child to organize experience and may be a way that the child can experience a sense of control even though this may not mirror reality (Landreth, 1991). The meaning of the play is not always what appears as the surface meaning but has deep or indirect meanings for the child which may not be apparent to the observer. It is often through this indirect meaning of the play that the child works through issues and problem solves (Brems, 2002).

CHILD-CENTERED PLAY THERAPY

Child-centered play therapy (CCPT) is based on client-centered play therapy as developed by Carl Rogers. The role of the therapist is to provide the child with the core conditions of unconditional positive regard, empathic understanding, and genuineness (Kottman, 2001). By being present with the child, the therapist can enter the world of the child. The uniqueness of the approach is seen in the five tenets of child-centered play therapy (Guerney, 2001, 17–19):

1. The child directs the content of the therapy. The responsibility for the child's behavior in the sessions rests with the child. . . .
2. The approach is not symptom specific or problem oriented. . . .
3. The internal frame of reference, or perceptions of reality of the child, is accepted by the therapist without challenge. . . . It is the therapist's task to make it safe and satisfying for the child to reveal his unique, personal world. . . .
4. CCPT is a system that must be followed in its totality. . . . The full power of the therapy is dependent on the use of the whole system.
5. Those using CCPT must believe in the power of this therapeutic system. . . .

Power refers to the power of the child: The child can work out the problem with minimal intervention from adults; children have the capacity for self-healing and will work on whatever needs to be resolved (Kottman, 1991, 1995). It may not be necessary for the therapist to know the meaning of the play for it to have a therapeutic benefit for the child.

There are a number of descriptions of playroom, and lists of toys to include (Kottman, 1991, 1995; Landreth, 1991). Guerney (2001) suggested that which toys they are is not as important as the fact that they say to the child that a great range of behaviors is permitted in the session. She proposed that toys that support the playing out of aggressive, regressive, independence, and mastery are important. I would add that for the grieving child nurturing should be added to the list.

The application of play therapy for children who have suffered a loss is the focus of this chapter. That will be followed by a discussion of expressive therapies in the playroom and a support group for children and families. The approaches include sandtray, art, bibliotherapy, and storytelling as well as hippotherapy and support groups.

CASE EXAMPLE

Mark's brother had died. Usually a happy three-year-old, Mark was having trouble sleeping and wanted to sleep in his parent's bed. He was also much more aggressive in his play with his peers and at home. Mark came into the playroom easily and explored the playroom. He tells me that he will play in the sand. Looking for miniatures and other toys to put in the sand, he is careful to ask first before putting anything in the sand. He smiles when he is told that he can decide what goes in the sand. The first day lots of toys go in the sand and he often checks to see if I am watching him. When told he has five minutes left, he easily leaves the playroom.

At the start of the second session, he asks if he can play with the doll house. I respond that in here you decide what to play with. He smiles and pulls out two dolls and proceeds to take all of their clothes off and puts them in the pool together and tells me he is giving them a bath. Then he moves to the stove and makes dinner for us. Today leaving is harder. He tells me he is not ready to go. It takes us about 10 minutes before he goes to Mom. Telling Mom about his play, she says that he and his brother were bathed together and now they are having a hard time getting him into the tub.

During the third session, Mark told me the story of how his brother died, acting out parts of it. After that there was sand play. Nurturing play was added during the next few sessions in which he fixed dinner for us. During the next two sessions, nurturing play continued and doll play continued. Sometimes he was the parent taking care of the child by putting the doll to bed or fixing dinner or bathing the doll. Sand play was burying and finding what was buried, or using the clay just making shapes and showing what he made. Checking in with the parents, there was a decrease in the problems with bedtime and more talking about good memories.

We moved to every other week and then to once a month for a total of 10 sessions.

EXPRESSION OF GRIEF IN CHILDREN

While not all children verbalize their concerns, some talk about what is different about their family. Some express concerns about being different from other families. Redefining who they are in relationship to the others in their families and to the deceased is one of the major issues for many preschool children. The feeling of being different and developing a new understanding of the current family constellation is an issue for all who have lost someone in their immediate family. For children whose parent has died, the children are often working on a redefined relationship with the remaining parent or other grieving adults.

The understanding of grief is related to the level of cognitive development of the child. The understanding of death is limited in the very young child (2–4 years of age) who does not understand permanence, universality, and the nonfunctional aspects of death (Oltjenbruns, 2001). These concepts develop during middle childhood and by the age of 11 most children have a more realistic understanding of death. For the preschool child, limited language skills and an inability to describe and name emotions limit the ability to verbally communicate. The school-age child, too, is limited in the ability to verbally describe what he or she is feeling. Grief is primarily expressed in art and play and in the interaction with others but the child is able to verbalize being sad and the differences in life now. The grief of children is often characterized by a shift back and forth between grief and normal activities. It is thought that young children cannot tolerate long periods of intense emotional pain and thus move between periods of grief and those of engaging in other activities (Baker & Sedney, 1996; Oltjenbruns, 2001). To understand the child's reaction to loss, it is important to understand what the child has lost. Baker and Sedney (1996) identified three types of losses:

- the loss of a personally meaningful relationship,
- the loss of an attachment figure, and
- secondary losses.

The secondary losses are all the ways that the child's life changes after the primary loss.

Secondary losses are stressful for the child; they are powerful losses. They may include moving to a new house which means a new school and loss of a friendship group, economic changes which may be felt by the child, the return of the remaining parent to work, and perhaps a new caregiver among others.

The death of a loved one is experienced and expressed in different ways depending on the developmental phase of the child (Worden, 1996). The way the child copes with grief may mirror the coping strategies seen in the adults in the family. Children often pick up spoken or unspoken rules for grieving from the adults. Thus, the child may take a message that he or she is not to cry from adults who are trying to control their emotional expression or are told that they have to be strong for the surviving parent. Other children are told they are now the adult and the child defines that to mean that emotional expression is not allowed. Children may take what people say concretely and model their behavior accordingly. For example, if a child is told that a parent is with God and that God only takes good people, the child's response may be to behave poorly to prevent his or her being taken. What adults understand in the context of a religious belief may be taken in a different and much more concrete fashion by the school-age child. A school-age child took grandpa's statement to take care of grammy when he was away to heart and thought he should move in with her so he could keep his promise to his grandpa.

Children's grief often seems less intense than those of adults but the duration is often longer (Baker, & Sedney, 1996). Children will benefit from consistent parenting and discipline and the maintenance of daily routines. However, the parents may not be as available to the child when facing their own grief.

The grief of the child is always within the developmental context. The grief experience can be an opportunity for positive growth of the child. But at the same time it is often difficult to identify what is a developmentally appropriate grief response and what is simply bad behavior. Parents are often hesitant about disciplining a child who is grieving and may be more permissive. While this is certainly understandable, the result may be the reinforcement of undesirable behaviors that are difficult to extinguish later on. One example is letting the child stay in the parents' bed. Sleeping problems are very difficult to change even under the best of circumstances.

Worden (1996) looks at the process of adapting to the loss in children. He identifies four tasks of mourning:

Task 1: Accepting the reality of the loss
Task 2: Experiencing the pain or the emotional aspects of the loss
Task 3: Adjusting to an environment in which the deceased is missing
Task 4: Emotionally relocating the deceased within one's life and find ways to memorialize the person.

In addition to the developmental overlay for the grieving process, the child will experience the loss in an individual way (Worden, 1996) as will adults. There are environmental and contextual aspects to the loss including sources of support for the child and areas of strength and vulnerability. Worden (1996, pp. 16-17) identified a number of mediators that influence the process of adapting to the death of a parent:

1. The death and rituals surrounding the death.
2. The relationship of the child with the deceased parent both before the death and after.
3. The functioning of the surviving parent and his or her ability to parent the child.
4. Family influences such as size, solvency, structure, style of coping, support, and communication, as well as, family stressors and changes and disruptions in the child's daily life.
5. Characteristics of the child including age, gender, self-perception, and understanding of death.
6. While these refer to the death of a parent, they can also apply to any death of a loved one faced by a child.

Seeing a child's grief as unique to the child and different from that of adults is critical. Being present with the child as he or she processes her grief is a gift to the child as well as the therapist. Sometimes all the child wants to know is that someone is there who listens and hears. The next section of the chapter presents therapeutic interventions with children.

PLAY THERAPY WITH GRIEVING CHILDREN

A child should not be deprived of his [her] right to grieve and to mourn. He [she] should be free to feel the sorrow in the loss of someone loved. (Ginott, 1956, p. 171)

Through play, the child expresses feelings and processes grief. A child's play is the way in which feelings are expressed and in which grief can be processed. The spontaneous paintings of the children and their themes in their sandtray worlds express a number of recurrent themes. Play represents the child's attempts to organize experiences: To organize the world of the child (Landreth, 1991). Children are much more likely to be comfortable using toys and play, as opposed to language, to express themselves and to show how they feel about people and events (Kottman, 1995). According to Landreth, the process of play can provide the opportunity for the child to experience being in control even though the reality of the circumstances may dictate otherwise. In play, the child expresses himself or herself creatively; the expression can be physical, emotional, or cognitive (Landreth, 1991). Children's metaphors separate the play from the reality until the reality is bearable (Frick-Helms, 1997).

Not all children need therapy; many do well without specific interventions (Worden, 1996). Some parents may see their grief reflected in the child and it is the adult who needs the additional support. Some children struggle with adapting to the loss and will benefit from therapy. Additionally, those children for whom grief is a secondary issue to serious emotional or psychological health issues, early intervention and therapy are beneficial.

The goals of play therapy with grieving children include providing a safe place for children to express grief. Children often get the message from adults, intentionally or not, that it is not alright to get upset and cry. A second goal is to promote the expression of grief. Normalizing the grief experience and encouraging the grief process are also goals. Often children come into grief therapy because of a noticeable behavior change such as acting out behavior in school or at home, regressive behaviors, an increase in misbehavior at home or school, a negative change in grades, and sleeping problems among others. For the parents, the goal of therapy is to alleviate these problems not realizing that these may be expressions of grief. As an adjunct of therapy for the child, parent consultation focusing on parenting skills may be helpful to the family as may referral for group or individual therapy for the adult. While the therapist may develop a list of goals for the therapy, we may not know what the child wishes to establish as a goal or what the child's goals are for their time in the playroom.

Termination

Termination may be an issue for the grieving child. The potential exists for the loss of the therapist to be an additional secondary loss for the child. Often with the grieving child, there will be a change in the play indicating a movement in the bereavement process. This is often accompanied by some of the signs Brems (2002) has identified such as the child not wanting to start the session, asking to leave early, or stops playing before the session is over. Moving from weekly sessions to every other week and then once a month is optimal or using a natural break such as the child going on vacation are ways to make the termination less traumatic to the child. Leaving the option to come back often decreases the anxiety for older children.

Worden's (1996) tasks are often seen in the playroom. An example of accepting the reality of the loss is the preschool child who would set up a scenario of a family in which Dad went off to work every day and came home every night. Dad had died in an accident. She did this same activity for five weeks. When she moved on to other play activities, her mother reported that her night terrors had ended. Experiencing the emotional pain of the loss is seen in the child who buried a ball in the sand and sang happy birthday to his sister. The play of children adjusting to the reality of the loss may include play of changes in the family life. One child played with the dolls doing the bath routine the way it was before her sister died and switched to portraying the way it is now.

Filial Therapy

An alternative therapy with preschool children and their parents is combining play therapy and filial therapy. The process involves play therapy for a number of sessions followed by filial therapy. Filial therapy is a strategy for teaching parents the primary skills involved in CCPT. Developed by Bernard and Louise Guerney, it has been modified by a number of others including Landreth (1991). Filial therapy is based on the premise that the parent is the best therapeutic agent for the child. With a grieving family, I have found that when the parent is able to process his or her own grief and is willing to do filial therapy with his or her child, that filial therapy can strengthen and restore the parent-child bond (Glazer & Clark, 1999). This is not appropriate with all families of grieving children; the parent has to be at a place in his or her grief where he or she can invest in the process and wants to do it. As the family attempts to restore order to their lives following a death, filial therapy can provide the opportunity to take 30 minutes out and be together in a playroom without evaluation or teaching. Filial therapy offers an opportunity for the parent to learn about grieving children and how to play with the child.

EXPRESSIVE THERAPIES WITH GRIEVING CHILDREN

Sandtray

Jungian approaches have used the development of a sandtray world to encourage expression by children (Kottman, 2001). The inclusion of the sandtray and miniatures in the playroom can be used in child-centered play therapy where the child may select to use the sandtray in any way that he or she chooses. The miniatures selected should represent a variety of animals, houses, trees and bridges, and people. But children will use miniatures to represent what they need, which may not be what it is seen to be by the therapist. I prefer dry sand while others prefer wet sand. Having a wet sandtray and a dry sandtray may be an option in some settings. Some children put together a sandtray world while others develop a story using the sandtray as a stage. One recurring theme in many sandtrays of grieving children is the family. Children put together sandtray worlds in which the animal and people, families, are central. One preschool child grouped the miniatures and put them around the room on the floor in groups. Some groupings appeared to be families with adult and baby animals, some had two adults and some groups had one. Others do a sandtray with no people or animals. Often they create a similar sandtray over several sessions. A preteen did a variation on a sandtray theme five times: An island was formed in the center of the sandtray with

one tree and one animal. The greatest amount of time was spent making the island and clearing the sand around it. The island was separated from land on either side. What varied were the placement of bridges and the use of fences in front of the other tree and the animals. One five-year-old boy noted in a second sandtray of families that he was only going to use happy animals and make happy families. Children may also develop a sandtray world of cemeteries or portray burying of animals and uncovering of them by other objects or people. A four-year-old did a cemetery scene that was so close to the cemetery in which her brother and grandfather were buried that her mother commented on it bringing a smile to the child's face. Another young child used the sandtray to work on her concept of death as being a parallel universe. The child did a sandtray of the cemetery and then, putting her hands under the sand where she had placed the markers, moved her fingers around and said that they were playing together! Some children will do the sandtray silently and some will keep up a running dialogue while building the sandtray world. One four-year-old tells a story about trains and how the machines save the train caught in the snow with the details of the role of each machine as he put them in the sand. The analogy may be how he feels about the paramedics not being able to save his grandfather but it is the meaning for him that is important as he never makes the connection verbally in the session. I offer to take pictures of sandtrays and then give the pictures to the child. There are times when they want to be in the picture, times when they do not want to be in the picture, and times when they do not want a picture to be taken of the sandtray.

A group sandtray is also possible. I orchestrated a family sandtray to help the parent and three-year-old child understand what each one saw as being the family unit after the death of a child. The directions were to do a series of sandtrays of their family life. They put together first the newlywed house, the house with one child, the house with two children, and now. The parents were able to understand how the child now saw himself as an only child. I took Polaroid® pictures of the sandtrays which I gave to the parents.

Art

A variety of art materials should be part of every playroom. Chalk, crayons, markers, colored pencils, washable paints, and finger paints (if the space permits) can be made accessible to the child. Children's drawings can have different levels of meaning. A four-year-old child whose brother had died of SIDS did a detailed painting of her house three weeks in succession. She would tell me about the house and which window was her brother's room etc. The background was detailed. When the house and background were complete and she had shared with me some of the details, she used a long brush and covered the entire paper with black paint. With all of the colors in the house, the resulting painting was never totally black, it was streaked with color. She never shared with her mother what was beneath the black. While interpreting the meaning of the colors can lead one to connect the black with grief and anxiety (Malchiodi, 1998), caution should be used in interpreting the meaning of color as it may be unique to the child. After three weeks, she did not cover the house with black. She never drew the house again. While some of the symbolism may appear obvious, the true meaning to the child and the impact on her grief process is within the child. The importance of her therapy was evident when the center was one of the places she wanted to say goodbye to when the family was moving out of state. The Serial Drawing technique of John Allan (1988) can be used effectively with a number of theoretical orientations and, as in the example, may be initiated by the child without direction from the therapist.

In addition to free drawing, specific art activities can be used to encourage processing and emotional expression. The choice of techniques should be consistent with the theoretical orientation of the therapist. Books such as *101 More Favorite Play Therapy Techniques* (Kaduson, & Schaefer, 2001) contain a variety of art and play activities.

The processing of grief can be seen in the change over time in children's drawings. We conducted a study of this using the Rosebush Technique developed by John Allan (Glazer, 1998). After the guided fantasy, the children are asked to draw the rosebush. We found that for children attending a grief support group there was a change in the background of their drawings between the pretest and the posttest. For many, the difference was not in the rosebush as expected but in the background. One child had divided the background in half – half-day and half-night perhaps expressing the sadness in her life at the start and had a single background of day at the end with a happy sun wearing sunglasses.

Storytelling

Storytelling also is part of the play therapy process either in spontaneous stories or used more directively. One nine-year-old who has had multiples losses of primary caretakers has used her sessions to tell intricate stories using puppets and miniatures. The first three stories were about dinosaur families and the birth and growth of children to the time they left the cave to be on their own. The focus of the next story was an animal family with the central character being the mother and her care of the children. All the stories end with the young successfully leaving the nest.

Mutual storytelling as developed by Gardner can also be an effective technique in the playroom (Muro & Kottman, 1995). In mutual storytelling, the therapist asks the student to tell a story with a beginning, middle, and end after which the therapist retells the story with a more adaptive ending (Muro & Kottman, 1995). This technique can be adapted to meet the requirements of the situation and the developmental level of the child. One example of this was a project in which we developed a story stem and asked children to complete the story. The story was about moving from home and noted some of the primary and secondary losses suffered by children. Our hope was that in finishing the story the children would insert some of their concerns and feelings into the story. Children in our support groups were asked to participate so they were familiar with the teller and storytelling. We discovered that there were a number of themes related to grieving that appeared in the children's stories.

A school-age child may use metaphors as a way to process the loss without direction. The variety of toys and puppets in the playroom will support the child in designing his or her story. Often children will tell the same story for a couple of sessions changing it as the child moves through the therapeutic process. Children often use puppet shows to tell a story and to include the therapist in their process. Some children even want to invite the parent into the playroom to hear the story.

Bibliotherapy

Journaling for older children, puppetry, and writing stories are processes that can also be used as effective interventions. A favorite with school-age children is *Tear Soup* by Pat Schwiebert and Chuck DeKlyen (2001), which touches many of the feelings associated with loss without specifying a specific loss. I have used this in grief groups where after reading the book, we make our own grief soup putting our feelings and thoughts into the pot.

Hippotherapy

Animal-assisted therapy has been shown to be beneficial as an adjunct to psychotherapy. Specifically, therapeutic riding can be an adjunct to other grief therapy. A hippotherapy program was designed as a summer program offered to children in a grief support program. Reactions of the children, the volunteer handlers, and the parents were collected. Analysis of those reactions revealed the following categories of responses: Building confidence included overcoming any fear of the horse and the development of a sense of independence (Glazer, Clark, & Stein, 2004). The study demonstrated the potential of animal-assisted therapy as part of an integrated program for children and teens. The relationship with the horses provided a safe place for the expression of grief (Glazer, Clark, & Stein, 2004).

GRIEF SUPPORT GROUPS FOR CHILDREN

One of the grief issues for many children is that they now not only feel different but their family is different. Many do not know another child who has suffered a loss. Additionally, it is easy for adults to say that everyone feels this way or you are not the only child who . . . but for the child to internalize what the adult is saying and accept it is not often easy or possible. Meeting other children who have lost a loved one and are being provided with opportunities to express and process grief together can be beneficial. Peer support groups can provide a safe place for children to process their grief. The shared group experience may be the most important part of the group process for the grieving child.

The Dougy Center

One of the first, if not the first, grief support groups for families was the Dougy Center in Portland, Oregon. The Dougy Center trains others in its model and offers a wealth of resources for those in grief and those who work with grieving individuals. The Dougy Center site offers a nationwide list of available programs.

> The mission of The Dougy Center for Grieving Children is to provide to families in Portland and the surrounding region loving support in a safe place where children, teens and their families grieving a death can share their experiences as they move through their healing process. Through our National Center for Grieving Children and Families we also provide support and training locally, nationally, and internationally to individuals and organizations seeking to assist children in grief. (http://www.dougy.org/about.html)

The Evergreen Program

The Evergreen Program of Mount Carmel Hospice and Palliative Care Center of Columbus. Ohio is a family support group program. There are peer support groups for children and parents led by trained facilitators and supported by a clinical staff of licensed mental health providers. The Center has as part of the volunteer and professional staff a storyteller, a drama therapist, a play therapist, and a therapy dog. The director of the center is the clinical manager for aftercare of the hospice. Facilitators go through hospice volunteer training. Meeting twice a month the evening begins with a pizza supper followed by a one hour group session. Group sessions are designed around program goals with a focus on expression of grief.

The program goals are: To increase grief awareness, to build relationships, to establish a sense of belonging to a community, to explore feelings, to respect and understand diversity, to increase self-esteem, and to normalize the grief process. While not group therapy, many of the activities for the groups use expressive therapy techniques including storytelling, drama therapy, art therapy, games, and puppetry. Clinical staff support the facilitators as needed. Summer programs have used hippotherapy and other animal-assisted therapies to encourage emotional expression and the other program goals.

CONCLUSION

One of the major therapeutic goals for grieving children is increased emotional expression which will facilitate the process of grieving.

Accompanying the child in his or her grief journey is a gift to the child and therapist. Child-centered play therapy provides a safe place for child to express and process grief. Expressive therapies integrated into the individual and group experience are primary interventions. These include art, storytelling, sandtray, and bibliotherapy. Additionally, support groups and hippotherapy can support the child's grief process.

REFERENCES

Allan, J. (1988). *Inscapes of the child's world.* Dallas, TX: Spring.

Axline, V. M. (1964). *Dibs in search of self.* New York: Ballantine Books.

Baker, J. E., & Sedney, M. A. (1996). How bereaved children cope with loss: An overview. In C. A. Corr & D. M. Corr (Eds.). *Handbook of childhood death and bereavement*, pp. 109–129. New York: Springer.

Brems, C. (2002). *A comprehensive guide to child psychotherapy.* Boston: Allyn and Bacon.

Dougy Center http://www.dougy.org/about.html

Frick-Helms, S. (1997). "Boys cry better than girls:" Play therapy behaviors of children residing in a shelter for battered women. *International Journal of Play Therapy, 6*(1), 73–91.

Ginott, H. (1956). *Between parent and child.* New York: Avon.

Glazer, H. R. (1998). Expressions of children's grief: A qualitative study. *International Journal of Play Therapy, 7*(2), 51–65.

Glazer, H. R., & Clark, M. D. (1999). A family-centered intervention for grieving preschool children. *The Journal of Child and Adolescent Group Therapy, 9*(4), 161–168.

Glazer, H.R., Clark, M. D., & Stein, D. S. (2004). The impact of hippotherapy on grieving children. *Journal of Hospice and Palliative Nursing, 6*(3), 171–175.

Guerney, L. (2001). Child-centered play therapy. *International Journal of Play Therapy, 10*(2), 13–31.

Kaduson, H. G., & Shaefer, C. E. (Eds.). (2001). *101 more favorite play therapy techniques.* Northvale, NJ: Jason Aronson.

Kottman, T. (2001). Adlerian play therapy. *International Journal of Play Therapy, 10*, 1–12.

Kottman, T. (1995). *Partners in play: An Adlerian approach to play therapy.* Alexandria, VA: ACA.

Kottman, T. (1991). *Play therapy: Basics and beyond.* Alexandria, VA: ACA

Landreth, G. L. (1991). *Play therapy: The art of the relationship.* Muncie, IN: Accelerated Development Press.

Malchiodi, C. A. (1998). *Understanding children's drawings.* New York: Guilford.

Muro, J. J. & Kottman, T. (1995). *Guidance and counseling in the elementary and middle schools.* Madison, WI: Brown and Benchmark.

Oltjenbruns, K. A. (2001). Developmental context of childhood: grief and regrief phenomena. In M. S. Stroebe, R. O. Hansson, W. Stroebe, & H. Schut (Eds.). *Handbook of bereavement research*, 169–197. Washington, D.C.: American Psychological Association.

Schwiebert, P., & DeKlyen, C. (2001). *Tear soup.* Portland, OR: Grief Watch.

Worden, J. W. (1996). *Children and grief: When a parent dies.* New York: Guilford.

Biographical Statement

Hilda R. Glazer, EdD, is a Registered Play Therapist and Supervisor, a licensed psychologist in Missouri, and a Professional Clinical Counselor and Supervisor in Ohio. She has a private practice, The Playful Therapies Center, in Columbus, Ohio and works part-time as a bereavement counselor with the Mount Carmel Hospice and Palliative Care Center. She also holds adjunct teaching positions. Dr. Glazer is Vice-President of the Board of Directors of the Foundation for Play Therapy.

Chapter 11

MOVING WITH MEANING: THE HISTORICAL PROGRESSION OF DANCE/MOVEMENT THERAPY

LAURICE D. NEMETZ

INTRODUCTION

The body is the first and primary means of movement and creative human expression, from the moment a baby first enters and interacts in the world. Unlike other forms of art, dance is unique in that the instrument and tool of expression is the human body itself, making it both a profound form of expression, as well as often elusive and transient. As the dance historian, Wosien (1974) noted, " . . . before man expresses his experience of life through materials he does so with his own body" (p. 8). The emergence of dance/movement therapy has developed formally as a field during the past century, but the use of dance as a therapy has been in existence as long as humans have felt a need to express, even prior to organized language, or other extensions of expression through musical instruments and art. There is a clear historical precedent in ancient forms of dance and movement healing; from the Greeks with their healing rhythmic patterns to Eastern cultures which combined dance into the major attributes of their deities. Almost all common dance forms developed from early ritual dance (Lawson, 1955; Wosien, 1974). Humanity has always used dance to express and reflect the world, creating and using cultural and individual dance to release psychological needs.

A variety of converging factors led to the direct rise of the modern field of dance/movement therapy including historical use of dance as healing, the growth of modern dance, the study of nonverbal behavior, and the field of modern psychology. As with the other creative art therapy fields, dance/movement therapy uses a number of specific tools and techniques for assessment and work,

and indeed often utilizes other forms of art for expression, as appropriate. However, at its core is the inherent need for people to express themselves on a most basic movement level, creating dance that emotes individual needs, as well as one's connection to the rest of the world. In exploring the history of the field, one reaffirms the reason for it: Humanity moves and creates art as part of the very essential aspect of living. Today, the American Dance/Movement Therapy Association (ADTA) has defined dance/movement therapy as the "psychotherapeutic use of movement as a process which furthers the emotional, social, cognitive, and physical integration of the individual" (ADTA, 2004). Please see Appendix for the timeline for the history of the dance/movement therapy field.

HISTORICAL PRECEDENTS

Dance is connected to emotional expression, and in dance/movement therapy today, the goal is to reconnect with this creative process, rather than produce a performance piece. As observed by one dance/movement therapist, "the aim is not to move more freely or more perfectly, which may be the aim of therapeutic dance activities, but to use movement experimentation to explore new ways of being and feeling, and to gain access to feelings that cannot be verbalized" (Stanton-Jones, 1992, p. 3). Traditionally, the original cultural creation of dance is to express these feelings both individually, and as a community. It is only through the recent few centuries that traditional forms of dance, such as ballet, have separated the audience from the dancer so clearly. While the art form of ballet has achieved a level of technical and artistic beauty, it has left many Westerners unfamiliar with the process of dance making. Further, separation of the body and spirit in the Judeo-Christian traditions had left a historically long period of believing the mind and psyche to be separated from the body. The modern dance movement, and the dance/movement therapists that followed, looked toward ancient dance forms as they began their exploration of the mind/body/spirit connection that has been recently reaccepted culturally. These dances are truly the beginnings of the field and it is often noted that "dance therapy has roots that extend back to ancient times in dances of celebrations and crises, in dances that define individual and group identity, and in dances of death and exorcism" (Schmais, 1974, p. 7). Likewise, as dance anthropologist Judith Hanna notes, "the shaman or medicine person in non-Western dances is an avatar of the dance therapist" (Hanna, 1988, p. 31).

The great difficulty in looking at historical dance is the lack of ability to witness the movement as directly as one can view an ancient painting, or decipher lines of poetry. The transient form of dance makes it difficult to study. Even with the modern interventions of film, video, and other recordings, the live qualities of dance are difficult to record and subject to great interpretation by the viewer. Cultural dance, with its constant evolution of form, becomes a great reflector of the psychological mood of that entity, and therefore, is constantly changing to reflect the current group of those performing the dance.

It is believed that dance is found in all human societies. Dancing serves a variety of purposes, but it is essentially a means of communication, whether to other members of society or to one's own god or gods. Basically, it serves to make the extraordinary in life understandable and to empower the common actions of daily activity with special meaning. Furthermore, whenever more than one dancer is present, the resulting dance is a reflection of the cultural ideas and ideals of interaction. In essence, dance helps to ritualize the ordinary movements of daily life, and endow them with meaning and purpose. The daily task of gathering fruit or chasing an animal for food is given purpose and meaning. In cultures such as the ancient Egyptians, there appear to have been dance/dramas performed to reflect significant agricultural occurrences such as the rise and fall of the Nile River (Kraus, Hilsendager, & Dixon, 1991, p. 38). The dances

Figure 11.1.   Ancient Egyptians danced in groups as well as expressed themselves in acrobatic poses.

were often depicted as either slow, pedestrian movement, or quite acrobatic in nature, including backbends and other physical feats (Kraus et al., 1991; Sachs, 1937).

Likewise, dance can be a means to also make the extraordinary and unexplainable into manageable concepts. Thus, the earthquake, or even an act of thunder and lightning, can be experienced on a creative level. Making those that are overwhelming less threatening through movement and organizational thought has historically helped individuals overcome great emotional strife. Perhaps one of the best-known examples is the tarantella dance from Italy, where folklore has spread the story that the dancer dances to give a potentially fatal spider bite a ritualized movement outlet, as well as to physically move the venom out of the body's systems through the frenetic dance. While the exact origin continues to be questioned, another such dance, the French Provencal Danse des Tripettes, was said to be created as a cure for epilepsy: "St. Marcel was held to have been able to cure epilepsy, and in the same way that in southern Italy they will dance to sweat out certain disorders, so the leaps of the Danse des Tripettes are employed in church, sometimes for hours on end, to cure the malady. The evil spirit of the illness is literally sweated out" (Jaffé, 1990, p. 273).

In addition to serving as a means for curing the sick, folk dance, particularly throughout Europe, developed to honor and ritualize daily movement. On the island of Madeira (near Portugal), for example, there is a folk dance based on the sweeping movement of a needle and thread, highlighting the very important trade of lace making that has been a staple of the culture for hundreds of years. In other cultures, such as in sub-Saharan Africa, dance has historically been part of life so fully that even when two Bantu greet each other, they ask the question, "What do you dance?" (Jonas, 1992, p. 33).

In India, both the yogic traditions of movement as well as their dance tradition were created as a means of gaining spiritual connection with the gods. The Far East, as well as ancient cultures such as Egypt, served as great inspiration to the work of dancers, Ruth Denis and Ted Shawn, known collectively as Denishawn in the early 1900s, as they created exotic and spiritual choreographic pieces. Denishawn studied Indian dance, and was one of the first to take an interest in yoga, soon to be followed by movement explorers such as Joseph H. Pilates in the heyday of modern dance. Yoga has gained great popularity in recent years, but it is founded upon a 3,000 year-old tradition of using movement patterns for the well-being of body, mind, and spirit. Further, it was originally studied in a guru-student relationship, not unlike the modern therapist and client. The asanas, or postures, in yoga were originally practiced as a means to prepare the body for remaining still for long periods of meditative practice. Long, rigorous, physical work is meant to be a means to transcend the body, and reach a higher state of mental well-being. Yoga is one of the clearest body systems that stress a non-competitive system of movement. Along with yoga, Indian dance was so critical to its culture that even the deities of India are commonly depicted as dancers. The critical book on drama and dance, the Natya Sastra, was one of the first books in Far East culture to classify human emotion into nine main rasas, or essences of emotion from wondrous to fierce (Gupta, 2000, p. 150). Each of these has a clear movement component expressed through dance. Indian yoga also states the body/mind connection that would become clarified in dance/movement therapy:

> What happens in the body likewise occurs in the mind, and what happens in the mind likewise occurs in the body . . . when tension of the organs is relieved, the mind becomes still. This process can be reversed. Relaxing the mind by controlling your thinking causes relaxation of the body. However, this method is more difficult. Thus, yoga places the emphasis on moving from the physical to the mental. (Kriyananda, 2002, p. 104)

Of course, the emphasis on yoga is to transcend the body, whereas dance therapists would later work this connection to provide a means for people to feel connected to themselves and each other in the present time.

Another means of connection that comes historically is the use of space in relationship to other people. Throughout all ancient dances, there are several basic patterns that are used, notably the circle, the serpentine line, and couple formations as well as two opposing lines. All of these patterns served different purposes in how the dancers related to each other. For obvious reasons, the circle is a rather universal form that allows those participating to see and be with each other. This appears historically from images in Japanese dance, European and African group dances, as well as in most Native American Indian dances. After the courts of Louis the XIV made the performance of ballet popular, these primitive shapes were utilized less as dance became an event to be watched. The emergence of Denishawn and other early pre-modern dance companies would refocus attention on the more natural patterns of movement interaction that would be further utilized by dance/movement therapists as a natural way of group interaction.

Figure 11.2. The circle is one of the universal forms utilized in dance and dance/movement therapy. © 2004 Museum of Fine Arts, Boston.

Modern Groundwork for Dance/Movement Therapy

Early studies in nonverbal communication led to a whole new interest in behavior and movement patterns, establishing an important piece of the foundation for the field of dance/movement therapy. In the late 1800s, scholars began to realize the limitations of studying human behavior in terms of linguistics alone. However, this formal study of nonverbal communication would begin to gain acceptance in the 1960s and 1970s (Levy, 1988, p. 19). Theorists in modern times began to recognize the subtle nuances of nonverbal interaction that are constantly sending messages are often more important emotionally than purely relying on language.

The first major theorist in nonverbal communication was Charles Darwin, better known for his theories of evolution, who wrote about these ideas in his book *The Expression of the Emotions in Man and Animals* (1872). Darwin contributed many ideas to the area of nonverbal communication, among the ideas later articulated by modern dancer Martha Graham, that movement never lies. In 1872, Darwin wrote that, "the movement of expression in the face and body . . . reveals the thought and intentions of others more truly than do words, which may be falsified" (p. 364). Around this time, Sir William Osler (1849–1919), who is considered the father of modern medicine, also noted the significance of emotional factors in the healing process, and that nonverbal aspects of treatment were critical to healing (Osler, 1932).

The next major contribution to nonverbal study came with the arrival of Raymond Birdwhistell's *Introduction to Kinesics*, published in 1952. Birdwhistell is credited with giving the name, kinesics, to describe "the study of all bodily motions that are communicative" (Morain, 1978, p. 3). Stark (1982) notes that Birdwhistell's research is particularly relevant to the field of dance/movement therapy as it deals with movement interaction. Birdwhistell also took his study of kinemorphology and compared it to the study of linguistics. In the same manner that linguists divide language into parts, movement can be subdivided into small subtle actions. The advent of film assisted in the deconstruction of movement into small elements. Genelle Grant Morain (1978) added greatly to this field by taking the ideas that while basic emotions are universal, there are many subtler movement interactions that are unique to the culture from which they originate.

During the whole early half of the twentieth century, the field of psychotherapy was likewise developing rapidly, and with it came many important ideas that would be critical to the future work of dance/movement therapy. Psychology provided a system to understand normal human behavior and its deviations. Ancient roots of psychotherapy begin with *De Anima* (*On the Soul*) by Aristotle that links the heart to mental activity (1987). However, the field took a big step with the new recognition of different types of mental illness during World War II. This war was startling to the American culture both because of the large number of men who were unable to serve due to mental problems, as well as the new difficulties that arose in mental health for those who served in the war (Schmais, 1974). Psychotherapy was beginning to both recognize a diverse level of mental health needs, as well as acknowledge the importance of different modes of expression to release that trauma.

This foundation of the body/mind connection was quite an important shift from the previous century. As Dr. Fran Levy notes,

> Much of Western thought at the turn of the century subscribed to the credo of dualism, or the distinct separation of body and mind. Formal dance developed as a performing art, emphasizing technique, with little attention to how it affects the dancer. Medicine and psychotherapy developed as forms of treatment, with the former focusing on the body and the latter focusing on the mind. Psychotherapeutic treatment approaches were almost entirely verbal and nonactive. During the first half of the 20th century, a trend began within many fields to break away from the limitations of these traditions. (Levy, 1988, p. 1)

The development of new aspects in psychotherapy during this time would be paramount to all of the arts therapies, as well as impacting the general creative community. The work of Carl Jung (1875–1961), so critical to new explorations in many modern dances, would be important in providing themes of universal unconscious. A younger colleague of Freud, Jung began his explorations after having several haunting dreams, around the time of World War I. These images, which he worked through utilizing all the art forms, began to appear to him as part of the larger community's thoughts and visions and were highly symbolic. Influenced by Buddhism, Kabala, and other religious teachings, Jung defined the idea of active imagination, which places value on the artist invoking the primitive unconscious.

William Reich also followed Freud's early work on the body, and became more concerned with the general relationship of the body and mind. Many of his concepts centered on the idea that people show physical tension patterns in "character amour," or fixed body positions that hold repressed feeling (Reich, 1943). This work was later more widely accepted, particularly with the reworking of his theories by Alexander Lowen during the 1960s, a more receptive time for thinking about the body in psychodynamic terms.

Shortly after Reich's initial work, the humanist movement, led by Carl Rogers and Abraham Maslow, appeared during the 1950s. This introduced the idea that is an unspoken tenet of many dance/movement therapists: that clients wish and, indeed, strive to reach their fullest potential. Called the "actualizing tendency," this is the will of every person to reach the best possible level of wellness (Rogers, 1961; 1995, p. 351). Therefore, the role of the therapist is to guide and to help the client toward this path, while allowing the client to do the work. Important in this process is the role of the therapist to hold the client in positive regard. This is very clear in the work later developed in dance/movement therapy in working the unspoken dance between therapist and client by modeling appropriate and caring behavior. Mental illness is seen as a break in the sense of self, while health involves, among other issues, creativity.

Of course, there have been numerous references to madness in creative arts from Vincent Van Gogh's psychosis to ballet dancer Vaslav Nijinsky's bouts of depression. However, these are examples of a select few, highly driven performers devoted to their creative quest. Indeed, the use of creativity may have brought a small sense of order or purpose to what otherwise was surely an unbearable means of existence for some of these artists. Again, the ancients' use of the arts was to order and express the universe around them. Creativity can be seen as a means of coping, a unique form of human expression and growth. Returning to Rogerian theory, a healthy individual participates in life through creative expression, whether in the arts, sciences,

or fulfillment in one's job or chosen role (Rogers, 1995, p. 193). Similar to Eric Erikson's idea of generativity in his outline of the eight stages of human development, this expression is due to a desire to connect with others in a healthy manner.

During this post-Freudian period, many other psychotherapists were developing their ideas. In addition, there was growing research in the study of communication. Most importantly, during this time period, as psychology was opening up new ideas, the world of dance reflected upon this, and presented a new way of integrating these modern ideals into expressive art. Dance in the late 1800s had primarily consisted of chorus girls who strove to perform acrobatics (Au, 1988). In contrast, the founders of Denishawn, Ruth St. Denis, Ted Shawn, as well as Isadora Duncan, employed multicultural dance forms in their choreography with an emphasis on artistry. Born in 1877, Isadora Duncan began her work inspired by her own natural body and the images from ancient Greece. Before reaching twenty, she had already proclaimed, "I have discovered the dance. I have discovered the art which has been lost for two thousand years" (Jonas, 1992, p. 193). Though boastful, Isadora soon had her following of dancers and admirers who moved full of emotion and danced barefoot. She also reflected and advanced the psychological atmosphere of the time. Highwater (1978; 1985) notes:

> . . . it is clear that the Freudian emphasis upon the interior world influenced the emergence of modern dance and the cult of personality which Isadora Duncan symbolized. This relationship between the driving forces of culture and the forms of dance demonstrates the way in which experience is ritualized. (p. 21)

Contemporaries to Duncan, Ted Shawn, and Ruth St. Denis also began their exploration of foreign and ancient movement, pulling from Egyptian mythology and Indian dance. While seldom ethnologically accurate, they began to realize the power of ritual in dance and in the expression of emotions. As Shawn (1974) stated, "body movement is life itself . . . and to move is hence to satisfy a basic and eternal need" (p. 3). The importance of ritual in the working of dance/movement therapy groups became important as early pioneers recognized that humans are comforted in movement rituals whether as formalized dance step, or brushing one's teeth in the same manner

Figure 11.3. The image of Isadora Duncan both reflected and inspired art in the twentieth century with her interpretation of ancient forms of dance, paving the way for the modern dance movement.

each morning. Denishawn embedded ritualized movement with great pageantry, but they were quite correct in recognizing the emotional significance of this movement.

This interest in ethnic dance reached its height in the Denishawn era, which lasted from 1914–1931 (Jonas, 1992). It was truly through the creativity and leadership of Ruth St. Denis that many of these changes in dance occurred. Important to her development as a choreographer was her exposure to performer Genevieve Stebbens. Stebbens was a follower of the philosophy of Francois Delsarte (1811–1871), who "observed people in public places . . . in order to understand the correspondence between mood and movement" (Mazo, 1977, p. 64). Thus, the foundation of body/mind connection, a primary dance movement therapy principle, was being established and developed by St. Denis.

Modern dance began to develop rapidly during the 1930s and onward, both in the United States as well as abroad (particularly in Germany), feeling the impact in particular of Isadora Duncan and this new round of dance exploration. In Europe, the influence of teachers such as Rudolph Laban and

Mary Wigman is noted as quite influential while in America, Denishawn, Martha Graham, Doris Humphrey, Merce Cunnigham, and José Limón were most important references for dance therapists (Levy, 1988). Hanya Holm, who came to America, and Alwin Nicolas, who was born in the United States, greatly impacted both modern dance movements. Unlike ballet, which requires a technical vocabulary practiced from a young age, modern dance was much more accepting of different body types and levels of training. Many students became interested in the use of modern dance in nonperformance domains, as well as creating artistic expression on stage.

The use of dance also became important in creating a psychological release of expression. Choreographer Martha Graham commented that dance would, "make visible the interior landscape" (as cited in Polcari, 1990, p. 3). A graduate of the Denishawn school, Graham took the interest in the ancient themes and combined them a step further with the growing interest in psychology. While Denishawn had thrived on the exotic and elaborate costumes of pageantry, Graham began to strip her works down to the bare essentials. In her dance,

Lamentation (1930), for example, she uses a piece of flexible cloth as both shroud and extension of her raw emotional language. The audience is witness to her process of grief, taking in the movement in a similar manner to witnessing authentic movement. This is a technique often used in which the witness, by their presence, helps the process of emotional release.

Graham was influenced by Sigmund Freud in her early work. Dance writer Joseph Mazo notes, "Freudian theory helped condition the ideas of the generation between the two World Wars, and was used by artists to interpret their reality. During the 1920s when Graham was maturing as an artist, Freud's teachings were being seriously discussed among the intelligentsia and absorbed by less scholarly sophisticates by a form of intellectual osmosis. Graham gained a solid understanding of the psychoanalytic conception of human motivation and, as her work developed, began to use the articulations of the body to explore the motions of the mind" (Mazo, 1977, p. 167). Graham would continue through her career to explore psychological themes, mythology, religion, and general societal issues.

Later influenced by Jung, Graham utilized the themes of universal unconscious in her works to further these explorations. Dance critic Anna Kisselgoff wrote about her moody work, *Dark Meadows* (named for Plato's Dark Meadow of Ate) and connected Graham with global themes in Jungian thought: The encounter between the woman and the embodiment of a male principle, hurried along by an earth mother priestess, is meaningful to us precisely because Graham is dealing in archetypes. (Kisselgoff, 1999). Mythology, with its large themes of sexuality, life, and death, is often used for symbolic exploration as well as to tell a story.

Other early choreographers from the modern dance period, including Doris Humphrey, began to explore deeper psychological themes as a way to express that dance should be experienced on a more profound level than mere entertainment. Though Denishawn saw itself as rooted in the ideal of ancient culture, these forms were portrayed on a somewhat superficial level, and evoked more of the mood and general feel of what Denishawn thought ancient and exotic cultures were. On the other hand, the modern choreographers "wanted to confront the problems that real people faced – including, in a post-Freudian era, sex . . . Graham's works

usually explored the individual psyche, while Humphrey was fascinated by the interactions of the individual and the group" (Au, 1988, p. 119).

During this period, the dance movement had also been influenced by such thinkers as James G. Frazer, who published *The Golden Bough* in 1890, as an examination of folk culture and religious ritual. As noted, the release of this book "created an anthropological revolution which added more fuel to the dance revolution and hence to the emergence of dance therapy. Primitive ritual became a source of inspiration for modern dance, as the older concept of dance as expression of magic, religion and spirituality was revived" (Levy, 1988, p. 3). Suddenly dance was not pure entertainment, but once again was infused with the power of mythology, symbolism, and meaning.

While the modern dance pioneers were changing the landscape of dance and making space for dance therapy to emerge, a man named Rudolph Laban (1879–1958) was not only creating dance, but also creating the very means to record the language of dance, a system that is often referenced by movement therapists to describe what they see, and to record pattern changes. In addition to Laban Movement Analysis, other nonverbal assessment tools for dance/movement therapy currently include the Kestenberg Movement Profile and elements from Body-Mind Centering work. Although Laban's work predated dance movement therapy, his interest in observing the basic interactions between individuals led to his desire to record the nonverbal language between people. Later, this would become a language that dance/movement therapists could use to communicate with each other, and to record changes in a patient's movement qualities.

The entire system of movement analysis is complex but some of the most basic ideas involve the concept of the effort dimension which looks at movement dynamically through height, space, time, and flow. Each of these dynamics consists of two opposite elements, for example, a person's use of time can either be thought of as quick or sustained. These descriptions helped dance therapists describe pathological movement. For example, the repetitive motions associated with autism can be further clarified by the use of descriptive terms such as quick time and bound flow. In general, a neurotic person can access all the efforts, but will clearly have personality preferences. On the other hand, someone struggling with mental illness is often locked into certain movement patterns, and has great difficulty accessing other qualities.

Warren Lamb (1965) later expanded upon Laban's original concepts, adding the idea of shape in describing how the body interacts with the space around it, referring to these actions as shaping, directional, or directional arc-like in nature. For example, the action of a mother cradling a child is called shaping whereas a businessperson walking to work with intention may be described as directional in nature. The four aspects of Laban Movement Analysis (with Lamb's contributions) are known as BESS and include: Body, effort, shape, and space (Lamb, 1965). These aspects deal fully with the many ways different parts of the body interrelate to each other, and how movement is sequenced. BESS addresses aspects of any movement event with the complementary areas of perception including: sensing (body), feeling (effort), intuiting (shape), and thinking (space).

Irmgard Bartenieff, a German dancer, was instrumental in taking Laban's ideas to America, and established the Laban School in New York City. She expanded upon the ideas of Laban, observing cultural dance forms and more pedestrian interactions of movement, and developed innovative ways to treat polio patients. She developed the Bartenieff Fundamentals, a series of six movement exercises designed to help connect body sensation with emotion (Bartenieff, 1980). In addition, she consulted with the musicologist and ethnographer Alan Lomax in his important work studying folk dance forms, and relating these movements to common work actions.

Lomax's system of studying cultural movement rhythms, called choreometrics, was based upon the assumption that dance embodies the movement of everyday life (Lomax, 1968). Often the movements of dance are culturally derived from a group's work actions. The ground-hugging shuffling of many Asian and African dances relates to the work done in cultivation. In contrast, people such as the Turkish and Bretans were horse riders, and the pointing and leaping steps of their dances are meant to highlight their equestrian skills (later adapted into the ethereal qualities deemed in the French courts in the performance of ballet).

Another branch in the Laban lineage is Judith Kestenberg, whose work began and overlapped with Laban and Bartenieff. Concerned primarily

Figure 11.4. Marian Chace, pioneer, in a dance/movement therapy session. Photo courtesy of Marian Chace Foundation.

with developmental theory (based on Anna Freud's work), she trained at the invitation of Dr. Paul Schilder, beginning in 1937, at Bellevue Hospital (Sossin, Loman, & Merman 1999). Her Kestenberg Movement Profile draws on some of the concepts from Laban, and merges them with developmental theories and rhythm patterns, creating a system of tension flow rhythms that would later provide a recordable language and theoretical basis for a branch of dance/movement therapy that works with these developmental patterns.

Emergence of Dance/Movement Therapy

The great evolution of modern dance, particularly in the early 1900s, had many exploring momentous works, and noting its emotional impact. Up to this point, though, no clear delineation of the field of dance/movement therapy existed. While all the elements, as well as the clear historical precedents for the use of movement in relieving psychological distress, were in place, it took the work of several pioneers to begin the formation of a clear field of professional work. The atmosphere in the early-mid 1900s had become a ripe time for the emergence of this new field of dance/movement therapy. As seen, the growing interest in psychology and new explorations in dance led many to explore these concepts together. Many of the early pioneers of dance/movement therapy emerged from this creative exploration occurring in modern dance. They also furthered their education in psychology and other relevant mental health work through varied studies.

In the United States, the growth of dance/movement therapy grew rapidly on both the East and West coasts. On the East coast there were pioneers including Marian Chace, Blanche Evan, and Liljan Espenak, and on the West coast, Mary Whitehouse, Trudi Schoop, and Alma Hawkins (Levy, 1988). Of the early dance/movement therapists, Marian Chace is considered to be the primary founder of dance/movement therapy (Bernstein, 1979; Stanton-Jones, 1992). Chace had her roots in the beginnings of modern dance and was originally a dancer with the Denishawn dance company. In her early career, she opened a dance studio and observed that many students came simply to better their own mood, without an agenda for professional careers in dance. In 1942, she brought dance to the psychiatric ward at St. Elizabeths in Washington, D.C. and was the first to make a clear connection between dance psychotherapy: "The dance therapist is not teaching dance in order to develop performing artists, but is using her technical skills and her personal creativity and spontaneity to enable people to become more aware of themselves on a human, realistic level" (Chace, 1964, p. 46).

Also critical to Chace's development was the work of the theoretician Harry Stack Sullivan, who created the idea of a participant observer, who witnesses, but also chooses to interact in the therapist process, rather than being a complete observer (Sullivan, 1953). In general, although his name is largely forgotten, Sullivan's ideas on interpersonal relationships added greatly to the field of dance/movement therapy. He furthered ideas that personality is about perception of self in relationship to others, and that this perception of self also changes throughout the developmental stages. Marian Chace applied these ideas in the way that she worked with individuals by either subtly mirroring physical gestures, or responding emotionally with another movement expression (Schmais, 1974). Chace always saw her work as helping to fur-

ther the individual toward an appropriate means of human expression.

Along with honoring the individual dance, Chace stressed the importance of focusing on what is healthy, instead of labeling pathological problems. As noted by Fischer and Chaiklin (1993), the dance between patient and therapist ". . . is the meeting of two people, each with their own dance, and the purposeful use of movement by the therapist which is healthy in each of them" (p. 152). Later, second generation therapists such as Sharon Chaiklin, Claire Schmais (1986), and Judith Fischer (1993) would create theoretical frameworks for understanding Chace's work in addition to connecting it with the evolution of developmental theory.

Blanche Evan helped to further the field through her work with both adults and children, as well as through her writing. She came from a diverse dance background that included dance improvisation with Bird Larson as well as Spanish dance with Viola and La Meri. Evan's interest in the modern urban adult came from a concern that modern society forces the individual to lose contact with the body and its emotions (Evan, in Benov, 1991). She created a system of movement work, called Fundamental Technique, which aims to rehabilitate the body with an emphasis on spinal alignment. Part of her ideas came from the observation that humans are unique in their upright posture, and that the spine reflects the body's movement and expressive capabilities.

Liljan Espenak had her own journey through a variety of movement studies and styles, including folk dance, work with the movement of Dalcroze, as well as brief study with Marian Chace. Important among her contributions was the formation of the first postgraduate school program in dance/movement therapy at New York Medical College. The core curriculum included the importance of studying folk and ancient forms of dance as vital to the training for a dance/movement therapist. She wrote that, "In a certain sense, dance therapy seeks to reproduce, working with patients in the psychological environment, the evolution of the history of dance, providing within a clinical setting the opportunity for the acting out of fears and anxieties through the archaic, primitive movements . . . then seeks to develop the fragmentary experiences into more integrated expression" (Espenak, 1981, p. 19). Again, the process of dance/movement therapy seeks, as ancient dance did, to both normalize the human experience as well as elevate expression.

Meanwhile, in the West, particularly in California, another group of dance/movement therapists (DMTs) were pioneering their work. Mary Whitehouse developed the area within dance/movement therapy known as authentic movement, originally know as "movement-in-depth." Having trained as a Jungian therapist, and often identifying herself with his work, she was also greatly influenced by the psychoanalytic ideas developed during WWII. This is particularly utilized with private practice work, as it involves the therapist witnessing whatever movement occurs, and describing this with statements such as "I move" or "I am moved" depending on the emotionality (Whitehouse, 1979, p. 57) of what is seen. Like Jung, she worked with the idea that the creative process, in her case using improvisational dance, tapped into a deep level of the unconscious.

Originally from Switzerland, Trudi Schoop began her work in psychiatric settings in southern California and came to formulate many of her ideas independently during the 1950s. She had strong influences from Duncan, Jacques-Dalcroze, as well as a foundation in European mime (Schoop, 1974). She described her first workings in the field through her book, *Won't You Join the Dance?* (1974). Much in the same manner as Martha Graham's statement that movement never lies, Schoop put this into terminology in her book, "with chapters such as the body is a blabbermouth" (Schoop, 1974, p. 59). As she describes,

> It seems to me that each body I see radiates its own nonverbal message, and that this message represents the sum total of an individual's various characteristics. By means of its unspoken projection, I can sense a personality as being fundamentally open or closed, active or passive, aggressive or defensive . . . the most significant of all body statements is the one that indicates a person's feeling about his own body. He may love it, hate it, or take it for granted. But whatever his prevailing attitude, it will surely influence his relationship to the world around him. (Schoop, 1974, p. 61)

Much of her technique centers on observing the individual, then delving into their world to find how they can open to larger community around them. Communication is critical to her work.

Whether through a folk dance rhythm or other expression, communicating frees an individual from isolation (Schoop, 2000).

The last of the West Coast therapists, Alma Hawkins (1964), based her work on the instinctive power of dance to heal. In her book, *Creating Through Dance*, she states the concept of dance being both the most ancient, as well as the most basic, form of expression. She also was greatly influenced by the humanist movement. In Rogerian thought, the role of the therapist is to help the client reach an area of health through the concepts of congruence, empathy, and unconditional acceptance. In dance/movement therapy terms, congruence would be expressed through the technique of mirroring (using the same movement as a client) or shaping and nonverbally reflecting a complementary quality nonverbally. Empathy is reflected through "kinesthetic empathy," a term coined by Miriam Roskin Berger to describe the empathic body connection (Berger, 1956, p. 170). Finally, the field of dance/movement therapy developed around the acceptance that everyone's dance is important, valid expression, whether performed publicly or expressed privately.

Other early leaders in dance therapy included Franziska Boas, who worked with children at Bellevue Hospital in the 1940s, Elizabeth Rosen, who wrote the first book of dance/movement therapy entitled *Dance in Psychotherapy* (1957), and Norma Canner, who began her work in the 1950s with children. Franziska Boas, the daughter of the famous anthropologist Franz Boas, was deeply influenced by the history and original meaning of dance, as much as in the new psychological language of her time (Levy, 1988). Rosen influenced many with her writings. Her own technique relied both on a free association reaction to words and movement, as well as utilizing simple, taught movement. As noted in one description of her work, ". . . the patients gradually developed a repertoire of movement techniques and simple folk dances which provided them with a feeling of accomplishment" (Levy, 1988, p. 118). Norma Canner began as an actress, later moving into creative movement, and then exploration dance therapy through a number of styles including Jungian, Gestalt, Neo-Reichian as well as utilizing authentic movement techniques. Like many dance/movement therapists that followed, her work has been strongly influenced by both traditional movement work as well as psychology.

American Dance Therapy Association

By the end of the 1950s, dance/movement therapists were organizing themselves and beginning to connect with each other. In 1964, there were three documented groups of dance/movement therapists based in Washington, D.C., New York, and California (Stark, 2002). The ADTA officially became organized in1966 with Marian Chace presiding as its first president. It came into being to create standards for education and a level of professionalism and conduct. The creation of the ADTA and the ongoing work to create a professional standard of study is largely considered the major accomplishment of the second generation of dance/movement therapists (Beaudry, 1997). One of the important steps taken was the establishment of a two-tiered process for the system of accreditation. The first level, DTR, or Dance Therapist Registered, is obtained after study and receiving a Master's degree from an approved program, or equivalent work through independent programs. The DTR is considered an entry-level clinician and has performed a minimum of 700 hours of supervised clinical internship. The second tier, the ADTR, or Academy-level Dance Therapist Registered, is achieved after several more years of supervised clinical work (at least 3,640 additional hours), as well as defining one's theoretical leanings in the field. At this level, the dance/movement therapist is qualified for private practice work, as well as being able to teach dance/movement therapy and provide supervision, an important part of maintaining the integrity of the field.

Currently there are more than 1,000 registered dance/movement therapists in 46 states and working in approximately 30 different countries. Still quite a small field, the 2nd and 3rd generation dance/movement therapists have worked hard in establishing graduate school programs as well as to publish and lecture in more venues. In joining with other creative art therapies, dance/movement therapy has been included in a number of different resolutions and grants throughout the past few decades. An important step in the historical progression of recognition was in 1993 when the National Center for Complementary and Alternative Medicine of the National Institutes of Health (formerly know at the Office of Alternative Medicine) awarded the ADTA an early grant to look at the effects of dance/movement upon medical illnesses (ADTA website).

The reality for the current generation of dance/movement therapists is finding avenues to be paid, while expanding the field. Like other creative arts therapists, dance/movement therapists search for work under several titled areas, such as therapeutic recreational specialist, mental health worker, as well as more oblique job classifications. Few have full-time jobs, and even fewer still have a job with the sole title of dance/movement therapist. As Beaudry (1997) ruminates, "before committing the field to any alliance, however, it seems critical for DMT leaders and educators to reach a consensus about what is the core identity of DMT in the U.S. at the present time" (p. 21). A recent decision to align with the National Board of Certified Counselors was intended to help create job opportunities, but states vary widely in both licensure and reimbursement possibilities for the DMT field. Many dance/movement therapists have gone through additional training to broaden themselves in the market, but there is a strong desire to also remember the roots of dance, and to respect the traditions that have created the field. There remains a societal distance from the world of dance, but as alternative health therapies have emerged, there is a new acceptance of exploring the body/mind connection, and returning once again to move and be moved by the power of dance.

Dance/movement therapy is useful for a wide range of patients and issues due to its movement component. It is particularly useful for those areas where traditional talk therapy may be inadequate due to unique nonverbal issues, for example, work with Alzheimer patients, who remember body sensations, but may lose track of a verbal conversation. Likewise, DMT is particularly useful for populations with eating disorders, victims of sexual abuse, emotional disturbed children, and those with sensory issues or trauma. Even in the most physically restricted body, there is interaction in the eyes, or a subtle movement in the hands. This is a place to begin the dance. Interestingly, yoga and Pilates have gained great acceptance in modern culture because of their accessibility to most of the normal neurotic population. It is often easier to be given an exercise than to tap into the creative process which can be a far scarier proposition. However, this is the very strength of dance/movement therapy, and the trained dance therapist works to meet a client at their level, and work through the dance itself.

CONCLUSION

Humans have long used the inherent power of dance to promote healing on a body, mind, and spiritual level. The modern field of dance/movement therapy developed into a professional domain that maintains a high level of educational competence and skills in therapists who are committed to guiding others towards well-being. Primary to this work is the belief that through the expressive power of movement, we further the emotional, cognitive, social, and physical integration of both individuals and groups in this healing art.

It is important to state that psychology has had a tremendous effect on the development of dance/movement as therapy, and has provided a language in which therapists can discuss pathology and development. However, it is the dance itself that remains a vital part of dance/movement therapy. The human urge and desire to express itself is a powerful and basic need, no matter what form of expression it takes.

The field of dance/movement therapy continues to grow and provide a means for people to connect to themselves, to each other, and to the world around them. In honoring the dance, the dancer moves, quite literally, to heal, to express, and to create. Dance is, at its most basic level, a way of being human in the present. It reveals the innermost self, as well as reflecting the universe as the individual perceives it. That is why it is quite critical never to judge personal or cultural dance, but to always understand that expression as an honest piece of self-illumination. The therapist is a skilled guide to join in this dance and to help move it quite literally onward.

REFERENCES

American Dance Therapy Association. (n.d.). *Fact sheet.* Columbia, MD: ADTA National Office.

American Dance Therapy Association. *Examples of recognition by the federal government.* Retrieved August 1, 2004, from http://www.adta.org/whoweare.html.

Aristotle. (1987). *De anima [On the soul].* New York: Penguin Books.

Au, S. (1988). *Ballet and modern dance.* London: Thames and Hudson.

Bartenieff, I., & Lewis, D. (1980). *Body movement: Coping with the environment.* New York: Gordon and Breach Science Publishers, Inc.

Beaudry, I. (1997). Reenvisioning dance/movement therapy. *American Journal of Dance Therapy. 19*, 16–23.

Benov, R. (Ed.). (1991). *Collected works by and about Blanche Evan.* New York: Blanche Evan Dance Foundation.

Berger, M.R. (1956). Bodily experience and expression of emotion. In *A collection of early writings: Towards a body of knowledge.* vol. 1, 1989. Columbia, MD: American Dance Therapy Association.

Bernstein, P.L. (1979). The use of symbolism within a Gestalt movement therapy approach. *Eight theoretical approaches in dance-movement therapy.* Dubuque, Iowa: Kendall/ Hunt, 1979, pp. 111–130.

Birdwhistell, R. L. (1952). *Introduction to kinesics.* Louisville, KY: University of Louisville Press.

Chace, M. (1964, July). Dance alone is not enough. *Dance Magazine*, pp. 46–47, 58.

Chaiklin, S. & Schmais, C. (1986). The Chace approach to dance therapy. In P.L. Bernstein (Ed.). *Eight theoretical approaches in dance-movement therapy.* Dubuque, Iowa: Kendall-Hunt.

Darwin, C. (1872). *The expression of emotions in man and animals.* London: John Murray.

Espenak, L. (1981). *Dance therapy: Theory and application.* Springfield, IL: Charles C Thomas, Publisher, Ltd.

Fischer, J, & Chaiklin , S. (1993). Meeting in movement: The work of the therapist and the client. In S. Sandel, S. Chaiklin, & A. Lohn (Eds.). *Foundations of dance/movement therapy: The life and work of Marian Chace.* Columbia, MD: The Marian Chace Memorial Fund.

Frazer, J. (1981). *The golden bough.* Avenel, NJ: Gramercy Books. (Originally published 1890).

Gupta, R. (2000). *A yoga of Indian classical dance.* Rochester, VT: Inner Traditions.

Hawkins, A.M. (1964). *Creating through dance.* Englewood Cliffs, NJ: Prentice-Hall.

Hanna, J. L. (1988). *Dance and stress.* New York: AMS Press.

Highwater, J. (1985). *Dance: Rituals of experience.* New York: Alfred van der Marck Editions.

Jaffé, N. (1990). *Folk dance of Europe.* West Yorkshire, England: Folk Dance Enterprises.

Jonas, G. (1992). *Dancing.* New York: Harry N. Abrams, Inc. Publishers.

Kisselgoff, A. (1999, February 18). From Graham, via Jung, a journey through an erotic landscape [Review of *Dark Meadow*]. *The New York Times*, p. 5.

Kraus, R., Hilsendager, S., & Dixon, B. (1991). *History of the dance in art and education.* Upper Saddle River, NJ: Prentice Hall.

Kriyananda, G. (2002). *The spiritual science of Kriya yoga.* Chicago: The Temple of Kriya Yoga.

Laban, R. (1935). *A life for dance.* London: Macdonald and Evans, Ltd.

Laban, R. (1985). *The mastery of movement.* New York: Macdonald and Evans, Ltd.

Lamb, W. (1965). *Posture and gesture: An introduction to the study of physical behavior.* London: Gerald Duckworth & Co.

Lawson, J. (1955). *European folk dance*. London: Sir Isaac Pitman and Sons Ltd.

Levy, F. (1988). *Dance/movement therapy: A healing art*. Reston, VA: The American Alliance for Health, Physical Education, Recreation, and Dance.

Lomax, A. (1968). *Folk song style and culture*. New Brunswick, NJ: Transaction Books.

Mazo, J. (1977). *Prime movers: The makers of modern dance in America*. New York: William Morrow and Co., Inc.

Morain, G. (1978). *Kinesics and cross-cultural understanding*. Arlington, VA: Center for Applied Linguistics.

Natya Sastra. (1987). Sydney, Australia: Orient Book Distributors.

Osler, W. (1932). *Aequanimitas*. New York: McGraw-Hill.

Polcari, S. (1990). Martha Graham and abstract expressionism. In *Smithsonian Studies in American Art*. New York: Oxford-Press.

Reich, W. (1943). *Character Analysis* (3rd ed.). New York: Orgone Press.

Rogers, C. (1995). *On becoming a person*. Boston: Houghton Mifflin Company.

Rosen, E. (1957). *Dance in psychotherapy*. New York: Teachers College Press, Columbia University.

Sachs, C. (1937). *World history of the dance*. New York: W.W. Norton and Company, Inc.

Schmais, C. (1974). Dance therapy in perspective. In K. Mason (Ed.). *Focus on dance* VII (pp. 7–12). Reston, VA: AAHPERD.

Schoop, T. (1974). *Won't you join the dance?* U.S.A: Mayfield Publishing Co.

Schoop, T. (2000). Motion and emotion. *American Journal of Dance Therapy. 22*, 91–101.

Shawn, T. (1974). *Dance we must*. New York: Haskell House Publishers Ltd.

Sossin, K., Loman, S., & Merman, H. (1999). Remembering Judith S. Kestenberg, our mentor and friend. *American Journal of Dance Therapy, 21*, 53–56.

Stanton-Jones, K. (1992). *Dance movement therapy in psychiatry*. London and New York: Tavistock and Routledge.

Stark, A. (1982). *The newer therapies: A source book*. New York: Van Nostrand and Reinhold.

Stark, A. (2002). The American journal of dance therapy: Its history and evolution. *American Journal of Dance Therapy. 24*, 73–95.

Sullivan, H. S. (1953). *The interpersonal theory of psychiatry*, New York: W.W. Norton & Co.

Whitehouse, M.S. (1977). The transference and dance therapy. *American Journal of Dance Therapy, 1*, 3–7.

Whitehouse, M.S. (1979). Jung and dance-therapy: Two major principles. In P.L. Bernstein (Ed.). *Eight theoretical approaches in dance movement therapy*. Dubuque, Iowa: Kendall-Hunt.

Wosien, M. (1974). *Sacred dance: Encounter with the gods*. London: Avon Books.

APPENDIX

Dance/Movement Therapy Timeline

2000 B.C.	Religions dances in Crete, ancient Egypt, etc. are documented through writing and art.
441 B.C.	Euripides incorporates dance in his dramas.
350 B.C.	Aristotle writes *De Anima* (*On the Soul*) that links "heart" to "mental activity."
860 A.D.	Shiva appears as Lord of the Dance (Nataraja) in Indian cultures.
1448 B.C.	First ballet (in France) – dance was less participatory for mainstream.
1811	Francois Delsarte was born – led study in understanding mood and movement.
1850	*The Golden Bough*, published by James G. Frazer, explores folk culture and religious ritual, and led the way for a new interest in dance.
1872	*The Expression of the Emotions in Man and Animals* is published by Charles Darwin, on nonverbal behavior.
1877	Isadora Duncan, born in San Francisco, ushers in a new era of dance and the natural body.
1879	Rudolph Laban born – theorist, philosopher, movement educator, he is known for pioneering a system of movement notation used by many dance/movement therapists.
1894	Martha Graham, pioneering modern dance was born – connected dance, ritual, and psychology.
1900	Freud's *Interpretation of Dreams* begins modern psychology movement.
1903	Freud outlines the stages of childhood development (oral, anal, genital).
1911	Emile Jacques-Dalcroze found institute for study of eurhythmics in Germany.
1914–1931	Denishawn era – founded by Ted Shawn and Ruth St. Denis, explores ancient dance, ritual, and opens doors for the modern dance movement.
1921	Carl Jung publishes *Psychological Types*.
1930s on	Modern dance grows, exploring connections in dance and psychology.
1937–38	Judith Kestenberg begins her intensive movement studies, leading to her developmental movement profile system.
1942–43	Marian Chace, primary founder of DMT, brings dance movement therapy to St. Elizabeths.

1950s	Trudi Schoop is part of the West Coast dance/movement therapy movement, publishing her work in *Won't You Join the Dance?*
1950s	"The humanist movement" led by Carl Rogers and Abraham Maslow focuses on client desire for wellness.
1952	Raymond Birdwhistell publishes *Introduction to Kinesics* dealing with movement interaction.
1954	Erik Erikson outlines his development theory on the "Eight Ages of Man."
1957	Elizabeth Rosen writes the first book of dance/movement therapy entitled *Dance in Psychotherapy*.
1962	Piaget defines cognitive stages of development.
1964	Three documented groups of dance/movement therapists organize, based in Washington, D.C., New York, and California.
1965	Warren Lamb adds to Laban's theories and movement observation work.
1966	American Dance Therapy Association officially organized.
1977	Dance/movement therapy, art therapy, music therapy, and psychodrama were represented on President Carter's Commission on Mental Health.
1980	Irmgard Bartenieff publishes *Body Movement* on her expansion of Laban's work, including relevance to dance/movement therapy.
1993	The Office of Alternative Medicine of the National Institute of Health awarded one of its first exploratory research grants to explore dance/movement therapy for those with medical illnesses.
1996	Dance/movement therapy, art therapy, and music therapy are recognized by the Health Care Financing Administration (HCFA) of the Department of Health and Human Services that may constitute covered elements of a partial hospitalization program in Medicare facilities.
	Dance/movement therapists celebrate their 40th annual conference.

Photo Credits

Figure 11.1

Dancing Girl. Limestone ostracon of irregular shape. Egyptian, New Kingdom, 17th dynasty (16th BCE). 16.8 x 10.5 cm.

Museo Egizio, Turin, Italy
Photo Credit: Erich Lessing/Art Resource, NY

Figure 11.2

Artist Unknown, Japanese
Circle Dance
Japanese, Edo Period, late Kan'ei (1624–1644) to Kanbun (1661-1673) era
Object Place: Japan
Panel; ink and color on gold-leafed paper, 19 3/8 x 22 3/8 in.
Museum of Fine Arts, Boston
Denman Waldo Ross Collection, 17.687

Figure 11.3

Anonymous, 20th century. Untitled [Three female nudes dancing on the beach]. 1931.
Oil over relief wood carving. 17 1/4 x 27 5/8 in.
Ricco-Maresca Gallery, New York, NY
Photo Credit: Ricco/Maresca Gallery/Art Resource, NY

Figure 11.4

Photo of Marian Chace in dance/movement therapy session.
Photo courtesy of Marian Chace Foundation

Biographical Statement

Laurice D. Nemetz, MA, ADTR, RYT, is an academy-level dance/movement therapist and registered yoga teacher with a diverse background in the arts and healing. Educated at Goucher College with a Master's degree in dance/movement therapy and at Wellesley College with degrees in art history and French. Lauri has performed dance extensively in the United States and France in various disciplines, including European folk dance, modern, and improvisation, and has worked and performed at the prestigious American Dance Festival. She has been a therapist in a variety of settings from children to geriatrics, as well as trauma work post-9/11. A well-known lecturer, she has also published in several professional journals.

Chapter 12

THEORETICAL PERSPECTIVES IN D/MT: VISIONS FOR THE FUTURE

SABINE C. KOCH

INTRODUCTION

In this chapter, I will describe a number of theoretical perspectives that can amplify and support dance/movement therapy (D/MT) theory, development, and advancement. Many theoretical developments have been triggered by cross-fertilization between different scientific disciplines. The young field of dance/movement therapy within the creative arts therapies has much to learn from and to offer to adjacent scientific fields. Existing trends of integrative body-based theories promote this endeavor at present.

Dance/movement therapy has always used a variety of theory from other fields for its work (mainly from psychology and psychiatry). Some of those have been introduced by Nemetz as well as Cruz and Hastie, contributors to the *Collage of Creative Therapies*. Genuine D/MT working models are rare and a central D/MT theory is still missing (Cruz, 2001). A brief overview of major contributions to working models within the field of D/MT is given in the Appendix. The cogent reader may move from there to where these D/MT sources can be found (Bernstein, 1979; Lévy, 2004; Pallaro, 2000).

Theoretical Assumptions in D/MT

The basic and primary theoretical assumption of D/MT can be found in its definition: "Dance/movement therapy is the psychotherapeutic use of movement as a process which furthers the emotional, social, cognitive, and physical integration of the individual" (ADTA, 2004). This definition is similar to the web pages of other countries' professional organizations, e.g.,

Germany BTD, England ADMT, and Spain ADMTE. We can distinguish two main components of this definition: (a) emotional, cognitive, and physical integration of the individual (psychophysical union), which forms *the individual component* and includes the possibility of the unions disintegration (e.g., by traumatic events) and reintegration, and (b) the social component, which focuses on the individual's relationship to others and includes communicative pathologies and healing. Some further tenets resulting from D/MT's assumption of the psychophysical union and its intent to affect it are, for example, the assumption of the arbitrary starting point of interventions (systemic thought). D/MT starts at the body level assuming that changes on the body level will cause or bring with them changes on the cognitive and emotional levels. In talking about the moving experience, it also starts at the cognitive-emotional level, assuming that changes on this level will cause or stabilize changes on the body level. This can also be called the assumption of the bi-directionality of cognitive/emotional and motor components. The critical reader will have noticed that this assumption leads to a paradox: D/MT needs to assume the very dualism of body and mind it wants to overcome by its work. Nevertheless, the body-mind connection is necessary for the communicability of how D/MT works. In the creative process, the core process of D/MT, there is, however, no separation between emotional, cognitive, and physical components.

In D/MT treatment, the healing power of the creative process, the common ground with other creative arts therapies, is used to arrive at a working metaphor or symbolic expression of the persons' core theme (usually related to their struggle between illness and health). D/MT assumes a place of inner truth or authenticity related to feeling at home in one's body (ADTA, 2004). Another core assumption is that healing should in many respects start from the healthy parts of an individual. This supports the psychological stability and ego strength (Antonovsky, 1997) and minimizes passivity and stigmatization of the person in treatment. Furthermore, D/MT works under the assumption of a body memory, "the body and its memory (body memory) enables the therapist to go back to pre-language experiences" (BTD, 2004). This last assumption about a distributed memory across the body challenges traditional models of memory (see discussion of the social embodiment approach below).

There are further important assumptions and building blocks of D/MT theory, and readers are called upon to complement this enumeration with their own wisdom on how D/MT works. The purpose of this chapter, however, is to introduce recent theories and findings from outside D/MT that have powerful potential for the field, support what D/MTs do, and provide opportunities to amplify the scientific basis of D/MT.

Farewell Descartes

"When will physics finally catch up with D/MT knowledge?" said Christine Caldwell in her opening lecture at the 38th annual conference of the ADTA in Denver, Colorado, 2003. Ever since Descartes' philosophy of the separation of body and mind has been established as a primary paradigm of Western thought, it has had a huge impact on the development of the theoretical underpinnings in the sciences. Descartes' assumption that vital movement is a material process and, therefore, needs to be explained in mechanical and functional terms has tacitly influenced physics, biology, physiology, medicine, and psychology up to the present (Descartes, 2001/1637). In classical physics, for example, everything happens without anything being done. If you ask a physicist about the qualities and character of the forces, she may only feel comfortable to explain the force in terms of a common formula. Similarly, a psychomotor researcher in psychology will not feel comfortable to talk about movement qualities, as they are not a fact that one seems to be able to measure objectively. This reluctance of scientists to treat subjective

aspects of the human body and its movement has begun to become rehabilitated with the theories of the biological scientists Jakob v. Uexküll (Uexküll & Kriszat, 1940/1956) and the medical Viktor v. Weizsäcker (Weizsäcker, 1940/1996), who have formulated that impressions are not adapted in an objective way by the organism, but only insofar as they have a meaning for the individual (Buytendijk, 1956; Kafka, 1950; Wallbott, 1990). For a treatment approach based on this philosophy, see Uexküll, 1994.

> I think, that all the nerves and muscles can serve (memory), so that a flute player, for example, has a part of his memory in his hands: for the ease of bending and disposing his fingers in various ways, which he has acquired by practice, helps him to remember the passages which need these dispositions when they are played. (Descartes, Letter to Mersenne, April, 1640; cited in Casey, 1987, p. 146)

How could the man who wrote the above lines about body memory more than 350 years ago possibly be identical to the man who has introduced the body-mind split into our thinking and cultural heritance? Interestingly, Descartes had chosen the philosophy of the body-mind split for a very pragmatic reason: The Pope would only allow him to do research on corpses when he declared that the soul of the person would remain untouched by the procedures implicated (Casey, 1987). With this approach of a pragmatic researcher, he went ahead, and, in consequence, has influenced Western philosophy deeply. Now that the sciences finally realize that the body-mind-split conception is not a universal given but just as culturally relative as a great number of our philosophical assumptions (e.g., the long proclaimed superiority of humans over animals or of men over women), and that science might be better off moving to embodied theories and situated approaches. Now that all this happens, the D/MT body of knowledge has a fair chance to receive an adequate place within the scientific disciplines. At present, introduced by literature such as Damasio's "Descartes' Error" (Damasio, 1994), there is a trend to include (or rather rehabilitate) the body and its movement into the research of the social and behavioral sciences. Within the sciences, the body is looked upon in its behavioral components (motor behavior) and in its perceptive components (e.g., proprioception as the sense of the position of one's own body in space and the orientation of the body parts towards each other even when one's eyes are closed (Sherrington, 1906). In current psychology, for example, there is a clear trend that after the decades of behaviorism and cognitive psychology, the body regains interest. Interestingly, within the cognitive paradigm (embodied cognition; embodiment of mind; Lakoff & Johnson, 1999; Wilson, 2002; Varela, Thompson, & Rosch, 1993). This development is strongly fueled by recent findings in the neurosciences. The neuroscientists Rizzolatti, Fadiga, Fogassi, and Gallese (2002), for example, have been detecting mirror neurons in the so-called brain area F5 that they have been able to brain-map. These neurons are activated not only when a motor action is actively imitated but also when the same motor action is merely observed suggesting sensory simulation as the basis of thought (Barsalou, in press). The back-to-the-body interest can be observed in anthropology, ethnology, linguistics, and diverse sub-disciplines of psychology: Clinical psychology (especially psychotraumatology) and psychotherapy research, in developmental psychology, social psychology, and cognitive science. Each of the psychological areas will be exemplified in this chapter. But beforehand the philosophical basis of the recent embodiment approaches will be introduced.

Body and Movement-Based Theories

Contribution of Phenomenology

"The body is in the world like the heart is in the organism" (Merleau-Ponty, 1966, p. 94). Phenomenology and its most popular representative, Maurice Merleau-Ponty, for the first time took an ontologically fundamental position on the body (Fuchs, 2000; Merleau-Ponty, 1966). Merleau-Ponty distinguishes between the body in its objective aspect (French: corps proper; German: Körper) and the body in its subjective aspect or the lived body (French: corps vivant; German: Leib; cf. T. v. Uexküll, 1994; Zaner, 1964). In Cartesian philosophy, the objective body is the one that results when separated from the mind and the soul, the one that has guided the medical model up to present. Even neuroscience still places the mind within the brain and is reluctant to acknowledge mind and memory within the body (distributed thought/memory), even though some of its most popular recent findings point strongly in this direction. The subjective

body or the lived body, on the other hand, is the subject of perception and of motion. As Merleau-Ponty puts it, it is neither mere content nor external instrument of consciousness. It constitutes our perception and our existence; it is our "anchor" in the world, our way of "being to the world" (être au monde). In his main work, *Phenomenology of Perception* Merleau-Ponty (1966) analyzes the lived body based on the best available neurological, physiological, psychological, and psychopathological observations of his time. The body for the first time gets a central place in philosophy. I cannot think nor perceive without inhabiting my body. My body has been communicating with the world, long before there was thought. Merleau-Ponty overcomes the priority of consciousness and thought of his teacher Husserl and proclaims a counterposition: Consciousness never existed without the body. All intentional contents of consciousness have always been pervaded by bodily-sensory structures (Fuchs, 2000). Before I was there, the body had already marked my place.

Contribution of Developmental Psychology

The realization, of course, that the body already exists before consciousness is born, is a part of the body of knowledge of developmental psychology. Piaget (1969) was one of the first scientists who systematically described the sensory-motor underpinnings of all human development. Recently, our knowledge of the first stages of human development has undergone a revolution (Dornes, 1993; Stern, 1998). Their research results suggest that next to comfort and discomfort the newborn can already distinguish the mother's voice from other voices, can recognize her face, realize her emotional expression, even imitate her facial expressions, and communicate with others via spontaneous mimesis. These research results support Merleau-Ponty's thesis of a primary "être au monde" (being to the world) of the body, a prereflexively given intercorporite (inter body relationship), in which all humans are embedded before they become thinking subjects (Fuchs, 2000).

Recent research in developmental psychology suggests that the distinction between self-moving and moved objects is one of the very first categories the infant develops ontologically (Pauen & Träuble, 2002, Träuble, 2004). In inventive experimental designs, the authors demonstrate that the distinction (and thus causal attribution) of self-initiated motion and externally caused motion, already takes place at the age of seven months. Further, research supporting the developmental theories of D/MT comes from Esther Thelen of the Indiana University, Bloomington. Thelen (1995) was able to find evidence for the influence of motor behavior on the cognitive and affective development of the young infant. Among other issues, she does research on developmental rhythms. Nava Lotan (2001), a scientist and D/MT researcher from Israel, adapted Thelen's new approaches for her work on the behavior of small children with the Kestenberg Movement Profile (Lotan, 2001). Thelen (1995) writes about rhythms as fundamental properties of infant movement. The human body is a dynamic system, and "the hallmark of such systems is the formation of patterns often themselves complex in time and space, in an entirely self-organized fashion. That is, there is no recipe for a clout, or the whirlpools in a mountain stream. This organization arises from the confluence of the components within a particular environmental context" (Thelen, 1995, p. 83).

Judith Kestenberg (1973; 1995) already demonstrated in the 1970s the enormous impact that rhythmic patterns have on self-organization and the organization of social interaction. She described in detail the differentiated semantic and developmental sequence of children from birth through the age of six years. Due to the development of her movement profile, clinical diagnosis, and intervention can be accomplished not only for children but also for adults with a high degree of precision. The Kestenberg Movement Profile (KMP) allows the description of motor behavior, related strengths and weaknesses of the patient, and the evaluation of the implications for their cognitive and emotional development (Koch 1999; Loman, 1996). It can be applied to all age groups as well as cross-culturally (Kestenberg-Amighi, 1990). New theoretical accomplishments within Kestenberg's system are the developmental movement rhythms, and the movement expression of defenses and learning styles in the so-called pre-efforts. Research on the competent infant (Dornes, 1993; Pauen & Träuble, 2002; Stern, 1998) demonstrates the enormous meaning preverbal motor development has for the integrative development of cognition, emotion, and the ability to symbolize in the course of the developmental process.

Contribution of Social Psychology

There is nothing more practical than a good theory; it is a guide to practice. Preverbal motor development does not happen in the individual space, but in the interpersonal space. We are social beings and social psychology has contributed a new line of body-based research culminating in the social embodiment approach of Barsalou, Niedenthal, Barbey, and Ruppert (2003). By embodiment Barsalou et al. (2003) mean that "states of the body, such as postures, arm movements, and facial expressions, arise during social interaction and play central roles in social information processing" (Barsalou et al., 2003, p. 43). Four types of embodiment effects have been reported by social psychologists. First, perceived social stimuli next to cognitive states produce bodily states as well. Second, perceiving bodily states in others produces bodily mimicry in the self. Third, bodily states in the self produce affective states. Fourth, the compatibility of bodily states and cognitive states modulates performance effectiveness (Barsalou et al., 2003). Movement therapists might be strongly reminded of the empathy theory of Theodor Lipps (1903) for the first three findings. The social embodiment approach bundles single empirical results and other body-based research strings and develops an alternative theoretical model of the workings of the mind (and memory) that is not driven by the computer metaphor, but rather by recent results in the neurosciences. It assumes that:

> Embodied theories of cognition depart from traditional theories in their assumptions about knowledge representation. In traditional theories, knowledge consists of amodal symbols that redescribe sensory, motor, and introspective states . . . . Traditional theories assume that knowledge of . . . experiences does not consist of the sensory, motor, and introspective states that constituted the experiences originally. Instead, these theories assume that a symbolic system redescribes these states, producing amodal descriptions that reside separately from sensory, motor, and introspective systems. . . . In memory, recalling an episode activates an amodal redescription of the episode. In language, comprehending a text produces amodal propositions that represent its meaning. . . . Conversely, embodied theories represent knowledge as partial simulations of sensory, motor, and introspective states. . . . When an event is experienced originally, the underlying sensory, motor,

and introspective states are partially stored. Later, when knowledge of the event becomes relevant in memory, language, or thought, these original states are partially simulated. Thus, remembering an event arises from partially simulating the sensory, motor, and introspective states active at the time. Similarly, understanding a text about an event induces a simulation of the experience . . . this approach does not entail that actual bodily states are executed obligatorily, as in James' (1890) ideomotor theory. Instead simulations of bodily states in modality-specific brain areas may often be the extent to which embodiment is realized. Depending on the situation, embodiment may range from simulation, to traces of execution, to full-blown execution.. . . these embodiments are not merely peripheral appendages or epiphenomena of social information processing—they constitute the core of it . . . based on the assumption that simulations represent knowledge of social situations . . . we illustrate how this theory . . . unifies social embodiment effects (Barsalou et al., 2003, p. 44).

Bidirectionality of Affect/Cognition and Motor Behavior

One major complex of *social* embodiment effects is the one around the body feedback hypotheses. Findings within this experimental paradigm suggest that the incorporation of distinct facial expressions or postures leads to distinct emotions or evaluations. Starting out with research on the facial feedback hypothesis (Adelman & Zajonc, 1987; Buck, 1980; Laird, 1984, Strack, Martin, & Stepper, 1988), followed by research on postural feedback (LaFrance, 1985; Riskind, 1984; Rossberg-Gempton & Poole, 1992; Stepper & Strack, 1993), and vocal feedback (Hatfield, Cacioppo, & Rapson, 1992), this line of research supports that next to emotions/cognitions causing certain motor behaviors (bodily expressions), certain motor behaviors cause certain emotions/cognitions. The resulting postulate of the bidirectionality of affect/cognition and motor behavior is exactly supporting the basic maxim according to which D/MTs have been working from the beginnings of the profession. Yet, only recent research in social psychology has rendered convergent evidence that seems to secure this assumption.

Approach and Avoidance Motor Behavior

While behavior may vary strongly, behavioral patterns guided by emotions or attitudes are less com-plex and serve the same general goals: to approach pleasant stimuli and to avoid unpleasant ones (Neumann & Strack, 2000, p. 39). A further interesting social embodiment effect is the influence of approach and avoidance motor behavior on attitudes (Cacioppo, Priester, & Bentson, 1993; Neumann & Strack, 2000). Cacioppo, Priester, and Berntson (1993) placed participants at a table and asked them while studying arbitrary Chinese signs to either activate the flexor or the extensor of their arm muscles by pressing against their table either from below or from above (from the table surface). The resulting movement was thus either an approach or an avoidance movement, either towards the body or away from the body. The signs that had been studied while pulling the arms towards the body were later on judged as significantly more positive than the signs that had been studied while pushing against the table. This finding is consistent with other motor congruency effects (Förster & Strack, 1996). For a dance/movement therapist this result is probably not surprising, the parallels to shape-flow and shaping dimensions are obvious (Laban, 1960), and it is a direct proof of the KMP theory about Unipolar Shape Flow (Kestenberg, 1973/1979; 1995; Kestenberg-Amighi, Loman, Sossin, & Lewis, 1999).

The evolutionary significance of motion has been described by Todd and colleagues (Blythe, Todd, & Miller, 1999; Todd, Barett, Blythe, & Miller, 2004). With their contribution, the authors add an important perspective and methodology of motion research.

Contribution of Clinical Psychology

If we accept the idea that peptides and other transmitters are the biochemical substrate of feelings, then their distribution in the body is of primary importance. Sigmund Freud, would he have lived today, would have enthusiastically taken this idea as the molecular support of his theories. The body is the unconscious. Repressed trauma caused by unbearably intense feelings which can be stored in one body part and influence our ability to sense or even move this part of the body. Recent research findings support the idea that there is an almost endless number of transmission pathways (at our disposition) to reach the body and the unconscious and to change it (Pert, 1997, pp. 213–214; biochemist at George Washington University, Washington, D.C., USA; author translation).

The fields most familiar to dance/movement therapists are probably clinical psychology and psychotraumatology. Many dance/movement therapists in Germany have joined a supplementary training in psychotraumatology. In the course of the 1990s, clinical emotion research and neuropsychology have experienced substantial theoretical and methodological advances. New technologies such as fMRI-scans allow stating precisely which regions of the brain are activated in different behavior(s). This allows us to brain-map dance/movement therapy interventions and effects on a cognitive level. Similarly, the effects of other creative modalities such as art, music, or drama therapy can be mapped by this technique. On a theoretical level the interdependence of cognition and emotion has increasingly been demonstrated and the discovery of the bodily basis and neurological correlates of many therapeutic processes has taken a big step forward (Caldwell, 2004; Cozolino, 2002; Damasio, 1994; LeDoux, 1995; Pert, 1997; Schore, 1994). In addition, psychotherapy research has to offer new scientific evidence on the effectiveness of body-based therapies. As an example, I will introduce the research on Eye Movement Desensitization and Reprocessing (EMDR) (Shapiro, 1995).

EMDR is a confrontational (body-based) therapy that has entered the therapeutic field in 1987. Dr. Francine Shapiro had discovered it in a self-experiment, when she used to deal with her cancer diagnosis. In moments in which she was overflowed by negative thoughts, emotions, and memories she employed saccadic eye movements (quick rhythmic eye movements in horizontal direction with sharp reversals) and was able to alleviate and finally cure her cancer. Meanwhile there are thousands of trained clinicians who partly travel all over the world to treat post-traumatic stress disorder (PTSD) patients in regions of natural or manmade disasters. The core of the therapy consists of imagining the event that caused psychological stress/PTSD as vividly as possible and to remember an accompanying cognition (such as "it was my fault/I should have done x, y, z," etc.). Thereby the patient is asked to focus on the experienced anxiety and accompanying bodily sensations and at the same time to visually follow the therapist's index finger that moves from side to side in about 30 to 35 cm distance from the patient's face causing saccadic eye movements. After 12 to 24 repetitions, the patient is then asked to switch off the stressful memory and to breathe deeply. The patient is now again asked to monitor his bodily sensations and to imagine an incompatible cognition such as "I have done my best/It is not my fault/I have learned from it/I am in control." The therapist then assesses the stress level with the Subjective Units of Distress (SUD) scale and depending on the progress measured repeats the intervention or moves on to the next stressful event. The new cognitions are tested with the SUD scale regarding authenticity. One session takes between 45 and 90 minutes and with two sessions treatment is usually complete except in very major cases. Shapiro assumes that the therapeutic effect of EMDR can also be reached by other rhythmic movement such as alternating touch of the right and left arm rest with the hand. Consequently the primary effective factor of the therapy might not be the eye movement, but the rhythmic alternation.

EMDR has been developed on a pragmatic background and thus, is characterized by a relative lack of theory to account for its effects. Many attempts have been made to explain the success of EMDR and much interesting research has been conducted over the years. The space of this chapter is too limited to start a detailed presentation. However, one of the main ideas is that EMDR simulates a coping process and thereby increases the coping speed. Another important idea is that the mind is part of the body and therefore the body is a good place from which to implement processes of change.

The body therapy aspects of the model are quite striking: Rhythmic movement as a major treatment component has been used and investigated by dance/movement therapists. Findings are that rhythmic movement is implementing structure, that it is physiologically stimulating but cognitive-emotionally relaxing (cognitions go from active to passive). Approaches from dance/movement therapy would also assume that it is important *how* the movement is performed: The horizontal plane of the saccadic eye movements, for example, is related to observation and communication (in the active mode). It is also related to attention and orientation. Our functioning in the horizontal plane is acquired throughout the first year of life. It is our earliest available movement plane and related to the most primitive defenses. This is why horizontal movement is best suited to reach the most primitive regions of our brain which are affected by traumatic experiences. The movement qualities implied in those saccadic eye movements are indirect or flexible, i.e., movement that is suited to discover possibilities for fight or flight. Usually the PTSD patient is trapped in the inner world of his recurring memories (cognitions and emotions). EMDR does now on a motor level redirect the behavior of the patients to the outer world. Thereby, the heightened arousal level is met on a motor level and can thus stepwise be reduced to a normal level. This technique is also employed in grounding a dissociative patient when she switches, has a flashback or an abreaction. The latter two reactions can also be found in PTSD patients. EMDR provides an anchor in the here-and-now, while the patient is in control and determines the tempo. Here, approaches from dance/movement therapy can explain the decrease of the arousal level, which is one of the crucial factors that can stop the compulsion to relive the trauma.

Contribution of Cognitive Science, Linguistics, and Communication Research

Our ability to move in the ways we do and to track the motion of other things gives motion a major role in our conceptual system. The fact that we have muscles and use them to apply force in certain ways leads to the structure of our system of causal concepts. What is important is not just that we have bodies and that thought is somehow embodied. What is important is that the peculiar nature of our bodies shapes our very possibilities for conceptualization and categorization (Lakoff & Johnson, 1999).

In psycholinguistic and linguistic approaches as well as in the neurosciences, embodied mind theories gain influence in the context of explaining situated social behavior (Lakoff & Johnson, 1999; Varela, Thompson, & Rosch, 1993). In their 1999 work, *Philosophy in the Flesh*, George Lakoff and Marc Johnson define an embodied concept as "a neural structure that is actually part of, or makes use of, the sensorimotor system of our brains. Much of the conceptual inference is, therefore, sensorimotor inference" and not just preceded by or followed by sensorimotor inference (Lakoff & Johnson, 1999, p. 20). They state that the embodied mind hypothesis radically undercuts the perception-conception distinction. In an embodied mind, it is conceivable that the same neural system engaged in perception (or in motion) plays a central role in conception. That is, the very mechanisms responsible for perception, movements, and object manipulation could be responsible for conceptualization and reasoning. This implies that movement is a direct part of reasoning. Lakoff and Johnson (1999) emphasize that replacing traditional disembodied concepts with embodied concepts is a gain, and not a loss, for science, as it is in line with the best neuroscience and cognitive findings of the present time. Traditional scientific thought misses that "what has always made science possible is our embodiment, not our transcendence of it, and our imagination, not our avoidance of it." (Lakoff & Johnson, 1999, p. 93). It is exactly the human embodiment, the human experience, and the use of metaphor and imagination that makes science possible. The authors add an entire theory on how metaphor is a central human capacity. Their theory could benefit from D/MT's input on how metaphor on a body-level is part of that capacity.

Communication research has long been a domain closely related to D/MT. Ever since Darwin (1965/1872) published his book *The expression of emotions in men and animals*, the movement-affect link has been an issue of scientific investigation. The body-mediated relation of affect and cognition has been excellently compiled by social psychologists Zajonc and Markus (1984) and comprehensive overviews of nonverbal phenomena are given by Burgoon (1994) and DePaulo & Friedman (1998). Ray Birdwhistell (1955) was probably the most consequent researcher trying to establish a semantic system of nonverbal communication. Nowadays, communication researchers have increasingly started to investigate the interplay of nonverbal and verbal communication. This is partly due to recent development of methods and tools that help advance the integrative analysis of communication (Grammer, 1999, 2003; Koch & Zumbach, 2002; Krämer, 2001; Magnusson, 2000). Approaches focusing on movement dynamics are missing almost entirely.

CONCLUSION[1]

As we have seen from this brief excursion into adjacent fields and their theories, there is a current trend to strengthen the theoretical underpinnings

1. Acknowledgments: Thanks to Heather Hill and Robyn Cruz for valuable editorial comments on earlier drafts of this chapter.

Table 12.1.
Movement theories and working models of D/MT

Author	Theoretical Background	Title and year of main work
Laban, Rudolph v.	Choreographer, Architect	The mastery of movement, 1960; Efforts (with Lawrence), 1947 (movement qualities and shaping)
Chace, Marian	Harry Stacks Sullivan	Sandel, Chaiklin, & Lohn (Eds.), Foundations of dance/movement therapy: The life and work of Marian Chace, 1993
Whitehouse, Mary	Jungian Analysis	Jung and dance-therapy: two major principles, 1979
Espenak, Lilian	Adlerian Analysis	Dance therapy, 1981
Siegel, Elaine	Freudian Psychoanalysis	Dance therapy, 1986
Bartenieff, Irmgard	Laban, Physiotherapy	Body movement: Coping with the environment (with Lewis, D.), 1980
Kestenberg, Judith S.	Medical doctor, Freudian Psychoanalyst, Laban, Anna Freud	Parents and children, 1975; The role of movement patterns in development, Vol. 1 + 2 (with Sossin), 1973/1979 (KMP; movement rhythms, defenses, learning styles, developmental sequence)
Kestenberg-Amighi, Janet, Loman, Sossin, & Lewis	Kestenberg, Anthropology	The meaning of movement, 1999
Lamb, Warren	Laban	Gesture and posture, 1965 (movement shape; The Action Profile)
Davis, Martha	Laban, Bartenieff, Nonverbal communication research	(e.g.) An introduction to DaNCAS, 1983
Schmais, Claire	Laban, Chace; Group Dynamics	Healing processes in dance therapy, 1985
Lewis, Penny (Bernstein, Penny)	Drama Therapy, Kestenberg Depth Psychology	Eight theoretical approaches in dance therapy, 1979
Dulicai, Dianne	Systems Theory	Nonverbal assessment of family systems, 1977
Adler, Janet	Work with Autistic Children, Self-Study	Integrity of body and psyche, 2000
Chodorow, Joan	Jungian Analysis, Emotion Theories	Dance therapy and depth psychology, 1991
Pallaro, Patrizia	Object relations theory	Self and body-self: D/MT therapy and the development of object relations, 1996

Note: This table is not complete. It is culturally biased toward models known in the English speaking D/MT community. For more recent models see, for example, Pallasch (2002), Best (2000)/Parker& Best (2001), Tortora (2004), or Trautmann-Voigt & Voigt (2001).

of the bodily basis of cognition and emotion. This trend has many implications for the field of dance/movement therapy. Especially promising for cross-fertilization are theories of embodied cognition and the social embodiment approach. These theories attribute new scientific value to experience-based approaches. Those approaches, in turn, enable new theory formulation (Kestenberg, 1973; 1995; v. Uexküll, 1994; v. Weizsäcker, 1996). Some empirical findings resulting from tests of embodiment theories directly support the work of D/MTs and validate major theoretical assumptions in D/MT. In turn, D/MT can offer its well-developed assessments and movement theories and a higher degree of exactness and differentiation to some of these theories. The analysis of movement qualities, for example, may become the subject of established scientific fields and no longer remain in the half-scientific, half-esoteric realm. In any case, movement itself can be used as a direct way to validate one's feelings, attitudes, and cognitions, and in a second step one's home base scientific theories. If cognitions do not resonate in the body, they are probably not important to the self at a given time. They cannot be truly understood nor can they be truthfully adapted as a theory. Listening to one's body may thus be of greater value to scientists than ever assumed. This chapter has tried to clarify the advantages of a theoretical cross-fertilization of D/MT and adjacent disciplines. The time seems advantageous for D/MTs to approach the broader scientific community. Let us expand and spread the word!

REFERENCES

Adelman, P. K., & Zajonc, R. B. (1987). Facial efference and the experience of emotion. *Annual Review of Psychology, 40,* 249–280.

Adler, J. (2000). Integrity of body and psyche. In Pallaro, Patrizia (Ed.). *Authentic movement: Essays by Mary Starks Whitehouse, Janet Adler and Joan Chodorow* (pp. 121–131). London: Jessica Kingsley.

ADTA (2004). Homepage of the American Dance Therapy Association. Retrieved on September 12, 2004 from www.adta.org

Antonovsky, A. (1997). *Salutogenese: zur Entmystifizierung der Gesundheit [Salutogenesis: The demystification of health].* Tübingen: DGVT.

Barsalou, L.W., Niedenthal, P. M., Barbey, A. K., & Ruppert, J. A. (2003). Social embodiment. In B. H. Ross (Ed.). *The psychology of learning and motivation* (Vol. 43, pp. 43–92); San Diego, CA: Academic Press.

Barsalou, L. W. (in press). Situated simulation in the human conceptual system. *Language and Cognitive Processes.*

Bartenieff, I. & Lewis, D. (1980). *Body movement: Coping with the environment.* New York: Gordon and Breach Science Publishers, Inc.

Bernstein, P. L. (1979). *Eight theoretical approaches in dance/movement therapy.* Dubuque, Iowa: Kendall/Hunt.

Best, P. (2000). Theoretical diversity and clinical collaboration. *The Arts in Psychotherapy, 47,* 197–211.

Birdwhistell, R. (1955). Background to kinesics. *ETC, 13,* 10–18.

Blythe, P. W., Todd, Peter, M., & Miller, G. F. (1999). How motion reveals intention. Categorizing social interactions. In Gerd Gigerenzer, Peter Todd, & the ABC Research Group (Eds.). *Simple heuristics that make us smart* (pp. 256–285). Oxford: Oxford University Press.

BTD (2004). Homepage des Berufsverbands der TanztherapeutInnen Deutschlands, e.V. Retreived 09/12/04 from http://www.btd-tanztherapie.de

Buck, R. (1980). Nonverbal behavior and the theory of emotion: The facial feedback hypothesis. *Journal of Personality and Social Psychology, 38,* 811–824.

Burgoon, J. K. (1994). Nonverbal signals. In Marc L. Knapp, & Gerald R. Miller (Eds.). *Handbook of Interpersonal Communication* (pp. 344–390). London: Sage.

Buytendijk, F. J. J. (1956). *Allgemeine Theorie der menschlichen Haltung und Bewegung* [General theory of human posture and movement]. Berlin: Springer.

Cacioppo, J. T., Priester, Joseph R., & Bentson, G. G. (1993). Rudimentary determinants of attitudes II: Arm flexion and extension have differential effects on attitudes. *Journal of Personality and Social Psychology, 65,* 5–17.

Caldwell, C. (2004). American Dance Therapy Association 38th Annual Conference Keynote Address. The power of stillness, the glory of motion. *American Journal of Dance Therapy, 26,* 9–15.

Casey, E. S. (1987). *Remembering: A phenomenological study.* Bloomington: Indiana University Press.

Chodorow, J. (1991). *Dance therapy and depth psychology.* London: Routledge.

Cozolino, L. J. (2002). *Rebuilding the brain: Neuroscience and psychotherapy.* London: Norton. (The Norton Series on Interpersonal Neurobiology).

Cruz, R. (2001). Perspectives on the profession of dance/movement therapy: Past, present, and future. *Bulletin of Psychology and the Arts,. 2*(2), 74–78.

Damasio, Antonio R. (1994). *Descartes' Error. Emotion, reason, and the human brain.* New York: Putnam.

Damasio, Antonio R. (1999). *The feeling of what happens: Body and emotion in the making of consciousness.* Orlando, FL: Harcourt.

Darwin, Charles (1965/1872). *The expression of emotions in men and animals.* Chicago: University of Chicago Press.

Davis, Martha (1983). An introduction to the Davis nonverbal communication analysis system (DaNCAS). *American Journal of Dance Therapy, 6,* 49–73.

DePaulo, Bella M., & Friedman, H. S. (1998). Nonverbal communication. In Daniel Gilbert, Susan T. Fiske, & Gardner Lindzey (Eds.). *The handbook of social psychology* (4th ed., vol. 1, pp. 3–40). Boston: McGraw-Hill.

Descartes, René (2001). Bericht über die Methode. Discours de la Méthode [Discourse on method]. Stuttgart : Reclam. Originally published in 1637.

Dornes, M. (1993). Der kompetente Säugling. Die präverbale Entwicklung des Menschen. [The competent infant. Preverbal development of a human being] Frankfurt a.M.: Fischer.

Dulicai, D. (1977). Nonverbal Assessment of family systems. A preliminary study. *The Arts in Psychotherapy, 4,* 55–62.

Espenak, L. (1981). *Dance therapy: Theory and application.* Springfield, IL: Charles C Thomas, Publisher, Ltd.

Förster, J., & Strack, F. (1996). Influence of overt head movements on memory for valenced words: A case of conceptual-motor compatibility. *Journal of Personality and Social Psychology, 71,* 421–430.

Fuchs, T. (2000). *Leib Raum Person.* Stuttgart: Klett-Cotta.

Grammer, K. (1999). Signale der Liebe. Frankfurt a. M.: Fischer.

Grammer, K. (2003). E-motion communication. Retrieved on January 20, 2003 from http://evolution.anthro.univie.ac.at/institutes/urbanethology.html

Hatfield, E., Cacioppo, J. T., & Rapson, R. L. (1992). Primitive emotional contagion. In M.S. Clark (Ed.). *Review of Personality and Social Psychology: Vol. 14, Emotions and social behavior* (pp. 151–177). Newbury Park, CA: Sage.

Kafka, G. (1950). Über Uraffekte. *Acta Psychologica, 7,* 256–278.

Kestenberg, J. S., & Sossin, K. M. (1973/1979). The role of movement patterns in development, Vol. 1 & 2. New York: Dance Notation Bureau Press.

Kestenberg, J. S. (1995). *Sexuality, body movement and rhythms of development.* Northvale: Jason Aronson, Inc. (Originally published in 1975 under the title *Parents and children*).

Kestenberg-Amighi, J. (1990). The Application of the KMP Cross-Culturally. In P. Lewis & S. Loman (Eds.). *The Kestenberg Movement Profile: Its past, present applications and future directions* (pp. 114–125). Keene, NH: Antioch New England Graduate School.

Kestenberg-Amighi, J., Loman, S., Lewis, P., & Sossin, K. (1999). *The meaning of movement. Developmental and clinical perspectives of the Kestenberg Movement Profile.* Amsterdam: Gordon and Breach.

Koch, S. C. (1999). T*he Kestenberg Movement Profile: Interrater reliability among novice raters.* Stuttgart: Ibidem.

Koch, S. C., & Zumbach, J. (2002). The use of video analysis software in behavior observation research: Interaction patterns in task-oriented small groups. *Forum Qualitative Sozialforschung / Forum: Qualitative Social Research [On-line Journal], 3* (2), Retrieved from http://www.qualitative-research.net/fqs/fqs-eng.html

Krämer, N. C. (2001). *Bewegende Bewegung. Sozio-emotionale Wirkungen nonverbalen Verhaltens und deren experimentelle Untersuchung mittels Computeranimation* Lengerich: Pabst.

Laban, R.. (1960). *The Mastery of movement.* London: MacDonald & Evans.

Laban, R., & Lawrence, F. C. (1947/1974). *Effort: Economy in body movement.* Boston, MA: Plays.

LaFrance, M. (1985). Postural mirroring and intergroup relations. *Personality and Social Psychology Bulletin, 11,* 207–217.

Laird, J. D. (1984). The real role of facial response in the experience of emotion: a response to Tourangeau and Ellsworth, and others. *Journal of Personality and Social Psychology, 47,* 909–917.

Lakoff, G., & Johnson, M. (1999). *Philosophy in the flesh. The embodied mind and its challenge to Western thought.* New York: Basic Books.

Lamb, W. (1965). *Posture and gesture.* London: Gerald Duckworth.

LeDoux, J. (1995). Emotions. Clues from the brain. *Annual Review of Psychology, 46,* 209–235.

Lévy, F. (2004). *Dance/movement therapy: A healing art.* Reston, VA: Ahperd.

Lewin, K. (1935). *A dynamic theory of personality.* New York: McGraw-Hill.

Lipps, T. (1903). *Leitfaden der Psychologie (Kap. 14: Die Einfühlung,* pp. 187–201) [Guide to Psychology. Chapter 14: Empathy)]. Leipzig: Wilhelm Engelmann.

Loman, S. (1996). The KMP: A tool for dance/movement therapy. *American Journal of Dance Therapy, 18*(1), 29–52.

Lotan, N. (2001; June). *Hand movements of toddlers falling asleep.* Conference Presentation First Motor Development Conference, Amsterdam.

Magnusson, M. S. (2000). Discovering hidden time patterns in behavior: T-patterns and their detection. *Behavior Research Methods: Instruments & Computers, 32,* 93–110.

Merleau-Ponty, M. (1966). *Die Phänomenologie der Wahrnehmung.* Berlin: DeGruyter.

Neisser, U. (1967). *Cognitive psychology.* New York: Appleton-Century-Croft.

Neumann, R. & Strack, F. (2000). Approach and avoidance: The influence of proprioceptive and exteroceptive cues on encoding of affective information. *Journal of Personality and Social Psychology, 79*, 39–48.

Pallaro, P. (1996). Self and body-self: Dance/movement therapy and the development of object relations. *The Arts in Psychotherapy, 23*, 113–119.

Pallaro, P. (2000). *Authentic Movement: Essays by Mary Starks Whitehouse, Janet Adler and Joan Chodorow.* London: Jessica Kingsley.

Pallasch, D. (2002). Tief bewegt zum Ziel. Ein tanztherapeutischer Ansatz aus NLP und Authentic Movement [Deeply moved toward the goal. A D/MT-approach between NLP and Authentic Movement]. Retrieved from www.jungfernmann.de on September 12, 2003.

Parker, G., & Best, P., (2001). Moving Reflections. The Social Creation of Identities in Communication. In L. Kossolapow, S. Scoble, & D. Waller (Eds.). *Arts—Therapies—Communication: On the Way to a Communicative European Arts Therapy,* Vol. I, pp. 142–148). Münster: Lit Verlag.

Pauen, S., & Träuble, B. (2002, April). *Causal attribution of animate motion in 7-month-olds.* Paper presented at the biannual meeting of the International Conference on Infant Studies, Toronto, ON, Canada.

Pert, C. (1997). *The molecules of emotion: Why you feel the way you feel.* New York: Scribner.

Piaget, J. (1969). *Das Erwachen der Intelligenz beim Kinde.* [The awakening of intelligence in the child]. Stuttgart: Klett-Cotta.

Riskind, J. H. (1984). They stoop to conquer: Guiding and self-regulatory functions of physical posture after success and failure. *Journal of Personality and Social Psychology, 47*, 479–493.

Rizzolatti, G., Fadiga, L., Fogassi, L., & Gallese, V. (2002). From mirror neurons to imitation: Facts and speculations. In A.N. Meltzoff & W. Prinz (Eds.). *The imitative mind: Development, evolution, and brain bases. Cambridge studies in cognitive perceptual development* (pp. 247–266). New York: Cambridge University Press.

Rossberg-Gempton, I., & Poole, G. D. (1992). The relationship between body movement and affect: From historical and current perspectives. *The Arts in Psychotherapy, 19*, 39–46.

Sandel, S., Chaiklin, S., & Chaiklin, L. A. (1993), *Foundations of dance/movement therapy: The life and work of Marian Chace.* Columbia, MD: The Marian Chace Memorial Fund.

Schmais, C. (1985). Healing processes in dance therapy. *American Journal of Dance Therapy, 8*, 17–36.

Schore, A. (1994). *Affect regulation and the origin of the self.* Hillsdale, NJ: Erlbaum.

Sherrington, C. C. (1906). *The integrative action of the nervous system.* New York: Yale University Press.

Shapiro, F. (1995). *Eye movement desensitization and reprocessing: Basic principles, protocols and procedures.* New York: Guilford Press.

Siegel, E. (1986). *Tanztherapie. Seelische und körperliche Entwicklung im Spiegel der Bewegung. Ein psychoanalytisches Konzept.* Stuttgart: Klett Cotta.

Stepper, S. & Strack, F. (1993). Proprioceptive determinants of emotional and nonemotional feelings. *Journal of Personality and Social Psychology, 64*, 211–220.

Stern, D. (1998). Die Lebenserfahrung des Säuglings [The living experience of the infant], (6th ed.). Stuttgart: Klett-Kotta.

Strack, F., Martin, L. L., & Stepper, S. (1988). Inhibiting and facilitating conditions of the human smile: A non-obtrusive test of the facial feedback hypothesis. *Journal of Personality and Social Psychology, 54*, 768–777.

Thelen, E. (1995). Motor development - A new synthesis. *American Psychologist 50*(2), 79–95.

Träuble, B. (2004). Die Bedeutung von Kausalwahrnehmung für den frühen Wissenserwerb. Neue Befunde aus der Säuglingsforschung [The importance of causal perception for early knowledge acquisition. New findings from infant studies]. Berlin: Logos.

Trautmann-Voigt, S., & Voigt, B. (2001). *Bewegung und Bedeutung. Anregungen zu definierter Körperlichkeit in der Psychotherapie.* Köln: Claus Richter.

Todd, P. M., Barrett, C. H., Blythe, P. W., & Miller, G. F. (2004). *Accurate judgments of intention from motion cues alone.* Manuscript submitted for publication.

Tortora, S. (2004). Our moving bodies tell stories, which speak of our experience. *The multisensory world of the infant, 24* (5), 4–12.

Uexküll, J., & Kriszat, G. (1956). *Bedeutungslehre* [Theory of meaning]. Frankfurt a. M.: Fischer. (Originally published in 1940).

Uexküll, T., Fuchs, M., Müller-Braunschweig, H., & J., R. (1994). *Subjektive Anatomie. Theorie und Praxis körperbezogener Psychotherapie.* [Subjective anatomy. Theory and practice of body-related psychotherapy.] New York: Schattauer.

Varela, F. J., Thompson, E., & Rosch, E. (1993). *The embodied mind: Cognitive science and human experience.* Cambridge, MA: MIT Press.

Wallbott, H. G. (1990). *Mimik im Kontext. Die Bedeutung verschiedener Informationskomponenten für das Erkennen von Emotionen* [Facial expressions in context. The importance of different informational components for emotion recognition]. Göttingen: Hogrefe.

Weizsäcker, V. (1996). *Der Gestaltkreis. Theorie der Einheit von Wahrnehmen und Bewegen* [The Gestaltkreis. Theory of the union of perception and movement], 6th edition. Stuttgart: Thieme. (Originally published in 1940).

Whitehouse, M.S. (1979). Jung and dance-therapy: Two major principles. In P.L. Bernstein (Ed.). *Eight theoretical approaches in dance movement therapy.* Dubuque, Iowa: Kendall-Hunt.

Wilson, M. (2002). Six views of embodied cognition. *Psychonomic Bulletin & Review, 9,* 625–636.

Zajonc, R. B., & Markus, H. (1984). Affect and cognition: The hard interface. In C. Izard, J. Kagan, & R. B. Zajonc (Eds.), *Emotions, cognition and behavior* (pp. 73–102). Cambridge: Cambridge University Press.

Zaner, R. M. (1964). The problem of embodiment. Some contributions to a phenomenology of the body. Nijhoff: Den Haag.

Biographical Statement

Sabine C. Koch, PhD., M.A., DTR, Social Psychologist and Communication Researcher, studied psychology at the University of Heidelberg, Germany, and Madrid, Spain, and dance/movement therapy at Hahnemann University in Philadelphia, Pennsylvania. She did her PhD in verbal and nonverbal analyses of gendered communication in work teams and publishes in gender research and dance/movement therapy.

Chapter 13

THE KESTENBERG MOVEMENT PROFILE

SUZANNE C. HASTIE

INTRODUCTION

In dance/movement therapy, when engaging in individual and/or group work, we look at and work closely and sensitively with the nonverbal behavior of our clients. Because the nonverbal is integral to our work, it is important to know as much about it as possible. This chapter reviews and presents the Kestenberg Movement Profile (KMP), an assessment tool used in the field of dance/movement therapy.

Kestenberg's Background and the Development of the Profile

"My intuitive approach was not good enough. I needed to know more about how feelings emerged from movement, merged back into them and influenced the development of thought in successive developmental phases" (Kestenberg, 1967, p. 6). Judith Kestenberg, MD, a psychiatrist and psychoanalyst, had an interest in movement and children early in her life and went on to devote her entire work life to exploring, studying, and engaging with the nonverbal behavior and communication of children and parents. In 1953, she selected some newborns for a pilot project for the purpose of finding a way to capture the nonverbal qualities of interactions between mothers and babies. This pilot project served as a base for the longitudinal study she did of three individuals from birth through adulthood (Kestenberg & Sossin, 1979). The development of her profile involved years of observing, studying, notating, and collaborating before its completion in 1965. Direct applications of the material gleaned from completed profiles were made at her Center for Parents and Children

(1972–1990) in New York, as well as by many practitioners in the fields of psychology and the creative arts therapies. The theoretical underpinnings of the profile come most strongly from her work with Paul Schilder (Kestenberg, 1975), her own observations of children and parents, her studies of Laban and Lamb's work, and her observations and validation at Anna Freud's Hampstead Clinic. Additional influences on her work come from early psychoanalysts, as well as from other movement specialists (Kestenberg, 1975; 1985).

Overview of the Kestenberg Movement Profile

The Kestenberg Movement Profile (KMP), "a Laban-derived, developmentally grounded system of movement description" (Sossin, 1987, p. 23), was developed by the Sands Point Movement Study Group and is based on the work of Laban, Lamb, Bartenieff, North, Kestenberg, and the Sands Point Movement Study Group's own studies on infants and children. The KMP is a descriptive, systematic, and in-depth movement assessment tool that utilizes as well as expands upon the effort/shape system of movement observation and notation. The KMP provides an organized framework within which to describe, categorize, and evaluate a client's movement qualities. Further, it offers a refined movement language to the dance/movement therapist, as well as a psychological interpretation for what is seen in the body.

Movement Patterns of the KMP and Their Meanings

The KMP, developed to assess infants, children, and adults, is constructed purely from nonverbal

121

behavior and movement patterns. The profile includes a body attitude description and nine graphed diagrams (see Figure 13.1) that give information about 62 specific movement patterns.

The movement patterns captured in each of the nine diagrams are the following: tension-flow rhythms, tension-flow attributes, pre-efforts, efforts, bi-polar shape flow, unipolar shape-flow, shape-flow design, shaping in directions, and shaping in planes. The diagrams in the profile can be placed into two major systems: the diagrams on the left side of the profile (1–4) comprise System 1; those on the right side of the profile (5–9) comprise System 2.

System 1, the Tension-flow-Effort system, captures the feeling and substance of a movement.

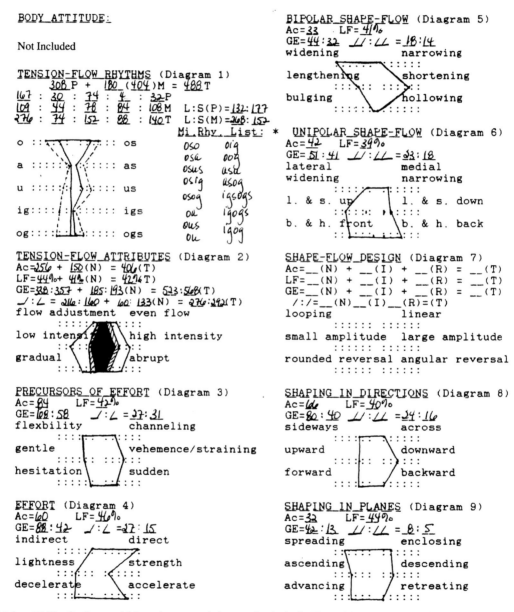

Figure 13.1. KMP of a 3-year-old boy (some statistics not included). From Hastie, Atley, S. (1991). In search of a standard form of assessment: The Kestenberg Movement Profile as diagnostic tool and treatment guide integrated into the practice of dance therapy. Unpublished master's thesis, Antioch/New England Graduate School, Keene, NH. Reprinted with permission of the author.

System 2, the Shape-flow-Shaping system, depicts the shape or structure of a movement quality and its relational development (Kestenber, Loman, Lewis, & Sossin, 1999). For example, visualize a man hammering a nail into a board below him: he is using strength to hammer the nail into the board in a downward fashion. In this example, strength is the substance of his movement (the Effort pattern reflected in Diagram 4), and the shape of his arm moving in a downward fashion is the affined (or complementary) structure for his strength (downward is a Shaping-in-Directions pattern represented in Diagram 8). Both Systems 1 and 2 follow a line of development beginning with movement qualities typical of the fetus and newborn, and ending with qualities typical of the adult, so that the top half of the profile (Diagrams 1, 2, 5, and 6) reflects early movement and the bottom half (Diagrams 3, 4, 7, 8, and 9) reflects more mature patterns of movement. All through life, all movement patterns are used; however, in infancy, the early patterns dominate (i.e., tension-flow rhythms, tension-flow attributes, bipolar shape flow, and unipolar shape flow). With development and environmental influences, patterns mature and build on top of one another so that in adulthood all patterns are fully established with the exception of those who have severe physical impairments or psychopathology.

In Diagrams 2–9, movement patterns representing the first three years of life are evaluated by looking at the top, middle, and bottom lines of each diagram. The top lines, representing the first year (approximately birth–1 year), are comprised of horizontal patterns that facilitate communication, attention, exploration, and investigation. The middle lines, depicting the second year (approximately 1–2 years), consist of vertical patterns that facilitate presentation of self and objects, showing intention, determining, and evaluating. The bottom lines, which represent the third year (approximately 2–3 years), are comprised of sagittal patterns that facilitate taking action, decision-making, timing, and anticipating. With regard to tension-flow rhythms, the first, second, and third lines represent the first through third years, and the last two lines represent the fourth through sixth years.

In the tension-flow-effort system, the movement patterns on the right side of Diagrams 2–4 are considered fighting in quality (i.e., high intensity, vehemence/straining, and strength); the patterns on the left are indulging in quality (i.e., low inten-

sity, gentleness, and lightness). In the Shape-flow-Shaping System, the movement patterns on the right are closed shapes (e.g., shortening, down, and descending) and those on the left are open shapes (e.g., lengthening, up, and ascending). Patterns that go well together between systems are fighting patterns with closed shapes and indulging patterns with open shapes (e.g., even flow with narrowing as seen when the brows are brought together, or flow adjustment with widening as seen in a smile). When learning about the KMP, it is very helpful to get a picture of or sense for the movement patterns being discussed. Therefore, in the sections that follow on body attitude and the nine specific KMP movement patterns, the reader will first be introduced to each pattern through a movement description or vignette to facilitate visualizing the pattern being presented.

The Body Attitude

A sample description of the body attitude as it might appear in a completed KMP can be seen in the case of Joey, whose completed KMP can be found in Figure 13.1. Joey is a three-year-old boy whose body is aligned primarily in the vertical and sagittal planes, conveying an attitude of mobility and fluidity typical of the urethral phase (Kestenberg, 1975). His torso is shaped with his belly bulging to the front (a sagittal quality). His arms are held at his sides, and he often lifts them up and down, letting his hands either dangle from his wrists or having them flap and shake in the fighting form of the urethral rhythm. At rest, he often holds his hands limply (in neutral tension and shape flow) in front of himself. Qualities he uses often that are left imprinted on his body are lightness, lengthening, widening, and even flow in a facial grimace, and neutral flow in his face and hands. Patterns he seems ready for at rest include gentleness, lightness, running, jumping, and an unpredictable taking off or lunging/moving forward. There is a neutral, apathetic quality about him that can turn into a burst of activity without warning. His entire body exudes a quality of light buoyancy (Hastie, 1991).

The body attitude description is placed on the top left side of the profile above diagram 1. According to Kestenberg, the body attitude is the "somatic core of the body image which changes in accordance with each new developmental phase" (1975, p. 236). When describing an individual's body attitude, the following aspects are assessed and included: (1) the alignment, (2) the way the body shapes itself, (3) the way the body parts are positioned, (4) the favored positions of the body, (5) the movement qualities used, often left imprinted on the body, and (6) the movement phrases and patterns "for which there appears to be readiness at rest" (p. 236). When writing about the body attitude in the profile, the aspects listed above may be included, as well as any general comments about how the individual looks (i.e., stubborn, jovial, etc.). When looking at the body attitude, the dance/movement therapist can see the dominant and preferred movement patterns of a client. Further, how clients hold and support themselves usually reflects, in some way, how they were held and supported as children (Kestenberg & Buelte, 1977).

The Tension-Flow-Effort System

At the base of the Tension-flow-Effort System lie two movement qualities – bound and free flow. Flow refers to the continuity and discontinuity of movement and the freedom and restraint of movement (Kestenberg, 1985). Bound flow serves to inhibit impulses (i.e., a child's tightly held fist). Free flow serves to release impulses (i.e., the flinging arms of a child). When one feels fearful or distrustful, bound flow may result, which can be very helpful in situations where there is danger. When one feels safe and unconcerned, free flow may result, enabling one to have facility in movement, a natural response to situations perceived as safe. In their extreme forms, too much bound flow can become immobilization and rigidity; too much free flow can become carelessness and accident proneness.

Neutral tension flow, which reflects the loss of elasticity in the muscle tissues, can be observed when one is daydreaming or sleeping, when one does not let oneself feel and appears shut down, or when one is tired or ill. In excess, neutral flow can be indicative of depression or severe pathology (e.g., a dissociative episode). According to Loman, "although it is adaptive when interacting with inanimate objects [such as machinery], an excess of neutral flow suggests numbness and blandness, and a loss of the distinct feelings of safety and danger" (1990, p. 55).

Tension-Flow Rhythms (Diagram 1)

Imagine, for a moment, a large family reunion is taking place in a park. On the periphery of this event, one of the relatives is standing back to observe all the different personalities and age groups present. What follows are some of what she sees. Susie goes on and on and never stops talking. Beverly is highly organized and rather stubborn. Mary walks with a bounce. Johnny is biting and sarcastic when he speaks to others. Sarah acts nurturing and supportive – kind of like an Earth mother. Peter likes to be the center of attention. Laurie is running around the park and stops only when she runs into her mother or one of the other family members. Little Jerry is pushing some of the other children. Emma is gulping when she drinks from the bottle. Brian is nagging his father and demanding a lot with endless "why" questions. David is "chillin" and taking it easy all the time. Lisa is constantly on the go. Stacey is verbally aggressive and intrusive. Paul is charming and flirtatious.

Tension-flow rhythms, which are present at birth and even earlier in the womb, lie at the base of all motor patterns; they express needs and drives, and seek satisfaction. Tension-flow rhythms are classified according to the body zone from which they originate; however, they do not only exist at their place of origin but may also be seen in various other body parts. Imagine being at a meeting at work consisting of ten people and deciding to take a look under the table to see all the different ways people are wiggling or moving their feet. These individual differences and unique ways of wiggling will reveal some information about each person's tension-flow rhythms. The developmental order of the ten rhythms, the approximate age at which each rhythm begins to dominate, and some examples of each of the rhythms observed in childhood and adulthood can be seen in Table 13.1.

The constellation of rhythms, obtained from notating and diagramming the tension-flow rhythms, can inform the dance/movement therapist about the developmentally-related issues and personality of a client. For example, Johnny, age 8, bites and chews frequently on the sleeves of his shirts to the point that he has holes in several of them. Oral snapping/biting is the rhythm associated with biting/down and chewing, and is connected with issues related to separation. Exploring Johnny's early history with his parents may be worthwhile, or it may be of value simply to be aware that Johnny may have unresolved separation issues that need to be further explored and addressed. Another possibility is to work with Johnny on redi-

Table 13.1.
Tension-flow Rhythms

Age	Rhythm	Movement Term	Behavioral Examples
0–1 year	oral	sucking	indulging manner; soothing oneself; rocking; enjoys talking and taking in food, sensations, and knowledge, etc.
6 months	oral	snapping/biting	tapping; snapping; chewing; patting;
9 months	anal	twisting	teasing; acting coy; using pincer grasp;
1 year	fighting		pulling hair; likes biting down; may be critical or have biting humor
1.5 years	indulging		adjusting to new positions; crawling; may be charming, flirtatious, messy
18 months	anal	strain; release	pushing; climbing; throwing; lifting;
2 years	fighting		acting stubborn; having a tempertantrum; may be neat, well-organized; controlled; can fixate on an idea
2–2.5 years	urethral	running; drifting	wandering aimlessly; passivity; letting go; indulging bubbling over with ideas or mobility; hanging out or "chill-in"; prefer to think/move without structure; may drift about, get lost, or lose things; good at just "being"
2.5–3 years	urethral	starting; stopping	squirting water; demanding things now; fighting turning switches on and off; telling others what to do; acting impatient; agitated; may be "on the go"; competitive; a list and goal maker; ambitious, a "doer"
3–3.5 years	inner genital	swaying	nurturing; acting like a baby and then indulging acting like a big boy/girl; asking lots of questions; being interested in pregnancy and mothering; may be easygoing and earthy
3.5–4 years	inner genital	surging; birthing	nagging; never being satisfied; expelling; fighting throwing; getting rid of feelings; birthing a child, an idea, or a large scale creative project/work
4–5 years	outer genital	jumping	interrupting; intruding; jumping everywhere; indulging identifying with a superhero; excitable; performing; may be outgoing and enjoy showing off; energetic; plunging wholeheartedly jumping into something interrupting; intruding; jumping everywhere; identifying with a superhero; excitable; performing; may be outgoing and enjoy showing off; energetic
4–5 years	outer genital	jumping	jumping interrupting; intruding; jumping everywhere; indulging identifying with a superhero; excitable; performing; may be outgoing and enjoy showing off; energetic; plunging wholeheartedly into something
5–6 years	outer genital	spurting/ramming	focused and penetrating; acting; fighting aggressive, shooting weapons, slam-dunking a basketball; ramming with precision; learning in bursts; may be assertive and explosive

*The ages in each phase may vary for individual children.
(Loman, 1988; Kestenberg et al., 1999)

recting his urge to bite and chew into a more accepted and appropriate manner (perhaps having something in his desk he could pinch when feeling stressed). On a personality level, this snapping/biting rhythm is manifested in his ability to "bite down and chew" on information in school and to be critical and discerning about it.

Tension-Flow Attributes (Diagram 2)

Imagine a group of workers embarking on a two month project. In the process of getting to know each other and working together, each worker becomes very aware of each other's temperament. The co-workers discover that John is very intense; Steve is laid-back and easygoing; Linda gets angry really slowly; Sue is steady and even-keeled; Matt is excitable and changeable; Karen is impulsive; Jim is not easily ruffled; Tina is perky and alert; and Carol is serene and patient. Tension-flow attributes are what create these basic temperamental and affective differences.

Tension-flow attributes are made up of six intensity factors "through which we express our feelings and attune to the feelings of others" (Kestenberg, 1985, p. 125); they are reflective of affect and temperament and stay fairly constant throughout life. These attributes, along with some ways in which they typically manifest, are: (1) evenness (steadiness), (2) flow adjustment (adaptability), (3) high intensity (intensity and moodiness), (4) low intensity (low-keyedness), (5) abruptness (alertness and impatience), and (6) graduality (patience and ability to endure) (Kestenberg, 1977; Loman, 1988). When a mother and child attune in attributes, empathy, understanding, and communication develop:

> Control over flow adjustment in free and bound flow is acquired in the first year of life. When mother and infant attune in these attributes, they develop empathy for change [flow adjustment] and sameness [even flow] in each other. . . . The regulation of ranges of high and low intensities of tension is the achievement of the second year. When mother and child attune in these attributes, they develop empathy in excitement [high intensity] and in calmness [low intensity]. . . . The regulation of ranges of graduality and abruptness of tension increases and decreases is the achievement of the third year of life. When mother and child attune in these attributes, they develop empathy in leisure [graduality] and alertness [abruptness]. . . .

> Attunement in tension-flow [attributes and rhythms] is the empathic core of communication, mutual understanding, and acting in consonance. (Kestenberg, 1985, pp. 131–132)

Tension-flow attributes inform the dance/movement therapist about the affect and temperament of a client. Awareness of the dominant and/or uniquely constelled attributes and rhythms of a client facilitates "starting where the patient is at," developing empathy through attunement, and creating a supportive therapeutic environment and transference relationship (Lewis, 1987).

Pre-Efforts (Diagram 3)

Imagine it is someone's first day of work at a new job or his first day of photography class. Or, perhaps, he just got off the bus in Montreal, a city to which he has never been. Imagine how he might act or move in each of these new situations. How will this day be different from when he is really comfortable and familiar with his new job or class and is really feeling at home in Montreal? How will his movement change? Consider also this person in a situation in which he feels threatened or defensive – how might he move? Pre-efforts are typically used in these new situations and/or in situations in which we feel defensive.

Pre-efforts "evolve from related tension-flow attributes and they merge and transform into related effort elements" (Kestenberg, 1985, p. 134). For instance, the tension flow attribute even flow (manifested in an infant trying to hold her hand steady) evolves into the pre-effort channeling (the child trying hard to reach an object), which develops into the effort directness (the child being able automatically and skillfully to reach the object). When an individual is moving in pre-effort she may be feeling anxious, uncertain, and vulnerable, which leads to her having an inner focus and concentration while attempting to cope with the outside environment (Loman & Kestenberg Amighi, 2002). Interpretively, pre-efforts are reflective of immature actions, learning style, and defensive patterns. When in a learning situation, the movement channeling facilitates defining; flexibility facilitates random generalization; vehemence/straining supports conquering; gentleness leads to learning without resistance; suddenness is manifested in having sudden insight; and hesitation is revealed by learning in a deliberate manner. Defensively, channeling can turn into isolating oneself; flexibility into avoiding; vehemence/straining into identifying with the aggressor; gentleness into reaction formation or appeasement; suddenness into defensive rushing and responding counterphobically when paired with moving forward; and hesitation into defensive dawdling (Kestenberg, 1985). Everyone needs defenses and having a certain amount of pre-effort behavior is considered normal. However, having a high amount of pre-efforts is indicative of being too defended and overusing one or two pre-efforts may be indicative of pathology, such as those of psychiatric patients (Loman & Merman, 1996; Merman, 1990).

Efforts (Diagram 4)

Imagine a man who has lived in the same apartment and city for many years and has worked at the same job for quite some time. Imagine how a typical day might be for him. He gets up in the morning, does his morning stretches, brushes his teeth and takes a shower, makes and drinks his coffee, reads the morning newspaper, writes a letter to his aunt, and proceeds out to the car for work. His entire day at work is routine and familiar. He is moving in the here and now with confidence and skill and doesn't miss a beat. If challenges come up, he engages his mind in problem-solving mode. Efforts are what he is using in this confident, comfortable place and the more effort patterns he has access to, perhaps the higher his creative intelligence and the more skilled at problem solving he will be.

Efforts have to do with one's coping style, ego strength, problem-solving ability, and creative intelligence. Their orientation is to reality. Coping with space involves paying attention with indirectness or directness. Coping with gravity (or weight) involves expressing one's intention through the use of lightness or strength. Coping with time involves making decisions in a decelerated or accelerated manner. As children mature, efforts develop: "only when specific skills become automatized and the child can maneuver well in the environment does he or she employ effort elements to adapt to the forces of nature which are either opposed or accepted" (Kestenberg, 1985, p. 137). Interpretively, efforts give the dance/movement therapist information about a client's ego strength, cognitive functions, creative intelligence, and problem-solving abilities. Efforts are seen in their clients' ways of functioning

in the world when feeling confident, skilled, and secure in their position at work or home.

Shape-Flow-Shaping System (Right Side of the Profile)

The most basic movement pattern underlying System 2 is shape flow (i.e., growing and shrinking, which is first experienced through the breath during inhalation and exhalation). Growing tends to be a smooth, continuous process having to do with feelings of comfort, intake, and approach behavior. In contrast, shrinking is an interruptive process, having to do with feelings of discomfort, expulsion, and withdrawing behavior (Kestenberg, 1977; Loman, 1989).

Shape flow can also be observed in the face (e.g., when smiling, bringing the brows together, bulging the eyes in surprise, etc.) and during any kind of flexion or extension of the body (e.g., curling oneself into a ball and then stretching out long). With infants and those with vivacious personalities, shape flow changes occur often; in contrast, those who are older or more solid and steady in personality exhibit few shape changes (Kestenberg, 1977).

Bipolar Shape-Flow (Diagram 5)

Imagine a woman is participating in a gathering with other women. As she interacts with the others, she begins to get a sense for those who seem grounded, centered, confident, or stable and those who are not. She notices those who are expressive, those who take up a lot of space, and those who are barely noticeable. The movement patterns that are reflective of the qualities she is sensing and seeing are the bipolar shape flow patterns.

In bipolar shape flow, feelings of comfort and discomfort are expressed via growing or shrinking, providing information about the stability and expressive range of an individual. Bipolar shape flow is symmetrical movement, manifested in expanding and contracting, which often involves the whole body and/or can be observed in facial expressions (Loman, 1989). It typically occurs in response to environmental factors such as temperature, air pressure, or noise level, as well as internal sensations (i.e., stomach pain or feeling inner shame). For example, if one is outside and very cold, the response is to pull in and shiver, in contrast to a warm and sunny day in which one may grow and expand into the environment.

Bipolar shape flow contributes to body-image formation, and can give an individual stability

(Kestenberg et al., 1999). The six bipolar shape-flow patterns are widening as in a smile (expressive of generosity); narrowing as in frowning (expressive of containment or stinginess); lengthening as in stretching from head to toes (expressive of elation); shortening when stooping (expressive of shame or feeling small); bulging when puckering lips (expressive of fullness or satiation); and hollowing as in pouting (expressive of emptiness or depletion) (Loman, 1989; Kestenberg Amighi et al., 1999). The balance between the growing and shrinking patterns conveys a solid body image and sense of oneself. If there is excessive growing (e.g., too much widening), the individual may be too generous or too vulnerable in the world. If there is excessive shrinking (e.g., too much narrowing), the individual may be too withdrawn. The capacity to both grow and shrink allows us to be in the world and return to restore ourselves. The data gathered and diagrammed on bipolar shape flow informs the dance/movement therapist about a client's body image and self-esteem. A client with a fair amount of each of the different qualities probably has good self-esteem and a solid body image. One who has mostly growing qualities may be narcissistic and/or too vulnerable, as contrasted to one with mostly shrinking qualities who may have low self-esteem.

Unipolar Shape-Flow (Diagram 6)

Imagine stimuli in life that are attractive and repulsive and how one might move in response. Some examples follow. He quickly pulled away from the mean dog. She went over to smell the freshly baked bread. He leaned in to snuggle with his mother. She pulled back from the shouting coach. He leaned back into the cozy chair. She reached over to touch the silky material. He jolted forward as a person he felt uncomfortable with passed closely behind him. Unipolar shape flow is what happens in the body when one moves in response to specific stimuli.

Unipolar shape flow involves growing towards beneficial and pleasant stimuli and shrinking away from unpleasant or noxious substances. With unipolar shape flow, the body part extends or contracts in one direction of the body axis. Unipolar shape flow is asymmetrical movement, providing an individual with mobility (Kestenberg Amighi et al., 1999). Unipolar widening and narrowing develop in the first year and facilitate turning over; unipolar

lengthening and shortening develop in the second year and facilitate climbing and standing on tiptoe; and unipolar bulging and hollowing develop between the second and third year and facilitate walking and running (Loman, 1989). Development of this movement pattern gives the infant a better understanding of body parts and their relationship to one another. Some examples of each pattern follow: unipolar widening: stretching an arm out to side to hold a friend's hand; unipolar narrowing: pulling an arm in close to get away from something unpleasant; unipolar lengthening: stretching up to get a book from a bookcase; unipolar shortening: flexing a knee to pull one's foot away from a nipping puppy; unipolar bulging: extending oneself forward to take in the wonderful smell of a flower; and unipolar hollowing: contracting back in the belly to stop oneself from running into a person ahead. The data and diagram on unipolar shape flow provide the dance/movement therapist with information about the client's feelings of attraction or repulsion to specific, discrete stimuli, as well as reveal if the client is overstimulated.

Shape-Flow Design (Diagram 7)

Imagine an observer of movement in an international airport sitting back to take note of the movement styles of people from all over the world. The observer in this environment may notice that there are those who make big gestures when speaking to others and those who are more contained with their gestures. The observer may notice folks who seem affable and permissive and those who seem curt and even rude. Shape-flow design is the movement that is representative of one's culture and interactional style.

Shape-flow design has to do with "the qualities of movements which individuals use to traverse the space around themselves known as the kinesphere" (Kestenberg Amighi et al., 1999, p. 139). These patterns are often influenced by one's cultural background. They reflect and capture movement directed towards and away from the body, with movement occurring in near, reach, or intermediate space. Interpretively, shape-flow design "reflects styles of relationships and manners, with linear, high amplitude and angular movement conveying a crude or forbidding attitude, and wavy, low amplitude and rounded movement conveying a polite or permissive attitude" (Kestenberg & Sossin, 1979, p. 155).

Shaping in Directions (Diagram 8)

Imagine situations in which one might move in a mechanical, robot-like, and/or linear manner. Some specific examples follow:

1. The construction worker signaled to stop moving forward.
2. The police officer indicated to cross there.
3. The little boy pointed to the bird and said "robin."
4. The school teacher directed her class to stop talking and look at her.
5. The aerobics class lifted their arms up and out to the side.
6. The weight lifter did bicep curls.
7. The soldiers turned to the right and saluted their captain.
8. The woman raised her hand to stop the advances of an aggressive stranger.

Shaping in directions involves dividing space in linear vectors to create bridges between oneself and objects; it often appears mechanical and robot-like. Further, shaping in directions provides the structure for learning and defending oneself. Movement occurs sideways or across, up or down, and forward or backward. Open shapes, such as sideways, upward, and forward, delineate the outer limits of access to the body and enlarge one's limits of exposure. Closed shapes, such as moving across, downward, and backward, bar access to and protect the body. The data gathered and diagrammed for shaping in directions informs the dance/movement therapist about her client's way of structuring his environment when learning something new and when defending himself and creating boundaries. Certain patterns may be helpful and beneficial in learning situations and when creating boundaries or protecting oneself; however, some patterns may hinder one's ability to learn, make new bridges, or defend himself.

Shaping in Planes (Diagram 9)

Imagine interactions with people that go beyond simply leaning towards and away from each other (as in unipolar shape flow) or relating in a linear, mechanical way (as in shaping in directions) but involve complexity and a higher level of relatedness. Some examples follow. They embraced and then walked side-by-side holding hands. They inspired others through their message of hope.

They got down to what mattered most as they worked on their campaign speech. They were able to reflect on their past and use what they learned as they looked to the future.

Shaping in planes is more complex and relational than shaping in directions, providing structure for multifaceted relationships to people and objects and for adaptation to reality (Kestenberg, 1985). Open and closed shapes, in this context, have to do with "two or three-dimensional concave and convex shapes which our movements sculpt in space" (Kestenberg & Sossin, 1979, p. 156). The shaping-in-planes patterns that create concave or open shapes are spreading, ascending, and advancing. The patterns that create convex or closed shapes are enclosing, descending, and retreating.

The data gathered and diagrammed on shaping in planes informs dance/movement therapists about how their clients tend to approach and relate to others. Work with these patterns alone or in combination with effort patterns can facilitate development of a wider range of approach and interaction styles. For example, a boy with communication and language difficulties has a habit of advancing (an open, shaping-in-planes pattern) towards people with acceleration (a fighting effort pattern). This approach style scares those he comes near, ultimately alienating him from others. Working with this boy on developing a more harmonious approach style (i.e., advancing with deceleration) would help him in his relationships with others (Hastie, 1991).

Using the KMP for Assessment

There are several ways to use the KMP for assessing others. Complete profiles or specific diagrams in the profile may be constructed. Pre- and post-profiling may done to evaluate treatment progress; and comparisons between profiles may be done when looking at parent/child relationships. Other ways to assess include notating and writing tension flow without scoring and making 'in the moment' assessments during individual and group sessions based on knowledge of the KMP.

Constructing Profiles

Kestenberg (1085) preferred that complete profiles be done. She felt that interpretations should be made based on looking at the whole profile. According to Kestenberg (personal communication, 1985), the most accurate and informed assessment of an individual could only be made by look-ing at the whole profile in all its breadth and complexity.

Profile construction begins with observing an individual naturalistically, in a live situation or through videotaped material. It is best to observe or have videotaped material of children in a variety of cross-contextual settings and at different times during the day, since their moods and feelings change often throughout the day and in response to different activities (Kestenberg, 1985; Kestenberg Amighi et al., 1999). It is best to observe adults when they are engaged in animated conversation and in varied activities, if possible. Also, it is important to note the immediate and broader context (i.e., cultural factors and recent significant events like 9/11), as well as the setting during each observation (Kestenberg, et al., 1999).

The entire process of observing, gathering data, and completing a profile takes approximately five to eight hours. The patterns that take the longest to identify, tally, and diagram are the tension-flow rhythms and tension-flow attributes. Making "in the moment" assessments and reflecting on sessions are based on knowledge of the KMP.

Often, there is not adequate time in one's clinical workday to construct complete profiles or even specific diagrams. Nevertheless, those trained in the KMP can still make "in the moment" assessments during individual and/or group sessions. A brief vignette of a client and an "in the moment" assessment and intervention follows:

> A nine-year-old male in 4th grade regular education has an extensive history in the foster care system. Also, he exhibits attachment disordered behavior and is diagnosed with ADHD. He also struggles socially.

Assessment

Client presents as highly distractible (spreading into his environment), impulsive (abruptness), and constantly moving (starting/stopping rhythm and perhaps excess unipolar – is overstimulated because he is attracted to lots of objects in his environment). Has great difficulty making any eye contact and twists away (using flexibility as a defense). Seems to have issues with the horizontal plane patterns of communication and paying attention, and with the shape-flow-shaping side of the profile. The boy is very mobile – seems to be using urethral and

outer genital rhythms. Decide establishing relationship with him is critical and take him to the gym to engage in running, jumping, and spurting activities. Including the spurting/ramming is one way of starting where he is at. Attuning to his abruptness, part of the urethral and outer genital rhythms, helps to quickly establish an empathic relationship and gets the boy to make eye contact and be more focused. Continuing to incorporate his movement preferences in therapy will help to firmly establish a therapeutic relationship and will help him feel seen and connected to which will enable him to be more receptive to other ways of moving and interacting. Knowledge of the KMP can be used as a guide throughout treatment to help in building attachment, communication, and social skills. Further, it can assist with ongoing assessment, understanding the developmental and psychological issues that emerge, creating a treatment plan, developing appropriate movement interventions, and evaluating treatment progress.

Research and Reliability of the KMP

In the past fifteen years, there have been increasing numbers of studies in dance/movement therapy research using the KMP in its whole or partial form (Binette, 1993; Bridges, 1989; Cruz, 2003; Daigle, 1993; Hastie, 1991; Lemon, 1990; Ojala, 1995; Williams, 1994). There have also been several interrater reliability studies on the KMP as a whole, as well as some focusing on specific diagrams in the profile (Burt, 1995; Hastie, 1991; Koch, Cruz, & Goodill, 2001; Sossin, 1983; 1987). The most current reliability study is anticipated to emerge in late summer 2004 and will look at tension-flow attributes, bipolar shape flow, and unipolar shape flow as part of a larger study on the KMP, parental stress, and parent-child interaction (Sossin, personal communication, June 6, 2004). Although the KMP demonstrates some reliability, future research is certainly needed.

Strengths and Limitations of the KMP

The KMP is an assessment tool that can be used with all ages. It is based entirely on the nonverbal and can be used on all clients. Further, it is a fairly unobtrusive tool, in that individuals can be observed and/or videotaped in natural settings. The complexity of the profile is similar to the complexity of working with movement in process. With the KMP, movement in process is captured on paper, tabulated, and diagrammed. The complexity of dance/movement therapy work requires an assessment tool that begins to capture the complexity of movement, which the KMP is capable of doing. Lastly, because the KMP movement terms describe universal qualities of movement, it can be used to assess individuals from diverse cultural backgrounds (Kestenberg et al., 1999).

One limitation of the KMP is that it requires time and study to learn; however, just like any language, the more one stays engaged with it and applies it (clinically or in research), the more one will truly come to understand it and be able to use it. Another limitation is that doing profiles takes time. However, the more practice one has in constructing profiles, the easier they are to do and the less time they take. Some additional limitations are: (1) profiles cannot be constructed on groups, (2) although the developmental norm research is essentially completed, it is not yet published or widely known, (3) interrater reliability is not fully established, and (4) the complexity of the profile can be challenging to understand and apply.

Benefits of the KMP

Knowing the KMP enriches one's work greatly, whether or not one constructs complete profiles. According to Loman (personal communication, 1991), the KMP heightens observation skills, further develops clinical skills (i.e., the ability to attune and adjust to clients, which supports the development of empathy and trust), facilitates the ability to assess and diagnose, aids in movement interventions and evaluation of the treatment process, and grounds the therapist in understanding both normal and abnormal development from a movement point of view. For Loman (1990; personal communication, 1991) and Levy (1988), the KMP assessments (of individuals or of parents and children) reveal areas of strength, vulnerability, compatibility, incompatibility, regression, and opportunities for growth. Lastly, they reveal the developmental level of an individual, which guides the dance/movement therapist in choosing the appropriate therapeutic intervention, such as attuning, providing support, creating structure, or instilling confidence (Loman & Sossin, 1983).

Studying and experiencing the KMP movement patterns on a body level – and then observing and kinesthetically attuning to those patterns – forever changes and grounds one's understanding and knowledge about development and nonverbal behavior. Familiarity with the profile facilitates communication about movement observation and assessment within the dance/movement therapy community as well as outside the field. Knowing the KMP brings the dance/movement therapist increased clarity, depth, and vision in all aspects of his/her work – facilitating sessions with individuals, families, and groups in all types of settings. Understanding and applying the profile in one's work balances intuition, enhances creativity, and most importantly, facilitates making new discoveries about movement and its meanings.

REFERENCES

Binette, L. (1993). *A KMP analysis of moshing: The study of communal ritual dance amongst adolescent males of the 1990s.* Unpublished master's thesis, Antioch/New England Graduate School, Keene, NH.

Bridges, L. (1989). *Measuring the effect of dance/movement therapy on the body image of institutionalized elderly using the Kestenberg Movement Profile and projective drawings.* Unpublished master's thesis, Antioch/New England Graduate School, Keene, NH.

Burt, J. W. (1995). *Body, face, and voice: Nonverbal expressions of emotion in infancy.* Unpublished doctoral dissertation, MCP Hahnemann University, Philadelphia, PA.

Cruz, R.F. (2003). Research Poster Session Abstracts, American Dance Therapy Association Conferences 2001 and 2002. *American Journal of Dance Therapy, 25* (1), 57–72.

Daigle, R. (1993). *Application of the Kestenberg Movement Profile to the clinical assessment of the mother-autistic child dyad.* Unpublished master's thesis, Antioch/New England Graduate School, Keene, NH.

Hastie, A. S. (1991). *In search of a standard form of assessment: The Kestenberg Movement Profile as diagnostic tool and treatment guide integrated into the practice of dance therapy.* Unpublished master's thesis, Antioch/New England Graduate School, Keene, NH.

Kestenberg, J.S. (1967). *Suggestions for diagnostic and therapeutic procedures in movement therapy.* American Dance Therapy Association proceedings, 2nd annual conference, 5–16.

Kestenberg, J.S. (1975). *Children and parents.* New York: Aronson.

Kestenberg, J.S. (1977). *The role of movement patterns in development I.* New York: Dance Notation Bureau Press.

Kestenberg, J.S. (1985). The role of movement patterns in diagnosis and prevention. In D.A. Shoskan and W.L. Roller (Eds.). *Paul Schilder: Mind explorer* (pp. 97–160). New York: Human Sciences Press.

Kestenberg, J.S., & Beulte, A. (1977). Prevention, infant therapy, and the treatment of adults: Toward understanding mutuality. *International Journal of Psychoanalytic Psychotherapy, Vol. VI:* 339–366.

Kestenberg, J.S., & Sossin, K.M. (1979). *The role of movement patterns in development.* New York: Dance Notation Bureau Press.

Kestenberg, A. J., Loman, S., Lewis, P., & Sossin, K. M. (1999). *The meaning of movement: Developmental and clinical perspectives of the Kestenberg Movement Profile.* The Netherlands: Gordan and Breach Publishers.

Koch, S.C., Cruz, R.F., & Goodill, S.W. (2001). The Kestenberg Movement Profile: Performance of novice raters. *American Journal of Dance Therapy, 23* (2), 71–87.

Lemon, J. (1990). *The use of dance/movement therapy in professional sport: A Kestenberg Movement Profile of Joe Montana.* Unpublished master's thesis, Antioch/New England Graduate School, Keene, NH.

Levy, F.J. (1988). *Dance movement therapy: A healing art.* Reston, VA: The American Alliance for Health, Physical Education, Recreation, and Dance.

Lewis, P. (1987). The unconscious as choreographer: The use of tension-flow rhythms in the transference relationship. *American Dance Therapy Association monograph, 4,* 22nd annual conference, 78–89.

Loman, S. (1988). Movement observation class notes. Keene, NH: Antioch/New England Graduate School.

Loman, S. (1989). Unpublished writings on shape flow.

Loman, S. (1990). Introduction to the Kestenberg Movement Profile. In P. Lewis & S. Loman (Eds.). *The Kestenberg Movement Profile, its past, present applications, and future directions,* (pp. 52–64). Keene, NH: Antioch/New England Graduate School.

Loman, S. (1991). Personal Communication.

Loman, S. & Kestenberg Amighi, J. (2002). The Kestenberg Movement Profile (KMP) as a tool for understanding diversity in learning styles and defense mechanisms. *Proceedings from the 37th annual conference,* Burlington, VT.

Loman, S., & Merman, H. (1996). The KMP: A tool for dance/movement therapy. *American Journal of Dance Therapy, 18* (1), 29–52.

Loman, S., & Sossin, K.M. (1983). *Clinical applications of the Kestenberg Movement Profile.* (unpublished manuscript).

Merman, H. (1990). The use of precursors of effort in dance/movement therapy. In P. Lewis & S. Loman (Eds.). *The Kestenberg Movement Profile, its past, present applications, and future directions,* (pp. 85–100). Keene, NH: Antioch/New England Graduate School.

Ojala, E. (1995). *Dance/movement therapy with a developmentally disabled adolescent utilizing the Kestenberg Movement Profile.* Unpublished master's thesis, Antioch/New England Graduate School, Keene, NH.

Sossin, K.M. (1983). Movement patterns of infant and mother and the ontonogenesis of aggression. Doctoral dissertation, Ferkauf Graduate School of Psychology, Yeshiva University, New York.

Sossin, K.M. (1987). Reliability of the Kestenberg Movement Profile. *Movement Studies: Observer Agreement 2,* 23–28. New York: Laban/Bartenieff Institute of Movement Studies.

Williams, A. (1994). *Dance/movement therapy and drama therapy as co-modalities with an adolescent population.* Unpublished master's thesis. Antioch/New England Graduate School.

Biographical Statement

Suzanne C. Hastie, MA, ADTR, NCC, LPC, is a registered dance/movement therapist who has worked in the mental health field with children, adolescents, women, families, and the elderly since 1989. She did part of her dance/movement therapy internship with Judith Kestenberg, MD at the Center for Parents and Children in Roslyn, New York in the late 1980s and is creator of *The Kestenberg Movement Profile Color Wheel* poster, a concise, visual representation of the KMP. In addition to working as a therapist, Ms. Hastie teaches courses on the KMP at Kinections in Rochester, New York and for the Drexel University Creative Arts in Therapies Program in Philadelphia, Pennsylvania. Ms. Hastie offers KMP-based supervision and consultation and may be reached at Lifemoving@aol.com.

Chapter 14

ASSESSMENT IN DANCE/MOVEMENT THERAPY

Robyn Flaum Cruz

INTRODUCTION

Dance/movement therapists use movement observations to provide important assessment data for the practice of dance/movement therapy (DMT). Regardless of the approach a dance/movement therapist uses, observing clients' movements and changes in movement including posture, integration of body parts, and other elements, makes DMT unique among the psychotherapies. No other psychotherapy focuses on the client's body and movement as the mediator for the relationship between the self and the external environment.

Dance/movement therapists use observations of movement in the DMT session to guide interventions used during the session; the ongoing assessment of the client's movement is the counterpart of listening by traditional verbal psychotherapists. For DMT research, changes in movement patterns are frequently a variable of interest or outcome indicator. Thus, movement observation serves a vital function in DMT and is the main form of assessment used by dance/movement therapists.

The purpose of this chapter is to describe the role of assessment in DMT practice and research and present information on specific ways in which assessment via movement observation is challenging. Means for supporting the credibility of movement observation assessment and a listing of available movement assessment tools are presented. Finally, two assessment tools, the Kestenberg Movement Profile (KMP; Kestenberg, 1979) and the Movement Psychodiagnostic Inventory (MPI; Davis, 1991), are presented and technological advances that may transform DMT assessment in the future are discussed.

DMT and Observational Assessment

DMT developed as a formal psychotherapy practice in the 1940s (Bartenieff, 1972). While international influences contributed to its development, the professional practice of DMT began in the United States. Today, DMT practitioners live and work in an impressive array of countries in different parts of the world including Argentina, Canada, England, Hong Kong, Ireland, Israel, Korea, Mexico, Norway, Puerto Rico, Scotland, Spain, Sweden, Switzerland, and the Netherlands.

At the genesis of DMT, pioneers Marian Chace, Mary Whitehouse, and Trudi Schoop, working independently of each other, took key elements of modern dance and began using dance and movement to address the needs of special populations, eventually creating the area of clinical practice known today as DMT (Chodorow, 1991). As Chace described it, "Dance therapy, as a discipline, did not move into the mental hospital full blown and as a bright idea to be sold" (Chace, 1975, p. 9). Instead, early dance/movement therapists had to discover and develop skills such as observation, interpretation, and the manipulation of dance elements such as rhythm and space to serve patients' needs. They observed their patients closely and extracted dance elements that could be used to make contact and communicate with them. The practice of DMT, especially with those who have very disabling conditions, remains similar today. DMT developed as an applied practice based on the assumption that movement reflects aspects of inter- and intra-personal functioning including pathological conditions (Bartenieff & Lewis, 1980). Dance/movement therapists regard movement as complex, individual, and expressive communication. Because the body and movement are the language of therapy, observation of movement is essential to assessment and intervention in DMT.

Observation and assessment of movement are functionally linked to what dance/movement therapists do in sessions. It is difficult to describe to individuals unfamiliar with DMT the immediacy of DMT clinical work and the demands it places on the therapist. The fact that the dance/movement therapist is unusually active compared to the standards of traditional verbal psychotherapy, is underscored by the reality that the dance/movement therapist and client are rarely seated in chairs unless the client has a physical mobility restriction. Dance/movement therapists are actually physically interactive in sessions in contrast to traditional verbal therapists and even some other creative arts therapists. This direct physical interaction in DMT and the dynamic quality of movement necessitate constant assessment and observation in the DMT session because many interventions are accomplished through movement. For example, the therapist frequently begins a session by observing subtle movements of clients and initiating a movement sequence that combines, reflects, and reproduces the qualities she or he observed. Dance/movement therapists refer to this as starting "where the client is," meaning the literal, observed physical expression of the client. From this beginning, the movement used in the session is similarly produced by the client first and expanded in quality, use of body parts, and other parameters via careful observation on the part of the therapist.

However, assessment in DMT is not limited to functional assessment of movement expression and interaction in the session. Dance/movement therapists also use clinical assessment in the traditional sense of collecting information on the client's functioning, diagnosis, and other means of understanding how to best meet the client's needs, to document progress, and set treatment goals. Movement observation serves as the core of clinical assessment in DMT; the therapist's observations are compared and contrasted to information from other sources. In addition, DMT researchers use formalized assessments of movement as important variables in studies that range from outcomes of treatment to identifying patterns associated with diagnosis. Of these three DMT assessment forms, functional and clinical assessments are more commonly used because of the profession's focus on practice.

Feder and Feder (1998) offered an excellent discussion of the many purposes for assessment that provides a worthwhile review for both seasoned and new clinicians (and researchers). The information they provide offers a solid introduction into any inquiry on assessment, including the importance of defining the (a) context, (b) purpose, and (c) precision of the information needed for the type of assessment that one desires (Feder & Feder, 1998). Readers will recognize these important elements in the remainder of this chapter, as they serve to focus any informed discussion of assessment.

In DMT, the context for assessment is significantly influenced by the population the client is associated with. For example, assessment of children necessarily differs from that of elderly individuals with Alzheimer's disease. Developmental stages and how they are embodied in children's functional and expressive movement are often a focus of DMT assessment for children, while impairments in range and quality of motion and affect frequently are the focus of assessment for the elderly with dementia (Berrol, Ooi, & Katz, 1997; Sossin, 2002).

DMT practice was originally focused on psychiatric hospital settings and those with mental illnesses or developmental delays. However, over time the populations with which dance/movement therapists work have expanded significantly to include such groups as medically ill children (Goodill & Morningstar, 1993; Mendelsohn, 1999), women with breast cancer (Dibbell-Hope, 2000; Serlin, Classen, Frances, & Angell, 2000), individuals with eating disorders (Krantz, 1999), individuals with Parkinson's disease (Westbrook & McKibben, 1989), trauma (Gray, 2001), and neurotrauma rehabilitation (Berrol & Katz, 1985). In a survey of dance/movement therapists, many reported working in the areas of wellness and personal growth, palliative care, medical illness, developmental disabilities, and addictions, yet 60 percent classified their work as psychiatric (Cruz & Hervey, 2001). Dance/movement therapists also work with infants and parents, children with autism and developmental disabilities, and the elderly, among other groups. As the range of populations seen in treatment by dance/movement therapists has increased, so has the need for assessment that is appropriate to many specific populations. Different assessment questions and tools are relevant for clients from different populations, for example, movement changes relevant to quality of life and coping style can be a focus in the treatment of women with breast cancer.

DMT practice settings have expanded to include public schools, clinics, and wellness centers. The characteristics of practice settings affect the context and purpose of assessments, including issues such as whether therapists work with individuals or groups, differences in length of stay related to control of health care costs, and the need to document effectiveness of services for insurance companies. For example, on an inpatient acute psychiatric unit, the dance/movement therapist may be part of a team that is focused on crisis intervention with a view to discharging the patient back to outpatient treatment in the community within seven days (see Riordan & Cruz, 2003). The purpose of assessment in this case might be to quickly determine if the patient has strengths that can be used to address their needs in the community. This type of quick, focused assessment is quite different from the type that can be done with someone in ongoing outpatient treatment over several years (see Lewin, 1998).

Dance/movement therapists may use existing movement observation tools or elements selected from them for clinical and formalized assessments. Movement assessment systems require very specific language for characterizing the movement parameters that are observed, and a popular movement language used in many DMT assessments is presented in the next section. In addition, important elements of observation and movement observation in particular are introduced.

DMT for Assessment

The first dance/movement therapists were professional dancers, and today dance/movement therapists continue to be individuals with substantial dance training. Thus, it seems natural that early in the development of DMT, a system of describing movement behavior devised by Rudolf Laban for notating dance choreography was adopted by many dance/movement therapists and remains the best-known system (Feder & Feder, 1998). Laban's system was influential in the development of assessment in DMT in that it provides both a vocabulary and a lens for focusing on the dynamic qualities of movement. Laban, a dancer and architect, developed an elaborate theory of movement, techniques of movement observation, and a system of notating movement that spread through Europe

after World War II. He had many students who carried his work to England and America where his theories had a profound effect on dance and dance education (Thornton, 1971). His system of observation and notation makes a key distinction between describing the spatial and dynamic aspects of movement apart from the actions performed, seeking to convey the qualities with which movement is performed. These qualities in turn impart feeling tones to movement. This distinction between spatial/dynamic aspects and action is important because it allows analysis of movement behavior apart from action so it can be used to describe functional and expressive movement as well as posture and the body at rest.

Laban's concepts were developed by Bartenieff, Lamb, and others into a system of movement assessment known both as effort/shape analysis (Dell, 1977) and Laban Movement Analysis (LMA). A concise introduction to the LMA concept of effort (weight, time space, and flow) and the flow and qualities of shape is beyond the scope of this chapter, but can be found in Feder and Feder (1998, pp. 288–291). DMT training programs in the United States teach movement observation using LMA and many dance/movement therapists obtain further training and certification in LMA. In addition, LMA provides a movement language that can be shared by dance/movement therapists. The basic concepts of the LMA system including effort, shape, space, and body context serve as a basis for diverse movement observation scales created by dance/movement therapists.

The Movement Psychodiagnostic Inventory (MPI, Davis, 1970; Davis, 1991) is a Laban-based scale created for observing the movement patterns of hospitalized psychiatric patients and used today to investigate involuntary movement disorder associated with severe psychopathology (Berger, 1999; Cruz, 1995). Kalish (1975) developed a body movement scale for autistic and atypical children that was influenced in part by the Laban descriptive language. North (1972) also used the Laban system to develop an assessment of personality for children, and the Kestenberg Movement Profile (KMP, Kestenberg, 1979) noting developmental movement patterns has a Laban base, and has been applied to a variety of populations with a focus on clarifying treatment issues (Kestenberg-Amighi, Loman, Lewis, & Sossin, 1999). The variability of these applications demonstrates the usefulness of

Laban's system in addressing various populations, contexts, and purposes for movement assessment. However, as Feder and Feder (1998) noted, not all DMT assessment scales are based on Laban's work.

Some examples of DMT assessments that are not based on Laban's work include Espenak's Movement Diagnostic Tests (Espenak, 1981), which combines elements of Adlerian psychology and psychomotor therapy, and the Functional Assessment of Movement and Perception (Berrol & Katz, 1985), which has a focus on rehabilitation after neurotrauma. Despite its title, Espenak's instrument does not involve diagnosis or testing. Rather it involves assessing body parts assumed to represent different psychological issues such as security and independence. Espenak did not attempt to validate or investigate the instrument empirically (Feder & Feder, 1998) so its application and appropriateness are not established. Berrol and Katz (1985) were careful to explicitly describe applications for their instrument and to develop it empirically as part of a large demonstration project (Berrol, Ooi, & Katz, 1997).

DMT assessment is as dynamic as movement itself, meaning that it must be flexible enough to address the many populations, contexts, and purposes for assessment that dance/movement therapists face on a daily basis in their work around the world. While it would be simpler if only one or two tools were available for all DMT assessment needs, the six different tools just mentioned and the range of populations and settings discussed should make it clear that this is not possible. Therefore, the most pragmatic and informative approach to DMT assessment is to consider the elements that must be tackled to make movement observation credible and useful. In the following sections, subjectivity, context and observer bias, validity, and reliability are presented as important elements in DMT assessment.

Elements of Movement Observation Assessment – Subjectivity

Any type of observation, including movement observation, has a subjective component created by the fact that perception can be compromised by the selectivity and prior knowledge of the observer, among other issues. As Cruz and Koch (2004) noted in a more extensive treatment of the topic, addressing the inherent subjectivity of movement observations begins with employing a system of descriptive terminology, such as LMA, for the movement behavior. The system serves to focus the observer on what to observe and provides a means of communicating it to others. This allows other observers to either confirm or disconfirm the observation, offering perspective on the original observation and its subjectivity relative to other observations. Subjectivity and bias affect clinical observations and observations for research purposes regardless of the observation tool. Observers must attempt to control their individual tendencies toward bias and selectivity in observing, and judging one's observations against those of another observer serves this important function. In clinical assessment, the therapist's intuition is a "synthesis of knowledge, experience, and recognition," (Feder & Feder, 1998, p. 216) from which clinical judgments arise. The subjectivity of these clinical judgments or assessments must be tested against observed clinical outcomes. Clinical judgments can be compromised by perception, assumptions, beliefs, values, and experiences – and scaling their subjectivity is vital.

Feder and Feder (1998) noted two different views on the subjectivity of clinical assessment that can also apply to formalized assessments. One view is that the clinician can work at minimizing subjectivity in assessment by using objective instruments or systems of observation based on empirical data, and the other view is that objectivity is unattainable and assessment is best left to the client. One DMT assessment procedure that has recently appeared in the literature does require clients to rate their own movement behavior by viewing videotapes made at different points in treatment (Bojoner-Horowitz, Theorell, & Anderberg, 2003, 2004). This is an interesting innovation in that it uses clients' subjective impressions of movement change as important research outcome data. Rather than seeing the two differing views articulated by Feder and Feder (1998) as opposing, clinicians and researchers might follow this example and effectively combine them to more rigorously address subjectivity and gain perspective that can be used to enhance the therapy or treatment.

In addition to addressing the subjectivity inherent in observing, observational assessments should be made systematically. Systematic observation implies that it is done the same way, in the same context, and at defined intervals. The research methods used for any research study dictate how, when, and where observations must be performed. Options such as choosing whether to structure the observation with explicit predefined categories, or employing a participatory stance by the observer are selected according to the research question and methods (Cruz & Koch, 2004). For clinical assessment, the dance/movement therapist must choose options that fit with his or her practice setting.

Elements of Movement Observation Assessment

Whether assessment is used for clinical or research purposes, the context for the observation is a truly relevant concern. Context is important because movement and the body can reflect any discomfort experienced by the individual who is assessed. Anxiety can be induced by clinical and research assessment settings and result in sweaty palms, shallow breathing, and other bodily signs or movement behaviors; context and its probable effects on individuals is an obvious area for consideration. Cruz and Koch (2004) made useful suggestions on enhancing naturalness in observing, but this may not always be possible. The therapist or researcher should always note how the context of the observation may have affected the movement behaviors of the client and exercise caution with interpretation.

The length of the observation is also relevant; depending on the length of the observation time, some noteworthy movement features with low baseline frequencies might not be observed. Length of observation time can also affect the practical use of an observation tool. Cruz and Koch (2004) noted that determining the required time frames for observations for many formalized DMT movement observation tools is an area for much needed research.

Observers, regardless of whether they are observing for clinical or research reasons, are subject to faulty observer tendencies that bias resulting assessments. For example, observers may base ratings on a general overall impression rather than the actual movement characteristics seen (a halo effect), observers may tend to use either the high or low end of a scale, or use the middle of a scale for all observations. McCoubrey (1984; 1987) suggested that observers using LMA may over- or underestimate the presence of their own personal movement preferences when observing others. It can be difficult to develop a sense of one's own

observer bias, but this is exactly the type of issue that can be addressed by regularly updating one's training with an observation tool. In addition, Koch, Cruz, and Goodill (2001) discussed generalizability theory as a technique useful for detecting observer bias that can be used in observer training.

All of the elements discussed to this point – subjectivity, context concerns, and observer bias – are of concern because they have an impact on the trustworthiness of the observations. In DMT as in other specialties, therapists and clients form relationships based on a common goal of moving the client toward greater health. Assessments are a part of that process, and therapists naturally want to trust that their observations contribute as they are intended. Likewise, observations used as part of research should be trustworthy or results will not be trustworthy.

Validity and Reliability of DMT

The trustworthiness of observational assessments is related to factors in assessment referred to as validity and reliability. To quote Cruz and Koch (2004), "validity is the degree to which an observation scale measures what it is supposed to measure (precision), while reliability is defined as the consistency or accuracy of the scores that result from the observation measurement process" (p. 45). When assessments are used to document the process or outcomes of the process for clinical or research goals, the meaning of the movement observed comes into sharp focus. Validity consists of the arguments and data that support how assessment observations can be interpreted. If a unique set of movement characteristics are interpreted to indicate that an individual has a personality disorder, for example, other types of evidence that support this interpretation of the movement assessment are needed. Reliability of assessment results can be supported by using more than one observer who independently arrives at the same rating of the movement characteristics. Validity and reliability of movement assessments can be supported by many different demonstrations that are beyond the scope of this chapter. However, an in-depth treatment of validity and reliability of movement observations is provided in Cruz and Koch (2004).

DMT assessment first requires a descriptive language for movement parameters. While LMA serves this function well, it is not a requirement as long as some other system or means for communicating clearly about the movement observed is provided. Although the descriptive language serves to address some of the subjectivity of the observer(s), control over bias and selectivity of the observer must also be maintained. Observations for clinical and research assessment need to be made systematically with attention to context and its potential to bias observed behaviors. Finally, evidence that can be used to argue for the validity and reliability of observations should be gathered. Specifications for all of these elements are usually easily addressed through selection and design for formalized assessments used in research, but may be problematic for clinical assessments. Some ideas and helpful guidelines to aide clinicians are thus in order.

Choosing and receiving regular training sessions in a movement observation system can benefit clinicians. One must choose a system that fits with the population that one treats the most. Grounding in an observation system can aid not only clinical assessments but also functional assessments. It provides a lens to focus observations in session and in more formal assessment, regardless of whether the therapist selects only elements of the system or uses the entire system. Active training with the system, even annual updates, helps address subjectivity and observer bias. If the training includes comparing one's observations to those of others, the therapist can get an idea of how reliable his or her observations with the system are. Setting up a regular time in or out of therapy sessions for systematic assessment observation is also helpful. As long as one chooses the same time for assessment, for example, even the first five minutes of every session, much is accomplished toward systematic assessment. Finally, developments in assessment systems and tools are ongoing. Staying in touch with the literature on DMT assessment can help the therapist martial cogent, evidence-based arguments on the validity of his or her assessment process.

DMT Assessment Tools

Two caveats are necessary before further exploration of formalized DMT assessment tools; all of these assessments require the user to be specifically trained; yet, most lack standardization to offer solid comparisons to a normative group. As opposed to pencil and paper assessments where users frequently read and follow directions for administration (e.g., Brief Psychiatric Rating Scale; Overall & Gorham, 1962), observational tools

require comparatively extensive training from a person who is an expert in using the system. This often involves onsite training using videotapes and can be time and labor intensive depending on the system. Part of the complexity of using the KMP or the MPI is that the task demand placed on the rater is intensive, even after the long and rigorous process of rater training is completed. Koch, Cruz, and Goodill (2001) studied the performance of a group of novice KMP raters who had 45 hours of comprehensive training. These raters had more difficulty observing unipolar shape-flow than bipolar shape-flow or tension-flow rhythms. Similarly, Cruz (1995) found differences in agreement among expert, experienced, and novice raters of the MPI, again indicating the importance of level of exposure and experience with an assessment tool.

Ideally, movement assessment systems for clinical or research use should offer comparative information about the individual assessed with regard to others from the same population and or individuals from contrasting populations. This requires that the assessment be extensively studied with large groups of individuals to generate normative data so that one can compare an individual's performance to what is typical of others. Table 14.1 displays a listing of movement observation tools with brief descriptive information. Of the assessment tools listed in Table 14.1, only the Body Movement Scale of the Behavior Rating Instrument for Autistic and Atypical Children (Kalish, 1975) used normative data in development, but the norm sample was relatively small.

Work is currently in process to develop norms for children for the KMP (Sossin, 2002), which will make a valuable contribution to this tool. There are several reasons why assessment tools for DMT lack comparative information: They reflect realities about the profession. Movement observation is time consuming and labor intensive, and developing large samples of individuals rated by more than one trained observer for reliability, requires financial research support resources. Historically, these resources have been scarce for dance/movement therapists, but there is some evidence that this may be beginning to change (Cruz & Hervey, 2001).

A range of formalized movement assessment tools are available for appraisal in DMT. The listing in Table 14.1 is not exhaustive, but it does include most of the tools that have been published or used in research. Complete reference material for locat-

Table 14.1.
Movement Assessment Tools for Dance/Movement Therapy

Movement Assessment Tool	Author	Population/Use
Body Movement Scale of the Behavior Rating Instrument for Autistic and Atypical Children (BRIAAC)	Kalish (1975)	Children with autism and other emotional/behavioral problems. Provides baseline for judging treatment progress.
Movement Diagnostic Tests	Espenak (1989)	Adults. Body dysfunction and personality traits.
Personality Assessment Through Movement	North (1972)	Normal children. Used to determine personality characteristics.
Kestenberg Movement Profile (KMP)	Kestenberg (1975)	See chapter text.
Movement Psychodiagnostic Inventory (MPI)	Davis (1991)	See chapter text.
Movement Signature Analysis (MSA)	Davis (1991)	Normal adults. Identifies individual "signature" patterns of movement.
Davis Nonverbal Communication Analysis System (DaNCAS)	Davis (1983)	Adults. Codes nonverbal aspects of psychotherapy.
Nonverbal Interaction and States Analysis (NISA)	Davis (1991)	Adults. Codes nonverbal interaction and emotional states.
Functional Assessment of Movement and Perception (FAMP)	Berrol & Katz (1985)	Individuals with brain trauma or injury. Behavioral assessment to identify motor dysfunction that impairs psychosocial functions.
Movement Observation Scale	Samuels (1972)	Adult psychiatric patients. Assesses movement repertoire and monitors changes in movement behaviors.
Psychiatric Movement Assessment Scale (PMAS)	Westbrook & Sing (1988)	Children. Psychiatric assessment.
Nonverbal Assessment of Family Systems (NVAFS)	Dulicai (1977, 1992)	Families, or child–caregiver constellations. Measures dynamics of interaction to guide treatment.
Functional Assessment of Movement (FAM)	Schappin (unpublished)	Adult psychiatric inpatients. Codes nonverbal interaction and interpersonal behavior. Also used in outpatient adults with developmental delays (see Sack, 2001; Sack & Bolster, 2002).

ing more information on each one is located by author(s) in the reference section of this chapter. The list is notable for its focus on psychiatric populations, and for the numbers of populations that are not included. It underscores the inclusion in this chapter of guidelines for clinicians for creating assessments that are relevant to their populations, settings, and purposes. The following sections provide more detail on two of the assessment tools that have often been used in clinical and research contexts.

The Movement Psychodiagnostic Inventory

Designed to be used in continuous observation and recording of videotaped sessions of one-on-one clinical interviews, the MPI can be used in live observation and was actually developed in this manner (Davis, 1970). A total of 65 items, some of which are LMA based, are contained in the inventory and rated throughout the observation. When ratings are made from videotape, raters are allowed to stop the action of the tape and view segments again in order to be confident of their ratings. The items are divided into two sections: The Action Inventory and the Primary Inventory. Items in the Action Inventory reflect the context of the observation, rating conventional, nonverbal behaviors associated with maintaining conversation. These items are organized into seven subscales: (1) Gesture, (2) Self-touch Action, (3) Instrumental Action, (4) Orienting Action, (5) Head Movement, (6) Facial Movement, and (7) Posture. An example of an item in the Action Inventory is item 10 in the Head Movement subscale, "head movements with speech: 0 = clearly accompany, 1 = nods or shakes only or very rare accenting moves, 2 = none" (Davis, 1991). The Action Inventory items are theoretically different from the Primary Inventory items. Davis (1991) described the Action Inventory as ambiguous and context sensitive. Further, Davis stated that the items are not considered indicators of pathology but parameters of nonverbal communication that are valuable as a frame for the observation.

The Primary Inventory is made up of specific patterns of involuntary and voluntary movement described by 51 items grouped into 10 categories. The 10 subscales of the Primary Inventory are (1) Disorganization, (2) Immobility, (3) Low Intensity, (4) Low Spatial Complexity, (5) Perseveration, (6) Flaccidity, (7) Diffusion, (8) Exaggeration, (9) Hyperkinesis, and (10) Even Control. An example of an item from the Primary Inventory is item five in the Disorganization subscale, sequence of weight shifts and/or weight in stillness disorganized. For example, one part shifts, then another in a different direction, etc., and/or body does not come to balanced rest. The MPI has been revised several times (Davis, 1974; 1991).

Clinically, the MPI has been used with its target population, adults with severe and persistent mental disorders, since the first version was developed in 1970. Originally, Davis (1991) hypothesized that certain MPI items indicated a more severe level of pathology than others. Yet, Cruz (1995) found that pattern across categories rather than the hypothesized items separated individuals with schizophrenia and borderline personality disorder. Patterns of scores in MPI categories distinguished using multivariate techniques, discriminated between patients with schizophrenia and those with personality disorders. Distinguishing between these groups based

on motor behavior might not be that difficult for untrained raters; yet, it was not degree or severity of scores but pattern across indicators that proved to be important. Further, Cruz (1995) found evidence for the validity of the MPI as a measure of motor disorder in the patterning of MPI items along the hyperkinesia–hypokinesia continuum traditionally used to classify motor disorder by neurologists. It was hypothesized that the MPI may represent a finer level of distinction of motor disorder than has been traditionally defined.

In a related study of movement characteristics in individuals with borderline and narcissistic personality disorders, Berger (1999) found that these two groups could be distinguished with 86 percent correct classification using the MPI, and again with a focus on pattern across categories. It is fairly easy to argue that untrained observers would not distinguish between these diagnostic groups based only on motor behavior. The surprising finding across these two studies is that a level of diagnostic specificity was obtained based purely on motor behavior indicators for diagnoses that are typically made based on extensive interview and history taking. The MPI appears to have potential for making diagnostic distinctions, but must be investigated more thoroughly with larger and more diagnostically varied samples of reliably diagnosed patients than used previously. Its use with children and adolescents with serious and persistent mental disorders has not been investigated, but motor signs related to severe psychopathology would not be expected to only occur in adults.

The Kestenberg Movement Profile

A more general measure of movement behavior than the MPI, the KMP measures the frequency of occurrence of a set of movement features, and provides interpretation for developmental and clinical issues, and personality traits. It combines LMA with frequency observations, and originally used Anna Freud's (1965) psychoanalytic theories and developmental assessment as the framework for interpretation. However, Kestenberg-Amighi, Loman, Sossin, and Lewis (1999) discussed the KMP as primarily movement assessment that can be integrated with other theoretical models such as the relational model and Body Mind Centering approaches.

The KMP was intended to measure the development of movement behavior of infants in an attempt to better understand normal development, prevent and treat developmental problems, and provide clinical diagnosis (Kestenberg, 1995). It has been adapted and successfully used for assessment of adults (Bridges, 1989) and individuals in intercultural contexts (Kestenberg-Amighi, 1990). The current version of the KMP is appropriate for individuals of all ages (Kestenberg-Amighi, Loman, Sossin, & Lewis, 1999). The system consists of nine categories of movement patterns whose elements are notated, quantified, and translated into frequency diagrams that represent developmental constructs. Observers also construct body attitude portraits based on assessment of persistent movement patterns. The KMP is designed to note everyday movement from video or live observation, and adult movement is usually rated from animated conversation (Koch, Cruz, & Goodill, 2001). The KMP differentiates more than 62 single elements.

The theory that underlies the KMP differentiates two major subsystems of movement behavior. The tension-flow/effort system (System I) describes the individual's needs, drives, affect, character, learning styles, defenses, and coping mechanisms. The shape-flow/shaping system (System II) describes both simple and complex ways of relating to environmental stimuli such as objects and individuals. Thus, the tension-flow/effort system assesses the dynamic qualities of movement, and the shape-flow/shaping system notes movement aspects that provide structure for expressing movement qualities.

The wide range of clinical applications of the KMP is well represented in Kestenberg-Amighi, Loman, Sossin, and Lewis (1999), and enhanced by the mention here of a few recent research applications. Koch (2004) has used the KMP to analyze gender specific movement behaviors of team leaders and team members in industry. They found differences in the use of tension-flow rhythms between male and female leaders with women using significantly more indirect efforts than men. Lotan and Yirmiya (2002) used elements of the KMP to explicate sleep problems in toddlers. The children's movements were analyzed as they were falling asleep, and results showed that movement variables predicted the length of the falling asleep phase significantly better than other variables associated with the falling asleep phase including duration of pacifier or thumb sucking and presence of objects in the bed. This research offers just two examples that nicely demonstrate the contribu-

tions DMT-based assessment methods can make to other important areas, such as the psychology of gender and child development.

CONCLUSION

Movement observation is an essential form of assessment for DMT, born of the therapist's need to build interventions based on the client's movement in the session. Early dance/movement therapists began this practice by using elements of modern dance to communicate symbolically with patients. As the profession has grown over the last six decades, the need for clinical and formalized assessments to guide treatment goals and provide data for research have served to increase the importance of movement observation to the profession. Because of the diverse nature of DMT practice, no single assessment tool is appropriate for all assessment needs in DMT. This chapter has presented an introduction to assessment in DMT and offered guidelines for practically addressing the issues surrounding movement observation useful for clinicians and researchers.

There are innovations on the horizon for movement observation that will most likely have an impact on assessment done for DMT research. Already, technology is available that tags videotape instances for observers to focus on that can improve reliability (Brugman & Kita, 1995; Noldus, 1996). But in addition, work is progressing on advanced software that recognizes and records LMA (Eisenberg, 2003). These improvements in technology have the potential to allow validity studies of many movement parameters that can inform DMT practice by providing empirical support for many of the assumptions that are held about the role of movement and the meaning of movement in therapy and everyday life. The future should prove to be exciting new terrain for DMT and DMT assessment.

REFERENCES

Bartenieff, I. (1972). Dance therapy: A new profession or a rediscovery of an ancient role of the dance? *Dance Scope, Fall/Winter*, 6–18.

Bartenieff, I., & Lewis, D. (1980). *Body movement: Coping with the environment*. New York: Gordon and Breach.

Berger, M. R. (1999). Movement patterns in borderline and narcissistic personality disorders. *Dissertation Abstracts International: Section B: The Sciences & Engineering, 60*(9-B), April 2000, 4875.

Berrol, C. F., & Katz, S. S. (1985). Dance/movement therapy with individuals surviving severe head injury. *American Journal of Dance Therapy, 8,* 46–66.

Berrol, C. Ooi, W. L., & Katz, S. (1997). Dance/movement therapy with older adults who have sustained neurological insult: A demonstration project. *American Journal of Dance Therapy, 19,* 2, 135–154.

Bojoner-Horowitz, E., Theorell, T., & Anderberg, U. (2003). Dance/movement therapy and changes in stress-related hormones: A study of fibromyalgia patients with video-interpretation. *The Arts in Psychotherapy, 30*(5), 255–264.

Bojoner-Horowitz, E., Theorell, T., & Anderberg, U. (2004). New technique for assessment of self-perception in fibromyalgia patients: A pilot study with video-interpretation. *The Arts in Psychotherapy, 31*(3), 153–164.

Bridges, L. (1989). *Measuring the effect of dance/movement therapy on body image of institutionalized elderly using the Kestenberg Movement Profile and projective drawings.*

Brugman H., & Kita, S. (1995). Impact of digital video technology on transcription: A case of spontaneous gesture transcription. *Ars Semiotica, 18,* 95–112.

Chace, M. (1975). *Marian Chace: Her papers.* H. Chaiklin (Ed.). Washington, DC: American Dance Therapy Association.

Chodorow, J. (1991). *Dance therapy and depth psychology: The moving imagination.* London: Routledge.

Cohen, L., Sargent, M., & Sechrest, L. (1986). Use of psychotherapy research by professional psychologists. *American Psychologist, 41,* 198–206.

Cruz, R.F. (1995). An empirical investigation of the Movement Psychodiagnostic Inventory. *Dissertation Abstracts International: Section B: The Sciences & Engineering Vol. 57*(2-B), August, 1996, 1495.

Cruz, R. F., & Hervey, L. W. (2001). The American Dance Therapy Association research survey. *American Journal of Dance Therapy, 23*(2), 89–118.

Cruz, R. F., & Koch, S. (2004) Issues of validity and reliability in the use of movement observations and scales. In R. Cruz & C. Berrol (Eds.). *Dance/movement therapists in action: A working guide to research options.* Springfield, IL: Charles C Thomas, Publisher, Ltd.

Davis, M. (1970). Movement characteristics of hospitalized psychiatric patients. *Proceedings of the Fifth Annual Conference of the American Dance Therapy Association, 25*–45.

Davis, M. (1972). *Understanding movement behavior: An annotated bibliography.* New York: Arno Press.

Davis, M. (1983). An introduction to the Davis Nonverbal Communication Analysis System (DaNCAS). *American Journal of Dance Therapy, 6,* 49–73.

Davis, M. (1974). *Analysis of movement styles and interaction in psychotherapy.* Paper presented at the First International Symposium on Nonverbal Aspects and Techniques of Psychotherapy, Vancouver, BC.

Davis, M. (1991). *Guide to movement analysis methods part 2: Movement Psychodiagnostic Inventory.* (available from [Martha Davis, 1 West 85th Street, New York, NY 10024]).

Dell, C. (1977). *A primer for movement description* (2nd ed.). New York: Dance Notation Bureau.

Dibbell-Hope, S. (2001). The use of dance/movement therapy in psychological adaptation to breast cancer. *The Arts in Psychotherapy, 27*(1), 51–68.

Dulicai, D. (1977). Nonverbal assessment of family systems: A preliminary study. *Art Psychotherapy, 4*(2), 55–62.

Dulicai, D. (1992). Nonverbal family therapy assessment: Evaluation and application. *Proceedings, 27th Annual Conference of the American Dance Therapy Association,* pp. 1–4. Columbia, MD: ADTA.

Eisenberg, A. (2003, October 9). Decoding the subtle dance of ordinary movements. *The New York Times.*

Espenak, L. (1981). *Dance therapy: Theory and application.* Springfield, IL: Charles C Thomas, Publisher, Ltd.

Feder, B., & Feder, E. (1998). *The art and science of evaluation in the arts therapies.* Springfield, IL: Charles C Thomas, Publisher, Ltd.

Freud, A. (1965). Normality and pathology in childhood: Assessments of development. In *The writings of Anna Freud, Vol. VI.* New York: International University Press.

Goodill, S., & Morningstar, D. (1993). The role of dance/movement therapy with medically ill children. *International Journal of Medicine, 2,* 24–27.

Gray, A. (2001). The body remembers: Dance/movement therapy with an adult survivor of torture. *American Journal of Dance Therapy, 23*(1), 29–43.

Kalish, B.I. (1975). Developmental studies using the Behavior Rating Instrument for Autistic and Atypical Children (BRIAAC) [Summary]. *Proceedings of the Ninth Annual Conference of the American Dance Therapy Association* (pp. 131–136).

Kestenberg, J.S. (1979). *The role of movement patterns in development* (Vol. 2). New York: Dance Notation Bureau Press.

Kestenberg, J. S. (1995). *Sexuality, body movement and rhythms of development.* Northvale, NJ: Jason Aronson, Inc.

Kestenberg-Amighi, J. (1990). The application of the KMP cross-culturally. In P. Lewis & S. Loman (Eds.). *The Kestenberg Movement Profile: Its past, present applications and future directions* (pp. 114–125). Keene, NH: Antioch New England Graduate School.

Kestenberg-Amighi, J., Loman, S., Lewis, P. & Sossin, K. M. (1999). *The meaning of movement: Developmental and clinical perspectives of the Kestenberg Movement Profile.* Amsterdam: Gordon Breach.

Koch, S., Cruz, R., & Goodill, S. (2001). The Kestenberg Movement Profile: Performance of novice raters. *American Journal of Dance Therapy, 23,* 71–87.

Assessment in Dance/Movement Therapy   143

Koch, S. (February, 2004). *Men and women at work: KMP analysis of movement qualities.* Poster presented at the 1st international dance/movement therapy research colloquium of the BTD, Hanover, Germany.

Krantz, A. M. (1999). Growing into her body: Dance/movement therapy for women with eating disorders. *American Journal of Dance Therapy, 21,* 81–103.

Lewin, J. N. (1998). *Dance therapy notebook.* Washington, DC: American Dance Therapy Association.

Lotan, N. & Yirmiya, N. (2002). Body movement, presence of parents, and the process of falling asleep in toddlers. *International Journal of Behavioral Development, 26*(1), 81–88.

Martin, P.R. (1989). The scientist-practitioner model and clinical psychology: Time for a change? *Australian Psychologist, 24*(1), 71–92.

McCoubrey, C. (1984). *Effort observation in movement research: An interobserver reliability study.* Unpublished master's thesis, Hahnemann University, Philadelphia, PA.

McCoubrey, C. (1987). Intersubjectivity vs. objectivity: Implications for effort observation and training. *Movement Studies: A Journal of the Laban/Bartenieff Institute of Movement Studies, 2,* 3–6.

Mendelsohn, J. (1999). Dance/movement therapy with hospitalized children. *American Journal of Dance Therapy, 21,* 65–80.

Noldus, L. P. (1996). *The Observer: Base package for Windows reference manual* (3rd ed.). Wageningen, The Netherlands: Noldus Information Technology.

North, M. (1972). *Personality assessment through movement.* London: Macdonald & Evans.

Nicholas, M.J., & Gilbert, J.P. (1980). Research in music therapy: A survey of music therapists' attitudes and knowledge. *Journal of Music Therapy, 17*(4), 207–213.

Overall, J., & Gorham, D. (1962). The brief psychiatric rating scale. *Psychological Reports, 10,* 799–812.

Riordan, K., & Cruz, R. F. (October, 2003). *Acute care dance/movement therapy practice in 2003: Descriptive data.* Poster presented at the 38th annual conference of the American Dance Therapy Association, Denver, CO.

Sack, J. (October, 2001). *Assessment in the creative arts therapies: When an assessment of movement is an assessment of functioning.* Poster presented at the 36th annual conference of the American Dance Therapy Association, Raleigh, NC.

Sack, J. & Bolster, G. (October, 2002). *Scoring and interpreting movement: Using the Functional Assessment of Movement (FAM) scale in multi-modal research.* Poster presented at the 37th annual conference of the American Dance Therapy Association, Burlington, VT.

Samuels (1972). Movement change through dance therapy: A study. *American Dance Therapy Association Monograph, 2,* 50–77.

Serlin, I., Classen, C., Frances, B., & Angell, K. (2000). Symposium: Support groups for women with breast cancer: Traditional and alternative expressive approaches. *The Arts in Psychotherapy, 27,* 123–138.

Sossin, M. (October, 2002). *Recent statistical and normative findings regarding the KMP: Implications for theory and application.* Paper presented at the 37th annual conference of the American Dance Therapy Association, Burlington, VT.

Thornton, S. (1971). *A movement perspective of Rudolf Laban.* London: Macdonald & Evans.

Westbrook, B. K., & McKibben, H. (1989). Dance/movement therapy with groups of outpatients with Parkinson's disease. *American Journal of Dance Therapy, 11,* 27–38.

Westbrook, B. K., & Sing, M. (1988). A psychiatric movement assessment scale with developmental considerations. *The Arts in Psychotherapy, 15* (1), 37–46. Unpublished master's thesis, Antioch New England Graduate School, Keene, NH.

Biographical Statement

Robyn Flaum Cruz, Ph.D., ADTR, is director of Creative and Expressive Arts Therapies at Western Psychiatric Institute and Clinic of the University of Pittsburgh Medical Center; Vice President, American Dance Therapy Association; Editor-in-Chief of *The Arts in Psychotherapy*; and contributor and co-editor of *Dance/Movement Therapists in Action: A Working Guide to Research Options* (Charles C Thomas, Publisher, Ltd.).

Chapter 15

IN-SCHOOL DANCE/MOVEMENT THERAPY
FOR TRAUMATIZED CHILDREN

Rena Kornblum and Robyn Lending Halsten

INTRODUCTION

The purpose of this chapter is to provide the reader with an understanding of how Dance/Movement Therapy (DMT) can be used in a school setting to help children who are dealing with trauma. An overview of DMT and trauma are provided, followed by a description of how the school staff and the therapists work together to make this program successful. Specific therapeutic techniques are discussed and illustrated with photographs and examples. This gives the reader a way to conceptualize some of the techniques used. All the names of the children have been changed to protect their privacy. Some of the photographs are from actual therapy sessions and some are not.

Theoretical Background

Dance/Movement Therapy (DMT) is the psychotherapeutic use of movement that supports integration of the mind, body, and spirit into the healing process (Levy, 1992). At the root of DMT is the premise that body movement reflects the inner emotional landscape. Change on a physical level, such as change in movement behavior, posture and muscular tension, will have an effect on emotional functioning. Unlike practitioners of traditional forms of psychotherapy, Dance/Movement Therapists (DMTs) believe that there is an intricate and undeniable connection between people's history, thoughts, feelings, behaviors, and their bodies (Levy, 1992).

> As DMTs we believe that the body is a vessel that contains all of who we are and that, when treating trauma, to leave our clients' bodies out of the therapeutic milieu would be ludicrous. What sets DMT apart from other body centered psychotherapies is that we incorporate all the elements of dance and movement while integrating traditional forms of psychotherapy into the therapy session. We are not afraid to have our clients literally move their bodies through space and help them to find satisfying ways to be in and connected to their bodies. Safe movement-based structures provide a frame/container from which clients can explore their creativity as well as their mental health issues. (Meekums, 2002)

Below is an example illustrating how movement through space was used to contain and settle strong feelings.

> It is 8:00 Monday morning and one of the boys in our DMT group is distraught. The weekend had been filled with domestic violence resulting in several visits from the police. His father sustained a broken arm, left home and has not returned. Sleep deprived and anxious, Rory is agitated. The rest of the group identifies strongly with him. They become fragmented, wiggling around and inter-

Figure 15.1. Moving through space.

rupting each other. They all have difficulty staying on task.

The group needs to move through space in order to mobilize their energy in a safe way. They stomp, jump, and slash with scarves; all to music containing a strong beat which served as an organizing tool. Afterwards, there was a sense of cohesion and settling. The boys requested an activity they had previously enjoyed: one boy at a time lay on a cloth while the others pulled him around the room. This allowed for regression and care taking (laying down, being pulled) while also stimulating the surface areas of their bodies that were in contact with the floor and cloth. This type of stimulation is nurturing and pleasurable; it helps to settle and reaffirm body boundaries. Working as a team to pull each other around supported building trust and connection. The initial overarousal and agitation transformed into feelings of being empowered and centered; they were ready to move on to another phase of the group.

Effects of Trauma

An overview of the effects of trauma provides the reader with a framework for understanding the therapeutic issues presented by the children we see in therapy. Trauma affects the body, impacting ego development, body image, emotional integrity, attachment, and interpersonal relationships. Trauma leading to Post Traumatic Stress Disorder (PTSD) involves events that are so disturbing that long-term (lasting more than a month) psychological, physical, and emotional effects are experienced (DSM-IV, APA, 1994). Feelings of intense fear, horror, helplessness, and hopelessness are prevalent. One result of this distress is that certain elements related to the trauma intrude upon people well after the actual event. Triggers bearing a vague relationship to the original trauma (sounds, smells, visual stimuli) may activate a physical and chemical response in the body that leads to overarousal (van der Kolk, 1996). It is as if the trauma is happening at that moment. PTSD in children and adults can result in avoidance of events associated with the trauma, a general numbing of responsiveness, irritability or outbursts of anger, difficulty concentrating, accepting nurturance, falling or staying asleep, nightmares, and an overactive startle or fear response. Disorganized or agitated behavior may be seen, with persistent re-experiencing of the trau-

matic event emerging via play themes and dreams (DSM-IV, APA, 1994).

Even if the trauma has not been physical in nature, i.e., witnessing abuse of another, it is the body that often becomes the battleground through which the trauma gets reenacted. This can come in the form of a fight-flight response, freezing, self-mutilating, self-injurious behavior, addictions, dissociation, and fragmentation, all of which can be observed in the body (van der Kolk, 1996).

Trauma and Children

Trauma not only impacts children's ability to play and negotiate but also fragments their internal experience of who they are. Two of the principal tasks of childhood are learning to negotiate collaborative relationships internally as well as externally. How one relates to his/her internal world will affect how one develops relationships with the outer world (van der Kolk, 1996). When children are traumatized, their most vulnerable parts of themselves are often exiled out of consciousness as a way to protect the self and survive. Other parts of themselves come forward to numb and disorganize, helping them to dissociate, lash out, escape, freeze – all in the service of protection and survival (Schwartz, 1995). Disorganized, impulsive, and sometimes dangerous movement often covers the more intact and healthy parts of the individual.

The following is an example of some typical movement qualities and behaviors that may be seen in children dealing with trauma.

> Travis had a history of severe trauma and was part of a group of 3rd grade boys seen in DMT. Travis easily became disorganized and had difficulty modulating his affect. It was hard for the other boys in the group to connect with him because of his out-of-control, unpredictable behavior. He regularly invaded others' personal space, interrupted and provoked anger.

During the movement warm-up, Travis often flailed about and fell on other people, necessitating an adult standing on either side of him to make sure he did not hurt himself or others. On this particular day, one of the boys took a turn leading the warm-up with movement containing sharp contrasts in speed and direction, moving towards the center of the circle and back out again. He kept the group from colliding by carefully watching and changing the direction whenever someone got too close. He received positive verbal and nonverbal feedback from the therapists and the other boys. When it was Travis's turn to lead, he emulated the other boys' carefully phrased movements and, for the first time, was able to organize his body so that the rest of the group could follow his movements. The rest of the group responded positively. He had found a way to make a satisfying connection! This session became a turning point.

In subsequent sessions, Travis asked to do solo "Warrior" dances (a theme we had been working on). The therapists had him choose and commit to moving and dancing in a prescribed space delineated by a large carpet. He was not to move off the carpet, for his safety and ours. It became a physical and emotional container for him and he tried with every fiber of his being not to step off or move outside this boundary. This was challenging due to his impulsivity and disorganization. The therapists worked with him to develop a clear beginning and ending ritual to center and ground him. Travis would stand with his feet together while reaching his arms up for a deep breath. His palms would meet over his head pressing together as he would bend his elbows and bring the focused energy down through his arms and torso while slowly bowing. Additionally, he would kick, punch, slash, and do karate chops in the air while making strong eye contact with the group. Travis was showing us his strength and he was being seen and celebrated. When doing these dances he stayed in control and learned to center/settle.

Collaborating with the Schools

One great advantage of providing DMT in the school is that for many children, it is their only access to therapy. Issues of drug and alcohol abuse, poverty, spousal abuse, and their own trauma histories often overwhelm the families of the children we treat, making the task of seeking and following through with therapy virtually impossible. In our role as DMTs, we meet with families/caretakers on an as-needed basis, providing education, emotional support, outside referrals, and occasionally family therapy. We attend team meetings with school staff and other professionals involved with the families outside of the school.

Successful DMT groups in a school setting require a regular place to meet, consistent times for the groups, a good working relationship with the support staff, and respect for the privacy of the ther-

apy session. That is not to say that we are not flexible and accommodating to the school's schedule and variability. While the size requirement is flexible, having the same room available on a weekly basis is critical. Trauma groups run for 60–90 minutes once a week for the entire school year. Sixty minutes is a minimum to allow deep material to emerge and to have time to work with it. Our groups are not open groups. We rarely add new children after the first few weeks the group has met. This provides consistency and allows trust to develop.

Our group size ranges from two to eight children, with the larger groups having adult volunteers acting as aides. In general, we do not lead trauma groups without a co-therapist because of the deep emotional material the children have to deal with and the potential need for one-on-one work when intense issues are triggered. Collaborative work with another therapist also provides an opportunity to deal with countertransference issues that may be activated.

DMT Process in Schools

The principal, social worker, and school psychologist, using input from school staff, decide who need services the most. As soon as permission for treatment is obtained from the school, we schedule an intake meeting. It can take two or three attempts before a parent shows up even when we arrange to come to their home due to the disorganized nature of the families we serve.

During the intake, we gather information about the family, provide an introduction to DMT with particular emphasis on the structure of our groups, and discuss the concept of confidentiality as it pertains to in-school therapy. We explore the child and parent's strengths and interests as well as their trauma background and other problem areas. Parents sign a permission for treatment form and releases enabling us to talk with any other agencies or professionals involved. In a school setting, the therapeutic contract is between the therapist and the family as well as between therapist and the school, thus extending the usual concept of confidentiality. We will not see a child in the school setting without permission to discuss issues with the school staff and vice-versa. We still, however, use discretion regarding what is shared.

Before the groups start, we meet with the children individually to orient them to the group and the room we will be using. We also meet with each

Figure 15.2.   There is no right or wrong way to move.

teacher to get information and share our goals for therapy. Teachers are much more supportive if they feel that their input is valued.

A View of a DMT Group

As DMTs, we start from a child's strengths and build on them. There is no right or wrong way to move or be creative as long as nobody is hurting themselves or others. This helps to build a sense of empowerment and trust. We believe that regardless of any child's history or experience there are always intact and healthy parts of themselves that may be upstaged by behavioral issues and internal states of overarousal. Movement experiences in the therapy session develop collaboratively between the therapists' assessment and observation, and input from the children.

General Goals of Trauma-Based DMT Groups

- Build a sense of empowerment
- Increase sense of safety and control
- Increase ability to feel pleasure
- Expand movement repertoire & increase self-awareness
- Improve ability to modulate feelings
- Increase ability to empathize with self and others
- Develop group synchrony
- Link internal experiences to verbal expression
- Increase awareness of others
- Increase ability to self-soothe

In the early stages of therapy, children will often ask why they are in the group. We try to elicit answers from the group so that we are not put in the position of authority. This sets the tone for a collaborative relationship and allows themes around trauma to organically unfold. At the same time, without the therapist bringing up the topic of violence or trauma, children usually feel that it is a taboo topic and do not talk about it. They need to know the adults in the group can handle the intensity of their experiences and are not afraid of their feelings (Friedrich, 1990; James, 1989). We usually include a statement to start the session off. For example, in a domestic violence group we might say, "Everyone in this group has experienced or witnessed violence. This group is a place for us to share our feelings, learn ways to be safe, and have fun together. We are here to learn and move together so that you can have safe relationships." Group guidelines for safety and confidentiality are discussed and developed with input from the children.

The discovery of common painful experiences, early in the course of therapy, creates a bond and many children begin to disclose material that may be anxiety-producing, leading to overarousal. We believe that anxiety is inherent when working with traumatized children. Containing, supporting, and making space for the exploration of anxiety helps to decrease overarousal and is critical to the work we do. Here are a few of the many ways we help children work with their anxiety:

1. Allowing the children to use movement to express their feelings while disclosing, or in response to the disclosure,
2. Slowing down the sharing by reminding the group about confidentiality or by checking in with group to see how everyone is feeling,
3. Using relaxation and grounding techniques such as abdominal breathing or rhythmic movement, and
4. Developing movement-based therapeutic stories, which act as a metaphor for working through intense feelings.

The following example illustrates how we support a child's need to disclose while providing structures that help her and the group deal with anxiety and overarousal.

In the initial session of the school year a girl named Preeta graphically revealed traumatic events surrounding her parents' fights. Over the next several weeks, after Preeta would tell the group about these fights her anxiety increased. She would either hide in the therapy room (she regularly hid in a closet when her parents fought) or become agitated, leaving the sharing circle to twirl and spin, as a way to self-soothe. We gave Preeta permission to move, accepting her behavior. We asked the rest of the group how they felt and how they thought Preeta might be feeling. The group was able to identify with Preeta's upset feelings and offered support by joining her in her hiding place, offering hugs or moving and twirling with her.

While the group was sympathetic with Preeta, they also got frustrated because she had difficulty regulating her intensity and frequently, though not intentionally, hurt others in the group. To help deal with this, we taught the group a technique we use in all our groups, in which anyone, at anytime, can call "times." At this point, everyone must stop what they are doing, sit down with hands on knees, and listen to whoever called "times." We tried to call "times" before Preeta got overaroused, asking the group to take some slow breaths or talk about what was happening in the moment. Over time, Preeta began to regulate her own excitement level, finding the control she needed to make safe connections with other children in the group.

Children depend on predictable routines to feel safe. We generally have the same five parts in each DMT session: (1) Opening ritual; (2) Verbal/nonverbal check-in; (3) Movement warm-up; (4) Theme, creative movement story; and (5) Snack and verbal processing. Opening rituals can involve intense gross motor movement as well as quiet meditation. The ritual depends on the needs of the group and once it is established it tends to remain stable for the duration of therapy. A simple gross motor ritual used with one high-energy group involved starting on one side of the room with the boys' feet on a line and running as fast as they could across the room, stopping on another line. Sometimes intensifying or matching high energy is needed before being able to bring it down to a more manageable level.

A meditation ritual was used in several groups to create a sense of calm readiness in preparation for inner exploration. This involved lighting a candle, and sitting quietly on a pillow while wrapped in a colorful piece of fabric. The cloth provided something for impulsive children to hold on to, decreasing the likelihood of touching a burning candle.

Wrapping in the cloth also provided the children with a tool for self-soothing and settling. Fabric can give tactually defensive children a way to be "held" without being touched. Physical contact can be overwhelming for some children and trigger a PTSD response.

The movement ritual is followed by a verbal/nonverbal check-in. This is a time for sharing, listening, and developing empathy. It is also a time for the therapist to get a feel for the themes and issues that are currently important to the group. What is not shared is just as important as what is talked about. The check-in is a time when commonalities/differences can arise. One group discovered that everyone had pets and siblings, a pleasant commonality to balance the pain of everyone having witnessed or experienced violence. We look for a range of commonalities so the group is not defined only by traumatic experiences.

Sometimes a child is too overwhelmed to share verbally. During one check-in, for example, a child curled up in a ball instead of sharing with words. Instead of pushing the child to talk, the therapist recognized that the child was showing the group how she felt. After checking with the client whether it was okay to try on her movement and body shape, the therapists and other group members mirrored her (matching her shape and energy). This supported our client, allowing her to feel understood and accepted on her level. Accepting clients where they are, seeing and being with them, with all their feelings, happens in many ways and on many levels. Being able to do this is an essential part of our work.

A movement warm-up follows check-in, consisting of both structured and unstructured movement

Figure 15.3. Building group cohesion through rhythmic movement.

experiences designed to help the children connect and develop awareness of their bodies, and feel settled and supported by the group. When check-in elicits intense feelings, the warm-up allows for a physical release of tension and anxiety. Strong rhythmic music is sometimes used to provide a sense of inner organization and structure for the movement. The warm-up provides opportunities for using strength and assertion safely, connecting to self and others, strengthening boundaries, sustaining synchrony, and pursuing other goals, which we decide are important for the group. The children are given the chance to move together rhythmically as well as to solve movement challenges creatively. They have opportunities to lead the group and they also practice following each other, which builds group cohesion. The warm-up is structured by the needs of the group on any given day and often sets the tone for the group. The following example illustrates how utilizing different levels of space and rhythm can help build group cohesion.

A group of boys finishes check-in. They are impulsive and intrusive. Warm-up usually starts with the group standing in a circle taking turns leading the group through full body movements, but today the boys are hitting each other, falling over, giggling nonstop, and are ignoring self-settling suggestions. The group is instructed to sit on the ground (lowering the center of gravity increases impulse control). The therapists start rhythmic openhanded drumming on the ground and chanting about getting in control (rhythmic movement provides organization). The boys join in spontaneously. After they are able to follow and lead different rhythmic patterns on the floor, we move the drumming to the body.

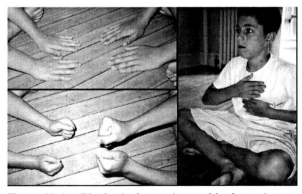

Figure 15.4. Rhythmic drumming and body patting settles and affirms the self.

This helps them to feel into themselves, almost as if with each self-directed pat of their hands they are saying, "I am me." Chanting in synchrony, the boys quickly become focused, settled, and grounded.

The movement experiences provided in the warm-up help children build and practice new skills. These skills function in a concrete way, for example, helping a child become more aware of his/her space so intrusion is diminished. They also build internal concepts/ ego functions, e.g., when children do not intrude in others' space and have safe ways to protect their own space, people interact with them differently, they feel more accepted socially, more aware and in-control. Behavioral choices increase. The warm-up works on these two levels in a creative, nonthreatening way. The facilitators also use this part of the group to gauge the group's energy level as well as to identify areas that need more work.

Following the warm-up, we decide, with the clients, what themes will be explored, either through a movement-based story or through structured movement experiences. These themes emerge out of the material presented in check-in and warm-up. Some of the more commonly occurring themes are safety, danger, dealing with conflict and anger, nurturance, trust, empowerment, and safe assertion. This part of the session allows the children to use movement, creative process, and verbalization as a metaphor for unresolved issues.

The following is an example of how material that emerged in the early parts of a session developed as themes in our therapeutic story time.

During check-in, the children described how their parents were fighting about visitation with them and how confusing and scary it felt. During the movement warm-up, we experimented with the different ways one could physically be pulled in two directions. This provided them with a way to physically explore their internal experience. The children then decided they wanted to do a story about parents fighting. Ground rules were set to establish safety when role-playing the fighting parents. The children set up two homes (with an adult in each home) on opposite sides of the room, as well as a "safe place" (with a helping adult) where the children could go for support whenever they needed to. The children told the adults what they should be saying and how they should be acting towards each other. This gave them the locus of control as opposed to being a passive witness/victim. They

Figure 15.5. A baby animal is born during a movement story. Child and therapist are wearing a spandex sack, symbolic of their animal skin. The child emerges from the therapist's sack.

were literally mobilized, able to move to a place of safety and comfort while they explored their feelings and thoughts. They could become a witness to their own process, naming how confusing, scary, and uncomfortable it was for them. They also had a chance to share how they would like things to be between their parents and what they could do in reality when their parents were fighting. Each child came up with a safe plan.

Assessment and Treatment

Movement observation is used as an assessment tool in evaluation and treatment. After observing a child moving over a period of time and notating his/her movement, we look at clusters of movement characteristics as being indicators of possible mental health issues. Below are some of the issues related to PTSD with corresponding movement parameters, client descriptions, and treatment approaches (Kornblum & Perry, 2003).

Dissociation

- Eyes glazed or fixed
- Limited movement expression
- Facial expression flat or fixed

- Limpness or extreme rigidity
- Shallow breathing
- Delayed/limited responsiveness to others

Case of Dissociation in a Child

Ashley, a pale six-year-old girl, with shallow breathing, looked frozen. Her body showed a high level of tension. She sat during verbal check-in without moving. Her expression was blank, showing no emotion or reaction to the other girls. There were almost no gestures when she spoke and her voice lacked inflection. When it was time for the group to move, she got up last, looking confused or dazed, stating that she did not know what to do. Her movements tended to be small, tense, and restricted.

Treatment Approaches

Directive rhythmic movement eliminated Ashley's anxiety over deciding how to move. A therapist stood next to her and modeled full body breathing. Ashley was able to move more fully and expand her breathing. Experimenting with exaggerated facial and body movement, she (intensifying her small, tense, and restrictive movement and then recuperating with a full breath, more open movement) got everyone, including Ashley, giggling. Humor at the right time is a wonderful antidote to disassociation.

Hyperarousal

- Fleeting or poorly sustained eye contact
- Difficulty focusing or attending to one object
- Energy/excitability – extremes high and low
- Energy not appropriate to task
- Tactually or spatially defensive
- Hypervigilance: frequent alerting to stimuli
- Difficulty self-calming
- Using extreme ways to self-settle
- Poor spatial awareness – intrusive – crashing into animate and inanimate objects
- Impulsive phrasing (starts with burst of energy), inability to inhibit action when aroused

Case of Hyperarousal in Child

Ray is a seven-year-old boy with a history of severe trauma and a pattern of tantrums at almost every transition in school. He would come into therapy in a disorganized way, throwing his backpack in one direction and his coat in another, all while talking very loudly and excitedly. During the movement warm-up he would move with large gestures that he had a hard time controlling. He would become physically intrusive and his gaze would shift rather quickly, never resting in one spot. If we would move physically closer to him in an attempt to provide support, he would move away. This ordinarily very coordinated young man would end up accidentally hurting himself or someone else. He never connected the "accidental hurting of someone" to anger.

Treatment Approaches

Giving Ray a solid structure to push against (the wall) helped him funnel his energy, feel empowered, and in control. He pushed his back into the wall with his knees bent and feet firmly planted on the floor. Additionally, he experimented with other ways to push. Using his weight and strength in this way helped Ray literally feel grounded and connected to his body. Ray was also invited to make any sounds or words that he wanted to while pushing. This not only deepened the use of breath to support the fuller, more integrated use of his body but also provided an opportunity to express emotions or thoughts. One time Ray yelled with a clear voice, "Get off me. Leave me alone." He repeated this several times. Perhaps this provided Ray with an opportunity to move and say what he had been unable to at other times in his life. Pushing with sustained strength helped Ray gain control of his impulsiveness.

Figure 15.6. Pushing with sustained strength against the wall.

Attachment Issues

- Manifestations of tension or anxiety
- Poor eye contact
- Excitability not always related to outward stimuli
- Low frustration tolerance
- Lack of sustained synchrony
- Difficulty with self-calming
- Tactually and/or spatially defensive
- Phrasing short and repetitive
- Gestural movements in kinesphere lack full range, breath shallow

Case of Attachment Issues in Child

Sy, a seven-year-old boy with a history of neglect and abandonment in the first year of life, showed clear signs of attachment issues. Whenever he did not get his way or he felt unsure of his ability, he withdrew, moving away from the group. His body was tight and rigid with collapsing in his upper torso, which made taking full breaths impossible. He would pull his arms tightly across his chest, an attempt to hold himself and protect his heart. Even though he was well coordinated he was unable to match and join the movements of others or let others join him (synchrony). His rigid and inflexible body was reflected through an inability to negotiate with others to get his needs met, feeding his feelings of hopelessness. When approached for comfort and problem solving, he would reject any attempts at connection.

Treatment Approaches

When Sy was upset, allowing him some space to withdraw to and some time to be alone was important. Finding ways to join him after a few minutes passed was a challenge. A slow indirect approach was necessary; moving toward him from the side, not head on. Matching his posture and mood (attuning) by sitting at his side in the same position as he was and verbally naming what was happening with him, ("I noticed you moved away from the group. You look like something is bothering you.") would be followed by Sy sharing his feelings of helplessness, powerlessness, and despair. Accepting his desire not to be touched and resisting the desire to suggest ways to become empowered were the only ways in. Providing the acceptance given to most children as infants allowed Sy the experience of being accepted for who he was with all his feelings. Pushing games and active fantasy games were other techniques that provided outlets for Sy's feelings and allowed him to remain connected to others for longer periods of time.

Depression (Withdrawn or Avoidant-Hyper)

- Body Attitude – Concave (or Convex if avoidant)
- Diminished use of breath
- Diminished gestural use – tends to be close or far, possibly lots of self-touch
- Energy level too low or high
- Facial expression neutral, or fixed
- Eye contact diminished
- Lack of spontaneity
- Physical expression of attention diminished
- Somatic concerns and poor hygiene

Case of Depression in a Child

Ann, a seven-year-old girl with a history of loss and abuse, presented herself as passive, withdrawn, and helpless. While the rest of the group danced to music with a strong beat, Ann would crawl around in slow motion with two pillows balanced on her back. She kept her head down and made no attempt to protect herself from other group members who might be dangerously close to her. There was no variety in her tempo or the intensity of her crawling, no change in her facial expression, which looked sad (quiet despair), and no attempt to interact with anyone while she crawled. Her breathing was shallow and all movements were close to the body and repetitive. This same slow, laborious

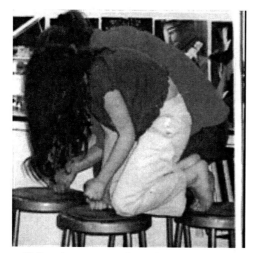

Figure 15.7. Attunement through mirroring.

crawling movement was repeated for several weeks with no variation.

Treatment Approaches

In our experience, it is not unusual to see children return to the developmental stage that the original trauma occurred. We see this in terms of the spatial level accessed (the floor), the movements (crawling), and body posture as well as through sounds and verbalizations. When we are able to attune to a child through our movement, at the developmental stage she or he presents, a dramatic shift occurs, allowing the child to mobilize. For example, after Ann was mirrored in her crawling position and symbolically held by the therapist through her movement, breathing and energy, and then she became more active. The turtle disappeared and a feisty, energized girl emerged.

Anger Issues

Anger in clients can trigger many feelings in therapists such as fear, anxiety, and anger. Many clients want to get rid of it permanently. We find that it provides useful material to work with, mobilizing clients and informing them about what they might want to change.

- Difficulty with self-calming and self-control
- Low frustration tolerance
- Intentional spatial intrusiveness
- High tension level
- Labile emotions – mood changes frequently
- Chest breathing – fast and shallow
- Facial expression – mouth tight, eyebrows down
- Strength and suddenness emphasized
- Movement tends to be impactive (accent at end such as in stamping or punching)

Case of an Angry Child

Rory, a 2nd grader with a background of domestic violence, had anger outbursts up to ten times a day. Happy one minute, and full of rage the next; his outbursts consisted of stamping, pushing others, yelling, and running away. Sometimes the anger seemed to be triggered from his own thoughts and feelings, and at other times by what was going on around him. He had a difficult time calming down and rejected any attempts at problem solving or comfort.

Treatment Approaches

Our willingness to match Rory's intensity with our movement and vocalizations let him know we were not afraid of his feelings. The entire group, including the therapists, warmed-up with high intensity movement such as punching, growling and stomping to strong rhythmic music and shouting, "No," or "I won't." This provided an energetic release, resulting in a decrease in arousal and an increase in relaxed attentiveness. We then taught the group a four-part movement technique for calming down called the 4B's of Self-Control (Kornblum, 2002).

1. *BRAKES:* Catch your energy, pushing the heels of your hands together close to your chest.
2. *BREATHING:* Take three slow calming breaths while lifting your arms overhead.
3. *BRAINS:* Rest hands on your head (fingers intertwined) and tell yourself, " I can calm down."
4. *BODY:* Put both hands on your chest and feel your body get calm and quiet.

We practiced abdominal breathing (stomach and chest rise together when inhaling, and sink when exhaling), a key element in calming down, and worked on recognizing early body signals of excitement, e.g., heart rate increasing or feeling ears or cheeks getting hot. We used the image of temperature rising in a thermometer to indicate higher arousal, signaling the need to do the 4B's.

One day while talking about what anger felt like inside the body, Carry, a girl in the group, provided an image the rest of the group could relate to. She said that her anger felt like balls were bouncing wildly inside her body. In response, the therapists structured an activity that allowed the group to experiment with this image. We all stood inside a purple circle of stretchy spandex cloth (the cloth metaphorically represented the body) that went over our back and hips, leaning back into the cloth so that we were all supporting each other. Each child was given a turn to enact her/his anger, running and bouncing into the cloth while the rest of the group anchored the "container." The children were wonderful as anchors, empowered by successfully supporting each other, releasing their anger, and seeing that nobody lost control.

Potential Treatment Approaches

- We always *start from a child's strengths* and *accept each child* where they are at the point of entering therapy.
- *Going with the resistance* can contain acting-out behavior by transforming it into something positive.
- *Acknowledging the positive* instead of focusing on the negative builds health and self-esteem. It works on behavioral control because its builds a positive model of reinforcement.
- *Synchrony* is used to develop attunement and group cohesion.
- *Rhythmic music or movement* serves as an organizing structure.
- A *circle formation* can increase awareness of others and develop group cohesion.
- The *calling of "Times"* is used to slow down the group process, thereby controlling arousal, leading to empowerment, providing the opportunity to express opinions and problem solve.
- *Directive movement* (structured activities) can be used to build skills and decrease anxiety.
- *Exaggeration/intensifying a characteristic movement or posture* invites recuperative movement in the opposite direction, allowing for the release of held patterns.
- Providing an *individual space* for each child (marked by a pillow, carpet square, or bean-bag chair), which no one may enter without permission, provides a place to retreat to when overaroused or threatened and develops a sense of safety and boundaries.

Figure 15.8. Comfort and nurturance in a child's individual space.

- *Humor* is a way to connect with difficult or disassociated children and reduce anxiety.
- *Being physically next to a child* helps with self-control and models new behavior options.
- *Pushing with sustained strength* against a wall or therapist builds control, centers, and grounds.
- *Movement stories* use metaphor to create distance and safety in the therapeutic process.
- *Mirroring* provides attunement experiences.
- *Asking clients questions about internal sensations (Tracking)* keeps clients in the present.
- *Concrete techniques, e.g., the 4B's of Self-Control,* de-escalate and build confidence and mastery.
- *Transitional objects* such as soft pillows, beanbag chairs, and stuffed animals provide security and nurturance. Cloth or fabric wrapped around the body develops boundaries and supports containment. Moving with transitional objects such as scarves or spandex bands provides an external focus and may be used to unify a group as well as inspire wider movement repertoire.

CONCLUSION

It is essential that therapists working with trauma survivors have a strong foundation to work from. Healing is not a linear process. It works like a spiral, cycling through defenses, emotional upheaval, trust, skill building, and periods of arousal and settling. The therapists' ability to be present with their clients physically, emotionally, and spiritually allows creative and spontaneous responses to emerge in therapy.

The way we provide trauma-focused DMT for children is through establishing a sense of safety and developing multiple movements, behavioral and emotional options. Variations in the techniques and approaches we create are unlimited because they continually develop and change in response to the individual or group. We actively engage the children in creating a safe space to explore their trauma internally as well as externally, putting the locus of control with the clients. This shows them that we trust their healing process and takes them out of the victim role. Our ultimate goal is for our clients to begin to internalize a sense of containment so they may learn to hold all the parts of themselves with love and compassion.

REFERENCES

American Psychiatric Association (1994). *Diagnostic and statistical manual of mental disorders* (4th ed.). Washington, DC: American Psychiatric Association.

American Psychiatric Association (2000) *Diagnostic and statistical manual of mental disorders* (4th ed.). Text Revision (DSM-IV). Washington, D.C.: American Psychiatric Association.

Dosamantes-Beaudry, I. (2003). *The arts in contemporary healing.* Westport, CT: Praeger Publishers.

Friedrich, W. N. (1990). *Psychotherapy of sexually abused children and their families.* New York: Norton & Co.

James, B. (1989). *Treating traumatized children: New insights and creative interventions.* New York: The Free Press, Simon & Schuster Inc.

Karp, C.L., & Butler, T. L. (1996). *Treatment strategies for abused children.* London, United Kingdom: Sage Publications, Inc.

Kornblum, R. (2002). *Disarming the playground: Violence prevention through movement and pro-social skills.* Oklahoma City, OK: Wood 'N' Barnes.

Figure 15.9. Moving with scarves.

Figure 15.10. Attunement through mirroring.

Kornblum, R., & Perry, Kristin. (2003). *Mental health assessment through movement (MHAM)*. Unpublished.

Lars. (Ed). (1996). *Traumatic stress*. New York: The Guilford Press.

Levy, F. (1992). *Dance/movement therapy: A healing art*. Reston, VA: National Dance Association, American Alliance for Health, Physical Education, Recreation, and Dance.

Meekums, Bonnie, (2002). *Dance movement therapy: A creative psychotherapeutic approach*. London, England: Sage Publications.

Schwartz, R. C. (1995). *Internal family systems therapy*. New York: The Guilford Press.

van der Kolk, McFarlane (1996). The black hole of trauma. In van der Kolk, Bessel A, McFarlane, Alexander C., Weisaeth, Lars (Eds.). (1996). *Traumatic stress*. (pp. 3–19). New York: The Guilford Press.

van der Kolk, M. The body keeps the score: Approaches to the psychobiology of posttraumatic stress disorder. In Van der Kolk, Bessel A., McFarlane, Alexander C., Weisaeth, Lars (Eds.). (1996). *Traumatic stress*. (pp. 214–241). New York: The Guilford Press.

Biographical Statements

Rena Kornblum, MCAT, ADTR, DTRL, brings over twenty-five years of professional experience as a dance/movement therapist to her therapy and prevention work in elementary schools. Ms. Kornblum obtained a Masters in Creative Arts in Therapy from Hahnemann University and is a member of the Academy of Dance Therapists Registered. She has been on the faculty at the University of Wisconsin-Madison for over twenty years. She developed the children and family program at Hancock Center for Movement Arts and Therapies, a center for Dance/Movement therapy where she recently became the Executive Director. Rena has written a book called *Disarming the Playground: Violence Prevention Through Movement*, published by Wood and Barnes Publishers, and edited two training videos by the same name, all of which describe her prevention curriculum in detail. She was recently selected to receive the 2002 Wisconsin Dance Council Research and Journalism Award and became licensed in the state of Wisconsin to practice psychotherapy specifically through the expressive arts therapies.

Robyn Lending Halsten, M.A., ADTR, DTRL, has been working in the field of Dance/Movement Therapy for 20 years. She has worked with children, adolescents, and adults dealing with trauma, mental illness, and eating disorders in inpatient clinical settings as well as in the community and public school settings. Ms. Halsten obtained her Masters of Arts in Dance/Movement Therapy from Columbia College in Chicago where she has taught, guest lectured, and supervised students working towards their Masters in Dance/Movement Therapy. She has lectured and presented her work nationally. She is trained in The Internal Family Systems Model of psychotherapy and integrates her Dance/Movement Therapy expertise with this model. In addition to Robyn's work as a Dance/Movement Therapist, Robyn also photographed all the pictures in Rena Kornblum's curriculum and book called *Disarming the Playground: Violence Prevention through Movement* and filmed and helped edit the two training videos that complement the book. She is on staff as a therapist at Hancock Center for Movement Arts and Therapies and has a private practice consulting.

Chapter 16

MEDITATION AND MOVEMENT THERAPY FOR CHILDREN WITH TRAUMATIC STRESS REACTIONS

Deborah A. O'Donnell

INTRODUCTION

Children around the world dance, sing, and play. They have vivid imaginations, enjoy moment-to-moment life experiences, and seem to intuitively understand the interconnections between mind and body in ways that far surpass most adults. Unfortunately and increasingly, children who dance, sing, and play also witness, are victims of, and perpetrate violence. When these frightening violent experiences are extreme enough to be characterized as outside the scope of normal human experience, the developing mind and body can develop traumatic stress reactions. These reactions to an overwhelming and confusing experience can take many forms, including disruptions in perception, cognition, and emotion. Sadly, if left untreated or if improperly treated, such reactions can lead to more treatment refractory forms of brain, mind, and body dysregulation that may persist into adulthood. Adults with long-term traumatic stress reactions may have difficulty in forming a stable sense of self and maintaining rewarding interpersonal relationships. The purpose of this chapter is to explore meditation and movement therapy with trauma survivors.

Contemporary trends in child trauma exposure paint a bleak picture. Both in inner-city neighborhoods and rural and suburban locales, witnessing of – and victimization by – violence among youth are alarmingly commonplace. More than 40 percent of youth in one inner-city community reported witnessing a shooting or stabbing in the preceding year and 74 percent reported feeling unsafe in one or more common environmental context (Schwab-Stone et al., 1995; Schwab-Stone

et al., 1999). Violent environments such as these produce their effects on multiple intra- and interpersonal levels, setting into motion a cascade of effects in a self-perpetuating cycle (Blair, 2002). This cascade of effects influences the full spectrum of psychological and biophysiological functioning, including brain mechanisms, gene expression, emotion, cognition, and behavior (Glaser, 2000; Kandel, 2001). These effects, in turn, influence the environment through a child's interface with the world.

It is at this intersection of the child and her environment that traumatic stress reactions develop. These defenses against an unforgiving environment appear to emanate from the sensory and perceptual level of processing and expand to affect cognition, emotion, and other higher order mental activities. As clinicians who engage and treat children exposed to trauma, meeting our child clients at this sensory-perceptual level will afford us maximum success in guiding a traumatized child through the recalibration of his sensory physiological functioning which has been damaged by its overwhelming encounter with a frightening and uncontrolled set of sensory experiences.

These physical body experiences, while impaired and often maladaptive among traumatized human organisms, are a source of deep enjoyment and expression among groups of humans in every part of the world. The motivation to create expressive body movement and its accompanying sensory stimulation seems an inherent part of the human condition. In many societies, movement, dance, and physical control of the automatic process of breathing are prominent components of family, community, and religious life. So central are these experiences to daily existence that physical, mental, emotional, and spiritual mind-body connections naturally emerge. These physical manifestations of human living do not take place in a vacuum. Rather, they occur within the context of language, culture, and other forms of mental abstraction. Culturally encoded in rites and rituals, movement and meditation accompany major life transitions and facilitate the integration of individual and society in much of the world. Of particular interest to the field of psychology, indigenous forms of traditional healing often incorporate movement and meditation into methods of releasing tension, relieving suffering, and providing spiritual calm (Vontress, 1999).

Western View of Movement/Meditation

Traditionally, Western society has not placed as much emphasis on movement and meditation as means of cultural scaffolding of daily life as have other cultures. The credo of dualism, or the distinct separation of body and mind, that became central to Western thought as scientific empiricism pervaded the intellectual community may have structured our understanding of the workings of life in a way that does not particularly value the role of automatic physical processes. As a result, an isolation of movement and meditation from everyday Western experiences and realities seems to have developed. Even in our highly technologically advanced society, in the absence of attention to automatic physical functions and survival mechanisms, higher order brain processes may lack a sound foundation (Levy, 1992). When this foundation has been shaken by exposure to trauma, the ramifications become even more pronounced.

Rebuilding a traumatized child's inner world in an attempt to restore a firm sensory-perceptual foundation should be the goal of traumatic stress interventions. These techniques, in the spirit of mind-body integration, will require the use of varied methods. Eclectic approaches to psychotherapy, which emphasize the use of a variety of therapy techniques tailored to the needs of the client, the nature of the therapeutic relationship, and the expertise of the clinician are becoming increasingly common. Some of these approaches incorporate movement and meditation techniques targeting the mind-body interface where traumatic stress reactions develop. This chapter explores the use of movement and meditative therapy approaches with children experiencing traumatic stress reactions, examining these techniques within a psychophysiological theoretical framework.

What Is Trauma and What Are Traumatic Stress Reactions?

The *Diagnostic and Statistical Manual of Mental Disorders (DSM-IV*; American Psychiatric Association, 2000) defines a trauma as "an event or events that involve actual or threatened death or serious injury, or a threat to the physical integrity of self or others" (p. 218). Traumatic stress reactions are mechanisms by which the human organism responds to trauma's impact on brain, mind, and body activities. Traumatic stress reactions arise from, and give rise to, a variety of processes.

Violent trauma leaves its mark on the developing human brain through changes in three main mechanisms: Brain anatomy, neurochemistry, and hormone production. In all of these phenomena, the concepts of neural plasticity and use-dependent development are crucial (McEwen & Magarinos, 1997; Nelson & Carver, 1998). These terms refer to the human brain's tendency to conform itself, through allocation of neurochemicals, production of neural connections, and speed of neural impulses, to its environment. A child growing up in a positive and stimulating environment, then, will experience brain development that emphasizes neural connections in brain areas devoted to adaptive responses to a welcoming world. Conversely, a child growing up in a violent, unpredictable, or negatively stimulating environment will experience more pronounced brain development in the neural areas devoted to detection of threat, automatic protective responses, and fear. A violent traumatic event overwhelms a child, disrupting homeostasis and creating a compensatory response that leads to a less functional new state of equilibrium (Perry, 2001). These neuroanatomical and neurophysiological changes secondary to trauma may directly decrease a child's ability to express feelings in words. Cognitive and academic impairment in traumatized youth have been consistently documented in a number of studies (Coster, Gersten, Beeghly, & Cicchetti, 1989; McFadyen & Kitson 1996). Wodarski and colleagues (1990) studied a group of physically abused youth, finding that 60 percent of the neglected and 55 percent of the abused youth had repeated at least one grade, compared with 24 percent of the comparison group.

Numerous stress reactions affecting brain function have been identified in individuals with Posttraumatic Stress Disorder (PTSD), such as smaller brain volumes and hippocampal size. The hippocampus plays an important role in memory formation, and its disruption may explain in part the memory impairment seen in victims of trauma (Bremner et al., 1995, 1997; DeBellis, Baum, & Birmaher, 1999). Others have shown decreased activity of the anterior cingulate, an area of the brain that inhibits the amygdala and other regions of the brain involved in the fear response (Shin et al., 1999). Studies have shown that the hypothalamic pituitary axis and autonomic nervous system, two body systems involved in stress reactions, can both over or under-react as a result of early traumatic experiences (McEwen & Magarinos 1997; Yehuda, Spertus, & Golier, 2001).

Trauma activates victims' stress-response system with either heightened or diminished physiological arousal when confronted with cues of the trauma (Keane, Kolb, & Kaloupek, 1998). Among children, the most readily accessible response to the pain of trauma often involves the activation of dissociative mechanisms consisting of disengagement from the external world through the use of primitive defenses such as depersonalization, derealization, numbing, and, in extreme cases, catatonia (Perry & Pollard, 1998). Dissociation is protective, allowing the child to psychologically survive the trauma. Over time, however, it can become maladaptive, emerging at inappropriate times during, for example, situations that may trigger verbal or bodily memories of earlier trauma.

If many of a child's experiences are characterized by violence or danger, future experiences – whether objectively violent or not – will likely be viewed through a "template" expectant of violence and danger. State-dependent recall is the process through which memory is triggered through exposure to sensory or affective stimuli similar to stimuli present when a memory is formed (Godden & Baddeley, 1975). In trauma survivors, state-dependent recall can be seen when internal and/or external cues that symbolize or resemble an aspect of the traumatic event (i.e., sights, smells, sounds, or emotional experiences present during the trauma) result in re-experiencing of the traumatic event. Research indicates that youth exposed to chronic violence are more likely to expect violence, hostility, and aggression in their environments and to perceive these traits to exist even when they objectively do not. The hostile attribution bias, the attribution of hostile intent to others when no such intent exists, is common among individuals exposed to chronic violence (Dodge, 1993). Unfortunately, such cognitive biases and distortions also serve to deplete brain and body resources, allowing a person to only narrowly focus on, and sometimes even misperceive, threatening cues denying them the opportunity to attend to other environmental cues and serving to push others away.

The presentation of posttraumatic stress symptomatology, which often arises as a child begins to understand that something terrible has happened and he or she is in danger, may initiate a process of encoding and storage of implicit and/or explicit traumatic memories. These processes in children differ in several important ways from adult responses (Terr, 1996). First, research indicates that children often display disorganized or agitated behavior rather than the fear, helplessness, and horror described in adults (Talbot, 2001). Such disorganized behavior may manifest itself in the form of sleep disturbances, nightmares with vague content often not about the trauma itself, increased autonomic arousal, and psychosomatic complaints (Green, 1997). It is also quite common for traumatized children to reveal the effects of their trauma exposure through repetitive play expressing themes of abuse, flashbacks, constriction of affect, or avoidance of events associated with the abuse (Pelcovitz, Kaplan, Goldenberg, & Weinblatt, 1994). This traumatic play may eventually develop into more clearly defined intrusive thoughts, fears, and repeated nightmares with specific trauma content (Terr, 1996). A foreshortened sense of the future, with accompanying reckless risk-taking behavior, is also common.

The epidemiology of PTSD among children following trauma exposure has been the subject of debate. Some research indicates that as many as 39 percent of maltreated children develop PTSD (Famularo, Kinscherff, & Fenton, 1992; Green, 1997) while other studies suggest that behavioral, emotional, and social difficulties are more likely outcomes than clear PTSD (Pelcovitz et al., 1994). There is increasing evidence that children who are victims of trauma are prone to behavioral and emotional difficulties. Cicchetti and Toth (1995) noted a wide range of effects including affect dysregulation, disruptive and aggressive behaviors, insecure and atypical attachment patterns, impaired peer relationships with either increased aggression or social withdrawal, and academic underachievement. The same authors also found a high rate of other co-morbid psychiatric disorders including depression, Conduct Disorder, Attention Deficit Hyperactivity Disorder (ADHD), Oppositional Defiant Disorder (ODD), and Post Traumatic Stress Disorder (PTSD). Others have reported abuse to be significantly associated with global impairment, poor social competence, major depression, conduct disorder, oppositional defiant disorder, agoraphobia, overanxious disorder, ADHD, and substance abuse (Famularo et al., 1992; Kaplan et al., 1998; Livingston, Lawson, & Jones, 1993).

A frequent outcome of trauma is aggression. Pathological defense mechanisms, including identification with the aggressor, may play a role. Preschool children who have been traumatized engage in more frequent aggressive behavior than their peers (Klimes-Dugan & Kistner, 1990) and more often attribute hostile intent to their peers (Dodge, Bates, & Pettit, 1990). Traumatized children have also been reported to be at risk for violent criminal behavior in adolescence (Herrenkohl, Egolf, & Herrenkohl, 1997) and adulthood (Widom, 1989).

A single event outside the scope of normal human experience, then, has the potential to give rise to numerous maladaptive responses. For a more detailed discussion of the neurological, physiological, and cognitive-affective reactions of a developing human organism to trauma, the reader is encouraged to refer to a recent review article by the author (Joshi & O'Donnell, 2003) from which some of the above empirical research descriptions are drawn. Locating a common sensory physiological mechanism underlying these varied reaction patterns and employing intervention strategies that target these mechanisms seems to be the most logical therapy approach. Movement and meditation strategies may prove useful in this regard.

Movement Therapy and How It Works

Movement, a physical process often driven by mental events outside the realm of conscious thought and intentional focus, serves many important functions and activates numerous interrelated brain, mind, and body resources. The locomotion, sensory activation, and tactile stimulation provided by movement can often initiate a positive response cycle centering on improvements in self-regulation, body esteem, and cognitive-affective processing. These results may be particularly marked among developing human organisms with traumatic stress reactions.

A common origin seems to exist between the tactile and nervous systems of developing human organisms. The nervous system and skin both develop from the ectoderm of the embryo, bestowing on the tactile sense the ability to provide important signaling and self-regulatory information to the central and peripheral nervous systems, especially early in life. This leads to a complex interreliance between the skin and nervous system (Cohen, 1993). As such, body movement, coordination, and control may serve a dynamic communication role with the brain and spinal column, the "command centers" of the human organism.

Movement therapy, which aims to incorporate and target the above-described processes, has taken many forms across its inception and development, and multiple theoretical frameworks have informed the various types of movement therapy. The three most influential contemporary conceptual understandings of the mechanisms and effects of movement therapy include those informed by Adlerian psychology, psychodrama therapy, and neuropsychological research on sensory-perceptual processing.

Adlerian Framework

Alfred Adler, a trained medical doctor who worked closely with Sigmund Freud until their relationship became strained due to disagreement over several theoretical issues, put forth a theory of personality emphasizing the importance of early life experiences within the family of origin (Nystul, 2003). Adlerian concepts such as the creative self, understanding of behavior from an interpersonal perspective, social interest, striving for significance, and a holistic psychology have been the most integral of his theories to movement therapy approaches of a psychodynamic origin (Levy, 1992). Many clinical approaches to movement techniques stress the ways in which body coordination, rhythm, and movement impact the development of Adler's creative self. The creative self is formulated as the point from which all life movement generates. Adler proposed that all humans possess the potential to creatively interact with the world in a self-deterministic manner (Nystul, 2003). This creative force of the individual can be harnessed and directed through movement.

In his emphasis on social interest, Adler posited that humans have an inborn tendency to cooperate and work with others toward common goals, and that this tendency represents a powerful motivational force. When movement therapy is conducted in a group setting with an emphasis on synchronized movement, group cooperation, and sense of common purpose, social interest can be nurtured and developed. As a holistic psychology, Adlerian theory understands the individual as indivisible and undivided. Adlerian therapists concentrate on the ways in which a given individual organizes himself as a whole person with coherent beliefs, perceptions, and goals, and on the interaction of mind and body. The primary focus of movement work from this perspective is on assisting children in understanding themselves and others through an organized and structured exploration of movement potential, and developing children's confidence and awareness through mastery and self-expression (Levy, 1992).

Psychodrama Framework

Moreno (1946) is the founder of psychodrama, one of the first systematic manifestations of drama as a form of therapy. Drama therapy, a related form of contemporary treatment, uses creative drama to promote emotional and physical integration and personal growth (Irwin, 1987). Spontaneous role playing serves as the foundation of most forms of drama therapy, and the therapist uses a variety of techniques including movement and mime to supplement this foundation (Fleshman & Fryrear, 1981). Movement, action, and bodily change are viewed as mechanisms through which inner conflicts can be expressed concretely and better understood. One typical mode of integration of movement and drama therapy involves simple body movements in combination with therapeutic discussion of how the movements are felt and experienced. Through this process, clients often begin to feel more comfortable with their bodies. As this comfort increases, drama therapy techniques are added to the movement work. This approach places great importance on the enactment of movements as soon as a thought or impulse appears, establishing a free flow of information between the mind and body (Levy, 1979).

Kinesthetic-Sensory-Perceptual Regulation Framework

This approach to understanding the correlates of movement therapy focuses on the interrelation among sensation, perception, movement, cognition, and emotion. The human as an organism is a complex entity in which actions and reactions in one domain invariably influence and are influenced by those in other domains. The goal of movement therapy stressed within this framework involves attuning bodily awareness of kinesthetic and sensory input in the service of increasing the experience and understanding of bodily, affective, and cognitive reactions toward oneself and the environment (Dosamantes-Alperson, 1974). In a sensory-motor feedback loop, sensation (the reception of information) informs perception (the comparison of previous experience to incoming sensory information and the interpretation of such information) which informs motor planning. The motor response, in turn, informs sensation in a self-perpetuating feedback loop, providing information about what happened during the response and how that movement should be interpreted cognitively and emotionally (Cohen, 1993). Rhythm and dance are often used as a way of activating responsiveness in withdrawn or dissociative youth, and as a way of teaching social control and rechanneling of behavioral impulsivity among aggressive or reactive youth. The overarching objective of such approaches is to guide the child in using movement to express and satisfy physical and psychological needs in place of relying on the external environment to provide regulation (Levy, 1992).

Movement therapy also serves to enhance perceptual-motor coordination. Perceptual-motor coordination involves the fluid relation between the ways in which an individual filters, interprets, and brings meaning to sensory experiences and the manner in which he or she moves or acts in his environment. Good perceptual-motor coordination allows one to synchronize perception and action in a way that allows for accurate perception, meaningful interpretation, and effective, adaptive action (Cohen, 1993). Movement therapists who focus on building perceptual-motor coordination stress the need for children to attend in the moment to both their movements (i.e., the action which stimulates) and their intentions (i.e., the intention, thought, or desire that drives movement and informs what action should be taken in reaction to the bodily stimulation). In this fashion, cognition, emotion, and action are linked and integrated.

Some movement therapists describe their technique as a mechanism by which preconscious knowledge is activated, understanding of the human body and organ systems as containing knowledge and information not readily accessible by cognition. Just as the immune system retains memory and knowledge of past invaders and the brain stores memories of past experiences, other body organs do the same. These theorists assert that the perception of movement provides access to bodily knowledge centering on the connection between affect and cognition (Hackney, 2002), and understanding of the human body as possessing individual organs that operate synergistically in a body system that interfaces with the world as a cohesive mind-body unit.

Meditative Therapy

Meditation as a practice encompasses diverse forms of relaxation, movement, and altered states of consciousness. Numerous definitions of meditation have been put forth, each describing a different form of basic meditational practices. For the purposes of this chapter, the following definition, which encompasses a broad spectrum of practices with common underlying processes, will be used (Shapiro, 1984):

> A family of techniques which have in common a conscious attempt to focus attention in a nonanalytical way and an attempt not to dwell on discursive, ruminating thought. There is an important meta-message implicit in this definition – the *content* of thoughts is not so important. They should be allowed to come and go. Consciousness, or awareness of the *process* of thoughts coming and going, is more important. (p. 6)

The type of meditation many clinicians view as most effective for self-regulation difficulties is concentrative meditation. Concentrative meditation involves narrowly focusing mental attention on a sound or symbol (Smith & Womack, 1987). Other forms of meditation, including Yoga, focus on the attainment of Samadhi, or union with the Universal Self. Yoga has been a central feature of the Hindu culture for over 2,000 years and takes various forms including physical posture (asana), breath control

(pranayama), fixed attention on an idea or image (dharana), and extended contemplation or meditations (dhyana) (Woolfolk, 1984a).

All forms of meditation rely on attention to breathing as a primary foundation for awareness of mind-body processes. Breathing is an automatic process, yet breath can be influenced by and is reflective of changes in consciousness, emotion, and cognition. By attending to breathing in a controlled and mindful fashion, children can become more highly attuned to both their inner states and the outside environment. Children can even be trained to consciously choose to alter breathing to affect emotional, perceptual, and cognitive processes (Hackney, 2002).

Which Traumatic Stress Processes Does Meditation Target?

Meditation achieves its effects through impacting the body's nervous system in such a way that a state of conscious relaxation is achieved. As with many animals, a physiological substrate of anxious or traumatic stress-reactions lies in the human fear response, which is seated in the sympathetic nervous system. The fear response propels individuals to react to threat in one of two ways: Marshalling body resources in preparation for fight or physically and psychologically retreating from the threat. This process is commonly known as the "fight or flight" response (Cannon, 1929; Hinde, 1985). Such impulses are undoubtedly advantageous to our survival in times of danger. The fight or flight response depletes considerable energy and attention, however, and cannot be activated all of the time because the human body and brain require stretches of homeostasis. Unfortunately, children living in much of the world today are not afforded the luxury of this "down" time. Living in homes, communities, or nations marked by perpetual aggression and violence, these individuals are in constant states of high alert. Such chronic states of fear and stress can be harmful to developing humans on multiple levels (Sapolsky, 1994), and meditative interventions targeting the relaxation response have been used to transform these fear states into the incompatible response of relaxation.

Relaxation Response and Meditation

The relaxation response is a mind-body state characterized by decreased blood pressure, heart rate, and oxygen consumption, increased body temperature, and increased regularity and amplitude of alpha activity. This state is sometimes also referred to as a hypometabolic state (Shapiro & Giber, 1984). The relaxation response is intimately linked to perception. Research indicates that relaxation significantly affects perceptual ability. Tension and anxiety interfere with accurate perception, resulting in narrow, rigid, and inflexible patterns of response, while relaxation allows one to remain open to a wide range of sensory data upon which to make realistic and informed perceptual inferences and interpretations (Levy, 1992).

Various therapeutic meditative techniques designed to induce the relaxation response have been employed by clinicians. One common and effective form of relaxation training used with children involves progressive muscle relaxation. This technique teaches children to be aware of varying degrees of muscle tension and consequent sensations throughout the body. Emphasis is placed on attending to the transition from muscle tension to relaxation through a series of exercises during which muscle groups are alternately tensed and relaxed (Smith & Womack, 1987). Achieving awareness of the sensations that arise from tensing and relaxing muscles helps children to become selective in deciding which forms of visceral sensory information merit acknowledgment and attention, and which should be ignored or allowed to pass. This is an important skill for children with traumatic stress reactions to develop, as much of the physiological underpinnings of traumatic stress reactions revolve around dysregulation of sensory processing. Allowing children to regain conscious control of their sensory and perceptual abilities can have a positive impact on their ability to self-regulate and express their physical and emotional states in words as opposed to unregulated behaviors.

This evolution from unregulated behaviors to verbalization is often achieved in meditative therapy through gradually increasing verbalization in movement and meditation. For instance, over the course of therapy clinicians may employ the repeated use of verbal and physical prompting of relaxation responses. These verbal prompts often focus on key words such as "calm" and "feeling good," while the physical prompts consist of touching the body parts to be tensed and relaxed. In this way, mental representations of physical sensations and abstract verbal concepts become linked. As therapy progresses, fewer prompts, particularly physical

prompts, are used. By the end of a successful course of meditative therapy, child clients have gained increased body awareness and control, along with an enhanced ability to engage in successful verbal communication about body, cognitive, and emotional states (Levy, 1992). A strength of this type of intervention strategy lies in its ability to effectively transfer to the nontherapy setting. When provided with these meditative techniques, children are equipped to achieve relaxation in whatever setting they happen to find themselves, making it a self-sufficient device useful in coping with transitory fluctuations in tension and arousal (Woolfolk, 1984b).

Research and the Positive Effects of Meditation

Mediators as a group have been found to be less anxious and more self-actualizing than nonmeditators. The relation between meditation and stress has been tested inferentially through operationalizing reaction to stress as habituation of skin conductance responses to tones. Compared to nonmeditators, meditators have been found to habituate more quickly, implying a more rapid recovery from stress-related arousal (Everly & Lating, 2004). This enhanced habituation extends to situations of emotionally complex stimuli. Overall, meditators seem to exhibit greater recovery from anticipatory arousal, a pattern consistent with their more positive affect and lower situational and trait anxiety levels (Alexander, Rainforth, & Genderloos, 1991). Another approach that researchers have taken to quantifying the effects of meditation employs measures of field independence, or the degree to which a child is able to mentally separate important environmental information from distracting background noise. It reflects a general disposition to perceive and think in a systematic and analytic fashion. One measure of this ability is the Children's Embedded Figures Test, which requires participants to discern a given form within the context of a distracting stimulus background. Meditation improves an individual's ability to focus her attention on an object or process ("figure") and to resist distraction from other sources of stimulation ("ground") (Gelderloos, Lockie, & Chuttoorgoon, 1987). Taken together, these research findings touch upon the component ways in which meditation induces its positive effects. What these findings fail to fully capture, however, are the less concrete and more difficult to capture processes through which children exposed to trauma ascribe a sense of personal meaning and worth to their lives. Although less conducive to empirical investigation, these too are important processes influenced by meditation.

Meditation and Self-Integration

In addition to its sensory physiological goals, meditation is often also used as a mechanism of spiritual development requiring no particular belief system. The manner in which meditation emphasizes and enhances the mind-body connection allows the meditative process to transcend religious boundaries while still nurturing spiritual oneness, transcendental experiences, and peaceful acceptance of natural processes. In doing so, meditation facilitates a greater integration of lower and higher-order areas of the brain, linking automatic processes such as breathing with sophisticated neuropsychological processes like attention, executive function, and language. This reunification of mind-body processes helps children whose cognitive, perceptual, and emotional worlds have become fragmented and disorganized due to traumatic stress. In short, meditation allows them to regain a sense of physical and mental wholeness (Alter & Alter, 2001). While these meditative processes of self-integration may appear at first glance to be better suited to adult clients due to their greater cognitive maturity, children's strengths in the domains of imagination and fantasy render them better poised to successfully achieve states of relaxed visualization.

Through these therapeutic experiences, traumatized children are encouraged to develop a more positive and forgiving sense of self and personal meaning. The self-transcendence nurtured through meditation allows a child to rewrite the trauma and formulate a personalized sense of meaning out of suffering, a sophisticated and important process for a traumatized child to navigate. When tailored to their developmental level, even young children can achieve this recalibrated state of self-acceptance.

CONCLUSION

As a nonverbal intervention which focuses on regulating sensory and physiological experiences as a springboard for regulation of cognition and affect, creative movement and meditative therapy techniques hold much promise as an adjunct treatment for children with traumatic stress reactions. Movement and meditative approaches can be both cost effective and time efficient. Group movement work may be indicated for those children who have gained sufficient self-regulatory ability to acquire social knowledge and skill in a group treatment setting. Children who have been trained in movement and meditative techniques can become self-sufficient, performing the techniques on their own and ultimately requiring less in-session time. Highly motivated children may teach their peers and family members the techniques they use, contributing to increased family cohesion and expression of positive emotion. These pragmatic considerations are of importance as many children struggling with traumatic stress reactions come from lower socioeconomic strata, have less access to consistent, high quality heath insurance and care, and are in need of alternative cost-effective treatment approaches (American Academy of Pediatrics, 2002; Elliot, Wilson, & Huizinga, 1996; Hoyle & White, 2003).

Creative movement and meditative techniques allow for flexibility in their application and can be tailored to each child's individual needs, strengths, and weaknesses. The pace of treatment can also be varied depending on the type, frequency, and level of creative intervention desired. Movement and meditative therapies have been found to be most effective when used in conjunction with, or integrated into, cognitive behavioral psychotherapeutic strategies (Smith & Womack, 1987). The pairing of physiological and cognitive focused techniques may prove ideal for traumatized youth who need such an integration of mind and body processes. The concrete didactic nature of cognitive-behavioral interventions, whose treatment aim is to increase awareness, understanding, and control of affective-cognitive-behavioral states, can usually be easily combined with movement and meditative approaches. Most importantly, creative movement and meditative techniques are active approaches to intervention that are fun and enjoyable for the children involved.

Reformulating one's understanding of self in the context of a traumatizing world through the bodily expression of emotions can have profound impact on a developing child's sense of self, safety, and security. Children are less able to express abstract thoughts and emotions in linguistic terms due to their less cognitively developed mental state. Creative movement and meditative therapies, when used in conjunction with traditional psychotherapy, have proven to be effective in reaching children on a level that allows them to process, understand, and integrate the confusing emotions they may be experiencing. The reestablishment of boundaries, feelings of safety, control, and body integrity facilitated by movement and meditative therapies allow for a developmentally-appropriate expression of meaning and identity (Barath, 2003).

As a child becomes increasingly autonomous and creative in developing personalized forms of movement and meditation, as should be encouraged as the course of treatment progresses, higher-order areas of the brain involving abstract reasoning are relied on more heavily. This activation of complex symbolic thought allows for the interpretation and integration of the fragmented sensations, memories, and experiences triggered by traumatic stress that originate in the lower, more primitive areas of the brain. This process, in turn, promotes creativity and imagination, skills that can serve as a catalyst for the development of other blossoming areas of interest such as athletics, art, and music.

Movement and meditative techniques hold much promise and merit further investigation. As therapeutic approaches that target multiple levels of a developing human organism's experience of trauma, treatment outcome research should involve a multidisciplinary approach that examines childhood traumatic stress reactions from a variety of perspectives. Not only should this approach investigate the effects of movement and meditative techniques on sensory, perceptual, and cognitive-affective processes, it should take care to do so within developmentally salient contexts during important developmental periods. Research indicates that family, school, and peer support differentially bolster resilience in violence exposed youth (O'Donnell, Schwab-Stone, & Muyeed, 2002), and these important environmental factors should be considered when designing and evaluating treatment. Traumatic stress reactions, as do the children they afflict, develop and change over time. Reactions that may be maladaptive at one developmental point in one setting may prove to be adaptive at a different stage of development and within a different environmental context. Theories, then, that take into account the complex interplay among physiological, neurobiological, and behavioral processes within a developmental framework

should inform the design of future preventive interventions (Brotman, Gouley, Klein, Castellanos, & Pine, 2003). Through this type of clinical and research attention, intervention strategies may begin to encompass a more holistic brain-mind-body approach.

Humans are more than verbal beings. We are sensory beings as well. The varied and wondrous forms of creative expression developed and engaged in by children often involve no verbalization at all. The human spirit is frequently moved most profoundly by those experiences that transcend verbal expression. Advanced linguistic mechanisms, while central to human evolution and civilization, need not always be activated and may in some cases hinder a traumatized child's journey from the frightening world of sensory dysregulation to the comforting world of well-controlled sensory and perceptual experiences. It is both a gift and honor for a clinician to witness and guide this courageous process in a child client.

REFERENCES

Alexander, C. N., Rainforth, M. V., & Gelderloos, P. (1991). Transcendental meditation, self-actualization, and psychological health: A conceptual overview and statistical meta-analysis. *Journal of Social Behavior and Personality, 6,* 189–247.

Alter, R. M., & Alter, J. (2001). *How long till my soul gets it right?: One hundred doorways on the journey to happiness.* New York: Harper Collins.

American Academy of Pediatrics. (2002). *AAP evaluates progress of SCHIP Program: Recommendations for improvements.* Washington, DC: American Academy of Pediatrics.

American Psychiatric Association. (2000). *Quick reference to the diagnostic criteria from DSM-IV-TR.* Washington, DC: American Psychiatric Association.

Barath, A. (2003). Cultural art therapy in the treatment of war trauma in children and youth: Projects in the former Yugoslavia. In S. Krippner, & T. M. McIntyre (Eds.). *The psychological impact of war trauma on civilians* (pp. 155–170). Westport, CT: Praeger.

Blair, C. (2002). School readiness: Integrating cognition and emotion in a neurobiological conceptualization of children's functioning at school entry. *American Psychologist, 57,* 111–127.

Bremner, J. D., Randall, P., Scott, T. M., & Bronen, R. A. (1997). MRI-based measurement of hippocampal volume in PTSD related to childhood physical and sexual abuse: A preliminary report. *Biological Psychiatry, 41,* 23–32.

Bremner, J. D., Randall, P., Scott, T. M., Capelli, S., Delaney, R., McCarthy, G., et al., (1995). Deficits in short-term memory in adult survivors of childhood abuse. *Psychiatry Research, 59*, 97–107.

Brotman, L. M., Gouley, K. K., Klein, R. G., Castellanos, F. X., & Pine, D. S. (2003). Children, stress, and context: Integrating basic, clinical, and experimental prevention research. *Child Development, 74*, 1053–1057.

Cannon, W. B. (1929). *Bodily changes in pain, hunger, fear, and rage,* (Rev. ed.). New York: Appleton-Century.

Cicchetti, D., & Toth, S. L. (1995). A developmental psychopathology perspective on child abuse and neglect. *Journal of the American Academy of Child and Adolescent Psychiatry, 34*, 541–565.

Cohen, B. B. (1993). *Sensing, feeling, and action: The experiential anatomy of body-mind centering.* Northampton, MA: Contact Editions.

Coster, W. J., Gersten, M. S., Beeghly, M., & Cicchetti, D. (1989). Communicative functioning in maltreated toddlers. *Developmental Psychology, 25*, 777–793.

Debellis, M. D., Baum, A. B., & Birmaher, B. (1999). Developmental traumatology part I: Biological stress symptoms. *Biological Psychiatry, 45*, 1259–1270.

Dodge, K. A. (1993). Social-cognitive mechanisms in the development of conduct disorder and depression. *Annual Review of Psychology, 44*, 559–584.

Dodge, K. A., Bates, J. E., & Pettit, G. S. (1990). Mechanisms in the cycle of violence. *Science, 250*, 1678–1683.

Dosamantes-Alperson, E. D. (1974). Carrying experiencing forward through authentic body movement. *Psychotherapy: Theory, Research, and Practice, 11*, 211–214.

Elliot, D. S., Wilson, W. J., & Huizinga, D. (1996). The effects of neighborhood disadvantage on adolescent development. *Journal of Research on Crime and Delinquency, 33*, 389–426.

Everly, G. S., & Lating, J. M. (2004). Neurological desensitization in the treatment of post-traumatic stress. In G. S. Everly, & J. M. Lating (Eds.). *Personality-guided therapy for Post-Traumatic Stress Disorder.* Washington, DC: American Psychological Association.

Famularo, R., Kinscherff, R., & Fenton, T. (1992). Psychiatric diagnoses of maltreated children: Preliminary findings. *Journal of the American Academy of Child and Adolescent Psychiatry, 31*, 863–867.

Fleshman, B., & Fryrear, J. L. (1981). *The arts in therapy.* Chicago, IL: Nelson-Hall.

Gelderloos, P., Lockie, R. J., & Chuttoorgoon, S. (1987). Field independence of students at Maharishi School of the Age of Enlightenment and a Montessori school. *Perceptual and Motor Skills, 65*, 613–614.

Glaser, D. (2000). Child abuse and neglect and the brain – A review. *Journal of Child Psychology and Psychiatry, 41*, 97–116.

Godden, D. R., & Baddeley, A. D. (1975). Context-dependent memory in two natural environments: On land and underwater. *British Journal of Psychology, 66*, 325–331.

Green, A. H. (1997). Physical abuse of children. In J. Weiner (Ed.). *American Academy of Child and Adolescent Psychiatry textbook of child and adolescent psychiatry* (pp. 17–38). Washington, DC: American Psychological Association.

Hackney, P. (2002). *Making connections: Total body integration through Bartenieff fundamentals.* New York: Routledge.

Herrenkohl, R. C., Egolf, B. P., & Herrenkohl, E. C. (1997). Preschool antecedents of adolescent assaultive behavior: A longitudinal study. *American Journal of Orthopsychiatry, 67*, 422–432.

Hinde, R. A. (1985). Expression and negotiation. In G. Zivin (ed.). *The development of expressive behavior* (pp. 103–116). Orlando, FL: Academic Press.

Hoyle, J. D., & White, L. J. (2003). Treatment of pediatric and adolescent mental health emergencies in the United States: Current practices, models, barriers, and potential solutions. *Prehospital Emergency Care, 7*, 66–73.

Irwin, E. C. (1987). Drama: The play's the thing. *Elementary School Guidance and Counseling*, 276–283.

Joshi, P. T., & O'Donnell, D. A. (2003). Consequences of child exposure to war and terrorism. *Clinical Child and Family Psychology Review, 6*, 275–292.

Kandel, E. W. (2001). The molecular biology of memory storage: A dialogue between genes and synapses. *Science, 294*, 1030–1038.

Kaplan, S. J., Pelcovitz, D., Salzinger, S., Weiner, M., Mandel, F. S., Lesser, M.L., et al. (1998). Adolescent physical abuse: Risk for adolescent psychiatric disorders. *American Journal of Psychiatry, 155*, 954–959.

Keane, T. M., Kolb, L. C., & Kaloupek, D. G. (1998). Utility of psychophysiology measurement in the diagnosis of posttraumatic stress disorder: Results from a department of Veteran's Affairs cooperative study. *Journal of Consulting and Clinical Psychology, 66*, 914–923.

Klimes-Dougan, B., & Kistner, J. (1990). Physically abused preschoolers' responses to peers' distress. *Developmental Psychology, 26*, 599–602.

Levy, F. J. (1979). Psychodramatic movement therapy: A sorting out process. *American Journal of Dance Therapy, 3*, 32–42.

Levy, F. J. (1992). *Dance movement therapy: A healing art.* Reston, VA: National Dance Association.

Livingston, R., Lawson, L., & Jones, J.G. (1993). Predictors of self-reported psychopathology in children abused repeatedly by a parent. *Journal of the American Academy of Child and Adolescent Psychiatry, 32*, 948–953.

McEwen, B. S., & Magarinos, M. (1997). Stress effects on morphology and function of the hippocampus. In R.

Yehuda, & A. C. McFarlane (Eds.). *Psychobiology of posttraumatic stress disorder* (pp. 271–284). New York: New York Academy of Sciences.

McFadyen, R. G., & Kitson, W. J. H. (1996). Language comprehension and expression among adolescents who have experienced childhood physical abuse. *Journal of Child Psychology and Psychiatry, 37,* 551–562.

Moreno, J. L. (1946). *Psychodrama, Volume 1.* Beacon, NY: Beacon House.

Nelson, C. A., & Carver, L. J. (1998). The effects of stress and trauma on brain and memory: A view from developmental cognitive neuroscience. *Development and Psychopathology, 10,* 793–809.

Nystul, M. S. (2003). *Introduction to counseling: An art and science perspective.* Boston: Allyn and Bacon.

O'Donnell, D. A., Schwab-Stone, M. E., & Muyeed, A. Z. (2002). Multidimensional resilience in urban children exposed to community violence. *Child Development, 73,* 1265–1282.

Pelcovitz, D., Kaplan, S., Goldenberg, B., & Weinblatt, M. (1994). Post-traumatic stress disorder in physically abused adolescents. *Journal of the American Academy of Child and Adolescent Psychiatry, 33,* 305–312.

Perry, B. D. (2001). The neurodevelopmental impact of violence in childhood. In D. Schetky, & E. Benedek (Eds.). *Textbook of child and adolescent forensic psychiatry* (pp. 221–238). Washington, DC: American Psychiatric Press.

Perry, B. D., & Pollard, R. (1998). Homeostasis, stress, trauma and adaptation – A neurodevelopmental view of childhood trauma. *Child and Adolescent Psychiatric Clinics of North America, 7,* 33–51.

Sapolsky, R. M. (1994). *Why zebras don't get ulcers.* New York: Freeman.

Schwab-Stone, M. E., Ayers, T. S., Kasprow, W., Voyce, C., Barone, C., Shriver, T., & Weissberg, R. P. (1995). No safe haven: A study of violence exposure in an urban community. *Journal of the American Academy of Child and Adolescent Psychiatry, 34,* 1343–1352.

Schwab-Stone, M. E., Chen, C., Greenberger, E., Silver, D., Lichtman, J., & Voyce, C. (1999). No safe haven II: The effects of violence exposure in urban youth. *Journal of the American Academy of Child and Adolescent Psychiatry, 38,* 359–367.

Shapiro, D. H. (1984). Overview: Clinical and physiological comparison of meditation with other self-control strategies. In D. H. Shapiro, & R. N. Walsh (Eds.). *Meditation: Classic and contemporary perspectives* (pp. 5–12). New York: Aldine.

Shapiro, D. H., & Giber, D. (1984). Meditation and psychotherapeutic effects: Self-regulation strategy and altered state of consciousness. In D. H. Shapiro, & R. N. Walsh (Eds.). *Meditation: Classic and contemporary perspectives* (pp. 62–69). New York: Aldine.

Shin, L. M., McNally, R. J., Kosslyn, S. M., Thompson, W. L., Rauch, S. L., Alport, N. M., et al. (1999).

Regional cerebral blood flow during script-driven imagery in childhood sexual abuse related PTSD: A PET investigation. *American Journal of Psychiatry, 156,* 575–584.

Smith, M. S., & Womack, W. M. (1987). Stress management techniques in childhood and adolescence. *Clinical Pediatrics, 26,* 581–585.

Talbot, J. A. (2001, October 26). Look behind classic symptoms to spot PTSD in affected kids. *Clinical Psychiatry News, 12.*

Terr, L. C. (1996). Acute responses to external events and posttraumatic stress disorder. In M. Lewis (Ed.). *Child and adolescent psychiatry: A comprehensive textbook.* Baltimore: Williams and Wilkins.

Vontress, C. E. (1999). Interview with a traditional African healer. *Journal of Mental Health Counseling, 21,* 326–336.

Widom, C. S. (1989). Child abuse, neglect, and adult behavior. *Criminology, 27,* 251–271.

Wodarski, J. S., Kurtz, P. D., Gaudin, J. M., Jr, & Howing, P. T. (1990). Maltreatment and the school age child: Major academic, socioemotional, and adaptive outcomes. *Social Work, 35,* 581–589.

Woolfolk, R. L. (1984a). Psychophysiological correlates of meditation: A review. In D. H. Shapiro, & R. N. Walsh (Eds.). *Meditation: Classic and contemporary perspectives* (pp. 369–375). New York: Aldine.

Woolfolk, R. L. (1984b). Self-control meditation and the treatment of chronic anger. In D. H. Shapiro, & R. N. Walsh (Eds.). *Meditation: Classic and contemporary perspectives* (pp. 550–554). New York: Aldine.

Yehuda, R., Spertus, I., & Golier, J. (2001). Relationship between childhood traumatic experiences and PTSD in adults. In S. Eth (Ed.). *PTSD in children and adolescents* (pp. 117–146). Washington, DC: American Psychiatric Publishing.

Biographical Statement

Deborah A. O'Donnell, Ph.D., received a doctorate in clinical psychology from Yale University in 2002. She completed her doctoral clinical internship at Children's National Medical Center, Washington, DC. She is Assistant Professor of Psychology at St. Mary's College of Maryland, Research Consultant to the International Center to Heal Our Children at Children's National Medical Center, and Clinical Consultant to Child Nurture and Relief, a nonprofit organization working for the psychosocial rehabilitation of orphaned and vulnerable children in conflict areas. She is the faculty supervisor for undergraduate directed research projects in cross-cultural psychology in the St. Mary's College of Maryland Summer Field School Program in The Republic of The Gambia,

West Africa. Research interests include cross-cultural processes of risk and resilience among violence-exposed youth, the role of self-regulation in overcoming adversity, and prevention and intervention design focusing on the use of meditative and movement therapy approaches for children with traumatic stress reactions. She is a licensed psychologist in Maryland and has written numerous chapters and peer-reviewed manuscripts on a variety of topics related to her clinical and research interests.

Chapter 17

THE HISTORY OF MUSIC THERAPY

JOKE BRADT

INTRODUCTION

The use of music in healing practices can be traced back as far as 20,000 years with shamanic drumming practices for healing (Rudhyar, 1982). With evolving medical theories, the relationship between music and healing underwent several transformations. However, music and healing remained partners throughout history, eventually resulting in the formation of music therapy as a profession.

This chapter will take a historical and evolutionary approach to the role of music in healing. It does not attempt to give a complete and detailed history of the growth of the music therapy field. Rather, its purpose is to create an understanding that music and healing have been connected since preliterate times and that, even if music therapy only became organized as a profession in 1950, it is a profession with a long and interesting history (Weldin & Eagle, 1991).

History

Music in Curative Rituals

In preliterate cultures, music, dance, magic, and spirituality were an integral part of healing and illness-prevention rituals. People believed that magical forces controlled their daily lives and well-being. In order to protect themselves against evil forces, tribe members developed and engaged in many rituals. It was believed that music, in the form of rhythms, songs, and chants, had supernatural power and was, therefore, used to assist the tribal healer in medicinal practices. In many primitive cultures, illness was viewed as a punishment for sins committed against the tribal god. For healing to take place, the patient's body had to be liberated from the evil spirit. Music served as a prelude to the healing rituals and was very often an active component of the exorcism treatment (Weldin & Eagle, 1991). The *San*, believed to be the original inhabitants of Botswana, Namibia, and northwest South Africa (20,000–15,000 BCE), portrayed many rituals in their cave paintings and ornaments. Their art, representing one of the most widespread forms of prehistoric art in Southern Africa, illustrated a variety of musical instruments used in ritual healing practices (Page, 2001).

Even, today, music plays an active role in tribal healing practices across the globe. In shamanic healing rituals, the shaman travels into an altered state of consciousness, known as the spirit world. Rhythmic drumming is aimed at helping the shaman reach this altered state, allowing him to listen to the spirits and re-establish a connection between the person and the healing spirits. Through specific songs, the shaman then attempts to drive out the illness of the person. Without knowledge of the proper song, treatment cannot be provided (Boxberger, 1962; Weldin & Eagle, 1991; Winn et al., 1989). The Kung San, inhabitants of Kalahari (bordering Botswana), believe that misfortune, death, or sickness can be directed at a person via invisible arrows shot by spirits. They use music and dance to influence the spirits and stop the arrows, preventing adversity from happening (Page, 2001). In Tumbuka healing practices (Northern Malawi), musical experiences form the "structural nexus where healer, patient and spirit meet" (Friedson, 1996, p. xvi). In Songhai society (now Republic of Niger), the *godji*, a one-string violin-type instrument, has long been considered a sacred instrument and is used to call healing spirits into action. Other Nigerian tribes, such as the Yoruba and Tiv, have traditionally used drums, along with specific songs and dance, to induce spirit possession and to evoke mystical power (Page, 2001).

A close link between music and healing was also present in rituals of ancient societies. In ancient Egypt (c. 5000 B.C.), high priests-physicians used chant therapies in their medical practice. Certain melodies, attributed to the goddess Isis, were used to regulate emotions, to purify the soul, and call upon the gods. The fact that it was a requirement in Egypt for all priests to be musicians as well as physicians, attests to the strong connection between medicine, music, and religion (Weldin & Eagle, 1991). The Babylonians (c. 1850 B.C.) were convinced that disease resulted from punishments inflicted by the gods. Healing rites, including music, were meant to appease the gods (Boxberger, 1962; Davis et al., 1999).

Music and Homeostasis

By the sixth century B.C., a shift had taken place in the conceptualization of illness in ancient Greece. Illness was no longer attributed to gods and spells, but rather to a lack of homeostasis. Rational medicine took over from magical healing practices. For the first time in history, empirical evidence became important in the study of health and disease. This, of course, greatly affected the role of music in medical practice (Davis et al., 1999).

A crucial theory in the evolution of medicine was Hippocrates' physiological theory of the four humors. This theory held that physical health – and by extension mental health and character – depended upon a balance among the four humors: blood, yellow bile, phlegm, and black bile. Good health resulted from equilibrium among these four humors. The four basic human temperaments, phlegmatic, sanguine, melancholic, and choleric, were each caused by a predominance of one of the four humors. Based on this theory, Pythagoras (582–500 B.C.) believed that the imbalance among the four humors could be restored by providing harmony and order. He believed music to be the essence of order and, therefore, having the power to restore equilibrium, a prerequisite for optimum well-being. Pythagoras and his followers believed that music, being ordered by numbers, represents the harmony of the cosmos and that the compositions of universe and man, the macrocosm and

microcosm, are based on the same harmonic proportions. Music, ruled by the same mathematical laws that operate in the visible and invisible world, is; therefore, they able to penetrate and restore harmony in the soul (Rudhyar, 1982).

Greek writers, such as Plato (427–347 B.C.), furthermore believed that music possessed moral qualities and could affect character and behavior. Aristotle (384–322 B.C.) wrote that music mirrors and arouses states of the soul, such as gentleness, anger, courage, self-control, and their opposites. Plato and Aristotle agreed that proper education needed to include gymnastics to discipline the body and music to discipline the mind. Plato even censured certain musical modes because of their negative effect on human behavior and recommended others because they fostered temperance and courage (Grout & Palisca, 1996).

The Pythagorean music theory and the theory of the four humors were enculturated the West during the early centuries of the Christian era. Most notable during this time was the work of Boethius (ca. 480–524), a leading expert in music in the middle ages. In the introduction to his *De Instituzione Musica (The Fundamentals of Music)*, Boethius divides music into three levels. The first is *musica mundana* (cosmic music), which consists of orderly numerical relations seen in the movements of the spheres, the changing of the seasons, and the elements. The second is *musica humana*, which controls the union of the body and the soul. Last is *musica instrumentalis*, an audible music produced by instruments, including the human voice, that exemplifies the same principles of order. Like Plato, Boethius also called attention to the influence of music on character and morals (Grout & Palisca, 1996). Even though the teachings of the antiquity continued to be practiced, medicine became dominated by religious dogma during this time (Tyson, 1981). Music became the servant of the Church and it was used to "mold the nature and . . . to avoid profane and pernicious influences on men's soul" (Tyson, 1981, p. 4), to protect against disease, and to honor the saints who protected people from illness. Disease was, once more, viewed as a punishment for sins and the belief in demonology, often resulting in cruel treatment of the mentally ill.

Music as Preventative Medicine

During the Renaissance, the Greek theories of balance and order revived and guided medical practice. The theory of the four humors was still the most influential medical theory. It is noteworthy to mention that during this time period, the four humors found their counterpart in four musical elements. The bass, tenor, alto, and soprano that corresponded respectively with earth, water, air, and fire – the four cosmic elements that formed the basis for theory of the four humors. These four musical elements form a complete harmony, just like the four cosmic elements make up the celestial harmony (Tyson, 1981).

Music theorists in this era, such as Gioseffo Zarlino, advocated that physicians should be trained as musicians as musical knowledge was needed to prescribe proper therapy for curative purposes. It was during the Renaissance that the use of music, with its beneficial effects on emotional health, expanded from purely curative medicine to preventative medicine. According to Feder and Feder (1981), it was recommended in the *Fasciculo di Medicina* (1493), or Medicine Booklet, that people guard against negative feelings by using music as preventative medicine. Music was believed to help build resistance against disease. This was extremely important in a time hallmarked by ravaging epidemics in Europe (Feder & Feder, 1981; Tyson, 1981). The use of music as preventative medicine continued in the Baroque and Classical Period (c. 1600–1800). Richard Browne, author of *Medicina Musica* (1729) or *A Mechanical Essay on the Effects of Singing, Music, and Dancing on Human Bodies*, recommended singing as a preventative medicine intervention. In addition, he attributed certain healing qualities to particular instruments (Weldin & Eagle, 1991). This is the first known English language book to extensively discuss and articulate fundamental principles of music therapy (Darrow, Gibbons, & Heller, 1985).

Music Medicine as a Science

With the arrival of the scientific approach to medicine came a growing disconnection of music and medicine. Whereas music and medicine had been integral parts of a physician's training and practice, the two fields grew apart during the late eighteenth and the nineteenth centuries. Even though music was no longer a part of medical practice, an increasing focus on the Cartesian worldview brought an interest in experimental studies on the effects of music on human behavior. The effect of music on physiological responses such as circula-tion, respiration, heart rate, electrical conductivity of tissues, and fatigue were scientifically measured. Furthermore, experimental studies investigated the effects of musical parameters on affective experiences (Tyson, 1981).

In the early 1800s, two essays addressing the physiological as well as psychological effects of music surfaced. Both authors, Edwin Atlee and Samuel Mathews, were students of Benjamin Rush, a noted physician and teacher at the University of Philadelphia. Mathews pointed out that responses to music are influenced by one's musical background and musical preference (Darrow et al., 1985). Today, music therapy assessment always includes questions concerning the client's musical choice as preference and is considered an important variable in music therapy treatment.

In 1878, a report appeared on a series of music therapy experiments that took place in Blackwell's Island's (now known as Roosevelt Island) insane asylum. Patients involved in the experiments received individual as well as group music sessions. The sessions consisted of listening to live music performed by instrumental and vocal soloists. More than 40 musicians were included in this study. Several physicians were in charge of measuring physiological and psychological responses to the music. This was the first time that music therapy services were provided to a large group of mentally ill patients. Another important contributor to the scientific development of music therapy during this time was James Leonard Corning (1855–1923), a prominent neurologist. He systematically recorded his patients' reactions to music before and during sleep. Based on these observations, he developed theories about the connection between sleep, emotions, and health (Davis et al., 1999).

Even though the increased emphasis on scientific thinking resulted in a decreased use of music in medical practice, the scientific studies on the effects of music on physiological and affective responses were essential to the growth of music therapy. The next section will provide a brief review of the early contributors to music therapy.

Early Pioneers in Music Therapy

In the nineteenth century, music therapy entered educational institutions in the United States. The Perkins School for the Blind (Boston, 1832), the New York School for the Blind (New York, 1840), and the American Asylum for the Deaf

(Hartford, CT, 1840) successfully incorporated music programs for their special needs populations. During this time, several articles were published in *Musical Magazine* on the use of music in the treatment of illnesses. Although these articles showed an ongoing interest in music therapy, it was only in 1874 that a substantial article on the matter was published. In his article *Music and Medicine*, the physician James Whittaker discussed at great length the connections between musical and physiological as well as psychological responses (Davies, et al., 1990).

Another important paper was published by George Blumer in 1892. In his *Music and Its Relation to the Mind*, he supported the use of music in institutional settings for the mentally ill. He is believed to be the first to have established an ongoing music therapy program in a psychiatric hospital, Utica State Hospital, (Davis et al., 1999).

It took until the twentieth century, however, for music therapy to become an organized profession. In 1900, Eva Vescelius, founder of the *National Therapeutic Society of New York City*, presented a lecture on *Musical Vibrations in the Healing of the Sick* at the International Metaphysical League's annual meeting. This presentation was followed by many presentations advocating the use of music therapy. In 1903, Vescelius established the *National Society for Musical Therapeutics*. Her theories of music therapy, based on the ancient concepts of harmony/disharmony, stipulated that the goal of music therapy was to replace discordant vibrations with harmonious ones. Vescelius developed a *Musical Pharmacopeia* to treat specific illnesses. Interestingly enough, Vescelius emphasized that the musical treatment should not be influenced by the personality of the therapist. In an attempt to separate out the effects of the therapist/performer, she had him perform music outside the patient's room. This, of course, is in great contrast with today's emphasis on the importance of the therapeutic relationship in music therapy. In 1913, Vescelius established the first American music therapy journal, *Music and Health*. Unfortunately, the journal did not include many substantial articles on music therapy, which may have contributed to its early termination after only three issues (Davis, 1993).

In 1918, Columbia University was the first university to offer a course in *Musicotherapy*. The focus of this course was on the use of music for neuropsychiatric and orthopedic issues and was taught by Margaret Anderton, a British musician. She had gained her knowledge from extensive work with Canadian soldiers in World War I. Whereas Vescelius had predominantly used music listening to affect the sick, Anderton believed that patients suffering from physical conditions should produce music themselves in order to obtain the desired healing effect (Taylor, 1981). This was the very beginning of active music therapy interventions or interventions in which patients actively participated in creating music.

Another woman who contributed significantly to the growth of music therapy as a profession was Isa Maud Ilsen. During her studies in nursing, Ilsen started to examine the effects of music on the terminally ill, the mentally ill, and the "mentally retarded." Like Anderton, Ilsen treated Canadian veterans with music during World War I. After her return to the United States, she promoted the use of music for injured American soldiers. In 1919, she followed Anderton at Columbia University, where she trained students to become music therapists. The training program, however, only took one semester to complete (de l'Etoile, 2000). In 1926, Ilsen founded the *National Association for Music in Hospitals*. The goal of this association was to have music programs as a complementary treatment in hospitals. As president of this new association, Ilsen insisted that only trained music therapists should provide music therapy services. The National Association even offered a limited amount of scholarships to train music therapists. Ilsen differed from Vescelius in that she underscored the importance of the personality of the therapist in the remedial process. She was in agreement with Vescelius, however, in her recommendation to solely use bright and cheerful music to arouse vital functions. Music in minor keys and sad lyrics were not appropriate for healing purposes (Davis, 1993; Taylor, 1981). This perspective would become strongly disputed by later music therapists. For many centuries now, music therapy had been prescriptive in nature and Ilsen's treatment was no different: a dose of Schubert's *Ave Maria*, for example, was prescribed by Ilsen as effective treatment for severe insomnia (Davis, et al., 1999).

In 1941, a third music therapy organization in the twentieth century was founded: Harriet Ayer Seymour established the *National Foundation of Musical Therapy*. Seymour was an accomplished pianist who taught at the Juilliard School of Music (then the Institute of Musical Art). She too had provided music therapy services to war veterans during World War I. She promoted the use of music in hospitals through writings, lectures, and practical demonstrations. She claimed to have trained more than 500 music therapists between 1941 and 1944. In 1944, Seymour wrote the first clinical manual for music therapy *An Instruction Course in the Use and Practice of Musical Therapy*. The book addresses clinical practice with a variety of populations including children, mental illness, and hospital patients, as well as promoting the combination of music and positive thinking during music therapy sessions (Davis, 1993).

Despite the tremendous efforts of these pioneering women to get music therapy accepted as a profession by the medical community, most physicians and hospital administrators provided little support to establish permanent jobs in hospitals. Even though several physicians played instrumental roles in promoting music therapy as an effective treatment, music therapy remained largely unknown and was often met with skepticism. Despite the founding of the three music therapy organizations, music therapy had not yet become an organized clinical profession. Moreover, the organizations were all demised after the death of their founders (Davis, 1993).

Music Therapy as an Organized Profession

World War II brought an unprecedented surge in interest in the use of music in hospitals. During World War II, the American Service Forces officially recognized music as a necessary treatment for its wounded soldiers. Music was included as a service in the Army's Reconditioning Program, designed to "return wounded military personnel to duty or to civilian life in the best possible physical and mental condition" (Rorke, 1996, p. 190). An official policy on the use of music in military hospitals stated that music should be used to assist in physical reconditioning, educational reconditioning, resocialization, and neuropsychiatric treatment. By 1946, most of the 122 Veteran Administration (VA) hospitals used music in the treatment of the wounded and 44 hospitals had a full-time music specialist on staff (Rorke, 1996; Tyson, 1981).

During the war and post-war period, many associations played an important role in bringing musicians to the wounded veterans. The American Red Cross, the National Federation of Music Clubs, the Musicians Emergency Fund, Sigma Alpha Iota, Mu Phi Epsilon, and Delta Omicron brought hundreds of musicians to the VA hospitals. In addition, music teachers were urged to participate in music therapy activities for wounded veterans (Rorke, 1996).

The widely spread use of music in VA hospitals slowly led to a greater understanding of the clinical uses of music. This resulted in an increased demand for trained musicians in hospitals. Several hospitals took it upon themselves to train musicians, initiating their own unique music therapy programs. At the same time, universities began to offer degree programs in music therapy including Michigan State University, University of Kansas, Chicago Musical College, College of the Pacific, and Alverno College. The majority of providers of music services in hospitals, however, were musicians and hospital workers. Most of them lacked adequate training and it became clear that the development of educational standards and procedures for certification of music therapists was urgently needed.

In 1950, the National Association for Music Therapy (NAMT) was founded thanks to collaborative efforts of the Committee of Functional Music of the Music Teachers National Association, the committee for Music in Therapy of the Music Educators' National Conference, and the National Music Council (Weldin & Eagle, 1991). In the early years of National Association of Music Therapy (NAMT), the focus was on improved education and clinical training as well as establishing standards and procedures for the certification of music therapists. In 1964, the association published its first quarterly periodical, *The Journal of Music Therapy*. The number of published studies on the use of music therapy increased dramatically. Soon after its inception, NAMT created the first music therapy credential: Registered Music Therapist (RMT). This was a very important event for the profession as it finally had established educational and clinical standards.

A pioneer in the early years of NAMT was E. Thayer Gaston (1901–1971). Gaston's relentless leadership and advocacy earned him the title of "father of music therapy." He worked closely together with the Menninger Clinic in Kansas, furthering the application and validation of music therapy with mentally ill adults. Under his leadership, the first graduate program in music therapy was initiated at the University of Kansas (Davis et al., 1999).

In 1971, a second organization, the American Association for Music Therapy (AAMT), was created. Training in an AAMT approved training program led to the Certified Music Therapy (CMT) credential. With a growing profession came additional journals. In 1980, AAMT published its first volume of *Music Therapy*, an annual periodical. In 1984, NAMT added a third music therapy periodical, *Music Therapy Perspectives.* In 1998, the two associations merged in an attempt to unify and strengthen the voice of music therapists in the United States. The *Journal of Music Therapy* and *Music Therapy Perspectives* continued to serve as the two official journals of the AMTA.

In 1986, the Certification Board for Music Therapists (CBMT), a separate and independent organization, was created. The CBMT, the only organization in the United States to certify music therapists, administered a national music therapy certification examination, which is officially recognized by the National Commission on Certifying Agencies. The examination evaluates the applicant's skills, knowledge, and ability to engage in professional music therapy practice. Qualified individuals who pass the national music therapy certification examination, earn the credentials of music therapist, board certified, or MT-BC. The purpose of board the CMBT certification in music therapy is to provide an objective national standard that can be used as a measure of professionalism by interested agencies, groups, and individuals. Nearly 4,000 music therapists have attained the MT-BC credential, and now participate in a program of recertification designed to maintain or increase initial competence in the profession of music therapy (CBMT, n.d.).

Current State of Music Therapy

Music therapy continues to grow rapidly. In the United States, there are currently 72 training programs approved by the AMTA, 27 of which offer graduate programs. Training is offered at the bachelor's level, the master's level, and the doctoral level. Music therapists work with a great variety of clinical populations, whereas music therapists predominantly work in psychiatric and educational settings in the beginning years of the profession. Now, they work in many different settings including psychiatric hospitals, rehabilitative facilities, medical hospitals, outpatient clinics, day care treatment centers, agencies serving developmentally disabled persons, community mental health centers, drug and alcohol programs, senior centers, nursing homes, hospice programs, correctional facilities, halfway houses, schools, and private practice (AMTA, n.d.).

Music therapists often work as a part of the interdisciplinary treatment team and, as such, to provide information and to help make decisions on assessment, treatment planning, and evaluation. Whereas listening to music was the primary music therapy intervention in the nineteenth century, a large variety of music therapy techniques are used by music therapists today. This is important as each client presents different needs and, therefore, requires individualized interventions. Music therapy treatment may include (a) listening or receptive techniques such as music-facilitated relaxation, music-guided imagery, music reminiscence, and lyric discussion, (b) recreative techniques such as playing pre-composed music, instructional music therapy, and rhythm bands, (c) compositional techniques such as song-writing, instrumental compositions, and music videos, and (d) improvisatory techniques such as free improvisations, structured improvisations, referential improvisations, and nonreferential improvisations (Maranto, 1993). A detailed discussion on these and other music therapy techniques has been presented by Maranto (1993).

Music Therapy Training in Practice

Depending on training and experience, a music therapist may practice at the supportive, reeducative, or reconstructive level. At the supportive or activity-oriented level, the goal of therapy is to promote healthy behavior and encourage active participation. Activities that are typically used at this level are group singing, playing instruments, music-related games, and listening to music. The focus of the therapy is to address maladaptive behaviors and symptoms, not to uncover underlying causes for the behavior. At the reeducative or process-oriented level, personal reflection on intrapersonal and interpersonal relationships becomes the focal point of therapy. This level of therapy requires the client to be capable of gaining insights and is characterized by a here-and-now approach. This means that the therapy will focus on present issues rather than unconscious processes. Finally, at the reconstructive level or analytical level, the goal is to identify, explore, and resolve through musical interventions the unconscious conflicts that are causing dysfunctional behavior. To work at this level, the music therapist needs advanced training and supervision (Davis, et al., 1999).

Because of music's complexity and diversity, it is an ideal medium to address a multiplicity of needs. Its omnipresence in our daily lives makes it a non-threatening tool that facilitates the development of a trust relationship and a safe environment, important prerequisites for effective treatment. Music therapy has grown tremendously during the past 50 years and it promises to continue to further expand itself as a well researched and well disciplined therapeutic approach.

REFERENCE LIST

American Music Therapy Association (n.d.) Retrieved January 13, 2005 from http://www.musictherapy.org.

Boxberger, R. (1962). *Music therapy 1961, eleventh book of proceedings of the National Association for Music Therapy, Inc. Part VI.* Lawrence, KS: Allen Press.

Certification Board for Music Therapists (n.d.). Retrieved January 31, 2005 from http://www.cbmt.org/default.asp.

Darrow, A. A., Gibbons, A. C., & Heller, G. N. (1985). Music therapy past, present, and future. *The American Music Teacher,* September–October, 18–20.

Davis, W.B. (1993). Keeping the dream alive: Profiles of three early twentieth century music therapists. *Journal of Music Therapy, 30*(1), 34–45.

Davis, W.B., Gfeller, K.E., & Thaut, M. (1999). *An introduction to music therapy. Theory and practice* (2nd ed.). Boston: McGraw-Hill College.

Darrow, A. A., Gibbons, A. C., & Heller, G. N. (1985). Music therapy past, present, and future. *The American Music Teacher,* September–October,18–20.

De l'Etoile, S. (2000). The history of the undergraduate curriculum in music therapy. *Journal of Music Therapy, 37*(1), 51–71.

Feder, E., & Feder, B. (1981). *The expressive arts therapies: Art, music and dance as psychotherapy.* Englewood Cliffs, NJ: Prentice Hall.

Grout, D. J., & Palisca, C. V. (1996). *A history of Western music* (5th ed.). New York: Norton & Company.

Maranto, C.D. (1993). *Music therapy international perspectives.* Pipersville, PA: Jeffrey Books.

Page, W. F. (2001). Spirit possession. *Encyclopedia of African history and culture.* Vol. 1, *Ancient Africa.* New York: Facts On File.

Rorke, M.A. (1996). Music and the wounded of World War II. *Journal of Music Therapy, 33*(3), 189–207.

Rudhyar, G. (1982). *The magic of tone and art of music.* Boulder: Shambhala.

Ruud, E. (2000). Music therapy—History and cultural contexts. Two major new texts on music therapy. *Nordic Journal of Music Therapy, 9*(2).

Taylor, D.B. (1981). Music in general hospital treatment from 1900 to 1950. *Journal of Music Therapy, 18*(2), 62–73.

Tyson, F. (1981). *Psychiatric music therapy. Origins and development.* New York: Creative Arts Rehabilitation Center.

Weldin, C., & Eagle, C.T. (1991). An historical overview of music medicine. In C. Maranto-Dileo (Ed.), *Applications of Music in Medicine I* (pp. 7–27). Silver Spring, MD: The National Association for Music Therapy.

Winn, T., Crowe, B., & Moreno, J. (1989). Shamanism and music therapy. *Music Therapy Perspectives, 7,* 67–71.

Biographical Statement

Joke Bradt, PhD, MT-BC, is Assistant Professor and Coordinator of Music Therapy at Montclair State University, New Jersey. As a clinician, she works with children with communication difficulties and women with chronic pain. Joke has presented her work at many national and international music therapy conferences. She is the author of several music therapy articles and book chapters.

Joke Bradt, Ph.D., MT-BC
Assistant Professor and Coordinator,
Music Therapy
Montclair State University
McEachern Music Building
Upper Montclair, NJ 07043, USA
Tel#: 973-655-7583

Chapter 18

MUSIC THERAPY THEORETICAL APPROACHES

E. MAGDALENA LAVERDIERE

INTRODUCTION

Music therapy is a field of study and practice that embraces a variety of theories. Forinash (2001) acknowledges that music therapy programs do not require specific courses across all music therapy programs; instead programs are competency based. This has allowed a great deal of flexibility in the training of music therapists. Such flexibility in the training of music therapists has enabled a variety of theories and methods to be utilized within the field. The diversity of theories being employed within the field of music therapy may foreshadow future divisions and development within the field (i.e. divisions based on association with specific theories or approaches to music therapy). For example, music therapy associated with having clients actually play instruments may be a division of music therapy and another division may be associated with music therapy that uses listening to music in order to assist clients' changes rather than actually playing an instrument. This information was covered in more detail in the previous chapter by Joke Bradt. The purpose of this chapter is to provide information regarding the theoretical approaches that are used in the field of music therapy.

Although a range of theories are recognized by music therapists, the defining purpose of music therapy remains relatively consistent. This purpose is to use music for the emotional and/or mental benefit of a client. The American Music Therapy Association (2004) defines music therapy as the following:

> Music therapy is the prescribed use of music by a qualified person to effect positive changes in the psychological, physical, cognitive, or social function of individuals with health or educational problems. (p. 1)

Organizations

The popularity of music therapy has assisted in the forming of associations that support music therapists. Such organizations and associations promote continuing education of music therapists (Certification Board for Music Therapists, 2004), provide professional support (i.e., conferences), and encourage research publications and professional writing opportunities related to the field (American Music Therapy Association, 2004). Lindberg (1998) states that music therapy associations provide a public awareness regarding the beneficial nature of music therapy for growth and healing in a variety of nonmusic-related areas including the development of communication skills, reducing inappropriate behaviors, reducing stress, improving attention span, and growth of self.

The two major organizations, within the United States, to which music therapists can be associated, are the American Music Therapy Association and the Certification Board for Music Therapists. The American Music Therapy Association (2004) cites that in 1998 the National Association for Music Therapy, founded in 1950, and the American Association for Music Therapy, founded in 1971, joined. These organizations merged to form the American Music Therapy Association.

The American Music Therapy Association

The American Music Therapy Association (2004) promotes music therapy for its multiple uses within a therapeutic environment. This association notes that music therapy can be used to assess the function of an individual (physically, cognitively, socially, and psychologically) by using music as a means for observation and assessment. In addition, the American Music Therapy Association (2004) also states that music therapists can utilize music to encourage social participation within group therapy. Musical imagery and music performance are also recognized by the association as approaches that are commonly utilized by music therapists within a client session.

The American Music Therapy Association (2004) accepts a wide variety of individuals into their group as the association envelopes nine categories of membership: professional, associate, student, inactive, retired, affiliate, patron, life, and honorary life. This association also professes that members are committed to promoting positive change among various groups of individuals through the use of music in the therapy environment. This theory is based on the belief that individuals from the following groups can be positively influenced by music therapy: "children, adolescents, adults, and the elderly with mental health needs, developmental and learning disabilities, Alzheimer's disease and other aging related conditions, substance abuse problems, brain injuries, physical disabilities, and acute and chronic pain" (American Music Therapy Association, 2004, p. 1).

The Certification Board for Music Therapists

The Certification Board for Music Therapists provides a national exam for potential members to take and if such exam is passed and the individual meets the other qualifications (i.e., education), the new member will receive the title "Music Therapist-Board Certified" (MT-BC). A positive aspect of this organization is that it is nonprofit. The Certification Board for Music Therapists (2004) also recognizes that music therapy is a multidisciplinary field and that there is no one form of music therapy, rather there are various approaches, methods, interventions, and applications utilized in this growing field of therapy.

Theories

A myriad of theories regarding music therapy have evolved through the years. Some theorists that are considered by researchers (e.g., Aigen, 1995; Bunt, 2002; Pavlicevic, 2002; Sharf, 2000) as cur-

rently popular and well known within the field for their practical applications include Bonny and Bruscia. Some current theoretical approaches that will be further discussed include African drumming, group music therapy, and songwriting. This section will take a historical and evolutionary approach to the development of music therapy theoretical development.

Bruscia

Bruscia explains music therapy as a well-defined sequence of interventions and approaches that are presented by a therapist in order to facilitate changes for a client's benefit. Recent researchers (e.g., Pellitteri, 2000; Wigram, Pedersen, & Bonde, 2002) recognize and find agreement with Bruscia's theory. Additionally, Bruscia (1998) focuses on the defining of music therapy: "Music therapy is a systematic process of intervention wherein the therapist helps the client to promote health, using music experiences and the relationships that develop through them as dynamic forces of change" (p. 20). Several levels of therapy assist in defining what type of music therapy is being practiced. These categories are the following (Bruscia, 1998):

1. *Auxiliary:* Use of music in therapy in a non-therapeutic manner, yet its purpose is still relevant in the therapy situation.
2. *Augmentative:* Use of music in a manner that supports other therapy modalities.
3. *Intensive:* Music is the central therapy modality.
4. *Primary:* Music serves as the only method of therapy in this level.

Areas of Practice

There are six major areas of music therapy practice. Each of these six areas of practice encompasses the four levels based on the criteria as listed above. Bruscia (1998) explains that music therapy includes six areas of practice, with each being based on criteria including therapy goals, the client-therapist relationship, and the client's presenting problem. The six areas of practice, as divulged by Bruscia (1998), incorporate the following: didactic, medical, healing, psychotherapeutic, recreational, and ecological. These six categories or areas of practice differentiate from one another according to their applications.

Applications of Music Therapy

A didactic application, according to Bruscia (1998) entails education. This area of practice focuses on assisting clients with obtaining knowledge or skills. Bruscia (1998) explains that the purpose in this type of music therapy is to help clients learn.

Medical approaches focus on the physical health and well-being of the client. Sidorenko (2000) used this approach in reducing anxiety among pregnant women who were pre-operative for Caesarian section. Additionally, Sidorenko (2000) reports that the women were assisted medically with music therapy methods, as the women subsequently required lowered dosages of painkillers during their medical stay. Sidorenko (2000) also reports that the patients participating in the music therapy study stayed an average of three fewer days when compared to other high-risk pregnancies. Furthermore, 62 percent of the patients participating in the music therapy program reported that they had only low levels of anxiety, which is significant when compared to the control group as 66 percent of control-group participants reported high levels of anxiety.

A third approach that clinicians utilize, as outlined by Bruscia, is that of healing. Bruscia (1998) explains that the applications within this category as making vibrations, music, and sounds for the purpose of restoring harmony. La Torre (2003) recognizes the usefulness of making sounds, tones, and vibrations as a form of music therapy. This form of therapy can assist in reducing stress and in providing a venue of expression for the client.

Another approach or area of music therapy is that of psychotherapy. Bruscia (1998) explains that psychotherapeutic music therapy approaches include all group and individual methods that focus on the client's mental and/or emotional changes. A fifth area discussed by Bruscia is recreational. This area of application includes practices that focus on personal enjoyment such as social interaction.

The final area of practice is ecological. Ecological practices involve music for the proposed improvement of the environment. Overall, the ecological approach is a little research topic in most disciplines, not just the creative therapies (Brooke, 2005). This includes improving the client's life environment or the actual therapeutic environment. However, the focus for such form of music therapy is placed upon the environment and the interaction with the client to such environment (i.e., attitude).

Practice within each of these six areas is dependent on the purpose of the client's presence in therapy. The health priority, according to Bruscia (1998), is the combination of several assessments that include the client's therapeutic needs, the agency's mission, and the motivation of the client in seeking therapy. The health priority is dually assessed in order to accommodate the client in the setting provided. Music therapy interventions are thus assessed according to this health priority.

GIM

The Guided Imagery and Music method, also known as GIM, was created by Helen Lindquist Bonny. Bonny (1999) cited that this theory of music therapy rests within two major theoretical frameworks. According to Bonny (1999), her theory is founded on Maslow's self-actualization model and Carl Rogers's client centered model of therapy. These theories appear within the GIM method in several forms. For example, within a session, the therapist will play specific music selections and the purpose of such choices is based on the therapist's belief that the selected music will promote self-understanding for the client. The emphasis of self-understanding as actualized by the client, rather than explained by the therapist to the client, is a form of client centered therapy. The role of Maslow's self-actualization theory can be revealed in the GIM method through the emphasis of metamorphasizing the client through the revealing of his or her own emotions and feelings (Bunt, 2002).

A feature that differentiates the Bonny GIM and music therapy from other methods of music therapy is the focus on classical music. Bonny (1999) states that three years of training focused on the Bonny GIM are required in order for a therapist to practice this method of therapy. This training primarily involves an acquisition of knowledge regarding classical music. Additionally, training in the Bonny GIM entails educating the therapist how to use music to enter an altered state of consciousness.

However, Bonny (1999) admits that her theory of GIM evolved from her work using Leuner's Guided Affective Imagery Therapy. Leuner's theory focuses more on a psychoanalytic approach, as Bonny (1999) cites that in working with Leuner's theory there are four steps that create an opportunity for the client to enter a different level of consciousness. The steps utilized in Leuner's Guided Affective Imagery approach involve the following (Bonny, 1999):

1. Allow the client to provide information regarding himself or herself by asking questions.
2. Assist the relaxation of the client by having him or her lie on a couch and focus on the next step of relaxation.
3. Play music selections, in a pre-selected order, that have been chosen for the facilitation of invoking emotions and images.
4. After the music experience allow the client to share the feelings and emotions he or she experienced during the music program.

The Leuner approach differentiates from the Bonny GIM therapy model in that Bonny's method entails five specific steps within a given session. The first step, the prelude, involves the use of journaling, playing music, or other forms of music/artistic expression (Bunt, 2002). Bunt lists the other stages of Bonny's theory as the following: induction (relaxation period while lying on a couch), listening and imagining, return (ending the music program and bringing the client's state of consciousness back to the therapy session), and finally the postlude. The postlude entails the client revealing thoughts, feelings, and images experienced during the music program.

A strength in using the Bonny method of GIM is the relatively new origination of the theory, as it was first presented to the World Congress of Music Therapy in 1999. This theory, being relatively new to the realm of music therapy, has had the opportunity to expand previous theories (i.e., the connections between Leuner's theory and Bonny's theory).

Current research has also indicated some of the strengths associated with the use of the GIM. McKinney, Antoni, Kuman, Tims, and McCabe (1997) investigated the use of GIM on mood changes. McKinney and colleagues (1997) cite that the GIM method can produce a decrease in depressed moods among participants. Furthermore, results from Blake (1995) explain that the Bonny's GIM is useful in treating psychiatric patients who are suffering from posttraumatic stress disorder.

A weakness associated with the practice of conducting Bonny's GIM of therapy is that three years of training are required (Bonny, 1999) in addition to other years of counseling. However, there is a good deal of support and organization provided for this practice of therapy, as the Association for Music and Imagery (2003) has been developed to support GIM practicing therapists. The Association for Music and Imagery (2003) requires that members be fully trained in the Bonny GIM for membership to be permitted.

Popular Approaches Within the Field

Music therapy in the clinical setting encompasses the use of music for the benefit of the client. Bruscia (1998) recognizes several factors that define current approaches to music therapy. The first factor is that music is not to be the priority in the clinical setting, rather the client's processing of emotions and his or her reactions to such music and musical experiences are to be the focus of the session. Another factor Bruscia (1998) recognizes is that successful music therapy includes goal setting, direction, and organization. Bruscia (1998) also asserts that the approach a clinician takes in a music therapy session depends on the clinician's theoretical orientation, the presenting problem, and the client's personality. Not all approaches and theoretical orientations will be applicable to all clients. It is important for clinicians to develop interventions that allow for growth according to clinician processes, as Bruscia (1998) states that clinicians using music therapy should apply the interpersonal process to a sequencing of events and stages in the therapeutic environment. For example, the establishment of rapport, developing trust, client history intake, etc., should be engaged throughout this sequence, even when the clinician is applying music therapy in the approach. Successful music therapy embraces three components in the clinical setting, as Bruscia (1998) describes these components as the following: "assessment, treatment, and evaluation" (p. 20).

African Drumming

African drumming is a new form of therapy and theoretical approach being utilized by clinicians (Longhofer & Floersch, 1993). Longhofer and Floersch cite that the use of drumming in therapy "complements the community integration goals of psychiatric rehabilitation" (p. 3). Furthermore, the use of African drumming achieves goals associated with the International Association of Psychological Rehabilitation, according to Longhofer and Floersch (1993), which include the use of group activities that "are designed to enhance individuals' skills and to foster a sense of community and healthy participation in normalizing adult activities" (p. 5).

Researchers (Longhofer & Floersch 1993; Stewart & Stewart, 2002; Wigram et al., 2002; Winkelman, 2003) find that drumming provides positive physical and psychological effects for some therapy clients. However, these researchers express that the emphasis must be placed on the client(s) conducting the drumming rather than listening or watching others drumming. Winkelman (2003) conducted research using drumming therapy among drug rehabilitation clients. Additionally, Winkelman reports that the results from this research indicate that the use of drumming in therapy can produce the following effects: feelings of relaxation, restored balance in opioid levels in the brain, self-awareness, emotional healing, spiritual experiences, and an overall feeling of social connectedness with others in the drumming group.

Longhofer and Floersch (1993) examined the use of African drumming in psychiatric rehabilitation. They cite that this form of music therapy provides the opportunity for clients to participate in a social experience. Longhofer and Floersch (1993) emphasized the use of "polyrhythmic music of the Dagbama from West Africa" in group therapy sessions to work with "the community integration goals" in rehabilitation settings (p. 3). Other researchers, such as La Torre' (2003) and Saroyan (1990), also emphasize the use of music therapy for the benefits of interconnectedness and group trust building.

Group Music Therapy

Group music therapy can be of value to clinicians as it can provide a basis for social interaction, which may be beneficial for clients with social introversion or shyness. Nayak, Wheeler, Shiflett, and Agostinelli (2000) reported that music therapy in a rehabilitation setting provides a positive effect on social and behavioral improvements among individuals with brain injury. Bunt (2002) purports that group music therapy can create a working alliance between group members, thus enhancing the socializing effects of this approach.

Group drumming and music performance within group therapy are recognized in current research (Hogan, 2003; Pellitteri, 2000) as favorable approaches within the realm of music therapy. Other theories of music therapy that have been utilized within group therapy settings include listening to music (Wimpory & Nash, 1999), singing (La Torre, 2003), songwriting (Gallant, Holosko, Siegel, 1997), and making musical vibrations (La Torre, 2003).

Saroyan (1990) explains that when using music in group therapy, initial tasks should be simple in nature and the therapy should progress to more creative or complex activities. This should assist in the encouragement of participation and improved comfort between group members, according to Saroyan's theory (1990). Further expressed by Saroyan (1990) are several goals of music therapy within group settings, which include the development of "trust, cooperation, and interaction" (p. 140).

Songwriting and Composing

Another current approach used in music therapy is songwriting. Songwriting is recognized by researchers (Hogan, 2003; Silber & Hes, 1995) as a valuable intervention in therapy. An article by Gallant and others (1997) presents clinical interventions related to their cumulative experience in the field of music therapy of more than 40 years. Gallant and colleagues (1997) stress that music interventions that integrate the use of poetry and songwriting can be beneficial to clients with addictions. The key to this form of therapy is recognizing that music can assist clients in getting "unstuck" (Gallant, 1997, p. 49). Clients with addiction may have developed issues (i.e., emotional problems) that are difficult to overcome and are related to their physical addiction (i.e., relationship problems leading to alcoholism). Songwriting is presented as a therapeutic device that can aid clients in confronting their issues and related addictions. It is asserted that the songwriting method can assist clients in recognizing their core issues that may have inevitably caused the addiction (Gallant, 1997).

CONCLUSION

The future of music therapy is very promising as researchers are proving that this form of therapy is beneficial to a myriad of clientele including children with cancer (Barrera, Rykov, & Doyle, 2002), children with autism (Wimpory & Nash, 1999), patients with psychosis (Hayashi et al., 2002), patients with addiction (Gallant et al., 1997), pregnant woman (Sidorenko, 2000), children with developmental difficulties (Duffy & Fuller, 2000), and individuals experiencing grief reactions (Bright, 1999), to name a few. Support for music therapy research and practice can be found with the American Music Therapy Association and the Certification Board for Music Therapists.

However, the development of a cohesive theory among the various schools that provide education to future music therapists may be required to promote this field to even greater levels. Bruscia (1998) recognizes that the definition and theories related to music therapy have been varied throughout time. Providing some cohesion, albeit through the American Music Therapy Association or the Certification Board or Music Therapists, may provide greater support and consistency in music therapy. Inclusion of the various forms of music therapy approaches, within the music therapy associations, may allow for further development and more recognition of the divisions, specializations, and areas of expertise in this realm of practice and study. Such action may provide even greater appreciation for the various approaches in the field of music therapy.

REFERENCES

Aigen, K. (1995). Interpretational research. In B.L. Wheeler (Ed.). *Music therapy research: Quantitative and qualitative perspectives.* Phoenixville, PA: Barcelona Publishers.

American Music Therapy Association. (2004). *About the American Music Therapy Association.* Retrieved May 5, 2004 from http://www.musictherapy.org/

Association for Music and Imagery. (2003). *Core elements of the Bonny Method of Guided Imagery and Music.* Retrieved May 5, 2004 from http://www.bonnymethod.com/ami/

Barrera, M.E., Rykov, M.H., & Doyle, S.L. (2002). The effects of interactive music therapy on hospitalized children with cancer: A pilot study. *Psycho-Oncology, 11,* 379–388.

Blake, R.L., & Bishop, S.R. (1995). The Bonny Method of Guided Imagery and Music (GIM) in the treatment of post-traumatic stress disorder (PTSD) with adults in a psychiatric setting. *Music Therapy Perspectives, 12,* 125–129.

Bonny, H.L. (1999, November 19). *History and development of the Bonny Method.* Presented at the World Congress of Music Therapy Plenary Session: Panel of Founders in Washington, DC. Retrieved May 5, 2004 from http://www.bonnyfoundation.org/bonny.html

Bright, R. (1999). Music therapy in grief resolution. *Bulletin of the Menninger Clinic, 63*(4), 481–499.

Brooke, S.L. (2005). Origins of the social mind: Evolutionary psychology and child development. *PsycCRITIQUES-Contemporary Psychology: APA Review of Books.* http://www.psycinfo.com/psyccritiques/

Bruscia, K.E. (1998). *Defining music therapy: Second edition.* Gilsum, NH: Barcelona Publishers.

Bruscia, K.E. (1995). The boundaries of music therapy research. In B.L. Wheeler (Ed.). *Music therapy research: Quantitative and qualitative perspectives.* Phoenixville, PA: Barcelona Publishers.

Bunt, L. (2002). Transformation, ovid, and Guided Imagery and Music (GIM). In L. Bunt, & Hoskyns, S. (Eds.). *The handbook of music therapy.* New York: Brunner-Routledge.

Certification Board for Music Therapists. (2004). Retrieved May 1, 2004 from http://www.cbmt.org/default.asp

Duffy, B., & Fuller, R. (2000). Role of music therapy in social skills development in children with moderate intellectual disability. *Journal of Applied Research in Intellectual Disabilities, 13,* 77–89.

Forinash, M. (2001). Music therapy in the United States. *Voices: Main Issue, 1*(2). Retrieved May 15, 2004 from http://www.voices.no/mainissues/Voices1(2)Forinash.html.

Gallant, W., Holosko, M., & Siegel, S. (1997). The use of music in counseling with addictive clients. *Journal of Alcohol & Drug Information, 42*(2), 42–52.

Hayashi, N., Tanabe, Y., Nakagawa, S., Noguchi, M., Iwata, C., Koubuchi, Y., et al. (2002). Effects of group musical therapy on inpatients with chronic psychoses: A controlled study. *Psychiatry and Clinical Neurosciences, 56,* 187–193.

Hogan, B.E. (2003). Soul music in the twilight years: Music therapy and the dying process. *Topics in Geriatric Rehabilitation, 19*(4), 275–281.

LaTorre, M.A. (2003). The use of music and sound to enhance the therapeutic setting. *Perspectives in Psychiatric Care, 39*(3), 129–131.

Lindberg, K.A. (1998). *Music therapy: Frequently asked questions.* Retrieved April 10, 2004 from http://www.members.aol.com/kathysl/questions.html.

Longhofer, J., & Floersch, J. (1993). African drumming and psychiatric rehabilitation. *Psychosocial Rehabilitation Journal, 16*(4), 3–11.

McKinney, C.H., Antoni, M.H., Kumar, M., Tims, F.C., & McCabe, P.M. (1997). Effects of Guided Imagery and Music (GIM) Therapy on mood and cortisol in healthy adults. *Health Psychology, 16*(4), 390–400.

Nayak, S., Wheeler, B.L., Shiflett, S.C., & Agostinelli, S. (2000). Effect of music therapy on mood and social interaction among individuals with acute traumatic brain injury and stroke. *Rehabilitation Psychology, 45*(3), 274–283.

Pavlicevic, M. (2002). Fragile rhythms and uncertain listenings: Perspectives from music therapy with South African children. In J.P. Sutton (Ed.). *Music, music therapy, and trauma: International perspectives.* Philadelphia, PA: Jessica Kingsley Publishers.

Pellitteri, J. (2000). Music therapy in the special education setting. *Journal of Educational and Psychological Consultation, 11*(3&4), 379–391.

Saroyan, J.S. (1990). The use of music therapy on an adolescent psychiatric unit. *Journal of Group Psychotherapy, 43*(3), 139–141.

Sharf, R.S. (2000). *Theories of psychotherapy and counseling.* Belmont, CA: Wadsworth/Thomson Learning.

Sidorenko, V.N. (2000). Clinical application of medical resonance therapy music in high-risk pregnancies. *Integrative Physiological and Behavioral Science, 35*(3), 199–207.

Silber, F., & Hes, J.P. (1995). The use of songwriting with patients diagnosed with Alzheimer's disease. *Music Therapy Perspectives, 31*(1), 31–34.

Stewart, R.W., & Stewart, D. (2002). See me, hear me, play with me: Working with the trauma of early abandonment and deprivation in psychodynamic music therapy. In J.P. Sutton (Ed.). *Music, music therapy, and trauma: International perspectives.* Philadelphia, PA: Jessica Kingsley Publishers.

Wigram, T., Pedersen, I.N., & Bonde, L.O. (2002). *A comprehensive guide to music therapy: Theory, clinical practice, research and training.* Philadelphia, PA: Jessica Kingsley Publishers.

Wimpory, D.C., & Nash, S. (1999). Musical interaction therapy: Therapeutic play for children with autism. *Child Language Teaching and Therapy, 15*(1), 17–28.

Winkelman, M. (2003). Complementary therapy for addiction: "Drumming out drugs." *American Journal of Public Health, 93*(4), 647–652.

Biographical Statement

E. Magdalena LaVerdiere, M.A., B.S., is currently a PhD (ABD) student attending Walden University. In 2002, she earned her M.A. in Professional Counseling from Liberty University. Former work experiences include that of sexual assault advocate and domestic violence advocate. She maintains a keen interest in helping victims of sexual assault through more current work with victims of sexual assault in crisis.

Chapter 19

A MOSAIC OF MUSIC THERAPY ASSESSMENTS

Eric B. Miller

INTRODUCTION

Assessment in music therapy is a vital and dynamic process of inquiry. The purposes for music therapy assessment include diagnostic evaluation, general needs, clinical intervention plans, and evaluation of ongoing treatment intervention. Assessment is necessary for accountability to creative therapists and clients, justification of services, and for the ongoing validity of music therapy approaches (Chase, 2002). The type of assessment technique a music therapist utilizes is driven by various music theoretical approaches that include improvisational models, psychoanalytic models, educational models, and biomedical models of music therapy. Each of these systems provides a unique view of the music therapy process and suggests somewhat different ways of approaching music therapy assessment within a continuum of passive to active participation on the part of the client.

This chapter will review the contributions of Bruscia (1998), Wigram, Nordoff, and Robbins (2002), Brunk and Coleman (2000), and other music therapy theorists who have developed practical assessment tools for use in the field. It will also take a brief glance at promising upcoming technologies in music therapy and the implications of current and future research on music therapy.

Until the late 1990s, articles on music therapy assessment were few and far between, with the bulk of research focusing on clinical intervention (Sabatella, 2004). Gradually, this changed as authors became more interested in the documentation of assessment measures. In 1999, at the 9th World Congress of Music Therapy in Washington, DC, assessment was a highlight of focus. This sparked two special journal issues devoted to assessment, the *Journal of Music Therapy* and *Music Therapy Perspectives* in the year 2000. Despite this influx of interest in assessment, music therapy still lags behind other professions in its development of cohesive assessment methods (Sabatella, 2004). The current paucity is expressed even more emphatically by Kristen Chase, who admonishes that "The music therapy profession lacks formal assessment tools" (Chase, 2004, p. 28).

Since music therapists tend not to use established assessment instruments (Wilson & Smith, 2000), it is important to understand the underlying constructs that compose a music therapy assessment. In a survey of music therapy assessment instruments used with children with disabilities, Wilson and Smith (2000) found that only 16 out of 41 studies used a named assessment, and only three of those 16 were used more than once. Original or untitled assessments were used in just over half (51%) of the studies. While the lack of replication makes for questionable cross-study comparisons, it does leave an opening for creative construction of assessment instruments that fit the individual therapist's purpose.

In contrast however, test instruments cited in the *Journal of Music Therapy* are reported by Gregory (2000) to be 25 percent researcher-constructed, 35 percent unpublished, and 40 percent published tests. I was intrigued by the seeming disparity of these two perspectives and performed a cursory manual re-analysis of Gregory, counting however only those tests that included a music-related word in their title. Of the 115 test instruments presented by Gregory, I counted 25 (22%) that included a music-related word in their title. Of those 25, 18 (72%) were researcher-constructed, five (20%) were unpublished, and only two (8%) were published. These findings appear to indicate that the majority of the published studies were actually borrowed from other disciplines, such as the Stanford Binet Intelligence Scale (Thorndike et al., 1986), or the Peabody Picture Vocabulary Test (Dunn & Dunn, 1997), which were borrowed from psychology. While research gains credibility from using established instruments that have proven reliability, in music therapy, care must be taken to use instruments that measure those core elements and processes that a music therapist is interested in using with clients.

Given the preponderance of researcher-constructed instruments, it is important to identify these authors and to watch for emerging data on their instruments. The high percentage of researchers who construct their own instruments also lends credence to the notion that there is a schism between music therapy clinicians and music therapy researchers, with each living in their own world (Aigen, 1993; 1998). The table includes only those instruments with a music-related word in the title, such as "music" or "rhythm" etc.

Consistent with what Sabatella (2004) describes as a fragmented organization of music therapy

assessment information in the field, this chapter will embark on a mosaic of diverse assessment perspectives. The following sections look at some basic theoretical approaches to music therapy assessment and the hands-on techniques that follow from these systems of thought.

Elements of Assessment

Consider the following scenarios. The phone rings. A caseworker from a local hospital is on the line asking if you can provide music therapy for her Alzheimer's syndrome client. A colleague requests permission to refer an autistic child who likes music to you for music therapy. You are a parent and would like to know if music therapy might help your fourth grader focus better in school. A national accrediting body has scheduled an institutional review of the music therapy program at the college where you teach. Each of these situations requires a music therapy assessment, however performed, in somewhat of a different fashion.

There are several recurrent themes that arise again and again throughout the various established and theorized music therapy assessments. At the heart of any assessment is a question (Cohen, 1978). Some questions on an assessment are as follows:

Table 19.1.
Music-related Instruments.

Test	Author	Application
Sound Perception Test	Flowers	descriptive
Music Therapy Physiological Measures Test	Sutton	descriptive
Vocal Range/Pitch Matching Test	Myers	descriptive
Pitch Discrimination Test	Grant, Share	descriptive
Rhythm Perception Test	Grant, LeCroy	experimental
Music/Activity Therapy Intake Assessment	Braswell et al.	descriptive
Pitch Discrimination Test	Ford	descriptive
Improvised Musical Play	Gunsberg	descriptive
Music Therapy Effect Scales	Thaut	experimental
MT Intern Assessment	Grant	descriptive
Functional Music Skills Checklist	DiGiammarino	descriptive
Music Interaction Rating for Schizophrenia	Pavlicevik et al.	experimental
Social and Music Behavior Importance Scale	Jellison, Duke	descriptive
Residual Music Skills Test	York	descriptive
Music Assessment Protocol	Lipe	descriptive
Music Major Satisfaction Questionnaire	Allen	descriptive
Appraisal of Music Performer's Stress	Brodsky, Sloboda	experimental
Music Performer's Stress Survey	Brodsky, Sloboda	experimental

(Adapted from Gregory, 2000, p. 91)

- Would this person benefit from music therapy?
- How might this person benefit from music therapy?
- How does this person relate to others (the therapist or group members) through music?
- How does this person communicate through music?
- How is (ongoing) music therapy affecting this person?
- How might the music therapist optimize or shift music therapy intervention for improved outcome?
- How could a music therapy program benefit a facility?
- What are the strengths and weaknesses of this music therapist, MT instructor, or MT department?
- What kind of music therapy would work best in this environment?

Another vital element found in music therapy assessments is an analysis of relationship through the musical idiom. While a common lens to view relational behavior is on passive-active, or an introvert-extrovert continua, I prefer a shift in syntax to a receptive-expressive scale (Wigram, Perderson, & Bonde, 2002) in conjunction with an indicator of musical response.

As an example of creating an instrument from these basic concepts, a crude but quick assessment can be constructed with a simple therapist's rating of responsiveness and expression. Putting the receptive-expressive scale on the X axis and responsiveness on the Y axis of a grid yields the matrix shown in Figure 19.1. In this graphic depiction of initial impressions, which I call the Quick Music Therapy Assessment (QMTA), observations on the X axis are not exclusive and may fall at both ends of the scale.

Observations of responsiveness on the Y axis, however, are exclusive and must be evaluated at a specific level. For the Y or Responsiveness axis, a value of 0 is equal to *Unresponsive*, and a value of 5 is equal to *Extremely Responsive*. In the Receptive-Expressive continuum, where dual points may be recorded, one each for Receptivity and Expression, the longer the connecting line between the two points, the greater the repertoire or range of expression.

Evaluation in this quick instrument is not criteria based, but grounded in the experience of the therapist and his or her subjective impression. Utilizing this format yields a very easy assessment at-

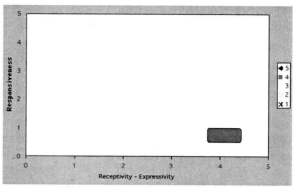

Figure 19.1. QMTA.

a-glance. For example, within a minute or two of improvisation with a music therapist, a young developmentally delayed client's QMTA might appear as shown in Figure 19.2.

The red box quickly tells us that this client is highly expressive; however, not very receptive and not very responsive. We might then assert that music therapy would be beneficial for this child to develop interpersonal skills and appropriate self-expression.

Specific techniques would then follow from the observed musical interaction within the first several sessions. While not suitable for cross-practitioner comparison, this kind of quick assessment provides information that a therapist builds while developing a therapeutic alliance with a client.

Other key concepts that recur in MT assessment are quantitative and qualitative assessment tools (Wigram, et al., 2002). Quantitative data consist of definable behaviors, while qualitative information relates to the experience of the music therapy session and phenomenological understanding of the

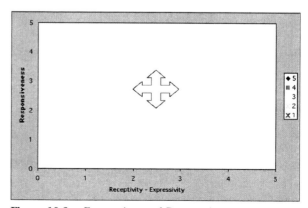

Figure 19.2. Expression and Responsiveness.

meaning of musical communication and interaction. In many ways, a music therapy assessment is a merging of quantitative data and qualitative information, or a balancing of these two ways of acquiring knowledge (Wheeler, 1995). The music therapist processes a musical experience into an analytical tool. Observable data can be quantified and compared; qualitative impressions can be described in ways to convey the essence of an experience. There are many qualities that music possesses, such as communication on multiple levels and inspiration for creativity, that lend themselves to qualitative study (Aigen, 1998; Smeijsters, 1997). Keeping these assessment components in mind during this tour of some of the different types of assessment in this chapter will help provide a cohesive framework for the construction of MT assessments in general.

Improvisational Music Therapy Assessment

The subject of improvisational music therapy assessment is vast and could easily take up a whole book in and of itself. In fact, Kenneth Bruscia (1987) has written a thought-provoking and comprehensive book on the subject, *Improvisational Models of Music Therapy,* that details the fundamental tenets of 25 models of music therapy in a uniform format for easy comparison. Bruscia goes even further and assists in codifying the work of other authors into cohesive and systematic theoretical approaches. In this section, we will scratch the surface of the improvisational approach.

Nordoff and Robbins (1971) identify thirteen categories of response and three musical response scales (Nordoff & Robbins, 1971; 1977) as assessment tools. They also present a tempo-dynamic schema that was not specifically constructed as an assessment (Bruscia, 1987), but helps to categorize normal versus pathological components of a child's music improvisation. These musical response scales may be some of the more widely used published instruments. They focus on describing the client-therapist relationship, musical communication, level of resistance and participation, instrumental responsiveness, and vocal responsiveness. Some of the Nordoff and Robbins' categories of response include the following (Bruscia, 1987, p. 37):

1. Complete Rhythmic Freedom
2. Unstable Rhythmic Freedom
3. Limited Rhythmic Freedom
4. Compulsive Beating
5. Disordered Beating
6. Evasive Beating
7. Emotional Force Beating
8. Chaotic-Creative Beating
9. Piano Playing
10. Responses by Singing
11. Response to Change
12. Responses to Mood

Each category is accompanied by a brief description of the response. In their evaluation scales 1 and 2, Nordoff and Robbins assess the child-therapist relationship and musical "communicativeness" respectively. In their Musical response, scale 3, Nordoff and Robbins rate levels of rhythmic organization, levels of ability/experience, expressive components, responsiveness, and singing responses (Nordoff & Robbins, 1971; 1977). The levels of rhythmic organization include ratings of rhythmic complexity, tempo range, and basic beating. Levels of ability/experience include establishing, finding, incipient, preservative, compulsive, reactive, undirected, and unaware. Expressive components include: Tremolo, Dynamic contrast, Loud/crescendo, among others. Levels of Responsiveness include: (M) musically expressive/perceptive, (S) self-expressively assertive, (B) becoming engaged, (N) nascent. Singing Responses are divided into ratings of level of melodic form, vocal responsiveness, and vocal participation (Bruscia, 1987). Here the themes of degree of expression and responsiveness are at center stage.

Nordoff and Robbins recorded their sessions and then went back over the tapes and rated each instance of behavior at a particular level (Nordoff & Robbins, 1977; 1985). A therapist utilizing the scales would likewise record their sessions, noting each instance of a behavior level, and then distributing 10 points across each of the observed levels of behavior and thus generating a point distribution percentage chart. These charts provide a method for trend analysis over time.

Improvisation Assessment Profiles

Kenneth Bruscia offers six profiles that may be used individually, but are designed to be used as a comprehensive battery. Each of the profiles contains musical element subscales. The initial battery typically takes several sessions, and the assessment

Table 19.2.
Bruscia's Improvisation Assessment Profiles.

Bruscia's Improvisation Assessment Profiles				
Integration				
Undifferentiated	Fused	Integrated	Differentiated	Overdifferentiated
Variability				
Rigid	Stable	Variable	Contrasting	Random
Tension				
Hypotense	Calm	Cyclic	Tense	Hypertense
Congruence				
Uncommitted	Congruent	Centered	Incongruent	Polarized
Salience				
Receding	Conforming	Contributing	Controlling	Overpowering
Autonomy				
Dependent	Follower	Partner	Leader	Resister

may continue as therapy progresses. Assessment by profile may even constitute a significant therapeutic activity within treatment. Table 19.2 presents the profiles and their subscale components.

Integration reflects the organization of simultaneous musical elements. Variability reflects the organization of sequential musical elements. Tension describes the sustenance, modulation, and release of musical tension within the musical improvisation. *Congruence* reflects the organization of simultaneous feeling, states, and role relationships. *Salience* indicates the prominence and control of certain musical elements of the improvisation. *Autonomy* describes the relationship between the improvisers. The middle three gradients represent the norm, while the outliers fall at each end. Scales are grouped together as either Rhythmic, Tonal, Textural, Volume, Timbre, Physical, or Programmatic. Tony Wigram utilizes primarily the Autonomy and Variability profiles in his work diagnosing children with communication disorders (Wigram, et al., 2002). He uses the Autonomy profile to look at the client/therapist interpersonal experiences. With the Variability profile, Wigram and colleagues look at the degree of rigidity or freedom present in client's music from excerpts of therapy sessions.

Additional areas of evaluation are contributed by Joanne Loewy (2000). Some areas that she includes in her assessment model are: degrees of concentration, range of affect, self-esteem, and risk-taking. Loewy is interested in the development of language through musical elements. Language and music share integral components such as pitch, rhythm, dynamics, and phrasing. Language evaluation is common in MT assessments.

Table 19.3 presents an example of a generic music therapy assessment instrument that I have compiled from a variety of approaches and is based on improvisation with a client.

Psychoanalytic Music Therapy Assessment

In the psychoanalytic or the Freudian approach, music as well as personality traits can be described in terms of their psychosexual stage of development. Here we might observe oral music, anal music, or phallic/genital music according to the Priestly Model of music therapy (Bruscia, 1987). Oral music is blissful and flowing. When playing with others, there is a sense of fusion or merging. Anal music is rebellious and immersed in self-awareness (Bruscia, 1987). When playing in a group, the player asserts his/her identity domi-

Table 19.3.
GMTA.

GENERIC MUSIC THERAPY ASSESSMENT (GMTA)

Client Name:		Music Therapist:	Date:
Date of Birth:	Age:	Diagnosis:	Case #
Contact Information:			
Referring Agency:			
Purpose of Assessment:			

Interaction (psychosocial)

Function	Rating	Criteria	Comments
Relates with therapist		1=resistant 2=not engaged 3=somewhat engaged 4=moderately engaged 5=highly engaged	
Maintains eye contact		1=minimal to no eye contact 5=high eye contact	
Responds to directives		1=does not respond 5=highly responsive	
Stays on task		1=minimal to no vigilance 5=high vigilance	
Behavioral inhibition		1=highly impulsive 5=higly self-regulated	
Exhibits appropriate affect		1=innappropriate or no affect (comment) 5=appropriate affect	
Follows multiple step directives		1=cannot follow multiple step directives 5=easily follows 3 step directives	

Sensorimotor/Cognition

Ability to use mallet		1=poor grasp of stick 5=accurately strikes target	
Use of both hands		1=little use of either hand 3=good use of one hand 5=good use of both hands	
Discriminates vocal pitch change		1=cannot detect any pitch change 5=easily detects pitch change at the semi-tone level	

Table 19.3.
continued

Function	Rating	Criteria	Comments
Discriminates Instrumental pitch change		1=cannot detect any pitch change 5=easily detects pitch change at the semi-tone level	
Discriminates dynamic (volume) change		1=cannot detect any volume change 5=easily detects pitch change at the semi-tone level	
Body awareness		1=little body awareness 5=high body awareness	
Oriented X3 (person, place, time)		1=not oriented 5=oriented X3	
Recounts history (long-term memory)		1=little long-term recall 5=excellent long-term recall	
Recalls immediate past events (short-term memory)		1=little short-term recall 5=excellent short-term recall	

Language

Verbalization		1=nonverbal 5=uses complete sentences	
Responds to questions		1=no response 2=appropriate response	
Initiates verbal expression		1=does not initiate 5=easily initiates verbal expressions	

Music

Improvises vocally		1=cannot improvise vocally 5=easily improvises	
Matches pitch		1=cannot match pitch 5=easily matches pitch	
Sings songs		1=does not sing songs 5=sings lyrics and melody easily	
Vocal range		1=little vocal range 5=wide vocal range	
Dynamic range		1=little dynamic range 5=wide dynamic range	
Sings intervals		1=cannot sing intervals 5=easily sing intervals	

Table 19.3.
continued

Function	Rating	Criteria	Comments
Sings harmonies		1=cannot sing harmonies 5=easily sing harmonies	
Improvises instrumentally		1=cannot improvise instrumentally 5=easily improvises	
Accompaniment		1=cannot accompany a soloist 5=provides solid accompaniment	
Reads notation		1=cannot read notation 5=sight reads well	

Summary & Recommendations

Overall impression:

Interaction (psychosocial):	Sensorimotor/Cognition:
Language:	Music:
Recommendations:	Specific objectives:

nantly over others. Tempos may be fast and end abruptly. Phallic/genital music may be evident through body messages, such as how the player holds his or her instrument. Genital music is characterized by reciprocity, awareness, and pleasure in playing. A tendency toward dyads may lead to competition for partners and conflicts around rejection (Bruscia, 1987). In this model, observable behaviors reflect unconscious conflicts, drive impulses, and ego defense mechanisms. Some ego defense mechanisms include denial, repression, projection, isolation, and rationalization, among others. Resistance is an attempt to work through issues of transference and counter-transference.

An analytic model may take a Jungian approach. In the Jungian system, key components to examine are symbols, archetypes, persona, shadow, story, dreams, anima, and animus. Austin (2001) describes the role of music from the analytic perspective as a mediator between the conscious and the unconscious. The music and accompanying words are the media that establish a dialogue

between conscious and unconscious content. Music can allow alienated or split-off aspects of the self, what Jung calls persona, to emerge and participate in the therapy process (Austin, 2001). I have pieced together diverse elements of psychoanalytic music therapy in the following assessment instrument shown in Table 19.4, which is the Analytic Music Therapy Assessment.

Receptive Music Therapy Assessment

The receptive models are those that rely heavily on listening. The music may be recorded, improvised live by the therapist, or read from printed music by the therapist or assisting musician. Helen Bonny (1975) based the theoretical premises of her Guided Imagery and Music (GIM) technique in Freud's concepts of ego psychology. Bonny pictures the ego at the seat of numerous concentric circles of consciousness (Bonny, 1975). The ego is normally conscious. Material nearby the center is close to conscious as in daydreams or music listening. The outer-reaches are the least accessible where such

Table 19.4.
AMTI.

Analytic Music Therapy Inquiry (AMTI)
Personality traits through music
Oral:
Anal:
Phallic/Genital:

Client musical depiction of parental conflicts
Mother/client music:
Father/client music:
Family music:
Musical Symbols and Archetypes:
Client identified symbols in music improvisation:
Client identified symbols in dreams:
Client identified symbols in music/guided imagery:

experiences as mystical oneness reside, or where repressed memories may be found.

In the Bonny model, recorded music serves as co-therapist and the music therapist functions as a guide. Music becomes a vehicle for accessing altered states of consciousness and the healing that can occur at the edges of consciousness. A GIM psychotherapy session consists of the four following stages (Rugenstein, 2000): (1) Preliminary conversation—prelude; (2) Induction, relaxation, and focus; (3) Music listening; and (4) Post-session integration—postlude.

It is in the prelude and postlude stages where much of the assessment occurs. In the prelude, the therapist and client discuss insights gained from and since the prior session. This is also the time when together they develop a plan for that day's session (Rugenstein, 2000). The second and third stages focus on the client's musical journey through imagery and sound. In the postlude, insights from that session are discussed and may be integrated via activities such as art, journal writing, discourse, music improvisation, or a combination of modalities. In this way, assessment is progressive and life changes can be noted in the prelude discussion stage. This gives the therapist a sense of how the therapeutic work is being generalized to the client's everyday world.

Family Music Therapy Assessment

One form of assessment that has received little attention in the literature is the family music thera-

py assessment. Within the context of family therapy, the music therapy assessment "provides the therapist with information about family roles, communication patterns, balance of power, and symptoms of dysfunction" (Miller, 1994, p. 45). Adapting a structural family therapy approach in the tradition of Salvatore Minuchin, a music therapist observes who does what to whom, and where power is seated (Miller, 1994).

The assessment begins with a simple directive from the music therapist, such as inviting the family members to choose an instrument and then begin playing and be sure to end together. Roles quickly become apparent. A child may be observed instructing a parent. The father may criticize mother, while aligning musically with one of the children. One child may withdraw and not participate, with no reaction from any of the other family members. Musically, the therapist notes who is playing rhythmically, who follows whom, who plays tonally, is the music adversarial, cohesive, disjointed, or tranquil. From observations of this nature, the music therapist then formulates a hypothesis about where power lies in the family, and where alliances and discords exist. The process by which the family communicates and engages in a task is also surmised. Once a formulation has been made, the therapist may design remedial music therapy intervention from the systemic, strategic, or structural family therapy approaches (Miller, 1994).

Figure 19.3 illustrates an example of a family music therapy assessment diagram. The picture is accompanied by a narrative that describes the nature of the musical interaction and the balance of power in the family. This family entered treatment upon recommendation of a crisis intervention team responding to the daughter's recent suicide attempt. Daughter has been placed temporarily in a therapeutic shelter facility. Music therapy is part of the treatment program and all families are encouraged to engage in one to three family music therapy sessions while their child resides in the placement.

In this case, the father does not connect musically with either mother or daughter, and his drum playing has an invasive or antagonistic quality. Mother and daughter come together with a light rhythmic melody in A minor. Daughter, however, clearly takes the leadership role in setting the tonal and rhythmic structure of the piece, while mother is adept at following. Son is present in a far corner

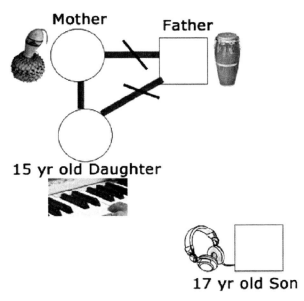

Figure 19.3. FMTA.

of the room and has withdrawn from the family improvisation, retreating into his own rap music via headphones.

The therapist may employ a number of strategies in an attempt to remediate the structural imbalances present. The first is to encourage and coach father to be able to enter a musical dialog with mother and daughter, with the aim of developing skills in reciprocal communication. Second, is to find a way to involve the son. This might occur through a sharing of his kind of music and maybe a family rap improvisation. Third, is to provide mother with opportunities that allow her to experience the role of leader, e.g., a conducting exercise. With successful experiences of being in charge, she may be able to re-assume her parental position in the family.

Educational Music Therapy Assessment

Music therapy may be beneficial in assisting children to benefit with special education needs, and may even be required by law (Brunk & Coleman, 2000). The key to determining whether a school is required to provide music therapy is based in proper assessment. The educational assessment therefore needs to take the legal framework of justification for additional support services into account to effectively produce a recommendation that can initiate or deny music therapy services. Brunk and Coleman (2000) emphasize therapist

knowledge of this legal backdrop, and particularly the need for both nonmusic as well as music based evaluation for direct comparison of response. Parent education of the music therapy assessment process is also important to help reduce the likelihood of confrontations between the school district and the parent. Nine steps are outlined in the Special Education Music Therapy Assessment Process (SEMTAP). They consist of the assessment request, documentation review, interviews, observation in a non-musical setting, assessment preparation and administration, preparation, and presentation of the assessment report (Brunk & Coleman, 2000).

An interesting aspect of the SEMTAP is that it allows for individualized or non-standard assessment. In the example presented by Brunk and Coleman, the therapist pulls together several songs that address specific Individualized Educational Plan (IEP) objectives. Additionally, the therapist even constructed a new song to evaluate a specific behavior peculiar to that child (Brunk & Coleman, 2000). The musical activities that were utilized in the case example include:

1. a greeting song;
2. a song to cue the child to match colored objects to words;
3. Six Little Fish (a counting song);
4. the "Cutting Song" (original tool to cue attention while using a scissors);
5. a song to cue the child to choose an instrument in context of an "I want" sentence;
6. Take Me Out to the Ballgame (pictures and cards to cue 3-step sequences;
7. Goodbye song.

Since each child presumably has their own individual IEP plan, their assessment must be individualized to be able to evaluate their performance on identified tasks.

Additional Types of Music Therapy Assessment Functions

While the most commonly described music therapy assessment may be the initial client evaluation for music therapy services, some other less analyzed purposes also deserve to be mentioned. These may include the evaluation of an institution's academic music therapy program, assessment of a music therapy supervisor, or evaluation of an existing clinic or facility's potential for incorporating a music therapy program. Assessment in these kinds of situations are similar to standard program evaluations.

Future Visions of Music Therapy Assessment

The advent of microcomputers, cyberspace, and innovative software assists music therapists in seeing through the music therapy experience according to Sr. Jean Anthony Gileno (Gileno, 1992). New developments in music technology promise new possibilities for music therapy assessment. Joseph Reilly is one of the pioneers of gesturo-musical assessment (Reilly, 1997). The Lightning module is one of a family of computerized devices that translate movements into music. Music and movement come together in this evaluation for a true multi-modal assessment. Preset scales can be assigned to motion input signals so the therapist can create a no-fault gesturo-musical improvisational space (Reilly, 1997). This means that improvisations can be musically pleasing regardless of client musical ability. The assessment is nicely presented in graphical form showing eight quadrants of motion and amount of variation among quadrants. Reilly shows that this procedure accurately discriminates manic from depressed patients (Reillly, 1997). I have recreated approximations of Reilly's graphs of manic and depressed patients (Figure 19.4).

The gesturo-musical space is recorded for a single hand moving a baton through the eight quadrants. The graphs make high density areas of movement easily distinguishable and Reilly shows that manic and depressed patients produce significantly different outputs of file size, zone use, and zonal spikes in the Lightning assessment.

Neuroimaging

New ways to graphically view brain function include neuro-imaging with Magnetic Resonance Imaging (MRI), Positron Emission Tomography (PET), Single Photon Emission Computed Tomography (SPECT) scans, and Quantitative Electroencephalograph, (QEEG). This author is currently investigating the use of QEEG responses to musical and nonmusical conditions in the assessment of Attention Deficit Hyperactivity Disorder children. The QEEG yields colorful topographic images of the brain showing what areas are active and in what frequency bandwidths. Alpha rhythms

Manic 1: Zone usage = 8, file size = 37.1K bytes, Zonal spikes = 33. Right hand baton.

Manic 2: Zone usage = 7, file size = 21.5K bytes, Zonal spikes = 47 Left hand baton.

Depressed 1: Zone usage = 4, file size = 4.7K bytes, Zonal spikes = 0. Right hand baton.

Depressed 2: Zone usage = 6, file size = 6.3K bytes, Zonal spikes = 0. Left hand baton.

Figure 19.4. Graphs of manic and depressed patients.

are produced when the eyes close or during a light meditation. Beta waves are associated with cognitive tasking, planning, and executive function. Theta is associated with reverie, deep meditation, and sometimes mystical experiences. In children with Attention Deficit Disorder, however, Theta is related to inattention, or "spacing out." The QEEG brain maps in Figure 19.5 show Theta and Alpha activity in the frontal region of this seven year ADHD child's brain during an eyes-open baseline reading.

The second set of QEEG brain maps in Figure 19.6 show reduced Theta and Alpha rhythms with increased Sensorimotor Rhythm (SMR), a low Beta wave, while the same child listens to Vivaldi. This

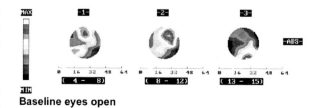

Baseline eyes open

Figure 19.5. QEEG of ADHD children.

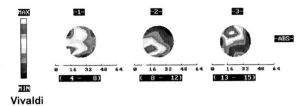

Vivaldi

Figure 19.6. QEEG response to Vivaldi.

pattern is more likely to correlate with increased attention.

These are just illustrative snapshots (each averaged over 2 seconds) from a current research project, and do not mean much until the entire length of each condition is cleaned of artifact, averaged, and graphed. What is exciting here is the method, and finding new ways to assess and analyze brain activity in relation to music therapy assessment.

CONCLUSION

Assessment in music therapy is a dynamic process that can be approached from different theoretical frameworks. Music therapy research can also be classified according to population (Aldridge, 1994). Different music therapy practitioners may approach the same standard assessment in somewhat different ways as a result of their experience and style of improvisation. They may even come to different interpretations of recorded music therapy assessments based on their individual values and interests (Ruud, 1998). Some argue that a qualitative approach to music therapy research is a good fit with the field (Aigen, 1993; Langenberg, 1996; Smeijsters, 1997), or that a balance of quantitative and qualitative measures produces more of a whole picture than either approach alone.

This chapter has briefly reviewed a sample of different theories, approaches, and styles of conducting music therapy assessments. The Quick Music Therapy Assessment (QMTA) may be useful for experienced practitioners to provide an at-a-glance assessment of two vital areas, expression and responsiveness. The Nordoff and Robbins evaluation lists provide detailed information on the child-therapist relationship, communicativeness, rhythmic organization, instrumental and vocal responsiveness, expression, and engagement. Kenneth Bruscia offers six improvisation assessment profiles that may be used as individual subtests or as a comprehensive

battery in initial assessment or ongoing evaluation. The *autonomy, variability,* and *tension* scales in particular provide new dimensions to previous approaches. Many therapists find value in the psychodynamic framework of therapy, with a focus on subconscious conflicts, drives, and ego defense mechanisms. I have presented an Analytic Music Therapy Inquiry (AMTI) to aid in acquiring an impression from the psychodynamic perspective. Family music therapy assessment offers a unique way to view family dynamics within a framework of communication patterns and power structures. The educational music therapy assessment typically occurs within the legal context of justification for services, and so must also include a nonmusic assessment for the purposes of comparison. New technology provides the ability to graphically represent brain function in visually understandable ways. These images can help our understanding of neurological oriented assessments and the way the brain works. There also exist many other valuable contributions to the field of music therapy assessment that were not covered in this chapter. It is hoped that you, the reader, will come away with some basic concepts of MT assessment, some questions that need answering, and a drive to explore further into this rich realm of inquiry.

REFERENCES

Aigen, K. (1993). The music therapist as qualitative researcher. *Music Therapy, 12*(1) 16–39.

Aigen, K. (1998). Creativity in qualitative music therapy research. *Journal of Music Therapy, 35*(3), 142–149.

Aldridge, D. (1994). An overview of music therapy research, *Complementary Therapies in Medicine, 2*(4), 204–216.

AMTA (2001). Standards of clinical practice. in Elkins, A. (ed.). *AMTA member sourcebook*. Silver Spring, MD: American Music Therapy Association.

Austin, D. (2001). In search of the self: The use of vocal holding techniques with adults traumatized as children. *Music Therapy Perspectives, 19*(1), 22–30.

Bonny, H. L. (1975). *Guided imagery and music therapy: Past, present and future implications*. Baltimore: ICM Press.

Brunk, B. K., & Coleman, K. (2000). Development of a special education music therapy process. *Music Therapy Perspectives, 18*(1), 59–68.

Bruscia, K. (1987). *Improvisational models of music therapy*. Springfield, IL: Charles C Thomas, Publisher, Ltd.

Bruscia, K. (1998). *Defining music therapy*: 2nd edition. Gilsum, NH: Barcelona Publishers.

Chase, K. (2002). *The music therapy assessment handbook..* Columbus, MS: Southern Pen Publishing.

Chase, K. (2004). Music therapy assessment for children with developmental disabilities: A survey study. *Journal of Music Therapy, 41*(1) 28–54.

Cohen, G., Auerbach, J., & Katz, E. (1978). Music therapy assessment of the developmentally disabled client. *Journal of Music Therapy, 15(*2), 88–99.

Dunn, L. M., & Dunn, L. M. (1997). *Peabody picture vocabulary test,* third edition. Circle Pines, MN: American Guidance Service.

Gileno, J. A. (1992). An introduction to cyberspace in music therapy. Paper presented at the *First Conference on Cyberspace in Music Therapy,* World Congress on Arts and Medicine, NY.

Goodman, K. (1989). Music therapy assessment of emotionally disturbed children. *The Arts in Psychotherapy, 16*(3), 179–192.

Gregory, D., (2000). Test instruments used by the Journal of Music Therapy. *Journal of Music Therapy, 37*(2), 79–94.

Kenny, C. & Stige, B. (2002). Contemporary voices in music therapy – Communication, culture, and community. Oslo: Unipub Forlag.

Langenberg, M., Aigen, K. & Frömmer, J. (1996). *Qualitative music therap research: Beginning dialogues.* Phoenixville, PA: Barcelona Publishers.

Loewy, J. (2000) Music psychotherapy assessment. *Music Therapy Perspectives, 18*(1), 47–58.

Miller, E. (1994). Musical intervention in family therapy. *Music Therapy, 12*(2), 39–57.

Nordoff, P., & Robbins, C. (1971). *Therapy in music for handicapped children.* London: Victor Gollancz, Ltd.

Nordoff, P., & Robbins, C. (1977). *Creative music therapy.* New York: Harper and Row, Gollancz, Ltd.

Reilly, J. F. (1997). LIGHTNING strikes: A correlational study of the gesturo-musical responses of in-patients with acute manic or depressive symptomatology using the LIGHTNING module. *Journal of Music Therapy, XXXIV*(4), 260–276.

Rugenstein, L. (2000). Music as a vehicle for inner exploration: The Bonny method of guided imagery and music (GIM). *Guidance & Counseling, 15*(3), 23–59.

Ruud, E. (1998). Science as metacritique. *Journal of Music Therapy, 35*(3), 218–224.

Sabatella, P. E. (2004) Assessment and clinical evaluation in music therapy: An overview from literature and clinical practice. *Music Therapy Today, 5*(1), retrieved from http://musictherapyworld.net

Sabatella, P. (1998) *How to evaluate music therapy?* Abstracts International European Music Therapy Congress.

Smeijsters, H. (1997). *Multiple perspectives: A guide to qualitative research in music therapy.* Phoenixville, PA: Barcelona Publishers.

Thorndike RL, Hagen EP, & Sattler JM. (1986). *Stanford-Binet Intelligence Scales.* (4th ed.). Itasca, IL: Riverside Publishing Company;

Wheeler, B. (Ed.). (1995). *Music therapy research: Quantitative and qualitative perspectives.* Phoenixville, PA: Barcelona Publishers.

Wigram, T., Pederson, N., et al. (2002). *A comprehensive guide to music therapy.* London: Jessica Kingsley.

Wigram, T. (1999). Assessment methods in music therapy: A humanistic or natural science framework? *Nordic Journal of Music Therapy, 8*(1), 6–24.

Wigram, T. (1995) A model of assessment and differential diagnosis of handicap in children through the medium of music therapy. In Wigram, Saperston, & West (Eds.). *The art and science of music therapy: A handbook.* London: Harwood Academic Publishers.

Wilson, B., & Smith, D. (2000) Music therapy assessment in school settings: A preliminary investigation. *Journal of Music Therapy, 37*(2), 95–117.

Biographical Statement

Eric B. Miller, Ph.D. MT-BC, is a psychotherapist, certified biofeedback therapist, board-certified music therapist, consultant, and author. Eric directs the Biofeedback Network, and serves as adjunct faculty in Music Therapy at Immaculata University, and has guest lectured at Bryn Mawr College, Pennsylvania State Medical College, Hahnemann University, and the Naropa Institute among other appointments. Eric is actively involved with the non-profit group Music for People and has served as Executive Director since 1997. He is also president of Expressive Therapy Concepts, a nonprofit organization dedicated to bringing the healing power of the arts to our communities. In his spare time, Eric chairs the Pennsylvania Badminton Association. He has been nationally ranked in the United States, and coaches the Bryn Mawr College varsity badminton team. Eric may be reached at Miller@Biofeedback.net.

Chapter 20

EMPOWERING WOMEN SURVIVORS OF CHILDHOOD SEXUAL ABUSE: A COLLABORATIVE MUSIC THERAPY-SOCIAL WORK APPROACH

SANDRA L. CURTIS AND GISÈLE C. T. HARRISON

INTRODUCTION

Women survivors of violence are being recognized as an emergent client population. In developing this new practice, music therapists are discovering music to be a particularly effective modality for these women, providing a unique and powerful way to assist them in their journey to recover from the harm of violence and to reclaim their lives (Curtis, 2000; Clendenon-Wallen, 1991; Hammel-Gormley, 1995; Lindberg, 1995; Rogers, 1993; Whipple, 1999). At the same time, social workers have been developing their own practice to best meet the needs of abused women. In so doing, some have informally discovered the power of music in this area (Berger, 2000; MacIntosh, 2003). An integrative approach—combining the experience of social work with the expertise of music therapy as a creative modality—could have much to offer clients. This chapter presents a look at a unique, collaborative Music Therapy-Social Work approach with women survivors of childhood sexual abuse. The nature of childhood sexual abuse and its impact on survivors is examined first. A review follows of current best practices in music therapy in this area and the connection to social work. The development and implementation of an integrative Music Therapy-Social Work program for women survivors of childhood sexual abuse is explored in detail, closing with stories of empowerment as heard through women's voices in interview and song.

Women Survivors of Childhood Sexual Abuse

Childhood sexual abuse is a violation of power and control from a position of strength, authority, or trust (Palmer, 1991). Abusers use sex as a weapon to humiliate, oppress, and force some type of sexual awareness on children. These children often grow up feeling betrayed by the adults who abused them, the family that failed to protect them, and the society that actively promotes the objectification of women and children (Brooke, 1996; Butler, 1985).

The prevalence of sexual victimization of children can be difficult to determine. Research has consistently shown that most children do not disclose their abuse and most adult survivors of childhood sexual abuse do not seek treatment to resolve abuse issues. As such, it continues to be a hidden and silent crime, shrouded in guilt and shame (Brooke, 1996; Hay, 1997). Researchers have, however, been able to estimate the prevalence of reported sexual abuse in the female population as ranging from 12 to 38 percent (Finkelhor, Lewis, & Smith, 1990; Schachter, Stalker, & Teram, 2001).

Understanding the root causes of childhood sexual abuse involves a thorough analysis of the damage done by a male-defined society and its assumptions about sex roles and expectations (Brooke, 2004; Butler, 1985). Although some may believe childhood sexual abuse to be a personal problem, a feminist analysis allows an understanding of abuse as "created and exacerbated by societal power imbalances" (Burstow, 1992, p. 40). Male entitlement is often at the root of this sexual exploitation (Brooke, 1997; Jacobs, 1994).

The impact of childhood sexual abuse is felt at the core of the survivors' minds, bodies, and spirits (Chew, 1998). In order to make sense of the sexual victimization, survivors often assume the blame, shame, guilt, and responsibility for what happened

195

(Brooke, 1996). This can lead to self-denigration and further revictimization or disconnections in adulthood (Chew, 1998; Jacobs, 1994). Childhood sexual abuse represents an extreme form of disconnection in survivors' relational experiences. This early violation in life can result in the development of skewed adaptive solutions, subsequently making mutually empathic and respectful relationships difficult. It can leave survivors with a sense of distrust in themselves and others, a distorted sense of self, and difficulties in identifying and voicing feelings (Fedele & Harrington, 1990). The abuse can make it difficult for survivors to separate their desire for safety from that for love (Jacobs, 1994).

As a result of childhood sexual abuse, adult survivors may display a variety of symptoms. These can include: unexplained grief or rage; numbness; confused thinking; significant memory lapses; denial of the impact of the traumatic events; hypervigilance; shame or distortion of reality; internalization of worthlessness; and overwhelming fear of injury, abandonment, or death (Brooke, 1997; Palmer, 1991).

Music Therapy with Survivors of Abuse

With increased awareness and understanding of childhood sexual abuse has come increased interest in exploring the uses of music therapy to empower survivors. This interest in sexual abuse is recent and as a result there is relatively little research literature to date (Hammel-Gormley, 1996; Lindberg, 1995). What does exist indicates that the expressive arts therapies can be very effective, with music therapy in particular offering a powerful medium for intervention with this population. It is music's capacity to evoke imagery and metaphors that makes it possible for survivors of childhood sexual abuse to reclaim their voices. It is music's unique capacity to evoke simultaneous physiological, cognitive, and emotional responses which makes it possible for abuse survivors to reclaim their lives where traditional therapies have failed (Lindberg, 1995; MacIntosh, 2003).

In terms of specific goals and outcomes of music therapy with survivors of childhood sexual abuse, the findings, although primarily anecdotal and derived from case studies, are quite consistent. Music therapy is being used by most creative therapists working in this area to effectively increase self-expression and self-esteem (Clendenon-Wallen,

1991; Lindberg, 1995; MacIntosh, 2003; Slotoroff, 1994). It is also being used by some to build trust, to explore personal boundaries, to connect mind and body, to examine issues of sexuality, and to develop problem-solving skills (Clendenon-Wallen, 1991; MacIntosh, 2003; Rogers, 1995; Ventre, 1994).

The techniques used in music therapy to empower childhood sexual abuse survivors are diverse. Songs provide a marvelous bridge to those recovering from childhood sexual abuse (Clendenon-Wallen, 1991; Hammel-Gormley, 1995). In listening to and discussing songs, abuse survivors can explore their feelings, connect with each other and with the therapist, regain a sense of self-worth, and make meaning of past experiences as they build new lives (Clendenon-Wallen, 1991; Hammel-Gormley, 1995; MacIntosh, 2003). In writing their own songs, abuse survivors are able to achieve emotional release, to validate their experiences, and to communicate their feelings in a deeper, more meaningful fashion. In telling their stories in song, they find their own voices and nurture their self-esteem (Clendenon-Wallen, 1991; Lindberg, 1995; MacIntosh, 2003). Other techniques used effectively with abuse survivors include clinical improvisation, drumming, and Guided Imagery in Music (MacIntosh, 2003; Rogers, 1994 & 1993; Slotoroff, 1994; Ventre, 1994).

Social Work and Music Therapy

Like its music therapy counterpart, social work has been developing its own practice to best meet the needs of childhood sexual abuse survivors. This social work practice has a longer history, with subsequently greater diversity of approaches (Burstow, 1992; Chew, 1998; Herman, 1997; Palmer, 1991). With this diversity, many social workers find themselves adopting an eclectic approach, as is the case at the Rape Crisis Center (RCC) involved in the collaborative Music Therapy-Social Work project. Subsequently, it is this approach that will be outlined here.

This eclectic social work approach draws on such theories and practices as feminist therapy, relational theories, cognitive behavioral therapy, and solution-focused therapy. The main premise rests on recognition that women have the inner resources to develop solutions that can bring them beyond their sexual victimization. Furthermore, women must have power and control over their healing process and this can be accomplished through a sense of partnership and collaboration within the therapy setting (Brooke, 1995; Burstow, 1992; Chew, 1998; Dolan, 1991; Herman, 1997; Matsakis, 1996; Palmer, 1991; Wells, Glickauf-Hughes, & Beaudoin, 1995).

Guided by principles of mutual empowerment, social justice, and feminist therapy, this social work approach provides opportunity for women to understand and honor the adaptive solutions used to survive their childhood; develop a sense of collective empowerment as each woman is helped to integrate her traumatic experience; break the silence imposed by abusers and by society, while dissolving feelings of isolation, shame, and stigma; and develop compassion for and empathy with other survivors and themselves (Brooke, 1997; Chew, 1998; Fedele & Harrington, 1990; Herman, 1997).

Techniques of this group approach include structured exercises with a cognitive, emotional, and moral context (Herman, 1997). Survivors work together to construct new interpretations of their sexual victimization through a growing awareness of oppression and its toll on the oppressed (Brooke, 1995; Herman, 1997; Matsakis, 1996; Chew, 1998). Through collaboration, empathy, and commitment to truth, women come to understand that sexual violence is a problem rooted in systemic oppression (Burstow, 1992).

In discussing collaboration, Graham and Barter (1999) contend that it is much more than a mere partnership between music therapy and social work. It involves a completely new way of thinking with the creation of common goals and innovative practices. Many maintain that collaboration is essential in today's increasingly complex society: "To collaborate may be included among the most significant of all social work verbs" (Graham & Barter, 1999, p. 12). To ensure successful collaboration, careful attention and concerted efforts are required. "A culture of collaboration does not just happen. It must be formed and fashioned" (Seaburn, Lorenz, Gunn, Gawinski, & Mauksch, 1996, p. 23). Essential components of successful collaboration include the following (Bronstein, 2003): interdependence; newly-created professional endeavors; flexibility; collective ownership of goals; and a reflection on the process by all stakeholders before and throughout the collaborative endeavor.

The Collaborative Project

This collaborative project arose out of initial interest in introducing music therapy as a new service at an RCC. It entailed a university-community collaboration, bringing together individual therapists, a music therapist, and a social worker from a community RCC. As preliminary discussions progressed, the advantages of a genuine, integrative collaboration became clear. Rather than simply include music therapy as an additional service, the plan evolved to encompass a new and unique Music Therapy-Social Work collaborative program. The success of such an endeavor was enhanced by the intersection of a number of shared interests on the part of the therapists: Interest in collaborative feminist approaches, as well as interest in social justice work the Music Therapy Centre's (Music Therapy Centre, 2003) mission. The endeavor reflected the hallmark components of successful collaboration outlined by Bronstein (2003): Interdependence with mutual respect, flexibility, newly-created professional endeavors, collective ownership of goals, and on-going reflection on the process.

The Program

The Music Therapy-Social Work program was developed in a close and thoughtful collaboration. As a music therapist and a social worker, we each brought with us our own program for empowering survivors of violence (Curtis, in press; Curtis, 2000). These goals were carefully reviewed and used as a jumping board for the creation of a new program reflecting the best of both disciplines. The final product, a 14-week collaborative program for groups, consisted of a series of modules that lead women through exercises and discussions on their journey to recovery. It was designed to provide the women with a greater appreciation of the abuse's impact on their past and present thoughts, actions, feelings of self-blame; and an understanding of the individual, cultural, and institutional forces responsible for the perpetration and perpetuation of sexual abuse (Brooke, 2004).

The first few modules were structured to foster safety and trust within the group through self-disclosure (Chew, 1998; Dolan, 1991; "Group work," n.d.; Matsakis, 1996). In these sessions, women explored their hopes, fears, and goals. Participants received song books and CD recordings of women's songs on a variety of themes – from violence, love, life, and empowerment. The singer-songwriters were equally diverse – from the likes of the *Dixie Chicks* to *Four Bitchin' Babes*. Listening to and discussing music written and performed by women served as a powerful medium for feminist analysis of power and gender role socialization (Curtis, 2000). This lyric analysis provided women in the first stage of the program with an opportunity to communicate their feelings about themselves and their past trauma. Songwriting was introduced as a technique to build group cohesion and gain a clearer picture of each woman apart from her abuse.

The modules in the next stage of the program focused on breaking the silence of sexual abuse with women supported in sharing pieces of their abuse history as a means of reclaiming power (Burstow, 1992; Chew, 1998; "Group work," n.d.). During this stage, lyric analysis concentrated on truth telling (Curtis, 2000). A documentary of survivors discussing their healing process was used to further facilitate the process. Should the opportunity arise, the women's participation at this point in outside community antiviolence events can underscore the connection between the personal and the political.

The third-stage modules explored issues of responsibility and power as they related to each participant's sexual victimization. An understanding of normative family dynamics provided the basis for looking at the misuse of power. Techniques used in this stage included letter writing, lyric analysis, and genogram analysis. At this stage, women also began writing their own original songs, with song analysis used to assist them in choosing a theme and style. These songs provided women with a chance to truly be heard.

Modules in the fourth stage focused on identifying the impact of sexual victimization on the core sense of self (Chew, 1998; Dolan, 1991; "Group work," n.d.; Matsakis, 1996). Participants were challenged to continue the process of dispelling false beliefs about themselves. They were also encouraged to explore any developmental areas that may have been neglected during their childhood. A variety of lyric analysis, writing, and discussion techniques were used in this stage (Curtis, 2000). Additionally, women continued to work on their original compositions.

Healing and nurturing the child- and adult-part of the self harmed by the abuse were the focus of the next stage (Chew, 1998; Dolan, 1991; "Group work," n.d.; Matsakis, 1996). Lyric analysis, medita-

tion, affirmation chant exercises, group discussion, and song writing were used at this point to assist women in connecting with themselves as well as in learning to honor, soothe, and nurture the child-part of the self, thus building a foundation for change (Curtis, 2000). Participants completed the finishing touches on their original songs, including designing artwork for their CD cover.

The final stage of the program included exercises in consolidating gains and working toward closure. Women had an opportunity to record their own songs or have them recorded for them. The final session included a "CD release party" where the women received a songbook of all of the participant's songs and CD of their own song. The celebration included music, food, and opportunity for recognition of the powerful songs written, recorded, and reflecting accomplishments achieved by each within the program. Figure 20.1 shows their pre and post test TSCS scores of the women who participated in the group.

The Women

The participants involved in the collaborative project were five women survivors of childhood sexual abuse ranging in age from 22 to 58 years. Their participation was voluntary as a result of their selection of the program from a number of services offered by the community RCC. Each woman provided informed consent and was invited to provide input prior to the start and upon completion of the project. The women were Caucasian, with diverse cultural heritages. Each woman had previously participated in other groups required by the RCC before participation in a specific childhood abuse group.

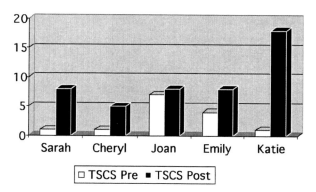

Figure 20.1.   Pre and post TSCS scores.

Their Story

The women participated in the collaborative program over a 14-week period, attending 2-hour sessions once weekly. To ensure that their true stories could be heard in their full, contextualized richness, a variety of measures were used – the Tennessee Self-Concept Scale (TSCS), an interview, the women's own songs and CDs, and an exit interview. The TSCS was selected since it had been used previously to effectively measure treatment outcomes for women survivors of violence (Curtis, 2000). The same holds true for the exit interview and participants' songs and CDs. The exit survey was used as a final measure since it was part of the standard procedures in place at the RCC. In listening to the women's voices on their experience in the collaborative program, attention was directed toward the group results and then to the individual women's responses.

Results of the TSCS showed an increased self-esteem for all of the women at the end of the program. While the increase is small, it is notable given the short time span and given that all of the women's pre-test scores were below the normal range (20th percentile minimum), indicating an extremely low initial self-acceptance and self-esteem.

In response to the exit survey, all of the women rated the quality of service as "excellent," indicating they would recommend the program to friends and they would return to the RCC should they desire further help. Concerning the services received, all participants indicated that the program helped them to deal more effectively with their problems. For confidentiality purposes, all names listed here are fictitious.

Sarah

Sarah was a single Caucasian woman of Canadian, French-Canadian, and British heritage. She had been abused between the age of 5 and 13 years by both a grandmother and two cousins. She was 32 years of age when she started the program, at which time she had ongoing feelings of anger, betrayal, shame, and guilt about the abuse.

Sarah completed the program, attending 12 of the 14 sessions. Full participation in the group was a struggle for Sarah, in voicing, and even acknowledging to herself, her deeper feelings. In fact, Sarah had started the program but had been unable to complete earlier social work programs at the RCC, dropping out at the point where relinquishing responsibility for the abuse was required. The Music Therapy-Social Work collaborative program reached Sarah where others did not. While reluctant to express her feelings in group discussion, Sarah selected songs which were clear reflections of her experiences. In one session, Sarah brought in her own CD – a recording of "A Warrior" by the Weird Sisters. This song aptly tells

BRING BACK THE DAY

Where did the sun go for this little girl?
Please bring back the day and keep me safe
I was happy then, wrapped in the sun's warm rays
Then he crept into my room and took that away

Chorus
I want to have happy dreams, with happy children
Laughing and dancing, tea parties, safe hugging
I want
I want

Playtime has gone for one more day
As Daddy settles in his comfy chair
He guards my room, then falls asleep
While the house is still, then the floor boards squeak

He's coming . . . I wait
Please Daddy, wake up
Wake up the sun
Another day over, fear has begun

Chorus

Figure 20.2. Sarah.

the story of a woman initially unable to fight against violence who, as she matures, learns to speak up and act for herself and other women: "I am an older woman now, and I will heed my own cries, and I will a fierce warrior be until not another woman dies." This recording was later included in the annual community Take Back the Night event. Sarah attended this event for the first time, connecting her therapy work in the private sphere with social justice work in the public sphere. While declaring herself unable and unwilling within the group session to write a letter to herself as a child, the original song she wrote in the program – Note to Self – ultimately became a song to herself as a child. The song reflects both her ongoing struggle with self-acceptance and her success. This was mirrored in her TSCS, which increased from 1st to 8th percentile, showing improvement, but still low.

Cheryl

Cheryl was a single, Caucasian woman of Canadian heritage. She had been abused between the age of 5 and 10 years, approximately once monthly by an extended family member. She was 22 years of age when she started the program, at which time her feelings about the abuse included anger, betrayal, fear, helplessness, and depression.

Cheryl did not complete the program, dropping out early and attending only 9 of the 14 sessions. At the time she dropped out, she indicated that she was in the midst of college exams and feeling stressed. As a result, Cheryl did not complete or record her own song and her TSCS reflected only a small increase – from 1st to 4th percentile. She did, however, return later to complete her final evaluations, collect a CD recording of all the other women's songs, and attended a few individual therapy sessions. In discussing her experience in the collaborative program, Cheryl described her song writing experience, saying " . . . it sounded pretty cool. I think that all of those feelings that were written on the page actually were what I felt and it was not sugar-coated. It was right there, it was pretty cool."

Joan

Joan was a single, Caucasian woman of Hungarian heritage. She was abused by her father over a 7-year period, starting around 5 years of age. She was 32 years of age when she started the program, at which time she felt anger and fear about the abuse.

Joan attended 13 of the 14 program sessions. She seemed to need to participate in most experiences of the collaborative program, although at times strong emotions were evoked. This journey for Joan brought her to an understanding of the sociopolitical underpinnings of the abuse she experienced

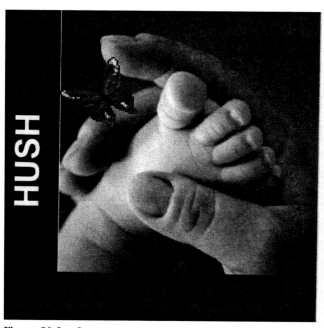

Figure 20.3. Joan.

and the connection between empowerment within therapy and within the community. She attended and was a very active participant at the Take Back the Night event. Although her TSCS indicated minimal change from 7th to 8th percentile, this was not the case in her songwriting-recording or her exit interview. The song she wrote, "Hush," tells the story of her abuse as a child and her sense of being silenced. It also reflects her ongoing struggles: "I'm almost all better now, but still afraid of the dark." Joan chose to record her own song. In so doing, she powerfully subverted society's imperative to "hush," reclaiming her voice and her story. In discussing what she learned in the collaborative program, Joan indicated "that I'm stronger than I think." She added further, "It was fun recording it . . . and nerve wracking . . . but then hearing it tonight, like in front of everybody . . . it was kind of strange, but it felt, it felt good . . . it felt empowering."

Emily

Emily was a married, Caucasian woman of Canadian heritage. She had been abused by her brother when she was between 8 and 10 years of age. She was 58 years of age when she started the program, at which time she felt angry, betrayed, disgusted, helpless, depressed, ashamed, guilty, and shocked about the abuse.

Emily completed the program, attending 12 of the 14 sessions. For her, recovery from childhood sexual abuse had been a lifelong struggle. In starting the collaborative program, she indicated some despair that she would ever be free of its harm. Initially, she was not hopeful that the program would be of much help: "I was so skeptical at the beginning." Yet as she progressed in the program, something changed: "At first I was going home . . . like this just isn't working . . . then all of a sudden you reach that plateau where you know it is working." While the progress was slow, her TSCS showed a small improvement from the 4th to the 8th percentile, and the work was challenging for Emily. Yet, it was ultimately a successful experience in her eyes:

> I've been dealing with mine for 47 years and um . . . this is another step in healing . . . This is more of a positive venture for me. I guess there's a lot of healing. Um, music is healing in itself. So it was easier to um discuss when you bring it into music . . . And it was really good. . . I would definitely do it again.

The songwriting did not come easily, but the final work told not only the story of her betrayal, but also of her hope for the future: "Where did the sun go for this little girl? Please bring back the day

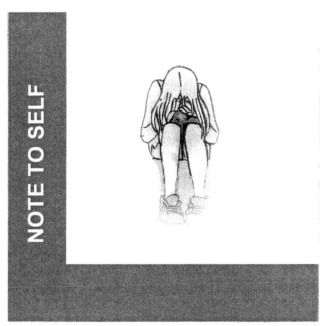

Figure 20.4.   Emily.

and keep me safe. . . . I want to have happy dreams, with happy children, laughing and dancing, tea parties, and safe hugging." In describing her response to her own song and those of the others, Emily commented, "I'll probably listen to the songs and that on the way home and play them over and over again . . . it's ah, . . . it's a reality when you have it on, on a CD."

Katie

Katie was a divorced Caucasian woman of French-Canadian and British heritage. She had been abused by her stepfather when she was between the ages of 5 and 13 years. She was 36 years of age when she started the program, at which time she felt acceptance about the abuse.

Katie joined the collaborative group after it was in progress and therefore, although she completed the program, she attended only 8 of the 14 sessions. While she indicated acceptance of the abuse, self-acceptance was a different matter—her initial TSCS score was in the 1st percentile. Her journey within the program towards self-acceptance reflected great success, with a final TSCS score in the 18th percentile. In describing her impressions of the col-

laborative program, Katie stated that it was "painful, difficult. . . . It was extremely hard. In the end it was quite enlightening." She added further that,

> We still feel that, that sense of loneliness like nobody, nobody can actually understand. Then you go to a group like this and you, you hear these songs that you've heard a hundred times before but you know . . . you don't ever put a connection to it . . . [then] that song comes on, you just realize that you're not [alone].

Katie's journey was also reflected in her song – the lyrics changed from the beginning "you had no right" to the closing words, "I have the right." The art work she chose for her CD also reflected this with the front showing an image of barbed wire and the back showing an image of a rainbow emerging from turbulent skies. The experience of songwriting for Katie was "quite powerful. It felt extremely, extremely good. It was like, um . . . finally putting it into something that can be heard if I want it to be. You know it's almost like having a voice – a secret voice." In the end, Katie chose to sing her song herself for the CD recording – an experience she

Figure 20.5. Katie.

found very powerful. "Singing it, well that was nerve-wracking . . . but it ended up being good too. It let me put the voice to the, to the words and allowed me to be THE voice that said the words."

There is no more powerful reflection of the profound impact of the Music Therapy-Social Work program than in the women's own voices. In survey, interview, and song, the women participants confirmed the unique contribution of this collaborative approach to their recovery that provided them with an extremely effective medium for healing from abuse, for changing, and reclaiming their lives.

Change was not restricted to these five women's lives – our lives as therapists were also changed. Our reflections on this are essential to the process in order to honor the tenets of feminist and collaborative practice. We created opportunity for this by means of individually-written reflections and weekly meetings. In our final reflections, we recognized that our commonalities made the collaboration possible – our shared values, flexibility, feminist practice, social justice framework, and understanding of the participants' healing as priority. Yet, it was our diversity that enriched the program – our differing techniques, as well as personalities and interaction styles. Our collaboration represented an evolution over time in which we moved from unfamiliarity with each other and to a comfortable relationship that merged our two approaches to create a single, seamless one with both of us participating fully in all aspects. This process paralleled our goal that we hoped the women participants would achieve. We enacted inclusivity and a mutually-respectful use of power, with both taking turns being learner and leader, both having roles of greater and lesser power. We enacted the process of gaining power individually without loss to another. Ultimately, the Music Therapy-Social Work program was successful in empowering women abuse survivors both through the unique therapeutic approach and through the process of collaboration itself. Through this creative collaboration, women survivors of childhood sexual abuse have a rich new resource for their journey towards recovery.

REFERENCES

Berger, L. M. (2000). Emotional and intellectual aspects of protest music: Implications for community organizing education. *Journal of Teaching in Social Work, 20*(1–2), 57–76.

Bronstein, L. R. (2003). Model for interdisciplinary collaboration. *Social Work, 48*(3), 297–306.

Brooke, S.L. (1995). Art expression: An approach to working with incest survivors. *The Arts in Psychotherapy, 22*(5), 447–466.

Brooke, S. L. (1996). *A therapist's guide to art therapy assessments: Tools of the trade.* Springfield, IL: Charles C Thomas, Publisher, Ltd.

Brooke, S.L. (1997). *Healing through art: Art therapy with sexual abuse survivors,* with foreword by Dr. Dee Spring, ATR. Springfield, IL: Charles C Thomas, Publisher, Ltd.

Brooke, S.L. (2004). Breaking down the myths surrounding sexual abuse. *Expository Magazine, 3*(1). Retrieved on April 7, 2004 from www.expositorymagazine.net/myths_sexual_abuse.php

Burstow, B. (1992). *Radical feminist therapy: Working in the context of violence.* Newbury Park, CA: Sage Publications.

Butler, S. (1985). *Conspiracy of silence: The trauma of incest.* Volcano, CA: Volcano Press.

Chew, J. (1998). *Women survivors of childhood sexual abuse: Healing through group work: Beyond survival.* Binghamton, NY: Haworth Press.

Clendenon-Wallen, J. (1991). Use of music therapy to influence the self-confidence and self-esteem of adolescents who are sexually abused. *Music Therapy Perspectives, 9,* 73–81.

Curtis, S. L. (in press). Feminist music therapy: Transforming theory, transforming lives. In Susan Hadley (Ed.). *Feminist perspectives in music therapy: Empowering women's voices.* Philadelphia, PA: Barcelona Publishers.

Curtis, S. L. (2000). Singing subversion, singing soul: Women's voices in feminist music therapy. (Doctoral dissertation, Concordia University, 1997). *Dissertation Abstracts International, 60*(12-A), 4240.

Dolan, Y. (1991). *Resolving sexual abuse: Solution-focused therapy and Ericksonian hypnosis for adult survivors.* New York: W.W. Norton & Company.

Fedele, N. M, & Harrington, E. A. (1990). *Women's groups: How connections heal. Work in progress no. 47.* Wellesley, MA: Stone Center.

Finkelhor, D.H., Gerald, L., & Smith, C. (1990). Sexual abuse in a national survey of adult men and women: Prevalence, characteristics, and risk factors. *Child Abuse & Neglect, 14*(1), 19–28.

Graham, J. R., & Barter, K. (1999). Collaboration: A social work practice method. *Families in Society, 80*(1), 6–13.

Group work with survivors of childhood sexual assault. (n.d.). Unpublished manuscript.

Hammel-Gormley, A. (1996). Singing the songs: A qualitative study of music therapy with individuals having psychiatric illnesses as well as histories of childhood sexual abuse. (Doctoral dissertation, New York University, 1995). *Dissertation Abstracts International, 56*(10B), 5768.

Hay, T. (1997). Child sexual abuse. Overview paper. Retrieved July 10, 2004 from Health Canada National Clearinghouse on Family Violence Web site: http://www.hc-sc.gc.ca/hppb/familyviolence/nfntsabus_e.html

Herman, J. L. (1997). *Trauma and recovery: The aftermath of violence – from domestic abuse to political terror.* New York: Basic Books.

Ivy, V. A. (1980). Music behaviors of social workers and music therapists: Characteristic profiles and their predicting factors. Unpublished master's thesis, University of Windsor, Canada.

Jacobs, J. L. (1994). *Incest and the development of the female self.* New York: Routledge.

Lindberg, K. A. (1995). Songs of healing: Songwriting with an abused adolescent. *Music Therapy, 13*(1), 93–108.

MacIntosh, H. B. (2003). Sounds of healing: Music in group work with survivors of sexual abuse. *Arts in Psychotherapy, 30*(1), 17–23.

Matsakis, A. (1996). *I can't get over it: A handbook for trauma survivors* (2nd ed.). Oakland, CA: New Harbinger Publications.

Mazza, N. (1999). Poetic in family social work. *Journal of Family Social Work, 3*(3), 69–73.

Music Therapy Centre. (2003). *Music Therapy Centre mission statement.* Retrieved July 12, 2004, from the University of Windsor, Music Therapy Centre website: http://www.musictherapycentre.org

Palmer, N. (1991). Feminist practice with survivors of sexual trauma and incest. In Bricker-Jenkins, Mary, Hooyman, Nancy, and Gottlieb, Naomi (Eds.). *Feminist social work practice in clinical settings* (pp. 63–82). Newbury Park, CA: Sage Publications.

Rogers, P. J. (1995). Childhood sexual abuse: Dilemmas in therapeutic practice. *Music Therapy Perspectives. Special Issue. International Music Therapy, 13*(1), 24–30.

Rogers, P. J. (1993). Research in music therapy with sexually abused clients. In Helen Payne (Ed.). *Handbook of inquiry in the arts therapies: One river, many currents* (pp. 197–217). Philadelphia, PA: Jessica Kingsley, Publishers.

Rogers, P. J. (1994). Sexual abuse and eating disorders: A possible connection indicated through music therapy? In Ditty Dokter (Ed.). *Arts therapies and clients with eating disorders: Fragile board* (pp. 262–278). Philadelphia, PA: Jessica Kingsley, Publishers.

Schachter, C., Stalker, C., & Teram, E. (2001). *Handbook on sensitive practice for health professionals: Lessons from women survivors of childhood sexual abuse.* Retrieved July 10, 2004 from Health Canada National Clearinghouse on Family Violence Web site: http://www.hc-sc.gc.ca/hppb/familyviolence/html/nfntsxsensi_e.html.

Seaburn, D. B., Lorenz, A. D., Gunn, W. B., Gawinski, B. A., & Mauksch, L. B. (1996). *Models of collaboration.* New York: Basic Books.

Slotoroff, C. (1994). Drumming technique for assertiveness and anger management in the short-term psychiatric setting for adult and adolescent survivors of trauma. *Music Therapy Perspectives. Special Issue. Psychiatric music therapy. 12*(2), 111–116.

Ventre, M. (1994). Healing the wounds of childhood abuse: A guided imagery and music case study. *Music Therapy Perspectives. Special Issue. Psychiatric music therapy, 12*(2), 48–53.

Wells, M., Glickauf-Hughes, C., & Beaudoin, P.. (1995). Ego/object relations approach to treating childhood sexual abuse survivors. *Psychotherapy, 32*(3), 416–429.

Whipple, J., & Lindsey, R. S. (1999). Music for the soul: A music therapy program for battered women. *Music Therapy Perspectives, 17*(2), 61–68.

Biographical Statement

Sandra L. Curtis, Ph. D., MT-BC, MTA, is Coordinator of Music Therapy and Associate Professor at the University of Windsor in Canada. She received a bachelor's degree in music from McGill University, Canada, a master's in music therapy from Florida State University, and an interdisciplinary Ph.D. in music therapy and feminist therapy from Concordia University, Canada. Her published articles, chapters, and reviews appear in the *Journal of Music Therapy*, *Music Therapy Perspectives*, the *Journal of Palliative Care, Interpersonal Violence, Health, and Gender* (W.C. Brown, 1994), *Research in Music Therapy: A Tradition of Excellence* (AMTA, 1994), and *Feminist Perspectives in Music Therapy* (Barcelona Publishers, forthcoming). She has been actively engaged in social justice work in Canada and the United States. Currently, she serves as chair of the International Relations Committee of the American Music Therapy Association.

Gisèle C. T. Harrison, BA, MSW, is a clinical social worker at the Sexual Assault Crisis Centre of Windsor-Essex County in Canada. She is also a seasonal instructor at the University of Windsor and has a small private practice. She received a bachelor's degree in international relations from the University of Windsor and a master's degree in social work from Wilfrid Laurier University, Canada. She has 15 years experience leading psychoeducational groups and has participated in social justice work in New York, Cameroon, Uganda, and Canada. She is passionate about women's issues and feels honored to work with survivors of sexual violence.

Chapter 21

MUSIC THERAPY WITH INNER CITY, AT-RISK CHILDREN: FROM THE LITERAL TO THE SYMBOLIC"

VANESSA A. CAMILLERI

INTRODUCTION

In working with inner city at risk children in a regular education elementary school setting, music therapists can address societal, environmental, and domestic stressors that may be preventing students from succeeding academically and socially. Stressors such as racism, poverty, and abuse can cause children to develop behaviors and emotions that may prevent them from making the most of their academic experience (McWhirter, 1998). These often manifest as withdrawal, fighting, lack of respect, or destruction of property (Brooks-Gunn & Duncan, 1997). Because these are the most disruptive, social skills are often the first areas to be addressed in music therapy groups. As behaviors modify and skills develop through the music therapy process, the group focus shifts to explore the roots of negative behaviors and associated feelings. Slowly, students are enabled to identify why they act in certain ways and how they feel about it. As patterns emerge, it becomes clear that behaviors and associated feelings elicited in the music therapy group are similar to those experienced in outside situations (Yalom, 1998). By working on behaviors and emotions in the music therapy group, students gain insight into how to deal with emotions and behavior in their everyday lives. The purpose of this chapter is to describe how music therapy can work in various ways to reach inner city, at risk children in ways that conventional forms of therapy may not.

The Inner City

The inner city is technically defined by the Office of Management and Budget (OMB, 2001) as a *central city.* This is defined as a core area containing a population nucleus of over 50,000 people. Surrounding the central city is a metropolitan area, defined as having communities with a high degree of economic and social integration with that central city (U.S. Census Bureau, July 2001). There are currently 276 metropolitan areas in the United States comprising 80% of the total U.S. population. Of this, 30% live inside central cities. Additionally, 60% of those living inside central cities are White, 21% are African American, and 19% are Hispanic. Of these, 16% of all households are headed by females, and 9% of all households are headed by females who have children below the age of 18 (U.S. Census Bureau, May 2001). The poverty rate of people living in central cities is 16.7%; however, 40% of all people living in poverty live in central cities. In addition, 26% of all households headed by single females live below the poverty level (U.S. Census Bureau, September 2003). Poverty and the lack of resources in the inner city begin a cycle of poor housing, inadequate schools, unemployment, dangerous neighborhoods, and a lack of a consistent support network. This often leaves children unattended, neglected, and lacking in very basic parental attention that would ensure their success and safety.

At Risk Children

Children who are considered "at risk" can be defined in many ways, and can be victims of many different circumstances. Depending on how the subject is approached, the definition will vary, as will solutions to the problem. Because the students described here are in an inner city elementary school setting, they are considered at risk due to environmental and domestic situations that may prevent them from succeeding academically. They are therefore at risk of failing or dropping out of school, which can lead to an inability to get a job, earn a living, have a place to live, start a family, and provide for themselves and others. These circumstances are setting students up for potential failure if intervention does not take place.

As described by McWhirter (1998), a series of cumulative circumstances lead to students being at risk. These circumstances exist on a continuum in that as more and more circumstances are prevalent in a student's life, the more at risk they will be. Such demographics include living in an impoverished neighborhood, having a low socioeconomic status, and being a member of a minority ethnic group. Students are not at risk because they have this background, but because students with this background are often victims of personal or material racism and discrimination causing trauma that can affect their quality of life.

The next circumstance involves family and school environments. These are the locations where students spend most of their time; therefore, what they experience in these places influences how they behave and view life. Families and schools that provide caring, nurturing, predictable, and safe environments can prevent students from being at risk. If on the other hand families and schools are chaotic, dangerous, unpredictable, and unpleasant to be in (for example, containing substance abuse and violence), students avoid being there; therefore, finding themselves on the street and in unsupervised situations. Students sometimes seek alternative family and school situations by running away or joining gangs. In addition, the lack of stable home and school environments reduces access to positive adult role models and potential support networks (McWhirter, 1998).

Another circumstance is experiencing psychosocial and environmental stressors, such as divorce, death, suicide, teenage pregnancy, abuse, incarceration, loss of a home or job, eviction, or loss of insurance. These can cause psychological trauma and can create physical circumstances such as homelessness, foster care, hunger, poverty, or illness that increase the potential for a student being at risk (McWhirter, 1998).

In dealing with significant stressors, the next important factor in determining whether students are at risk is their own psychological make-up.

Their personal characteristics determine how they deal with their circumstances and how they will be affected by them. The more negative their attitudes, the more at risk they will be. In addition, if their outlook is hopeless, this can lead to symptoms of depression, anxiety, and aggression, often recognizable as deficits in social skills and coping mechanisms.

Negative psychological states can lead to dangerous activities and behaviors (Brooks-Gunn & Duncan, 1997; Sagrestano, Paikoff, Holmbeck, & Fendrich, 2003). These may be self-destructive or destructive to others. Students may start to skip school, smoke, drink, do drugs, fight, or engage in crimes such as theft, mugging, or vandalism. These maladaptive behaviors may result in incarceration, hospitalization, or death.

Each of these circumstances taken alone can lead to students being at risk, but the risk increases as these circumstances accumulate in a student's life. These circumstances are not necessarily predictive of students becoming at risk, but are red flags for evaluating students. Factors leading students to being at risk are often overlooked by schools. At-risk students are often labeled special education students (Noguera, 2003) or problem students because they are often failing academically, or are socially inappropriate. Such students often end up in the special education system, juvenile justice system, or mental health system. In schools, there is rarely a consistent outlet for children to address emotional and behavioral issues that are a result of their environmental and domestic situations. Therefore, the roots of the problems faced by these students are rarely explored. The music therapy program described here fills this need and acts as a preventive measure. It provides a context for exploration and growth in the form of small group music psychotherapy.

Stages of Group Development

People are born into particular groups such as a family, neighborhoods, ethnic groups, or religious groups. Additionally, people find themselves in other groups throughout life. In school or in the workplace, individuals are on teams, on committees, or in groups that are given specific tasks such as completing a project, meeting a deadline, or coming up with a plan. It is therefore important to learn how to work with people in order to succeed and to complete tasks. This requires a specific set of social skills that will allow for positive peer or collegial interaction.

The students described here are identified by the classroom teacher and music therapist as lacking social skills that are necessary to succeed in their classrooms. Many of these skills are interpersonal in nature such as listening, sharing, cooperating, taking turns, and communicating. Working on these goals in a therapeutic group context is therefore the most logical method to be used.

As described by Dwivedi (1993), groups proceed through various stages of development as they move through time. Dwivedi describes three phases of group development specific to work with children and adolescents: early, middle, and later phases. In the early phase, students show a high level of dependency on the leader, and look to the leader to establish rules, rituals, structure, and boundaries. These limits are at times tested by students who try to see if the leader can be manipulated. Students may be aggressive, show off, talk, or refuse to participate. How the leader addresses these situations will set the tone for the remainder of the sessions. As group norms form, the group begins to develop an identity and a purpose, while individual roles emerge. Activities can involve introductions, getting to know you games, leadership games, bridging people together by sharing common experiences, and developing patterns of working together.

The middle phase is described as being a time when relationships within the group develop and are tested. Students shift in their loyalties and friendships as they get to know each other and experience working together. Patterns of behavior emerge, and the group is able to discuss and identify those behaviors that are appropriate and desirable. During the middle phase, students are encouraged to share feelings about each other, as well as help each other through difficult situations. Sharing intimate information helps to build group cohesion and trust. Students begin to disclose personal feelings about the group, and are able to hear feedback from fellow students.

The later phase in a group is a time of honesty and intimacy. Students trust each other, and the therapeutic relationship is fully developed. The therapist acts as a positive adult role-model and demonstrates that she is able to provide a safe and predictable setting that can contain emotions and behaviors. As trust builds, students disclose information about their feelings and lives, allowing for in-depth exploration in the group context. Group norms and limits are firmly established, allowing students to have a consistent and predictable group experience. Being part of a therapeutic group gives a child the experience of belonging and being essential to the functioning of the group. Self-esteem of students improves as they feel important and heard.

By the later phase of a group, students have fully developed roles that can be explored and modified. As described by Yalom (1998), often people who are involved in some type of group therapy have had a dissatisfying group experience in the past, usually in the family context. He goes on to describe how the therapy group begins to resemble the family group as roles develop and group members fall into similar roles that they held in their families (leading, submissive, controlling). Group members begin to interact with each other as they have in other situations as rivalries and power struggles emerge. As stated by Yalom, "patients will, over time, automatically and inevitably begin to display their maladaptive interpersonal behavior in the therapy group" (p. 34). Patterns of behavior and feelings emerge in the group that mirror those behaviors that occur outside of the group. Therefore, the group becomes a social microcosm that can be used for therapeutic growth.

Yalom goes on to emphasize that in order for therapeutic group work to be successful, work must be done on two levels. The therapist must firstly be attentive to the here-and-now interactions that are occurring between group members. Secondly, the therapist must encourage examination of the process and must enable group members to integrate the here-and-now experience into their larger experience in life. This requires self-reflection, as group members attempt to understand their feelings and behaviors in the group in the context of their personal histories.

The Music Therapy Group Process

Any relationship evolves through stages of development parallel to stages of increasing intimacy. Typically, as people get to know each other, the connection between them becomes deeper, and the relationship becomes more fulfilling. Similarly, music therapy groups progress through stages, each serving a different purpose, and providing new opportunities for therapeutic work. Transitions and stages are identified by the music therapist so that goals can be amended accordingly. Progression through the stages indicates client readiness to meet new challenges, and to enter deeper levels of personal and interpersonal awareness.

The benefits of using music therapy with inner city at-risk students is made evident in many studies. In her work with adolescents in chronic care, Brooks (1989) has shown how music is an excellent method of increasing communication between patients and the therapist. Where verbal communication may break down, nonverbal communication is ideal to bridge the gap. Music is already part of patients' lives; therefore, using it for healing is natural for a therapist and accepted by patients. She goes on to describe how music making can allow patients to interact with each other, and to form relationships. Self-esteem increases and patients develop a positive sense of self.

Farr (1997) describes the benefits of dance/movement therapy in her work with at-risk African American adolescents. Therapies that require clients to interact with one another, such as dance or music therapy, and to engage in social behaviors create opportunities for difficult interpersonal behaviors to emerge. As described by Farr, in safely contained groups, feelings can emerge as children release anxiety and withhold feelings. These can then be addressed by the group, and handled by the therapist. Similarly, during music therapy groups, the interactive musical experience is used as a working situation in which students have emotional and behavioral experiences that can then be discussed by the group. As the group music therapy process proceeds, students learn to navigate through conflict and to gain self-knowledge from peer comments and hands-on experiences.

In her work with multirisk mothers and their children, Shiraishi (1997) determined that music listening decreased levels of depression and raised self-esteem in the mothers. In addition, many of the mothers indicated that the music therapy sessions brought enjoyment to their lives, and helped them to escape from the difficult realities of poverty, hunger, and violence. The music therapy sessions allowed them the opportunity to interact positively with their children and to give them a sense of pride in being able to do something engaging for their children.

Wheeler (1987) describes three levels of therapy each with a distinct set of goals. Based on her work

in music therapy with adult psychiatric inpatients, she states that severity of the illness can often indicate what set of goals or interventions are most effective with that particular client. In the first level, for severely ill clients, music therapy as activity therapy is most appropriate, addressing goals such as attention span, self-esteem, and self-control. The second level is described as insight music therapy, in which music is used "to help clients achieve insight into material which is on a relatively conscious level" (p. 40). Music is used to elicit feelings, which are then discussed, targeting expression of emotion and communication. The third level described is music therapy with reconstructive goals that target the gaining of insight into unconscious material. This is done by projection or role reversal through words and music. It is suggested that depending on the severity of the affliction, a client will best be suited to and will gain the most from a specific set of goals and interventions.

Hibben (1991) describes how depending on the stage of development of the music therapy group, different activities can be implemented in order for individuals to make the most of the experience, and to attain individual goals. The first stage she describes is the pre-affiliation stage in which children are not yet able to interact with each other or the therapist. She goes on to describe the power and control stage during which children are resistant and are attempting to develop trust while at the same time testing the limits of the group and the therapist. The next stage she describes is the intimacy stage in which children are ready to try new behaviors, develop leadership, and take risks. The next stage Hibben describes is the differentiation/cohesion stage. At this point, children are emotionally invested in the group and they have developed a sense of pride in the group. The last stage she describes is the separation stage during which some regression could take place while the group deals with the prospect of ending the group. During each one of these stages, it is important that the therapist be aware of what students are going through emotionally and socially, and develop musical activities that are appropriate to the specific stage of group development.

As groups develop, intimacy increases and students gain more and more knowledge of themselves and awareness of others (Dwivedi, 1993). As is described here, this progression allows children to move from social skills-oriented activity music therapy to more insight-oriented music therapy. Taken in another light, it is suggested that as clients become healthier, they can progress through varying levels of treatment goals. In working with children, as social skills develop, so too do group cohesiveness and communication. These in turn develop trust and self-esteem, which are necessary for personal expression of feelings. Below is an account of how music therapy groups with at-risk children can progress from a very literal approach, targeting changes in behavior and development of social skills, to a more symbolic one of achieving insight into behaviors and feelings in and out of the music therapy context.

Music Therapy Groups

The music therapy work described here focuses on social skills development that will enable students to become positive and active group members. Social skills such as effective communication, sharing, listening, respect, impulse control, leadership, and interaction are addressed through carefully structured musical experiences, which are designed to meet the immediate social needs of students in the group.

As trust develops, steps are taken to move away from structured social skills development to more insight-oriented music therapy groups. Members discuss the group process, roles, behaviors, the music, and feelings that arise in response to the group experience. As described by Yalom (1998), feelings elicited form the immediate musical experience that are often similar to those experienced in life. By addressing them in the group context, students are enabled to better cope with them should they occur again in their lives. The shifting from social skills development to more insight-oriented music therapy occurs depending on student needs, and goals are organized accordingly.

In her work with adolescents in chronic care, Brooks (1989) describes how music therapy is used to modify behaviors so that patients become socially appropriate in the group context. In addition, negative behaviors are discussed to help patients understand why they are not socially acceptable. As patients gain insight into why their behaviors are not appropriate, they are enabled to replace negative behaviors with more socially acceptable ones, and to discuss the pros and cons of each. Not only does behavior change in this context, but patients gain understanding about the process they are going through. This awareness gives added meaning to the behavior modification that is occurring as patients understand why the process is necessary.

Literal Music Therapy

Often, issues preventing students from succeeding in school are behavioral such as yelling out, fighting, lack of respect, inability to share, destruction of property, bullying, isolation, or withdrawal. Roots of disruptive behavior can often be emotional, due to domestic or environmental situations. Inappropriate social behaviors are usually the reason a child is referred to music therapy, as these are the most visible and disruptive to learning.

Social skills are therefore the first areas to be addressed during the initial stages of the music therapy group process, with the understanding that more deep-seated issues may be the cause of outward disruptions. Students may demonstrate disruptive behaviors in the music therapy context by damaging property, talking back to the therapist, or refusing to participate. These are addressed in terms of how these behaviors are affecting them and others (not getting a turn or other group members being angry at them). Because music is motivating and students may see others enjoying it, often beginning an improvisation is enough to capture a disruptive student's attention. Their focus then becomes the music rather than the power struggle or the search for attention. At times, verbal processing of behaviors is necessary and suggestions about ways of joining in with the music are given by the therapist or other group members.

Through structured musical activities such as drum circles, songs, rhythm games, call and response, and following a leader, social skills learning is fine-tuned. Students learn how to wait for their turn, follow a leader, listen to each other, and try new things. They develop impulse control, turn taking, cooperation, and sharing, all of which are skills that they need to participate and succeed in their classrooms. It is important to stress that the social skills learning that occurs in the music therapy context does not happen in a vacuum. Students are challenged to apply what they learn in music therapy to the rest of their lives, by having to answer questions such as when else in your life will you need to learn how to cooperate or take turns. Bridging from the session to life outside of the session is an essential component of this style of music therapy in that students can begin to make connections, and apply what they learn. In his work with emotionally handicapped middle school students, Eidson (1989) found that in comparing students in a general music therapy group with those in music therapy groups targeting specific behaviors, those in the latter showed increased carry-over of newly acquired social skills to their classrooms. This was attributed to the fact that those students were taught how to generalize social skills to the classroom by use of tokens. verbal reinforcement, and instructions for next week.

In support of carry-over from learning that occurs in music therapy to the rest of a student's day, Haines (1989), conducted a study in which the hypothesis was that "certain nonverbal communication skills are prerequisite to successful verbal communication, e.g., listening, eye contact, attention span, tone discrimination, appropriate expression etc. . . .". (p. 80). Some students lack these very basic nonverbal skills, making communication and learning difficult for them. Nonverbal skills can be developed through music therapy, therefore improving communication ability, reducing frustration, and improving self-esteem. An improvement in social and communication skills can lead to improved academic ability.

Students in music therapy groups learn how to behave in a group through experiencing the process by trial and error, and by discussing the experience through sharing. As described by Frisch (1990), "words can increase the music's effectiveness when they are used in a way that structures, that directs or highlights the musical activities of the session" (p. 20). The process is discussed in terms of identifying skills that were used (watching, waiting, listening, sharing), what worked, what did not work, and what the consequences of those actions were for the group. Questions such as, who was playing too loudly, who always picks the largest instrument, and who did we not hear, are addressed, often jump-starting discussions about associated feelings and patterns of behavior.

Often the music therapy context mirrors home or classroom situations in that students fall into similar roles. As students gain awareness about their roles and behaviors, they may be able to develop new ways of behaving that may be more effective. Time for reparative experiences is provided based on group suggestions on how to improve the music or relationships, allowing students to experiment with their learning. The music therapy experience allows students to learn in the moment about skills that they need in other areas of life such as setting the table, playing basketball, and doing a class project. The point at which students can make the connection between "musical production and internal process" (Frisch, 1990, p. 20) is when therapeutic growth takes place.

Social skills are worked on at a very immediate and literal level in the context of the music therapy group. For example, if students are having trouble listening to each other, they will be asked to listen to a leader create short rhythms, and mirror the leader back, so that they are motivated by the knowledge that they will get a leadership turn themselves. If students cannot share, they may be asked to introduce themselves on an instrument and pass it around. Behaviors modify over time as students learn from the satisfaction of having their rhythms mirrored back, trying new instruments, hearing their name in a song, having a solo, or singing a favorite song. Positive behaviors are rewarded by external feedback as well as by the internal experience of physical and emotional pleasure as the students participate in the music. Tension is released, students are heard, and relationships are formed, all of which fill needs and contribute to an overall positive experience. It is the hope that social interactions through music, the personal experience of well-being, and the positive reinforcement of appropriate behaviors will teach students to become aware of their acting-out behaviors, take responsibility for them, and adjust them over time.

As described by Frisch (1990), students begin to use the music and the group context differently, expressing themselves and interacting in new ways that may be more appropriate. As they begin to listen to a peer playing a xylophone, they may begin to listen to their classroom teacher. As they navigate through musical changes in tempo and volume, they may become more at ease during transition time from class to class. How they manipulate the music and relate to it indicates how they may behave outside of the session. As they begin to play in a more organized and connected way, this may indicate a readiness to attend to a classroom activity and to complete it. As they control the music, they are in essence controlling themselves and their impulses. The music therapy context becomes a template for their lives, and learning that occurs through the music will over time translate into changes occurring in their behaviors.

Symbolic Music Therapy

The development of a strong and healing relationship with the music therapist paves the way for group trust and the development of self-esteem. As the group begins to come together as a solid unit, a sense of safety is established that enables the group to move into more intimate and vulnerable territory. As the group content changes, so does the music.

Friedlander (1994) describes how music therapy groups often reflect common stages of development of other groups or relationships. In the context of the music therapy group, students can experience power dynamics, rebellion against leadership, assuming of leadership, and development of trust, in appropriate and safely contained ways. The music lends itself to experiencing group dynamics, as students negotiate interpersonal interactions through the music-making process. New patterns of communication and leadership emerge through the music, as students define their roles within the group by trial and error. As described by Friedlander, in dealing with interpersonal issues within the music therapy group, a "corrective emotional experience" (p. 97) is provided for students as they learn appropriate ways of resolving conflicts and interactions through music and verbal processing.

Slotoroff (1994) describes a music therapy drumming technique used to address anger management issues in a short-term psychiatric setting with adolescents and adults, in which the music is used to purposefully elicit feelings, which patients are struggling with in their lives. The therapist drums with the patient and deliberately tries to disrupt the patient's playing or rhythm. The patient is given the directive to say "stop" at any time. By creating a situation in which the patient is losing control or getting angry, the therapist can address the emotion as it is occurring, asking the patient how they are feeling, what signs their body is giving them that indicates anger, and what made them say "stop" when they did. The therapist can then relate the experience to times outside of therapy by asking the patient to recall any other times when they experienced similar feelings. These focus questions help the patients to gain awareness of why they are feeling the way they are, and it gives them a chance to recognize when they are beginning to feel angry, and to address it before they lose control. This helps patients to develop new coping mechanisms and to gain a sense of control.

Activities shift from being structured to more improvised group and partner work. During these musical improvisations, students learn how to negotiate time and space, learning how to listen and to respond to one another. After modeling appropriate feedback, group members are encouraged to respectfully and constructively comment to each other about their playing, such as what they liked and did not like. Additionally they are encouraged to describe their experience of playing music with the group and during solos. They may be asked what their favorite instrument was and why, what they enjoyed or did not, and what it was like to be listened to or not.

The personal and interpersonal feelings elicited within the group through the music initiates more in-depth and personal discussions as the therapist bridges the gap between what is occurring in the immediate music therapy group and how these feelings relate to previous experiences outside of the group. The group shares about times in their lives when they have had similar experiences or feelings such as times when they have not been heard, or they did not get what they wanted.

Long and Soble (1999) describe a violence prevention project for sixth grade students in which a variety of art forms were used each week to explore the effects and causes of violence in their community. Art and drama activities were used as well as brainstorming and discussions. They found that students used artistic expression as a means of communicating with others, and expressing their feelings. Many students shared personal experiences involving violence by drawing them or acting them out and then talking about it. The art therefore was a vehicle for expression and sublimation of associated feelings.

Case Study

D, a fourth grader, participated very actively in an improvisation during one of his weekly small group music therapy sessions. The improvisation included two bass tone bars (C and G), a cymbal, a djembe, and a glockenspiel, with the music therapist at the piano. A Middle Eastern sounding improvisation developed which incorporated a musical cue on the piano indicating an instrument rotation. D particularly enjoyed the tone bars, standing up, and swinging his arms high above his head before hitting the instrument with his mallet. When his turn came to use the glockenspiel, he at first banged on it extremely rapidly, at times holding it up to his ear. His affect changed from enthusiastic animation to frustrated, frowning, and finally dejection. As the improvisation continued, he put down the glockenspiel, and lay down on his stomach, fingering the mallets but not touching the instrument. During our discussion after the improvisation, most and least favorite instruments were discussed. D said that he hated the glockenspiel because nobody could hear him. He said this felt bad because it was not fun. Other students agreed that the glockenspiel was too soft compared to other instruments. When asked if he had ever felt this way before, D shared about a time when there were many people over at his house and they were all in the living room watching TV and yelling. D realized that somehow his younger brother had gotten onto the fire escape. D tried to tell his father, but his father ignored him. D was very scared that his brother would fall, but nobody would respond to him or help him. In the end, his brother was unharmed, but D described feeling frightened and helpless because nobody heard him.

Other group members shared stories about not being heard as the musical improvisation provided a very concrete way to compare being heard and not and to remind students of other real experiences in their lives. As they related their musical experience to real life experiences, students discussed how they could deal with not being heard in the future, making the music therapy learning real and useful.

CONCLUSION

In working with inner city at-risk youth, a therapist must take into account domestic and environmental stressors that may be preventing students from succeeding academically and socially. Situations involving abuse, neglect, violence, and addiction can often lead children to develop emotional states (depression, anger, grief) and behaviors (violence, isolation) that may get in the way of them making the most of their academic experience.

The music therapy style described here targets those emotional states and behaviors, and provides a time and space during the school day to help students gain mastery over these feelings and behav-

iors. Beginning with structured musical activities, skills such as listening, sharing, and cooperating are addressed, making the music therapy session a very literal vehicle for students to become aware of their behaviors and modify them over time. As trust develops and group cohesion increases, the music therapy sessions become more insight oriented, allowing students to express feelings that emerge in response to the musical and group processes. They are then encouraged to identify other times in their lives when they may have felt similarly. By addressing deep-rooted feelings and group dynamics within the safe context of the music therapy session, students will over time begin to gain awareness of the roles they play, the behaviors they manifest, the emotions that come up for them, and the coping mechanisms that they use. As understanding through experience increases, music therapy may make these experiences more effective.

In making connections to other times in their lives when they are going to need to apply what they have learned during sessions, children begin to understand the relevance of social skills learning, as well as the importance of emotional awareness. Bridging what they learn during music therapy to other areas of their lives challenges students to apply what they learn, and to realize that they do have the ability to be academically and socially successful.

Future exploration of this topic should include research on how music therapy can help an at-risk population. Additionally, more in-depth investigation of how learning during music therapy sessions carries over into classrooms is needed. A student's response at each stage of group development should be investigated to evaluate the importance of each set of goals (social skills development and the gaining of insight). This would allow us to determine which methodology is the most influential over significant life changes.

REFERENCES

Brooks, D.M. (1989). Music therapy enhances treatment with adolescents. *Music Therapy Perspectives, 6*, 37–39.

Brooks-Gunn, J. & Duncan, G.J. (1997). The effects of poverty on children. *The Future of Children, 7*(2), 55–71.

Dwivedi, K.N. (1993). *Groupwork with children and adolescents: A handbook.* London: Jessica Kingsley, Publishers.

Eidson, C.G. (1989). The effect of behavioral music therapy on the generalization of interpersonal skills from sessions to the classroom by emotionally handicapped middle school students. *Journal of Music Therapy, 26*(2), 206–221.

Farr, M. (1997). The role of dance/movement therapy in treating at-risk African American adolescents. *The Arts In Psychotherapy, 24*(2), 183–191.

Friedlander, L.H. (1994). Group music psychotherapy in an inpatient psychiatric setting for children: A developmental approach. *Music Therapy Perspectives, 12,* 92–97.

Frisch, A. (1990). Symbol and structure: Music therapy for the adolescent psychiatric inpatient. *Music Therapy, 9*(1), 16–34.

Haines, J.H. (1989). The effects of music therapy on the self-esteem of emotionally disturbed adolescents. *Music Therapy, 8*(1), 78–91.

Hibben, J.K. (1991). Identifying dimensions of music therapy activities appropriate for children at different stages of group development. *The Arts In Psychotherapy, 18,* 301–310.

Long, J.K. & Soble, L. (1999). Report: An arts-based violence prevention project for sixth grade students. *The Arts in Psychotherapy, 24*(5), 329–344.

McWhirter, J.J. (1998). *At-risk youth: A comprehensive response.* Pacific Grove, CA: Brooks/Cole Publishing Company.

Noguera, P. (2003). *City schools and the American dream.* New York: Teachers College Press.

Sagrestano, L.M., Paikoff, R.L., Holmbeck, G.N., & Fendrich, M. (2003). A longitudinal examination of familial risk factors for depression among inner-city African American adolescents. *Journal of Family Psychology, 17*(1), 108–120.

Shiraishi, I.M. (1997). A home-based music therapy program for multi-risk mothers. *Music Therapy Perspectives, 15,* 16–23.

Slotoroff, C. (1994). Drumming technique for assertiveness and anger management in the short-term psy-chiatric setting for adult and adolescent survivors of trauma. *Music Therapy Perspectives, 12,* 111–116.

U.S. Census Bureau. (2001, May). *Profiles of general demographic characteristics: 2000 Census of Population and Housing.*

U.S. Census Bureau. (2001, July). *Cartographic boundary files: Metropolitan areas cartographic boundary files descriptions and metadata.*

U.S. Census Bureau (2003, September). *Poverty in the United States.*

Wheeler, B.L. (1987). Levels of therapy: The classification of music therapy goals. *Music Therapy, 6*(2), 39–49.

Yalom, I.D. (1998). *The Yalom reader.* New York: Basic Books.

Biographical Statement

Vanessa A. Camilleri, MA, MT-BC, studied Psychology and Education at Vassar College and completed her Masters in Music Therapy at New York University. She is a pianist by formation, but uses voice, guitar, and much drumming in her work with children. She began her career in Music Therapy at a school where she began the Music Therapy program, in Spanish Harlem, New York City. The school had predominantly Hispanic and African-American students from the highly chaotic and volatile neighborhood surrounding the school. She now works at The Arts and Technology Academy, Public Charter School, in Washington DC, where she began the Music Therapy program, and continues to work with an inner city African-American population. She is the author of several journal articles, has presented at conferences, supervises bachelor and masters level students, and is currently working on her first book about the use of the creative arts with inner city, at-risk children.

Chapter 22

ANCIENT AND MODERN ROOTS OF DRAMA THERAPY

SALLY BAILEY

INTRODUCTION

The word drama comes from ancient Greek and means quite literally "things done" (Harrison, 1913). Drama therapy is, in simplest terms, the use of action techniques, particularly role play, drama games, improvisation, puppetry, masks, and theatrical performance, in the service of behavior change and personal growth. It has its roots in religion, theatre, education, social action, and mental health/therapy. The National Association for Drama Therapy, created for promoting the field of drama therapy in the United States, was organized recently in 1979, as were many of the other creative arts therapy organizations, but drama therapy has been around much longer than that!

Ancient Roots: Religion and Theatre

Evidence in archeological records suggests that early humans began to make art – paintings, sculpture, music, dance, and drama – during the Upper Paleolithic period about 35,000–45,000 years ago. Experts marvel at the suddenness with which the arts burst onto the human scene and tie it to the beginnings of symbolic, metaphoric thought (Lewis-Williams, 2002; Mithen, 1996; Pfeiffer, 1982). Simultaneous with this creative explosion, shamans and priests began utilizing the arts in their healing and religious practices. The origins of the arts and religion seem to be intertwined because the arts naturally provided effective symbolic ways to express abstract religious ideas. Dance and drama, in particular, were extremely useful in rites to create sympathetic and contagious magic as well as to embody myths and rituals. Details about these ancient origins are sketchy, but many scholars have hypothesized about those origins, based on surviving cave paintings, artifacts, myths, and even on extrapolating from contemporary shamanistic practices (Lewis-Williams, 2002; Pfeiffer, 1982). Greek scholar and cultural anthropologist, Jane Ellen Harrison, for instance, theorizes that early art developed directly out of ritual from mimesis or imitation of an experience and became an abstract representation or metaphor, which was then available for magical use (Harrison, 1913). However, without a written record providing direct testimony, we cannot know exactly what those ancient practices entailed and how those ancient humans understood their ceremonies.

Eventually, the art form of theatre developed out of religious rites and rituals. Western theatre history usually begins its formal accounts with ancient Greek theatre. Religious festivals dedicated to Dionysus, god of fertility and revelry, featured theatrical competitions in which plays brought mythology to life for the community. The Great Dionysia, held in Athens in early spring, featured tragedies, comedies, and satyr plays written by citizen-poets and performed by citizen-actors for the entire populace. During a choral presentation at one of these festivals around 560 B.C., Thespis, the first actor, stepped away from the chorus to take on an individual character for the first time – theatre as we know it was born (Brockett, 1968).

The first written theoretical account of drama therapy can be found in connection with Greek theatre. In his *Poetics*, Aristotle says the function of tragedy is to induce catharsis – a release of deep feelings (specifically pity and fear) to purge the senses and the souls of the spectators (Aristotle, trans. 1954). These cathartic feelings are experienced empathically for the characters in the play by the individuals watching the performance and they share that theatrical/cathartic experience with others in the audience magnifying the release and allowing for an adjustment in the community's attitude as a whole. According to Aristotle, drama's purpose is not primarily for education or entertainment, but to release harmful emotions which will lead to harmony and healing in the community (Boal, 1985).

In his analysis of Aristotle's work, Brazilian director Augusto Boal (1985) suggests that this cathartic release helped preserve the status quo in Greek society, for a populace that is content and at peace will not rebel against the rulers in power. Aristotle's ideas about catharsis have influenced many psychotherapy models from Freudian psychoanalysis onward by focusing psychotherapeutic work on the idea that insight into troubling emotional issues and healing occurs only after the patient has achieved catharsis. This process is disputed as unrealistic and unnecessary by cognitive-behavioral therapists, rational-emotive therapists, and others who feel that catharsis and insight are not enough to induce healing or change, that new thoughts and behaviors must be learned to replace the old, and that change doesn't automatically follow emotional release and understanding (Seligman, 1993).

Mental Health Roots

Ancient physicians recognized the value of drama as a therapeutic tool. Soranus, a second century Roman, believed that the way to cure mentally ill patients was to put them into peaceful surroundings and have them read, discuss, and participate in the production of plays in order to create order in their thinking and offset their depression (Cockerham, 2000). In the fifth century, another Roman, Caelius Aurelius, took this a step farther. He states in his treatise, *On Acute Diseases and on Chronic Diseases,* that in order to achieve emotional balance, patients should go to the theatre and watch a performance that expresses the emotion opposite to their condition. For depression, see a comedy; for mania or hysteria, see a tragedy (Jones, 1996).

For the most part, however, people with mental illness were not treated by taking trips to the theatre or by reading and performing plays; they were locked away in horrible prisons and asylums where they were either forgotten or attempts were made to cure them through exorcisms and treatments, which could only be described as torture. Not until the late eighteenth century, with the beginning of the Moral Treatment movement, did some mental institutions provide occupational, horticultural, and artistic activities as part of their treatment regimen (Cockerham, 2000; Whitaker, 2001). This approach to treatment continued in enlightened institutions in Europe and America into the twentieth century and opened the door to the practice of drama therapy.

The groundwork for inclusion of the art therapies into psychiatric hospitals in the U.S. was laid after World War I. Talk therapy and medical interventions did nothing to help veterans recover from what at the time was called "shell-shock" (now called Post Traumatic Stress Disorder), the emotional response to traumatic combat experience. However, the arts did help. In the early '20s and '30s, inclusion of the arts in hospital programming began to expand. Occupational therapists at many psychiatric hospitals began involving patients in the rehearsal and performance of plays, pageants, and puppet shows. Interestingly, the genre of plays performed was limited to comedy, so as not to upset the patients (Phillips, 1996).

T. D. Noble, a psychiatrist at Sheppard-Pratt Hospital in the Baltimore, MD area, noticed that patients in his psychotherapy sessions who had acted in the hospital plays were able to understand and identify emotions better than other patients, could link their present emotional state and behavior to their earlier trauma more easily, and were able to experiment with alternative modes of behavior with more flexibility (Phillips, 1996). He wrote in a 1933 issue of *Occupational Therapy and Rehabilitation* that he found drama was a vehicle for the discovery and expression of conscious and unconscious conflicts. Playing other characters in the plays, he noted, helped patients release repressed emotions so that they could later deal with them directly in therapy. He also observed that drama was a useful diversion and encouraged socialization among patients (Phillips, 1996).

Social Roots of Drama Therapy

The social action root of drama therapy can be traced to Hull House and other sites of the settlement movement. Jane Addams opened Hull House in 1889 to serve as a socializing, civilizing, connective, and reforming force for the immigrant, working-class neighborhood of the Nineteenth Ward of Chicago's West Side (Jackson, 2001). She set up a series of what she termed "Lines of Activity:" courses, lectures, and group experiences that would bring culture, education, social connection, and change to the community living in proximity to the settlement house. The most popular activities were the drama clubs which provided socialization, a creative outlet, and an exciting group experience which led to a product shared with others (Jackson, 2001). Young people would join drama clubs at the age of seven or eight and found so much meaning in their work together that they would remain in them until they were in their thirties and forties. The Little Theatre or community theatre movement grew, in part, out of the enthusiasm for amateur performance that the Hull House drama clubs created (Hecht, 1991).

Movement and recreational groups were run for children at Hull House by Neva Boyd (Jackson, 2001). She used games and improvisation to teach language skills, problem-solving, self-confidence, and social skills. Boyd became a sociology and theatre professor at the University of Chicago and is one of the founders of the Recreational Therapy and Educational Drama movements in the U.S. Her student Viola Spolin, learned Boyd's techniques and developed them further, writing the widely-studied *Improvisation for the Theatre*, from which many theatre games and improvisation techniques used in American theatre training and in drama therapy originated (Spolin, 1963).

American Pioneers in the Field of Drama Therapy

The surge in the growth of educational theatre in the U.S. can be traced to this source and to the educational theatre program at Northwestern University in Chicago, which was helmed by Winifred Ward (Goldberg, 1974; Lease & Siks, 1952; McCaslin, 1971). Many founders of the National Association for Drama Therapy began as creative drama teachers. Drama therapists like Eleanor Irwin, Rosilyn Wilder, Naida Weisberg, Rose Pavlow, Jan Goodrich, and Patricia Sternberg discovered the therapeutic benefits of process drama through their work with young children and extended it to other populations in an intentional manner (Lewis & Johnson, 2000, personal communications).

Lewis Barbato is credited with coining the term drama therapy in print in an article he wrote in 1945 for the *Journal of Psychodrama and Group Psychotherapy*. Florsheim published a book in which she discussed utilizing the enactment of scripted plays as therapy in 1945 (Casson, 2004). However, Gertrud Schattner, a Viennese actress, is credited with popularizing the term drama therapy and providing the impetus to create a national organization in the U.S (Reiter, 1996). In order to avoid Hitler's invasion of Austria, Gertrud fled to Switzerland for safety during the Second World War on a temporary visa. When it expired, she used her acting skills to have herself admitted to a mental hospital as a patient, convincing the doctors that she was suicidal. She learned a great deal about mental illness from her stay at the hospital (Reiter, 1996). Gertrud ended up marrying Edward Schattner, a psychiatrist working with refugees and survivors of Nazi concentration camps in a Swiss tuberculosis sanitarium. While he was able to make his patients' bodies healthier, he had little success healing their utter desperation, depression, and despair. Edward asked Gertrud to come in to the sanitarium to do drama, storytelling, and poetry with the patients in a recreational vein. Through their participation in drama, they began to come back to life. Gertrud recognized what she was doing was something special and out of the ordinary – she called it drama therapy (Reiter, 1996; Schattner, 1981).

After the war, the Schattners moved to the U.S. and Gertrud practiced drama therapy in a number of social service organizations and psychiatric hospitals in the New York City area. She taught the first drama therapy courses at Turtle Bay Music Center on Long Island (Reiter, 1996). In the early 1970s, she and drama educator Richard Courtney began approaching other people who were doing similar work to collaborate on a publication which became *Drama In Therapy, Volume One: Children and Volume Two: Adults*, the first books in print about drama therapy (Schattner & Courtney, 1981). She and a number of those other pioneers, including David Read Johnson, Eleanor Irwin, Marilyn Richman, Rosilyn Wilder, Naida Weisberg, Ramon Gordon, Jan Goodrich, Barbara Sandberg, and others formed the National Association for Drama Therapy in 1979 in order to promote the training and education of drama therapists, to establish standards for registry, and to promote the field (Finneran, 1999).

European Roots of Drama Therapy

At the same time drama therapy was developing in Great Britain. The British put the two words together: dramatherapy. Sue Jennings reports that because psychotherapy is one word, British dramatherapists felt their modality should also be expressed in one word. Peter Slade, who as early as 1939 addressed the British Medical Association on the new modality, said he felt it had more force that way (Jones, 1996).

British origins can be connected to the educational drama work of Peter Slade in the 1930s in an arts center in Worchester. He wrote *Child drama* in 1954, the first book to connect drama with helping children develop emotional and physical control, confidence, observation skills, and abilities to be tolerant and considerate of others. In 1959, Slade began calling what he and others were doing dramatherapy in a pamphlet entitled "Dramatherapy as an Aid to Becoming a Person" (Jones, 1996). Brian Way developed similar ideas about the essential growth drama offers participants in his classic *Development through drama*, which collected ideas and methods from his work in educational drama from the forties through the mid-sixties (Way, 1967). Dorothy Heathcote used drama in education for teaching purposes, but also as a way for children to develop insight, understanding, and empathy. In 1964, Marian Lindkvist created the first dramatherapy training program, the Sesame Institute, which focused on drama and movement as forms of learning and expression, particularly in work with children with special needs. Peter Slade worked with her to expand their method through psychological training.

Another early pioneer was Sue Jennings, who began doing drama at a psychiatric hospital when she was a young drama student and called the work she was doing "remedial drama" (Jones, 1996). In the 1970s, she completed a Ph.D. in anthropology which focused on ritual and started referring to her work as "dramatherapy" (Jones, 1996). The British Association for Dramatherapists (BADth) was created in 1976 to promote the education and credentialing of dramatherapists in the U.K. (Jones, 1996). It is interesting to note that this is just three years before the National Association of Drama Therapy (NADT) was formed in the U.S. While the British and the American forms of drama therapy developed separately and had different theoretical emphases, they truly did develop along parallel lines.

Drama therapy also has a history in Russia and the Netherlands. Phil Jones, in *Drama as therapy: Theatre as living* talks about two Russian drama therapists who were influenced strongly by the work of Stanislavky (Jones, 1996). Nicholai Evreinov, a Russian director, created a method he called Theatrotherapy that focused on the internal and psychological processes involved in acting to create healing and well-being in participants and help them reframe or reimagine their difficulties into a new way of life. Vladimir Iljine also created a Therapeutic Theatre in the years before the Russian Revolution (1908–1917) using theatre games and improvisational training to encourage flexibility, spontaneity, expressiveness, and communication abilities. He used his methods with individuals and groups in many situations and locations: psychiatric patients, people with emotional problems, and actors in the theatre (Jones, 1996).

After the Revolution, there were others who carried on this work. One, Nikolai Sergevich Govorov, developed a theatrical storytelling technique that he used to help psychiatric patients and others develop social connections, self-confidence, and socially appropriate behavior (Martin, personal communication, June 2, 2004). He felt that much of mental health depended on people having the ability to socialize and support each other morally and humanly. Govorov was very aware of Evreinov's work and consciously built on it and other Western therapeutic theatre work (Martin, personal communication, June 2, 2004). His work developed between the1950s and the 1970s.

One other country in which drama therapy currently thrives is the Netherlands. In the late forties, activity leaders involved with social welfare and youth care in community and residential care centers began using the arts and play for self-expression and social interaction (Jones, 1996). This gave rise to The Netherlands Society for Creative Expressive Therapy in the 1960s; a branch for drama therapists was formed in 1981. There are, perhaps, more drama therapists per capita in the Netherlands than anywhere else in the world!

Other Influences

Two other individuals should be mentioned as important influences on drama therapy. The first is Constantin Stanislavky. Before Stanislavsky, theatre was not considered a psychological art. His work at the Moscow Art Theatre (1900–1938) set the stage, not just for actors training in the twentieth century, but also for the use of his methods as tools for connecting with the emotional mind by other educators and psychotherapy professionals (Blair, 2002). His intuitive utilization of the imagination (the brain's natural ability to create imagery and metaphor), the unconscious (as a gateway to connecting with true emotion), and given circumstances (embodying the actor in the physical and psychological details of the moment in which the character is) mesh with research that has been done on neurology and brain processes in the past fifteen years. The body-mind is essentially one, as Antonio Damasio explains in *Descartes' error* and *the feeling of what happens*, and as Stanislavsky's methods demonstrate (Blair, 2002). Stanislavsky's methods deeply influenced not just the Russian drama therapists, but also theatre artists from the West, most notably in our case, Viola Spolin and the American theatre educators who developed into the first drama therapists.

The other critical individual who must be mentioned is Jacob Levy Moreno, the father of psychodrama, sociodrama, and sociometry (Johnson in Lewis & Johnson, 2000). Moreno, born in Bucharest in 1889, grew up and studied medicine in Vienna. There, as an attending physician at a refugee camp at Mitterndorf at the end of World War I, he developed sociometry, a method of assessing the social choices made within a group by its members and then intervening in a systemic way to create social change (Garcia & Buchanan in Johnson & Lewis, 2000). He applied these new measurements and intervention tools to create order and improve living conditions in the displaced residents' lives. It worked! Later he started what amounted to a support group for Viennese prostitutes, using role play and improvisation to help them find solutions to social problems with which they were faced.

From 1920–24, Moreno led The Theatre of Spontaneity, an improvisational theatre in which professional actors created spontaneous drama based on current events. This work developed into sociodrama and later psychodrama as the focus changed from the community and social issues to personal and psychological issues of individuals. Moreno emigrated to the U.S. in 1925 where he continued developing his methods with the general public through the Impromptu Theatre at Carnegie Hall and by consulting at prisons, psychiatric hospitals, and residential treatment centers. In these latter institutions he helped individuals who had serious personal, emotional, or social problems learn how to function better (Blatner, 2000). The American Society for Group Psychotherapy and Psychodrama (ASGPP) was founded in 1942. Many of the pioneers of creative arts therapy movements, experiential therapy, and traditional talk therapy came to his sessions and were influenced by his work, including Marian Chace, Eric Berne, Arthur Janov, and Fritz Perls (Blatner, 2000; Johnson in Lewis & Johnson, 2000).

Psychodrama and drama therapy purists would argue that Moreno's work is not a subset of drama therapy, but there is a truth to the idea that Moreno was the "first drama therapist," as he identified role and social relationships as important therapeutic issues through his writing and work with clients long before American or British drama therapists became organized or began publishing (Johnson in Lewis & Johnson, 2000). My view of psychodrama is that it is part of the drama therapy toolbox; therefore, its story rightfully belongs as part of drama therapy history.

Current and Future Directions

Presently, there are two Master degree programs in the U.S. and one in Canada approved by NADT for training drama therapists: New York University in New York City, California Institute for Integral Studies in San Francisco, and Concordia University in Montreal, Quebec. NADT has also developed an alternative training program through which students can work with a Board Certified Trainer/ Mentor to create an individualized program of study in drama therapy in conjunction with a Masters degree in theatre, social work, counseling, special education, or another discipline related to drama therapy. Being an interdisciplinary field, training in drama therapy requires courses in psychology/therapy, drama therapy, and other creative arts therapy as well as internships in which students practice their skills and receive supervision from experienced professional drama therapists and other credentialed mental health professionals.

The professional credential for drama therapists in the U.S. and Canada is the R.D.T. (Registered Drama Therapist), which can be applied for after

Table 22.1.
Drama Therapy Time Line

43,000 BC–33,000 BC	*Homo sapiens* begin thinking symbolically and creating arts (painting, sculpting, dance, drama)		

TIME	EUROPE	RUSSIA	NORTH AMERICA
400–500 BCE	*Greece:* Origins of Greek Theatre		
534 BCE	*Greece:* Prize for Best Tragedy established at City Dionysia Festival.		
c. 560 BCE	*Greece:* Thespus steps out of Greek Chorus to become first actor.		
c. 335–323 BCE	*Greece:* Aristotle writes *The Poetics.*		
100–200 ACE	*Rome:* Soranus has mentally ill patients reading and performing plays.		
c. 500 ACE	*Rome:* Caelius Aurelius writes *On Acute Diseases and on Chronic Diseases.*		
1789	*Paris:* Moral Therapy reforms begun by Phillippe Pinel and continued by others in Europe.		Moral Therapy continued by others in America.
1889–1900			*Hull House, Chicago:* Theatre and theatre games with immigrants by Edith de Nancrede and Neva Boyd.
1900–1930		*Moscow:* Constantin Stanislavsky develops his psychological acting method at Moscow Art Theatre.	
1908–1917	*Vienna:* Jacob Moreno develops sociometry. (1917)		*Kiev:* Vladimir Iljine develops Therapeutic Theatre.
1920–24	*Vienna:* Moreno creates the Theatre of Spontaneity.	*St. Petersburg:* Nicholai Evreinov develops Theatrotheatre.	
1925			*Chicago:* Winifred Ward begins educational drama movement; Neva Boyd begins therapeutic recreation movement.
1926–40			*New York:* Jacob Moreno developing psychodrama in prisons/hospitals.
1930's	*UK:* Peter Slade begins working with children.		Occupational therapists using drama with residents in psychiatric hospitals. *Chicago:* Viola Spolin is developing her improvisation methods.
1940–47	*Switzerland:* Gertrud Schattner works with refugees in Swiss sanitarium.		

Table 22.1.
continued

TIME	EUROPE	RUSSIA	NORTH AMERICA
1942			*New York:* Moreno founds American Society for Group Psychotherapy & Psychodrama (ASGPP).
1947			*New York:* Schattner and Moreno work in schools & hospitals.
1950–70	*UK:* Peter Slade writes Child Drama (1954). *UK:* Peter Slade writes *Dramatherapy as an Aid to becoming a Person* (1959). *UK:* Sue Jennings begins doing "remedial drama" (1960). *The Netherlands:* The Netherlands Society for Expressive Therapy formed (1960).	*St. Petersburg:* Nikolai Govorov develops his drama therapy techniques.	*New York:* Schattner and Moreno work in schools & hospitals.
1964	*UK:* Marian Lindkvist opens The Sesame Institute (1964).		*New York:* Schattner teaches 1st DT training program at Turtle Bay Music Institute.
1975			*Chicago:* Toddy Richman founds The Institute for Therapy Through the Arts.
1976	*UK:* British Association for Dramatherapy (BADth) founded.		
1979			National Association for Drama Therapy (NADT) founded. National Coalition for Creative Arts Therapies (NCCATA) founded.
1981	*The Netherlands:* Drama Therapy Branch formed in The Netherlands Society for Creative Expressive Therapy		*Drama in Therapy, Vols. I and II*, published, edited by Schattner and Richard Courtney.
1982			*Pittsburgh, PA:* First Registered Drama Therapist: Eleanor Irwin. *New York:* 1st DT MA Program approved at NYU, created by Robert Landy.
1983			*California:* 2nd DT MA Program approved, created by Renee Emunah.
1999			*Montreal:* 3rd DT MA Program approved at Concordia University, created by Stephen Snow.

one has finished an appropriate Masters degree, the approved drama therapy and psychology coursework, an 800 hour drama therapy internship, a minimum of 500 hours of theatre experience and a minimum of 1,500 professional hours working as a drama therapist. Most registered drama therapists have much more than a minimum of 500 hours of theatre when they discover drama therapy since most begin as theatre artists or educators who discover the healing aspects of drama through their theatre training and work. However, more and more social workers, counselors, and special educators are discovering that talk therapy is not enough; that there is a need for insight and change to be effective for clients. As this happens, drama therapists with theatre origins are being joined by drama therapists with clinical mental health origins, who have discovered the magic and intrinsic healing value of drama. Among the ranks of drama therapy students, there are even ministers, priests, and rabbis who have discovered the healing power of drama therapy. Perhaps this is an indication that we are rounding the bend to complete the circle to the place where our drama therapy roots began.

REFERENCES

Aristotle. (1954). *Aristotle's rhetoric and poetics.* New York: The Modern Library.

Blair, R. (2002). Reconsidering Stanislavsky: Feeling, feminism, and the actor. *Theatre Topics. 12*(2), 177–190.

Blatner, A. (2000). *Foundations of psychodrama.* New York: Springer Publishing Company.

Brockett, O. (1968). *History of the theatre.* Boston: Allyn and Bacon, Inc.

Boal, A. (1985). *Theatre of the oppressed.* New York: Theatre Communications Group.

Casson, J. *Tribute to Peter Slade,* read at Peter Slade's funeral, June 30, 2004.

Cockerham, W. C. (2000). *Sociology of mental disorder.* Englewood Cliffs, NJ: Prentice Hall.

Damasio, A. (1994). *Descartes' error: Emotion, reason, and the human brain.* New York: Avon Books.

Damasio, A. (1999). *The feeling of what happens: Body and emotion in the making of consciousness.* San Diego: Harcourt, Inc.

Finneran, L. (1999). Beginnings: Letters to and from Gert. *Dramascope. 19*(2), 18–20.

Goldberg, M. (1974). *Children's theatre: A philosophy and a method.* Englewood Cliffs, NJ: Prentice Hall.

Gordon, R. (1999). Beginnings: Cell Block Theatre. *Dramascope. 19*(1), 13–26.

Harrison, J. E. (1913). *Ancient art and ritual.* Bath, England: Moonraker Press.

Hecht, S. J. (1991). Edith de Nancrede at Hull House: Theatre programs for youth. *Youth Theatre Journal. 6*(1), 3–10.

Jackson, S. (2001). *Lines of activity: Performance, historiography, Hull-House domesticity.* Ann Arbor, MI: University of Michigan.

Jones, P. (1996). *Drama as therapy: Theatre as living.* London: Routledge.

Landy, R. (1997). Drama therapy – The state of the art. *The Arts in Psychotherapy. 24*(1), 5–15.

Lease, R. & Siks, G.B. (1952). *Creative dramatics: In home, school, and community.* New York: Harper & Brothers Publishers.

Lewis, P. & Johnson D. R.(Eds.). (2000). *Current approaches in drama therapy.* Springfield, IL: Charles C Thomas, Publisher, Ltd.

Lewis-Williams, D. (2002). *The mind in the cave: Consciousness and the origins of art.* London: Thames & Hudson.

Martin, H. (2004, June 2). Personal Communication.

McCaslin, N. (1971). *Theatre for children in the United States: A history.* Norman, OK: University of Oklahoma Press.

Mithen, S. (1996). *The prehistory of the mind: The cognitive origins of art, religion and science.* London: Thames and Hudson, Ltd.

Pfeiffer, J.E. (1982). *The creative explosion: An inquiry into the origins of art and religion.* New York: Harper & Row.

Philips, M. E. (1996). The use of drama and puppetry in occupational therapy during the 1920s and 1930s. *The American Journal of Occupational Therapy, 50*(3), 229–233.

Reiter, S. (1996). Honoring Gert Schattner. *Dramascope, 14* (1), 1–3.

Schattner, G. & Courtney, R. (1981). *Drama in therapy, Volume One: Children.* New York: Drama Book Specialists.

Seligman, M.E.P. (1993). *What you can change . . . and what you can't.* New York: Fawcett Columbine.

Slade, P. (1954). *Child drama.* London: Hodder and Stoughton.

Slade, P. (1959). Dramatherapy as an aid to becoming a person. Pamphlet, Guild of Pastoral Psychology.

Spolin, V. (1963). *Improvisation for the theatre.* Evanston, IL: Northwestern University.

Stanislavsky, C. (1936). *An actor prepares.* New York: Theatre Arts Books.

Way, B. (1967). *Development through drama.* Atlantic Highlands, NJ: Humanities Press.

Whitaker, R. (2001). *Mad in America: Bad science, bad medicine, and the enduring mistreatment of the mentally ill.* Cambridge, MA: Perseus Publishing.

Biographical Statement

Sally Bailey, MFA, MSW, RDT/BCT, is director of the drama therapy program at Kansas State University, Manhattan, KS, a site for alternative training in drama therapy. She is a recent past president of the National Association for Drama Therapy and the author of two books: *Wings to fly: Bringing theatre arts to students with special needs* (1993) and *Dreams to sign* (2002).

Chapter 23

DRAMA THERAPY THEORETICAL PERSPECTIVES

YEHUDIT SILVERMAN

INTRODUCTION

For as long as humans have existed, we have been troubled. It is perhaps a defining characteristic of our race. With the ability to think, also comes the capacity to worry, and with the ability to imagine, comes the capacity for despair. For millennia, myths and stories have been used to express human conflicts. From Gilgamesh to Sophocles, myths and drama have enabled people to appreciate the joys and despairs common to everyone (Campbell, 1968). In more recent times, our understanding of the human mind and psyche has deepened, and the ideas of modern psychology imbued nearly every aspect of society. Therapeutic models and ideals abound, and the growing acceptance of the importance of psychology is encouraging. Yet, in its rise, something may have been forgotten. In the. pursuit of scientific acceptance, a primal function of the narrative and story has been left by the wayside. For the five thousand years of recorded history, stories of inner conflict defined and sustained us. They are no less important today. All of us have internal stories that provide meaning and purpose in our lives. To ignore our stories would be to ignore the human mind itself, and ultimately, the aim of any therapy is to reveal, examine, and work with our stories. The lessons of recent years have much to offer, but the lessons of thousands of years cannot be forgotten. Drama therapy combines the tools of modern therapy with an understanding of the stories within us to treat clients effectively. This chapter explains the fundamental principles of drama therapy, identifies its prominent techniques, and provides a detailed illustration of one form of it:

the use of myth and fairytale in therapy as a way to uncover, work with, and ultimately transform the client's self-narrative.

Origins of Drama Therapy

Drama therapy was born from the marriage of psychology and theatre. As in any marriage, each partner brought into it a different personality. Psychology provided a focus on personal processes, therapeutic alliances, and clinical interventions. It entered the union with great sensitivity. Next, in marched flamboyant theatre with its wild imagination, performance technique, and dramatic intensity. When these were combined, an amazing new form of therapy was born.

Drama therapy uses the dramatic techniques of theatre in a therapeutic context. It is an active form of therapy in which the client's creativity is developed, expressed, and explored (Jones, 1996). The creative process, with its symbolic expression, becomes a means of communication between therapist and client. This exploration of nonverbal and verbal avenues of communication frees clients to express themselves in a personal way and at their own safe pace. In therapeutic sessions, clients engage in a variety of dramatic processes to work through difficult psychological challenges. In each case, the goal is to foster the development of a profound relationship between the client's inner emotional world and his or her external dramatic form. This allows the client both a high degree of safety when working through difficult material, and the ability to discover new perspectives about his or her situation or problem. For example, Jones (1996) explains that projection, "as used in drama therapy, is the process by which clients project aspects of themselves or their experience into theatrical or dramatic materials or into enactment, and thereby externalize their inner conflicts" (p. 101). This use of projection is very different from its use in traditional psychology, which views projection as a defense mechanism, a way for clients to deny their own feelings by putting them outside themselves. Thus, Yalom (1985) describes projection as an unconscious process that consists of projecting some of one's own (but disowned) attributes onto another, toward whom one subsequently feels an uncanny attraction/repulsion (p. 117). In fact, the goal of many psychotherapeutic approaches is to assist clients in gaining insight about their projections and reclaim disowned feelings or parts of themselves through discussion or analysis. By contrast, projection as used in drama therapy is an expressive therapeutic tool that allows clients to gain insight into their problem or situation.

Pioneers

The theoretical framework underlying drama therapy evolved from the pioneers of psychology and experimental theatre. Freudian concepts of the unconscious, projection, transference, defense mechanisms, and symbolism are intrinsic to it and have been enriched by the ideas of Carl Jung, Melanie Klein, Anna Freud, and Erik Erikson (Lewis & Johnson, 2000). From these early pioneers came techniques such as active imagination, play therapy, and psychodrama that are central to drama therapy. In addition, the developmental perspective of Mahler (1963), which emphasized the child's struggle for psychological birth as a process of separation and individuation, influenced many drama therapists who integrate this perspective into their work. Winnicott's (1971) notion of the transitional object and transitional space is crucial to the idea of a play space in drama therapy. Winnicott (1971) explained the importance of a transitional object (blanket, teddy bear) for the child in that it becomes the "me" and the "not me," existing in the world as a concrete object; yet, also imbued with the child's subjective personal significance. He stressed how important it is for the mother to set up a psychological environment in which the child is free to explore his or her world. In drama therapy, the therapeutic space, or play space, can be viewed as a true transitional space becoming a bridge between the client's inner and outer world. Johnson (1992) described the play

space in drama therapy as an interpersonal and imaginary realm shared by the therapist and client.

In theatre, Stanislavsky (1961) linked acting techniques to the personal and psychological realm of experience. He developed the method of psycho-technique, which emphasized the actor's use of memory, the unconscious, and emotions in portraying a character. The actor expresses the character's feelings by entering into a similar emotional state. Through this empathetic connection with the dramatic character, an authentic feeling state is ultimately portrayed. A similar connection is used in drama therapy when clients enter into an intimate relationship with a character in role-play, with an object in personification, and with a feeling state in movement sculpting (Jones, 1996).

Brecht (1898–1956) developed a theatrical form with quite a different aim. For him, the actor does not enter into an empathetic relationship with the character, but instead maintains an emotional distance by commenting on the action and text of the play. Boal (1979) has developed this concept into his Theatre of the Oppressed, a method that uses performance as a tool for a social and personal revolution. Out of this idea of creating dramatic distance for personal, social, or political change came the techniques of sociodrama, playback theatre, and disability theatre groups. The notions of transformation through emotional authenticity and distancing are important roots of modern drama therapy theory.

One of the pioneers of drama therapy, Joseph Moreno (1889–1974), brought his vision of role theory and the theatre of spontaneity from Vienna to New York (Lewis & Johnson, 2000). Trained as a psychiatrist, he was an astute observer of children's role play and the sociodynamics of groups. From these observations, he developed the techniques of psychodrama and sociodrama. In psychodrama, clients enact scenes from their lives to gain perspective and insight about real-life situations and relationships. The client expresses a narrative about his or her personal story by creating a scene from a real-life situation, casting the characters, and directing them as they enact the scene. Sociodrama, on the other hand, is concerned with the roles and challenges that are common to most people (Lewis & Johnson, 2000). The group formally agrees to deal with a common problem, such as the loss of a parent, and then creates a dramatic scene based on this theme using fictional characters. As Moreno (1993) points out, "The true subject of sociodrama is the group... The sociodramatic approach deals with the social problems and aims at social catharsis" (pp. 59–60). For Moreno, however, the integration of psychology and theatre was not always easy. As his techniques were increasingly embraced by mental health professionals, his methods tended to stray from the aesthetics of their theatrical roots.

In contrast, Sue Jennings (1994), who created the British Association of Drama Therapy, stayed close to her theatrical roots. Although influenced by developmental psychology, she has continued to emphasize the healing properties of drama itself and the therapeutic importance of setting up a dramatic space. Jennings describes children's play as an evolving process of three stages: Embodiment, projection, and role play – known as the EPR method. Jennings correlates the normal stages of development with what she refers to as a drama therapy developmental paradigm. Her technique of drama therapy is known as the EPR method: Embodiment (movement system and gesture), Projection (sculpting, drawing, and painting), and Role (drama games, enactment, role play, improvisation). Jennings uses these three stages of play as a way of structuring her drama therapy sessions and has developed a condensed and expanded version of her EPR method. In her condensed version, Embodiment consists of finger play, moving specific body parts, and singing games, Projection uses sculpts and small worlds, while Role uses puppets, doll play, and stories. While in the expanded version, Embodiment would consist of larger movements and dance, Projection would use body and chair sculpts, and Role would employ role-play, dramatizations, and improvisations (Jennings, 1994).

By contrast, Eleanor Irwin (1975, 2000) made a transition from a dramatic emphasis into a psychoanalytic framework. She began her work with children using spontaneous drama to promote self-expression and growth. Over time, the orientation became increasingly psychoanalytic, emphasizing the unconscious symbolism of drama and play. Irwin integrates core concepts of psychoanalysis (resistance, transference-countertransference, and interpretation) into her drama therapy sessions (Lewis & Johnson, 2000).

Gertrud Schattner (1981) used drama therapy techniques with concentration camp survivors after

World War II. Although she studied with the psychoanalyst Karen Horney, she remained loyal to her previous profession as an actress and was fiercely committed to the union of psychology and theatre. Schattner was instrumental in making drama therapy a recognized profession in the United States.

The dedication and impassioned belief of these psychology and theatre pioneers has led to the formation of a professional identity. New vocabulary was created to describe drama therapy principles and theoretical models. As in any therapy, drama therapy required a way to evaluate progress, and to assess the client's self-growth and improved ability to function. Jones (1996) has developed a comprehensive definition of drama therapy by breaking its underlying themes into nine core processes:

1. Dramatic Projection is a technique that allows the client to project his or her inner feelings and issues onto a role or object.
2. Therapeutic Performance Process is the therapeutic use of a theatrical performance to work through specific themes and issues.
3. Dramatherapeutic Empathy and Distancing is the ability to engage or disengage from personal problems and inner conflicts.
4. Personification and Impersonation describes two different dramatic forms in which the client expresses his or her personal material in the form of a role-play or an object.
5. Interactive Audience and Witnessing is the client, group, or therapist, in the role of the audience or witness.
6. Embodiment: Dramatizing the Body is the way a client physically expresses and encounters personal material.
7. Playing is the attitude of playfulness within the session, the delineation of the play space, and a developmental model of play as intrinsic for therapeutic change.
8. Life-Drama Connection is the process in which clients connect their personal problems or conflicts with their dramatic projection.
9. Transformation is inherent in many aspects of the theatrical structure (role-play, props, and audience) and in the goal and process of drama therapy (development of the client through personal transformations). (pp. 99–100).

Importance of Drama Therapy

From Jones's concept of impersonation, we can examine the idea of role in drama therapy. What roles do we play in our life? How do these roles limit us and influence our self-image? What are the roles we feel stuck in and what roles feel forbidden and terrifying? Robert Landy (1993) has written extensively about the importance of role in drama therapy. He created a therapeutic approach that uses role-play and a formal assessment of the client's role repertoire in normal life. Drawing on the role theories of Moreno (1993), Landy (1993) stresses the importance of identifying the client's internal cast of characters and bringing them out into the open. The goal is to help clients increase the number of roles in their repertoire so that they do not become stuck in one or two destructive or ineffective roles. In his view, the ability to move from one role to another is a sign of health and social adeptness. Drama therapy is distinct among other forms of therapy in that it proceeds through role. Both client and therapist take on and play out roles in order to help the client discover and/or recover the most functional role system (p. 45). However, Johnson (2000) uses the psychoanalytic concept of free association in his spontaneous improvisation between therapist and client to help the client work through their role limitations and difficult relationships.

Performance

Therapeutic performance process is another way to assess a client's progress in terms of self-image and ability to work in a group. How do the clients work together? What is their commitment to the group, the group process, and their individual character? What qualities and challenges do they identify with in their theatrical character? Mitchell (1990) proposes that drama therapy is an artistic inquiry in which clients gain the dramatic tools they need to work through their problems within a theatrical structure. Meldrum (1993) views the role of the drama therapist as an empathetic director who guides clients to take responsibility for their own lives through theatrical metaphors. Jenkins (1991) approaches a text, such as Shakespeare's *The Tempest*, as a projective or metaphorical technique. Group members explore their personal issues within the context of the characters and relationships in Shakespeare's play. For these thera-

pists, the client's commitment, engagement, and ultimate insights in relationship to the theatrical play are what are assessed and evaluated.

A different perspective, and one that can include all of Jones's 1996 core concepts, is to look through the prism of a developmental context. From this perspective, life is an ongoing journey through different developmental stages. It is the working and re-working of these life stages that is the central theme of the drama therapy. Pathology is a blockage or a halt in development to be assessed and worked with creatively (Lewis & Johnson, 2000). Lewis (2000) describes the need for drama therapists to work with unresolved childhood themes. "Unresolved childhood dramatic themes and their prescribed roles interweave and repeatedly overlap, recreating the past as if it were the present. The work of the drama therapist is to not only view the fabric of the drama as a momentary gestalt, but also to identify the repetitive phenomena" (p. 129).

Dramatic Projection

Whether drama therapists evaluate progress by examining role repertoire, theatrical performance process, or development stage, there always remains the fundamental notion of dramatic projection. In clinical sessions, dramatic projection can take many forms: Role-play, masks, puppets, scene work, play, improvisation, artwork, or stories. These mediums provide an open representation that can be modified, witnessed, and addressed, and although kept at a distance, it still can be spoken to and listened to. The therapist follows the client's lead in relating the dramatic projection back to the client's own problem or inner conflict. The projection of difficult feelings onto an unthreatening object or role provides a safe way for the client to make hypothetical or imaginative changes to the projected form. Clients are the directors, the protagonists, the actors, and the mask makers. They have the opportunity to try out different roles, reactions, and solutions to their problems.

Working effectively with unconscious inner conflicts is challenging for all therapists. Often the client gets stuck in destructive emotional patterns, cannot access difficult feelings, circumvents the problem through intellectual justifications, or lacks the motivation to fundamentally change his or her behavior and relationships. Because of its inherently active and participatory approach, drama therapy can often engage such reluctant and "resistant" clients (Lewis & Johnson, 2000). Clients who refuse to confront their issues directly have an opportunity to work indirectly with a creative form such as a role or mask. Gradually, when they are ready, they can make a connection between the mask and their internal feelings. Resistance itself can be projected onto a dramatic form and worked with therapeutically. As Feldman and Jones (2000) assert, "in order to work through resistance, the therapist must join with it and enlist it into the therapeutic process. Thus, we employ various methods and techniques to "unwind" resistance in a playful, creative and supportive way" (Lewis & Johnson, 2000, p. 337).

Improvisation

Improvisation is such a method in drama therapy. A session begins with a warm-up, which helps the group or individual prepare for the dramatic activity. It also provides a way for clients to connect creatively with the current emotional state and spontaneously expresses this state through movement, sound, image, or improvisational play. Chesner (1995) writes that improvisation "provides a rough framework or starting point for action, and space for spontaneous input" (p. 68). As the warm-up continues, the thematic content from the group or individual emerges in a natural and organic way. These themes can be worked with during the main dramatic activity. The client learns through improvisational play that he or she can be flexible, spontaneous, and creative. These skills can subsequently be used when confronting life's challenges.

Course of Drama Therapy

When clients come to a drama therapy session, they bring underlying problems they want to work with. These problems may be clearly defined, such as a stressful job or family situation, or less defined emotions such as anxiety or desperation. The therapist and client begin an exploration to discover how to represent this problem in a dramatic medium. This is usually done either through impersonation (role-play, enactment through movement, sound, scene work) or personification (using objects such as puppets, toys, or material) to represent the feeling or problem. Once the medium is chosen and the dramatic projection begins, the therapist monitors the client's emotional engagement with his or her personal material. For a client who has difficulty in relationships and in feeling empathy for others, the development of an empa-

thetic response during dramatic work may encourage empathy in real-life interactions. On the other hand, for clients who are overwhelmed by emotional responses to situations or others, creating more emotional distance within the dramatic form can provide perspective on themselves and their issues.

Effective therapists offer their clients the right amount of safety or emotional distance. Landy (1993), Jones (1996), and Jennings (1994) describe three feeling states: under distance (when we feel overwhelmed by our feelings), over distance (when we are very removed from our feelings), and aesthetic distance (when there is a balance between the two). The goal in any therapy is to obtain aesthetic distance. The continual challenge for the therapist is how to maintain this balance so that the client feels safe while confronting difficult emotions. Inherent in drama therapy is an ability to monitor the feeling state through the degree of dramatic distance.

Drama therapy offers a unique opportunity for clients to have both a high degree of emotional empathy and a high degree of emotional distance. Through the dramatic medium clients can be inside a role as an actor, or outside it as a director or witness. They may use their own bodies as the dramatic medium or choose an object outside themselves. These dramatic possibilities permit the therapist and client to shift easily between the cognitive and the emotional.

One session might intensify the emotional engagement by an improvisational role-play, while another might encourage emotional distance by placing the client outside the role as director. As Jones (1996) states, "The Dramatherapist needs to consider the specific context – the client's needs at any particular point in an enactment and the relationship of an exercise or activity to the empathy/distancing phenomenon" (p. 106). All forms of drama therapy include this technique of shifting between empathy and distance. Whether in the context of a role-play, an improvisation, mask making, working with puppets or toys, directing or witnessing a scene, or writing a script, the therapeutic process continually shifts between empathy and distance.

The co-existence of both empathy and distance permits clients to discover their personal narrative and story. Drama therapy is unique among the creative arts therapies in that it uses all of the creative mediums to allow a detailed, nuanced, and infinitely variable development and expression of the narrative or story (Gersie & King, 1990). Despite their many approaches and techniques, all schools of drama therapy share the idea of the narrative in some form. The client's narrative guides the therapy, whether through spontaneous improvisations, structured enactment of family relationships, play therapy with puppets or figurines, or embodying different roles (Brooke, 2005). It is the expression, and ultimately the transformation, of the client's unconscious or hidden narrative that allows healing to take place.

Narrative

To illustrate the idea of dramatic projection and the use of the narrative in action, I will describe the use of myth and fairy tale in drama therapy. Bettelheim (1976) described the use of fairy tales as a way for children to confront and give form to archaic fears, anxieties, and longings, while May (1991) explained how myths form an essential component of an adult's sense of identity. Several drama therapists use myth and fairy tale as an integral part of the therapeutic process.

For Alida Gersie (1990), it is the story that is important, the rich tapestry of narrative that is encoded in traditional myths and legends. She believes that working with these stories helps to evoke memories, images, and eventually insights for her clients. Gersie (1997) selects stories from myths or fairy tales that she perceives as exemplifying themes emerging from her groups. She also encourages clients to relate their life experiences as stories. Her story-making structure contains a landscape, a dwelling place, a main character, an obstacle, a helpmate and, a resolution. Gersie's clients draw, act out, or tell a story. She listens to and observes the tone, message, as well as the content of the story and how it expresses of the client's personal struggles.

Jennings (1990) asks clients to create masks of different kinds as part of the therapeutic process; the masks are often fairy tale or mythic characters. For Jennings, (1990) the inherent aesthetic distance in theatre and drama is in itself therapeutic. She emphasizes the fictional and dramatic reality that she believes gives clients more options to deal with their real life situation. ". . . the nearer we work to a person's own life, i.e., the more proximity, the more limitations we impose on the exploration of their life story. The greater the dramatic distance we create, the greater the range of therapeutic choices available" (p. 111).

Snow (1991) focuses on the spontaneous mythic imagery of his psychotic patients. He views the process of psychosis as a rite of passage having an inherent mythic content. In his brief therapy with psychotic patients, Snow demonstrates how clients can embody mythological entities to represent their inner world and to help them navigate a distinction – between fantasy and reality.

Lahad (1992 has clients create myth-like stories as a way to assess and work with individuals coping with stress. He has developed a multi-modal approach that he believes reveals the underlying coping style of the client. Lahad's six-part story or BASIC Ph method is an acronym for the six underlying dimensions for coping with stress:

B – beliefs and values
A – affect
S – social mode
I – imagination
C – cognitive
Ph – physical

He is particularly interested in how the coping strategies of the client are expressed in each part of the narrative of his or her story making method.

My own work involves a different use of myth and fairytale. A key feature of it is that the client, rather than the therapist, selects the myth or fairy tale, character, and the specific dramatic situation or tension within the story to be worked on. In this process, each client works on his or her own personal story instead of working as a part of a group on a collective story. Unlike much of drama therapy, in which many roles are assumed, here the client takes on and moves deeply into one role for many weeks or months. In order to intensify identification with the story, clients are required to identify *one specific moment* in the chosen story that has special significance even though the reason for its importance remains obscure. During the sessions, clients move through different stages of creative process that frequently involve artistic media, such as mask making, artwork, movement, writing, and scene work. To establish a sense of distance and perspective the client directs other people (therapist, other members of a group) in dramatizations of his or her character. Throughout this process the client interprets the metaphors and symbols in the story within his or her own personal experience rather than within a Jungian or other established framework. It is the client's personal and unique relationship to the story that is emphasized and explored.

> Clients begin this process by carefully selecting a myth or fairytale that evokes a personal, although still not understood, sense of relevance to their central psychological issue. The process of discovering why this story is interesting and important represents the central activity of this therapeutic method. (Silverman, 2004, p. 3)

The process of finding and working with the right story, character, and dramatic moment provides a safe container within which to connect the challenge in the story with the client's own personal problem.

After choosing the story and character, the client embarks on the task of invoking and embodying the role. Through this process the client identifies with, and develops a deep relationship with, a single character. This makes the personal projection onto the character particularly intense and creates a setting in which the client can identify uncomfortable feelings without being threatened. There is also reassurance – here is a character that feels the same way he or she does.

Clients move through specific stages and exercises aimed to connect the challenge facing the client's mythical character and his/her own personal problem.

1. choosing the story, character, and dramatic moment;
2. becoming the character (creating a mask, costume, environment);
3. interacting with characters created by other group members;
4. facing the edge or obstacle in the chosen story;
5. directing someone else in the role of the character;
6. creative transformation (an artistic expression of the client's journey with his or her character).

These stages evoke an evolving relationship between the client and the therapist, the client and the other group members, the client and the chosen character, the client and the artistic creations, and ultimately, the client and his or her own personal story. This internal story, the one that is hidden, buried, and hardest to access, is gradually revealed. In the process of creatively and emotionally engaging with their character's problem and challenges, clients begin to see perspectives from the character's point of view. They form an intimate relationship with their chosen character and all of his or her complexities of behavior, motivations, and challenges. This process is almost always intense and deeply emotional. Clients come to live the reality of their character's journey and find themselves confronting their character's trauma or deepest fear which they gradually realize is their own (Silverman, 2004).

CONCLUSION

The aim of all drama therapists is to connect the fictional dramatic projection with the client's real-life situation. Drama therapists have developed a unique approach to clinical work bringing creativity, spontaneous dramatic play, improvisation, dramatic projection, the narrative, and a balance between empathy and distancing, into the therapeutic process. These tools provide an effective way to engage "resistant" clients who are often unable to access, articulate, or engage with their personal issues. Drama therapists are employed in hospitals, clinics, schools, and community centres around the world where they often see clients who have not responded to traditional verbal therapy. These clients are unable to discuss their problems or gain insight through discussion alone. Having the distance of working through a dramatic medium often allows these clients a way to gain insight and perspective.

Drama therapists view health as the capacity to continually adapt and respond throughout one's life span and to be able to be playful, creative, and spontaneous. Healthy individuals have a realistic sense of self and a varied and flexible role repertoire. They exhibit appropriate empathy and respect for themselves and others, and can develop intimate and positive relationships. Born from two powerful and dynamic parents, psychology and theatre, drama therapy uses the skills and concepts from both to offer a unique and effective form of therapy which can reveal and ultimately transform the hidden narrative or story.

REFERENCES

Bettelheim, B. (1976). *The uses of enchantment*. New York: Knopf.

Boal, A. (1979). *Theatre of the oppressed.* New York: Urizen Books.

Brooke, S.L. (2005). Metaphors as teaching tools for abnormal psychology. *Journal for Student Centered Learning,* (3), in print.

Campbell, J. (1968). *The hero with a thousand faces,* (2nd ed.). Princeton, NJ: Princeton University Press.

Chesner, A. (1995). *Dramatherapy for people with learning disabilities: A world of difference.* London: Jessica Kingsley.

Feldman, D., & Jones, S. F. (2000). Unwinding resistance and externalizing the unspoken: The enact method in the schools. In Lewis & Johnson (Eds.). *Current approaches in drama therapy.* (pp. 331–345). Springfield, IL: Charles C Thomas, Publisher, Ltd.

Gersie, A. (1997). *Reflections on therapeutic storymaking: The use of stories in groups.* London: Jessica Kingsley.

Gersie, A., & King, N. (1990). *Storymaking in education and therapy.* London: Jessica Kingsley.

Irwin, E. (2000). Psychoanalytic approach to drama therapy. In Lewis & Johnson (Eds.). *Current approaches in drama therapy.* (pp. 27–49). Springfield, IL: Charles C Thomas, Publisher, Ltd.

Irwin, E. & Malloy E. (1975). Family puppet interview. *Family practice. 14*(2) pp. 179–191

Jenkins, M., & Barham, M. (1991). *BADth Application to join the council for professions supplementary to medicine on behalf of the profession of drama therapy.* BADth

Jennings, S. (1990). Masking and unmasking: the interface of dramatherapy. In Jennings, S. *Drama therapy with families, groups, and individuals.* (pp. 108–128) London: Jessica Kingsley.

Jennings, S., Cattanach, A., Mitchell, S., Chesner, A., & Meldrum, B. (1994). *The handbook of dramatherapy.* London: Routledge.

Johnson, D. (1992). Developmental transformations: Toward the body as presence. In Lewis & Johnson (Ed.). *Current approaches in drama therapy* (pp. 87–110). Springfield, IL: Charles C Thomas, Publisher, Ltd.

Jones, P. (1996). *Drama as therapy – theatre as living.* London: Routledge.

Landy, R. (1993). *Persona and performance: The meaning of role in drama therapy, and everyday life.* New York: The Guilford Press.

Lahad, M. (1992). *Dramatherapy theory and practice 2.* London: Tavistock/Routledge.

Lewis, P. (2000). The developmental themes approach in drama therapy. In Lewis & Johnson (Eds.). *Current approaches in drama therapy* (pp. 129– 161). Springfield, IL: Charles C Thomas, Publisher, Ltd.

Mahler, M. (1963). Thoughts about development and individuation. *Psychoanalytic study of the child, 18,* 307–342.

May, R. (1975). T*he courage to create.* New York: Norton.

May, R. (1991). *The cry for myth.* New York: Bantam Doubleday Dell Publishing Group.

Meldrum, B. (1993). A theatrical model of drama therapy. *Drama Therapy, 14*(2) 10–13.

Mitchell, S. (1990). The theatre of Peter Brook as a model for drama therapy. *Drama Therapy, 13*(1).

Mitchell, S. (1994). The theatre of self-expression: A therapeutic theatre model of dramatherapy. In Jennings, S., Cattanach, A., Mitchell, S., Chesner, A., & Meldrum, B. (Eds.). *The handbook of dramatherapy.* (pp. 41–57) London: Routledge.

Moreno, J. L. (1993). *Who shall survive?* (Student edition). Roanoke, VA: Royal Publishing Co.

Schattner, G., Courtney, R. (1981). *Drama in therapy.* New York : Drama Book Specialists.

Silverman, Y. (2004). The story within – myth and fairy tale in therapy. *The Arts in Psychotherapy, 31*(3), 127–135

Snow, S. (1996). Focusing on mythic imagery in brief dramatherapy with psychotic individuals. In Gersie, A. (Ed.). *Dramatic approaches to brief therapy.* London: Jessica Kingsley.

Stanislavsky, C. (1961). *Creating a role.* New York: Routledge, Chapman and Hall Inc.

Winnicott, D. W. (1971). *Playing and reality.* New York: Penguin Books.

Yalom, I.D. (1985). *The theory and practice of group psychotherapy.* (3rd ed.). New York: Basic Books.

Biographical Statement

Yehudit Silverman M.A., DTR, RDT, is a registered Dance Movement Therapist and a registered Drama Therapist and assistant professor in the Creative Arts Therapies Graduate Program, Concordia University, Montreal, Quebec. In this position she teaches, supervises, is practicum coordinator for all Drama Therapy students, and has developed an arts-based research component. Ms. Silverman created a technique called The Story Within – Myth and Fairytale in Therapy, which is described in her article published in the *Arts in Psychotherapy* journal. She recently completed a documentary film based on this approach, which was shown at the 2004 NADT conference. In clinical practice for twenty years, she has worked at several Montreal hospitals and has presented at conferences internationally. As a professional performer in theatre and dance, she has created her own solo and group shows in Canada and the United States, most recently appearing in a solo performance of the stage and film versions of McGill University's Music Alive production of *JACK*.

Yehudit Silverman DTR, RDT
Assistant Professor
Creative Arts Therapies Graduate Program
Concordia University
1455 de Maisonneuve Blvd. W.

Montreal, Quebec, Canada H3G 1M8
tel: (514) 848-2424 ext. 4231
fax: (514) 848-4969
yehudit@vax2.concordia.ca

Chapter 24

THE USE OF ROLE-PLAY AS AN ASSESSMENT INSTRUMENT

TED RUBENSTEIN

INTRODUCTION

Although words sometimes fail us, we use words to know each other. We use words to discipline our children, express love for each other, vent our anger, and negotiate our daily business. Words cannot capture the depth of the experience of being human, but without words, we might live in isolation. Words fail and yet there are few other ways to know another. Therein lies a paradox. For the field of psychology, the core work is to understand the client, but an overwhelming majority of therapists rely on the most vague, most deceptive, and least descriptive way of one's own words. How else are we to understand the felt experience of another person? Sometimes role-play can help. Role-play has been widely used as a training tool In the cognitive behavioral literature, role-play is discussed as a viable strategy for practicing and demonstrating coping skills (Mahoney, 1991; Neimeyer, 1995). Role-play techniques are also widely cited as suitable training techniques in the business community (Dallimore & Souza, 2002; Edelstein & Armstrong, 1993; May & Kahnweiler, 2000).

By comparison, the use of role-play as a diagnostic instrument is not frequently cited in the scientific literature. The reasons for this will be discussed below. This chapter will operationalize the behavior of role-play from several theoretical perspectives. Based on the definition of role-play that is offered, the author will provide an overview of the various ways role-play has been used as an assessment tool. Finally, this chapter will discuss the psychometric and statistical challenges one is likely to encounter when using role-play as an assessment tool.

Psychological assessment is a process by which information is gathered about an individual or group of individuals. This information is collected, synthesized, and interpreted by a clinician. The clinician then uses the data from an assessment to provide a client or individual with a diagnosis or a hypothesis about a particular problem or recommendation for further treatment. Sattler (1988) has described this process as the four pillars of assessment: (a) norm-referenced tests, (b) interviews, (c) observations, and (d) informal assessments. This chapter will be primarily concerned with role-playing assessments that are either norm referenced or informal.

Formal assessments or norm-referenced are those tools that have been standardized using a large, clearly defined group of people. This group becomes the norm group. The assessment tool is scaled in such a way that any individual score can reflect a rank within that norm group (Sattler, 1988). The tool is then administered to other individuals using standard conditions, standard procedures, and interpreted based on the standard scores. Norm-referenced tests are invaluable to clinicians as they provide rich information about an individual's functioning, intellectual capacity, or coping skills. On the other hand, such tests are mere snapshots in time and can only suggest the way an individual functions by comparison to the norm group. Norm-referenced tests provide limited information about the psychological processes or ways to understand the specific problems of a specific individual. This is why multiple tools or pillars of assessment are necessary (Sattler, 1988). This is what Brooke (2004) terms a battery of assessments.

Informal assessments are those tools that are not norm-referenced but are criterion related. Such tools are created by the clinician in response to the specific needs of the client at a specific time. Informal assessments do not have norm references or any scaled scores. Such tools are only modestly standardized and present the clinician with unknown quantities of reliability and validity. On the other hand, such tools can be rich sources of information about an individual. Moreover, an informal assessment is a highly appropriate strategy in understanding how an individual processes information, experiences the world, or understands an experience. When surveying the land of formal and informal assessments, it is important that the clinician not place a value judgment or conclude that formal is better or worse than informal.

Role-playing assessments tend to be neither formal nor informal but rather inhabit a void area. Role-playing assessments are not quite able to exert the technical rigor enjoyed by the intellectual and some of the personality assessments. At the same time, researchers in the field of role-play assessment continue to struggle with finding ways to standardize role-playing tools without eroding the very spontaneity that role-play offers. This dialectic between formal and informal assessment as it applies to role-play tests will be addressed throughout the chapter.

In the following pages, the reader will be introduced to formal or partially formal assessments such as the Diagnostic Role-Playing Test and the Impro-I. The reader will also be introduced to some of the ways clinicians have attempted to create unique, individualized informal tests.

Origins of Role-Play

Freud (1900/1933) first said that the interpretation of dreams is the royal road to the unconscious. Melanie Klein (1955) extrapolated Freud's idea to suggest that for children, play was the royal road to the child's unconscious. From this we can assume that the myriad of stories, enactments, imaginary worlds, and make-believe of child's play form a sort of window into the child's inner wishes, drives, and concerns. It is this assumption that forms the foundation of the Thematic Apperception Test (TAT). Can an individual's imagination tell us about whom that person wants to become? If one's imagination is a window, then what of a person's enactments or role-plays? Is it possible that stories built from role-

plays or vice-versa can provide an x-ray with more depth and dimension?

Shakespeare wrote in his play, *All's Well that Ends Well*, "All the world's a stage, and all the men and women merely players: They have their exits and their entrances; and one man in his time plays many parts" (1598/1988, p. 34). As the metaphor offered by Shakespeare suggests, humans take on roles that are mediated by temporal and social contexts. With the development of society came certain norms of public behavior. These public expectations, or norms, are contradicted or confirmed by the individual's internal experience. However, as one begins to engage the society, a contradiction may arise between one's internal experience and the expectations of society. To reconcile these contradictions, an individual might begin to alter his or her behavior based on the external expectations imposed by the society that surrounds that individual. To play a role as described by Shakespeare then implies that one is in some way responding to and engaging with the environment. Put simply, people know us by the roles we play and we know which roles to play by the people we encounter.

The term role-play carries with it many connotations. Children commonly refer to role-play as pretend or make-believe. A child's act of role-play can be as grand as imagined trips into outer space or as simple as pretending to carry out the tasks of daily living, marriage, and child-rearing. Children will create characters and story lines that capture their fantasies, wishes, or expectations for the future. In so doing, children act upon the world and begin to master their internal and external experience (Singer & Singer, 1990).

Defining Role-Play

The *American Heritage Dictionary* (2000) defines role as, "a character, or part played by a performer, the characteristic and expected social behavior of an individual, a function or position" (p. 595). Additionally, the *American Heritage Dictionary* (2000) defines role-play as, "to assume or represent in a drama, to assume or act out a particular role" (p. 595). The word, role, comes from the Old French term, rôle, which meant parchment or paper, because in the theatrical presentations during the Middle Ages, the play script was written on parchment. Role is best described by its functional use or purpose. The functions of role-play that can be categorized as follows: (a) aesthetic, (b) sociodramatic, (c) social presentation, (d) making meaning of the self in social context, and (e) specific clinical applications.

Aesthetic role-play occurs when a trained actor creates a character as defined by the words and behavior found in the text of a play. In theatrical parlance, the actor strives to become the character or role but this is only accomplished after weeks or months of study of the theatrical text from which the character derives and in collaboration with other actors, theatrical directors, designers and, in some cases, the playwright (Stanislavski, 1949; 1987). The resulting role-play is then presented to an audience for the purposes of entertainment or artistic accomplishment for which the actor receives some form of monetary compensation or derives artistic satisfaction. Thousands of films and plays are produced each year in which tens of thousands of actors create thousands of roles to audiences of billions (Dow Jones & Company, 2002). To be sure, this kind of role-play is a cultural mainstay of contemporary life.

A second kind of role-play is called sociodramatic play or what children might call make-believe. In this activity, children enact characters and situations. This can be done alone or while interacting with other children. For children, this pretense play begins to emerge at about 18 months and reaches its peak at about 5 years of age (Santrock, 1983; Singer & Singer, 1990). Developmentally, this behavior is preceded by the emergence of symbolic play (Piaget, 1945/1962). The child begins to play symbolically by first allowing one object to stand for another. In this activity of object substitution, the child begins to transform and transcend immediate reality (Westby, 1991). The development of symbolic play is marked by the acquisition of discrete skill sets: (a) de-contextualization, (b) object substitution, (c) introduction of thematic content, and (d) the organization of self-other relationships (Piaget, 1962). As the elements of symbolic play become more complex, the child will develop the ability to engage in a fully invested sociodramatic play. The shift from symbolic play into sociodramatic play is marked by the addition of: (a) plot, (b) prop, and (c) role (Garvey, 1977).

The functions of role-play as a definition of self and as a form of social presentation are in some ways two sides of the same coin. Moreno (1960) defined role as the actual, tangible form that the self takes. According to Moreno, the self is known and is understood by the roles that are played.

Using Moreno's definition, the role is the smallest unit of expression of the self. Each role becomes an aspect of self, which later is amalgamated into a meaningful whole (Doyle, 1998; Landy, 1996). As Doyle (1998) states, "roles depict the myriad of pieces of the reality of who we are" (p. 225).

Borrowing a concept from the aesthetic form of role-play, an actor can only play those parts that live within the actor (Stanislavski, 1936; 1948). The same can be said of human experience. The most convincing role-plays are those in which the role demands are congruent with the person's beliefs (Sarbin & Allen, 1968). When the demands of a role and self-beliefs are incongruent, the roles that are played are hollow and unconvincing (Middleton, 1978). Sarbin and Allen suggest that the engagement and investment of role lies on a continuum. On one end of the continuum is a kind of noninvolvement in which self and roles are completely differentiated. At the other end of the continuum is a sort of bewitchment in which the role and self are fused. For example, a successful executive fuses roles when he behaves towards his family the same way he would behave towards his staff.

A role can also be viewed as a sociological construct in which an individual engages in a set of behaviors assigned by society (Mead, 1954). The self is a construction of a social process that in turn reflects the values of the larger societal context (Doyle, 1998). The individual, functioning in this context, plays roles based on the cues and actions of the others. Role becomes dependent upon other individuals involved in the social transaction of which the result is a presentation of self, or role, to the world.

This self-presentation or role is discussed at length in Erving Goffman's (1959) book, *The presentation of self in everyday life*. According to Goffman, people engage in two kinds of communication: expressions given and expressions given off. It is the communications given off that constitute the presentation of the individual. These impressions become social roles or parts that are performed based on the environmental context. Self, therefore, is a dramatic effect drawn from the set of roles that are presented. According to Goffman (1959), "all the world is not, of course, a stage, but the crucial ways in which it isn't are not easy to specify" (p. 72).

Finally, role-play can be used in a therapeutic endeavor to assess for specific problems, teach skills, or practice coping strategies. When role-play is used for a therapeutic purpose, it is referred to as drama therapy (Landy, 1996), psychodrama (Kedem-Tahar & Felix-Kellerman, 1996), or simply as role-play.

The use of role-play as a form of treatment dates as far back as the early part of the twentieth century when Moreno (1960) began using drama in spontaneous play groups for the purpose of health and healing. He termed this process psychodrama. In Moreno's psychodramatic approach, the focus is on the individual's reenactment of critical moments in life or internal conflicts. One's ability to be spontaneous was a keen interest of Moreno's and essential to the technique of psychodrama. The theory of psychodrama states that much, if not all, of psychopathology is the result of replaying old patterns in new relationships (Kipper, 1988). In psychodrama, the client is asked to enact memories of specific happenings, unfinished business, or to prepare, in the context of role, for future situations. These enactments either approximate the real-life situation or are the externalization of the imaginary internal process (Kedem-Tahar & Felix-Kellerman, 1996).

Role-playing in a clinical context has also been used as a behavioral simulation of a real or imagined event. The individual, when playing a role, identifies with another person, real or not, and then assumes the attitudes and characteristic modes of behavior for that other person (Schwebel, 1953). Kipper and Har-Even (1984) define these simulations as either spontaneous behavior or mimetic replication of behavior. As defined by Kipper and Har-Even, role behavior is a spontaneous, freely associated response to a simulated environment. Mimetic pretend behavior is the replication or imitation of behavior based on models or a combination of models.

In this context, role-plays are analogues that replicate a specific environment or a set of anticipated circumstances. The subject in a role-play imagines being in a prescribed environmental situation and then carries out behaviors that are in congruence with the demands of that situation (McReynolds & De Voge, 1977). The individual may be asked to take an unfamiliar role or to assume an *everyday* role but react to a novel set of circumstances (Mann, 1956). The individual is asked to respond as if a set of interactions or events were transpiring even though these interactions are not taking place.

Historically, the interest in role-play as an assessment tool coincides with an interest in the way in which people function in social situations. In the late 1950s and throughout the 1960s, research in the area of the social life of humans began to include processes and behaviors such as assertiveness, attachment, obedience, and the ability to make friends (Bellak, Hersen, & Turner, 1979). Many of these behaviors were studied using role-play based assessments. In attempting to define social competence, many researchers reached the conclusion that social competence is a complex set of behaviors that include eye contact, speech patterns, facial expression, and physical gesture (Kazdin, Matson, & Esveldt-Dawson, 1984; Williamson, 1983). In order to understand how these behaviors interact to form the construct of social competence, both molar and molecular levels of analysis were necessary (Bilodeau & Bilodeau, 1969). Role-play as an assessment tool held promise as an appropriate and powerful way of analyzing social behavior at the molecular level (Kazdin et al., 1984). Role-play offered the opportunities to create analogues of social interactions, while at the same time providing experimental control not available in naturalistic observations (Hughes, Boodoo, Alcala, & Maggio, 1989). Asking clients to self-monitor in real social situations, over extended periods was thought to be unrealistic and even counterproductive to achieving a level of social competence (Kern, 1991). Role-play was thought to be the best of both worlds, experimental control in a nearly natural setting (Hughes et al., 1989). As will be discussed in later sections, the use of role-play as an assessment tool did not deliver what had been promised. Herein lies the paradox. Social interaction is so complex that it is hard to recreate the various elements that might be main effects within a laboratory setting, making role-play a poor substitute for what might really happen in-vivo.

Role-Play as an Assessment Tool

In considering the breadth of role-playing assessments, it might be useful to consider a circle, divided from top to bottom and left to right. The line that separates the circle from top to bottom is a continuum of scripted to unscripted activity. This means that some role-play assessments are based on carefully written text assigned to each participant; these are called scripted. Conversely, unscripted role-plays are those in which one word or gesture serves as a starting point but what unfolds after that is improvisational, spontaneous, and idiosyncratic to the participants.

The line that cuts the circle from left to right is also a continuum of engagement or participation from the individual being evaluated. One end of the continuum can be called passive; the other end can be called active. Passive participation would mean that the individual is read to or presented with a scene or a role-play and then that individual is asked to respond to what was observed. Conversely, active participation implies that the individual being evaluated is asked to enact a role, either using a script or creating the script in the moment. Specific examples and the supporting research are discussed below. A diagrammatic representation is presented in Figure 23.1.

In role-play based assessments that fall within the scripted/passive quadrant, an individual or group of individuals watch videotaped or live scenes performed by trained or amateur actors. At the conclusion of the role-play, the audience may be asked to respond to the role-play. The comments made during the post-enactment discussion

or the reactions of the individuals as they watched the role-play become the assessment data. In one study, for example, college age students were asked to view a scene that represented typical peer interactions. The students were then presented with a response to this interaction and asked to rate the effectiveness of this response. The students' ratings served as an indicator of their ability to effectively assess and make decisions about appropriate social interactions (Hughes et al., 1989).

In another example, live theatrical performance was used to help counselors and school personnel identify at-risk youth in a program called the *Music Theatre Workshop – Under Pressure*, based in Chicago (Harding, Gibb, Kavanagh, & Bania, 1996). In this program, actors enacted various scenes about at-risk behavior such as drug use, unsafe sexual behaviors, and gang violence before an adolescent audience. After the short scenarios were presented, a group discussion ensued with professional counselors observing and documenting the reactions of the students. Based on comments from the audience and the counselors' observations, certain students were identified as potentially at-risk for the same behaviors that were shown in the role-play enactments (Harding et al., 1996). Social learning theory underpins the approach taken in this model and would suggest that observing the actions of another can evoke strong feelings and powerful internal experiences (Bandura, 1977; Davies, 1972).

Another set of role-play based assessments on the matrix mentioned above are those role-plays that are unscripted but ask little or relatively little in the way of participation. Structurally, these role-plays would resemble a number of popular television and theatrical productions that are referred to as *improv comedy or sketch comedy*. While this form remains quite popular in the mainstream culture, it is infrequently used in clinical settings and there is scant literature suggesting its use as a form of assessment. This type of role-play has been widely used in socio-political contexts to illuminate and identify the suffering of impoverished and oppressed people throughout the world (Boal, 1976; 1997).

The scripted/active quadrant in the matrix includes those role-play based assessments that are scripted but require active involvement from all the individuals involved in the activity. In these sorts of assessments, the individual is given a complete scene or portions of a scene and then asked to play one of the roles with either the researcher or

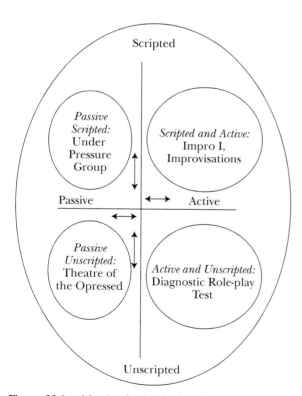

Figure 23.1.   Matrix of role-play based assessments.

another volunteer (Chiauzzi, Heimberg, Becker, & Gansler, 1985; Stanton, Back, & Litwak, 1956; Van Hasselt, Hersen, & Bellack, 1981). In these types of role-play based assessments, two kinds of data that are gathered are the subjective experience of the individual while engaged in role-play and the verbal and nonverbal responses (Chiauzzi et al., 1985; McReynolds & DeVoge, 1977; Williamson, 1983).

An example of a scripted, active role-play assessment in which the salient data set is the subjective experience of the participant can be found in a procedure developed by Kern (1991). Children were asked to recall a specific event that related to a type of interaction, such as "someone borrows something from you that you need or do not want to lend" (Kern, 1991, p. 19). After the child verbally recreated the details of this event from his or her experience, the event is recreated into a script. The child and one of the investigators then enact this script. If the child felt that the role-play was not an accurate portrayal, then it was replayed until the child was satisfied. This entire procedure was referred to as *The Idiographic Role-play Test*.

In some cases, the response to a scripted role-play is the salient data set. For example, during World War II, the Office of Strategic Services, a branch of the United States Army, turned to a psychologist at Harvard University for help in developing a set of assessments that would identify which soldiers would be able to withstand the stress of special missions behind enemy lines. That Harvard professor was Henry Murray, the author of the TAT (McReynolds & DeVoge, 1977). Under Murray's leadership, a team of psychologists developed a battery of tests that recreated stressful situations and then observed how candidates for these covert missions would respond to each situation. One of the subtests in this battery was entitled *Improvisations*. In this subtest, a series of one hundred and eleven scripts were written that involved quandaries of leadership. An individual would be asked, in role, to make decisions that would reflect on their overall management abilities and fitness for combat. Observers would make notes about the various leadership styles and the interpersonal relationships that were observed (Bronfenbrenner & Newcomb, 1948; McReynolds & DeVoge, 1977).

Impro-I

Inspired by the work of Murray, McReynolds and DeVoge (1977) developed a test entitled *The*

Improvisation Test for Individuals (Impro-I). In this test, several lines of dialogue are read to an individual and then the individual is asked to improvise the rest of the scene with an investigator. The individual's performance is evaluated based on the effectiveness of interpersonal style (McReynolds & DeVoge). This particular tool, while useful in creating heuristics about interpersonal style, was not able to establish a norm-reference partially because each response became idiosyncratic. Over time, this particular test also demonstrated validity issues because the construct of interpersonal style was difficult to rationalize. Moreover, tools such as the MMPI and the Meyers-Briggs became more reliable from a psychometric perspective (Groth-Marnat, 1990).

Almost functioning as a bridge between scripted and unscripted role-play, assessments that require active involvement by all participants, is a study conducted by Van Hasselt and colleagues (1981). In examining social competence, the researchers used scripted, partially scripted, and improvised role-plays within the same study. This study was not necessarily intended to compare forms of role-plays, but the results seemed to indicate that the partially scripted and partially improvised role-play activities yielded the richest data (Van Hasselt et al., 1981).

The last set of role-play assessments encompasses those instruments that are unscripted and require active involvement on the part of the researcher and the individual or group being studied. In this set of role-play assessments, the data being gathered includes: (a) verbal and nonverbal responses; (b) specific problem-solving strategies; (c) external reactions to novel situations; (d) subjective experiences of playing a role; (e) subjective experiences of reflecting on the role-played in comparison to real life; and (f) changes in behavior after the role-playing experience (Gallassi & Gallassi, 1976; McReynolds & DeVoge, 1977).

Some notorious examples of role-plays that are unscripted but require active participation are those studies in which individuals being observed are not entirely aware of the fact that they are role-playing. This lack of awareness or deception has been used in several famous or infamous studies such as the Stanford Prison Experiment and studies on the behavior of obedience and authority (Haney, Banks, & Zimbardo, 1973). These studies did not employ role-play as a form of assessment but rather as a part of the experience. These studies exemplify extreme examples of using a role-play experience in which one or more individuals participating in the study are unaware of the pretense or fictional elements of the situation.

There are other examples of unscripted and active participation that are more ethically sound in which the participant was aware of the role-playing activity. Swink and Buchanan (1984) used a sociodramatic method of role-play in which children were exposed to various role-plays that reflected situations that were socially awkward or difficult, such as being the new student or relating to authority figures. After the role-play, the group talked about their experience and all participants were offered an opportunity to replay the scenes. The way in which each individual chose to alter his or her behavior after the group discussions served as an indicator of problem-solving skills.

Higgins, Alonso, and Pendelton (1979) conducted experiments on assertive behavior in college students. Students who participated in this study were to receive extra credit in their undergraduate psychology course. When the student arrived, a confederate, male or female depending on the experimental group to which the student was assigned, was told that one of the examiners was running late. As the hour progressed the same confederate came into the room and said that they would run the experiment as if the other examiner were present. The student was presented with a series of social situations and asked to respond, although each student was reminded that the real examiner was not present. After these role-plays were complete, the student was told that the assignation of credit was in question. The student's response to this fabricated dilemma and each individual's ability to assert his or her needs was the focus of the study (Higgins et al., 1979).

To be sure, these studies and the more controversial ones mentioned above represent the far corners of the unscripted and active quadrant on the role-playing matrix. There are many examples of role-play assessment in which the content and process are completely unscripted and the participants are fully engaged, while at the same time all participants are aware of the fictional and pretend nature of the interaction.

Johnson and Quinlan (1980) examined the way in which individuals diagnosed with schizophrenia enacted scenes derived from a role-playing activity in order to study interpersonal relationships among a patient population. In this assessment,

participants were asked to enact ten different scenarios that represented various social roles that one might encounter in everyday life. The responses were analyzed with respect to the ways in which the patients maintained boundaries between the roles and the patient's everyday presentation. Two scales were created, the Fluid Boundary Scale and the Rigid Boundary Scale. Johnson and Quinlan (1980) measured boundary maintenance by observing a number of behaviors during the role-plays. These behaviors were defined as: (a) breaking role; (b) intrusion into role; (c) bizarre elaboration; (d) merging real life with the role's actions; (e) fusion of roles; (f) perseveration; and (g) speaking in the third person (Johnson & Quinlan, 1980). The investigators found that those individuals who were floridly psychotic also showed poor boundaries in the role-play. When comparing the data from the role-playing activity to each patient's records, a marked consistency was found between the progression of negative symptoms and lower scores on the ability to maintain role boundaries as defined by this study (Johnson & Quinlan, 1980).

Building on this work with role-play assessments, David Read Johnson (1988) developed an assessment called the *Diagnostic Role-playing Test*. He identified this as a projective test that can provide insight into the individual's inner world and identify symbolic modes of expression. In this test, the individual was asked to enact five social roles, one at a time. The roles identified in the test were: grandpa, bum, politician, teacher, and lover. These roles were selected based upon ratings of undergraduate students from a selection of 100 possible social roles. Those roles that were selected were believed to emphasize a particular dimension of social interaction such as, nurturance, control, sexuality, and personal competence. The individual was asked to enact each of these roles alone in an empty space based on the following directions (Johnson, 1988):

I am going to ask you to act out five separate roles, one at a time. In each case, show me what these people do. Make sure to try to act out as much about them as you can. Do them in any way, which you wish. You are free to choose whichever sex you want to be for each role. You may use any of the props you see here in any way that you wish, including talking on the telephone. On the table are the following items to be used as props: wastebasket, table, chair, stick, cloth, piece of paper, cup, book, hat, telephone, man's overcoat, woman's dress. Try not to plan out what you will do. Take your time and tell when you have finished. (p. 25)

The player is then asked to begin with the role of a grandfather. The scenes are stopped after about one minute and the next role is presented to the study participant. The session is videotaped and later assessed for spontaneity, ability to transcend reality, repertoire of role, organization of scenes, patterns in thematic content, and attitude toward enactment.

Role-playing has also been used as an initial assessment of one's ability to engage in the therapeutic process. Kelly (1955) defined a technique in which the client and therapist conjoin to re-write the roles that the client plays. In this approach, the client is asked to write a self-character sketch in the third person, which is then responded to by the therapist. The client is then asked to write the opposite of the character that the client has in mind, thus using fantasy as a means of initiating therapy.

Unstructured role-playing and puppetry have also been suggested as informal assessment tools to evaluate a client's ability to present and solve problems, tolerate frustration, or reflect on experiences (Irwin & Frank, 1977). For example, Halberstadt-Freud (1975) conducted a structured psychoanalytic psychotherapy with a four-year-old girl named Lara using dolls to create mini-plays that aided in his evaluation of her pathology. In this case, Halberstadt-Freud and Lara role-played and used dolls to create stories. Throughout the treatment process, the dolls were used as puppets or actors in her dramas and the clinician used the plot, roles assumed by the dolls, and eventual outcomes as guideposts to the progress of the therapy.

Psychometric Challenges of Role-Play Assessment

The literature on role-play assessments suggests that role-play is not as effective a tool as had been hoped (Kazdin, Esveldt-Dawson, & Matson, 1983; Kazdin et al., 1984; Michelson, DiLorenzo, Calpin, & Ollendick, 1982). Upon closer examination, it seems that the very processes that make role-play appealing as an assessment tool also create problems in relying on it as an assessment. Among the problems are generalizability, validity, and replicability.

Generalizability is contraindicated by definition because of the wide variations in response and interpretation that can be found when comparing even two individuals, let alone hundreds (McNamara & Blumer, 1982). Levenson and Herman (1991) draw the conclusion that for role-play to be an accurate portrayal of experience, then it must be idiosyncratic. If it is to be idiosyncratic, then generalization is contradictory to the aim of role-play. Mann and Borgatta (1959) studied the ecological validity of role-playing by comparing responses to role-play with projective tests and behavior in actual situations. The findings suggested that role-playing was related to projective techniques but not significantly related to actual behavior. In subsequent studies, the validity of role-playing when compared to real-life behaviors was more promising. However, the administration of role-play tests was so varied that these findings are suspect. Subsequent studies have found that role-play is a useful screening tool for identifying specific behaviors, but not at all effective as a predictor of in-vivo behaviors (Bellak et al., 1979). On the other hand, if an individual is asked to re-construct a specific set of events that occurred in real life and then a role-play is conducted based on these events, the ecological validity seems to improve (Swan & McDonald, 1978).

Experimenter effects also seem to hamper the effectiveness of role-play assessments. In two separate studies, people's behavior when engaging in a task that they know to be a pretense significantly differed from one's behavior when no pretense was implied (McNamara & Blumer, 1982). Another problem with generalizability is that if a role-playing task is created by an investigator and then given to a client, the client can be distracted from a here and now experience while focusing on the role-play. Simon and Smith (1985) make the argument that people can look like they are role-playing when in fact their behavior during testing is merely a function of the setting. There is even a risk that individuals create personal responses that match what the individual perceives as the intentions of the investigator. In other words, a person will act a particular way to get a presumed right answer, regardless of how that individual might really act in a similar situation that was not being evaluated by an investigator. It also seems that the more scripted the role-play activity, the less authentic the play. This would suggest that role-plays are most useful and telling when they are idiosyncratic and based on the singular experience of the individual engaged in the role-play (Kern et al., 1983).

Another recurring theme found in the literature on role-play assessment is the wide variability of procedures and methods thus complicating the ability to repeat the assessment. The wording of instructions and the nuances of modeling procedures have been shown to dramatically change results when using role-play assessments (Kipper & Har-Even, 1984).

Kern and Har-Even (1983) attempted to address this issue of methodology by applying a strict set of administration standards and then contrasting this with a more open-ended, idiosyncratic set of rules for role-plays. In the group where the administration of the role-playing exercise was standardized, there was significant improvement in criterion validity. The researchers also found that validity was increased by the specificity of the role-play scenarios that were selected. This finding would suggest that role-plays could be both structured, idiosyncratic, and still maintain their validity. The inter-rater reliability of these more structured but idiosyncratic role-plays was not analyzed and seems to be thinly addressed in the literature.

Similarly, Perri and Richards (1979) suggest a systemic approach to the development of role-playing assessments. The approach involves eight steps of scientific inquiry that take into account situational analysis, response evaluation, and scoring. Perri and Richards began by conducting a situation analysis of the various behaviors they sought to study, in this case hetero-social behavior. College age students volunteered to create lengthy diaries of their daily interactions. The researchers then analyzed these interactions and selected those that were problematic. These problematic interactions were given to a different set of students, all of whom read an account of these interactions. These students were asked to provide their personal responses to the situation. These responses were then presented to a third group of students who served as judges. Each student judge evaluated the effectiveness of each response. These responses were then converted into scripts that presented the circumstances of a particular situation, all of which included some problem in social interactions. A fourth set of students enacted these scripts with a trained volunteer playing one of the parts. These students would then be asked to complete the

interaction. The students in this final group were also given paper and pencil tests that measured assertiveness and social competence. The ways in which social problems were solved in role were compared to the way the students responded to written descriptions of social problems. The results suggested that this method of test development bolstered the validity of the entire assessment. The results of this study suggested that this approach to test development bolstered the validity of the role-playing assessment designed by Perri and Richards (1979). Another key finding from this study was that construct validity was far less important than inter-rater reliability in the development of role-play assessments. Perri and Richards (1980) caution that while the validity results were promising, the sample size was small and further research was required to assess the reliability of these results.

Conversely, Van Hesselt and colleagues (1981) found that inter-rater reliability in coding responses to role-playing tests was generally very strong, ranging from .78 to 1.00. They also found no significant differences between the ways in which the people behaved in the role-play and how they behaved when observed in naturalistic settings. What set this study apart was the fact that the role-plays were unscripted and therefore allowed for a more idiosyncratic response style (Van Hasselt et al., 1981).

Social skill performance can be significantly influenced by the instructional set, thus providing results that do not cohere with in-vivo experiences (Kazdin et al, 1983). It has been suggested that if a client believes that therapy will produce change, then the individual will begin to make change (Kirsh, 1976). The assumption therefore is that implicit and explicit messages are sent to the client about "healthy" behaviors (Horvath, 1984). If this is the case, the client plays a role of sorts, the role of the healthy client, and in so doing begins to infer and integrate desired behaviors. Elms (1966) identified that attitude changes were influenced by role-play and that empathic ability showed some relationship to role-playing tasks. On the other hand, given that instructional sets did seem to improve social skills exclusive to the laboratory setting, it is arguable that expectancies found in role-playing assessments can be useful for therapeutic change, just not assessment.

The issue here is that there are few notable examples of spontaneity as measured using role-playing. There are examples of the use of role-play being used to assess for certain dimensions of spontaneous behavior. For example, in studies looking at the way in which personal attitudes can be adjusted, it has been found that the more one becomes engaged in improvising an argument for or against a topic, the more deeply one becomes attached to that enactment and subsequently the more one can begin to adopt those same arguments (Sarbin & Allen, 1968). Such a finding does not entirely suggest that one has an ability to be spontaneous, but it does speak to one's ability to present novel behaviors in novel situations. It should be noted that one cannot adopt a new opinion about a topic if such an opinion involves attacking a strongly held truism or is antithetical to a strongly held belief.

CONCLUSION

In summary, role-play as an assessment tool shows some promising results for social skill assessments but has poor generalizability and weak validity. Role-play as an assessment of functional behavior is effective but also has psychometric challenges. Role-play as a detector of psychological disturbance has been used in some promising studies, but too few studies exist to provide any kind of normative database. In the area of personality functioning, role-playing also shows some interesting potential, but in most cases relies so heavily on idiosyncratic responses that the reliance on a clinician's judgment provides the field not much more than interesting hypotheses. While these criticisms may be accurate, they can also be said of many other psychological tests that rely on projection such as the TAT and the Rorschach (Exner, 1993; Watkins, Campbell, Nieberding, & Hallmark, 1995). Therefore, despite the methodological and validity problems of role-play assessments, their role in a psychological battery cannot be negated. While not discounted, the use of role-play has a checkered history and one that cries out for standardization.

REFERENCES

American Heritage Dictionary. (2000). Boston, MA: Houghton Mifflin.

Bandura, A. (1977). Social learning theory. Oxford, England: Prentice-Hall.

Bellak, A. S., Hersen, M., & Turner, S. M. (1979). Relationship with role-playing and knowledge of appropriate behavior to assertion in the natural environment. Journal of Consulting and Clinical Psychology, 47, 670–678.

Bilodeau, E. A., & Bilodeau, I. M. (1969). Principles of skill acquisition. Oxford, England: Academic Press.

Blake, D. D., & Andrasik, F. (1986). Between-measure consistency in social-skills assessment. Journal of Psychopathology & Behavioral Assessment, 8(3), 227–240.

Blass, T. (1999). The Milgram paradigm after 35 years: Some things we now know about obedience to authority. Journal of Applied Social Psychology, 29 (5), 955–978.

Blatner, A. (1985). The dynamics of catharsis. Journal of Group Psychotherapy, Psychodrama & Sociometry, 37, 157–166.

Boal, A. (1997). Theater of the oppressed. UNESCO Courier, 50(11), 32–37.

Boal, A. (1992). Games for actors and non-actors. (A. Jackson, trans.). New York: Routledge. (Original work published 1976).

Borgatta, E. F. (1951). An analysis of three levels of response: An approach to some relationships among dimensions of personality. Sociometry, 14, 267–316.

Bowers, P. & London, P. (1965). Developmental correlates of role-playing ability. Child Development, 36(2), 499–508.

Bronfenbrenner, U., & Newcomb, T. M. (1948). Improvisations – An application of psychodrama in personality diagnosis. Sociatry, 4, 367–382.

Brooke, S.L. (2004). A therapist's guide to art therapy assessments: Tools of the trade, (2nd ed.). with a foreword by Barry Cohen, ATR. Springfield, IL: Charles C Thomas, Publisher, Ltd.

Chiauzzi, E. J., Heimberg, R. G., Becker, R. E., & Gansler, D. (1985). Personalized versus standard role-plays in the assessment of depressed patients' social skill. Journal of Psychopathology & Behavioral Assessment, 7(2), 121–133.

Dallimore, E. J., & Souza, T. J. (2002). Consulting course design: Theoretical frameworks and pedagogical strategies. Business Communication Quarterly, 65(4), 86.

Davies, M. H. (1972). Social imitation: A neglected factor in psychotherapy? British Journal of Psychiatry, 121(562), 281–285.

Dow Jones and Company (2002). Gross Domestic Product for 2nd Quarter of 2002. Retrieved November 26, 2002, from onlinewsj.com/document/bbgdp.

Doyle, C. (1998). A self psychology theory of role in drama therapy. Arts in Psychotherapy, 25(4), 223–235.

Edelstein, B. C., & Armstrong, D. J. (1993). A model for executive development. Human Resource Planning, 16(4), 51.

Elms, A. C. (1966). Influence of fantasy ability on attitude change through role playing. Journal of Personality and Social Psychology, 4, 36–43.

Exner, J. E. (1993). *The Rorschach: A comprehensive system.* New York: John Wiley & and Sons.

Freud, S. (1933). The interpretation of dreams. In A.A. Brill (Ed. and Trans.). *The basic writings of Sigmund Freud.* New York: Modern Library (Original work published in 1900).

Gallassi, M.D., & Gallassi, J. P. (1976). The effects of role-playing variations on the assessment of assertive behavior. *Behavior Therapy, 7*(3), 343–347.

Garvey, C. (1977). *Play.* Cambridge, MA: Harvard University Press.

Goffman, E. (1959). *The presentation of self in everyday life.* New York: Doubleday.

Groth-Marnat, G. (1990). *Handbook of psychological assessment, Second Edition.* New York: Wiley-Interscience Publication.

Haney, C., Banks, C., & Zimbardo, P. (1973). Interpersonal dynamics in a simulated prison. *International Journal of Criminology & Penology, 1,* 69–97.

Harding, C., Gibb, S. L., Kavanagh, J., & Bania, R. (1996). Using live theatre combined with role-playing and discussion to examine what at-risk adolescents think about substance abuse, its consequences, and prevention. *Adolescence, 31*(124), 783–796.

Higgins, R. L., Alonso, R. R., & Pendleton, M. (1979). The validity of role-play assessments of assertiveness. *Behavior Therapy, 10,* 655–662.

Horvath, R. L., Alonso, R. R., & Pendleton, M. (1979). Demand characteristics and inferential processes in psychotherapeutic change. *Journal of Consulting and Clinical Psychology, 52,* 616–624.

Hughes, J. N., Boodoo, G., Alcala, J., & Maggio, M. (1989). Validation of a role-play measure of children's social skills. *Journal of Abnormal Child Psychology, 17*(6) 633–646.

Johnson, D. R. (1988). The Diagnostic Role-playing Test. *The Arts in Psychotherapy, 15*(1), 23–36.

Johnson, D., & Quinlan, D. M. (1980). Fluid and rigid boundaries of paranoid and non paranoid schizophrenics on a role-playing task. *Journal of Personality Assessment, 44*(5), 523–531.

Kazdin, A. E., Esveldt-Dawson, K., & Matson, J. L. (1983). The effects of instructional set on social skills performance among psychiatric inpatient children. *Behavior Therapy, 14*(3), 413–423.

Kazdin, A. E., Matson, J. L., & Esveldt-Dawson, K. (1984). The relationship of role-play assessment of children's social skills to multiple measures of social competence. *Behaviour Research & Therapy, 22*(2), 129–139.

Kedem-Tahar, E., & Felix-Kellerman, P. (1996). Psychodrama and drama therapy: A comparison. *The Arts in Psychotherapy, 23,* 27–36.

Kelly, G.A. (1955). *The psychology of personal constructs: Volume 1.* New York: W. W. Norton and Company.

Kern, J. M. (1991). An evaluation of a novel role-play methodology: The standardized idiographic approach. *Behavior Therapy, 22*(1), 13–29.

Kern, J. M., Miller, C., & Eggers, J. (1983). Enhancing the validity of role-play tests: A comparison of three role-play methodologies. *Behavior Therapy, 14*(4), 482–492.

Kipper, D. A. (1988). On the definition of psychodrama: Another view. *Journal of Group Psychotherapy, Psychodrama & Sociometry, 40,* 164–168.

Kipper, D. A. & Har-Even, D. (1984). Role-playing techniques: The differential effect of behavior simulation interventions on the readiness to inflict pain. *Journal of Clinical Psychology, 40*(4), 936–941.

Kirsh, B. (1996). A narrative approach to addressing spirituality in occupational therapy. Exploring personal meaning and purpose. *Canadian Journal of Occupational Therapy, 63*(1), 55–61.

Klein, M. (1955). The psychoanalytic play technique: Its history and significance, In M. Klein, P. Heimann & R.E. Money-Kyrle (Eds.). *New directions in psychoanalysis,* pp. 3–22. New York: Basic Books, Inc.

Landy, R. (1996). *Essays in drama therapy: The double life.* Bristol, PA: Jessica Kingsley Publishers.

Levenson, R. L., & Herman, J. (1991). The use of role-playing as a technique in the psychotherapy of children. *Psychotherapy: Theory, Research, Practice, and Training, 28,* 660–666.

Mahoney, M. J. (1991). *Human change processes: The scientific foundations of psychotherapy.* New York: Basic Books.

Mann, J. H. (1956). Experimental evaluations of role-playing. *Psychological Bulletin, 53,* 227–234.

Mann, J. H., & Borgatta, E. F. (1959). Personality and behavior correlates of changes produced by role playing experience. *Psychological Reports, 5*(3), 505–526.

May, G. L., & Kahnwiler, W. M. (2000). The effect of a mastery practice design on learning and transfer in behavior modeling training. *Personnel Psychology, 53*(2), 353.

McNamara, J. R., & Blumer, C. A. (1982). Role-playing to assess social competence: Ecological validity considerations. *Behavior Modification, 6*(4), 519–549.

McReynolds, P., & DeVoge, S., (1977). Use of improvisational techniques in assessment. In P. McReynolds (Ed). *Advances in psychological assessment, 4,* pp. 222–277. San Francisco: Jossey-Bass.

Mead, M. (1954). *Cultural discontinuities and personality transformation.* New York: Association Press.

Michelson, L., DiLorenzo, T. M., Calpin, J. P., & Ollendick, T. H. (1982). Situational determinants of the behavioral assertiveness role-play test for children. *Behavior Therapy, 13*(5), 724–734.

Middleton, P. (1978). A test of Sarbin's self-role congruency theory within a role-playing therapy analogue situation. *Journal of Clinical Psychology, 34*(2), 505–511.

Moreno, J. L. (1960). Definitions of group psychotherapy. *Group Psychotherapy, 13,* 57–72.

Neimeyer, G. J. (1995) The challenge of change. In R.A. Neimeyer & M. J. Mahoney (Eds.). *Constructivism in Psychotherapy* (111–126). Washington, DC: American Psychological Association.

Perri, M. G., & Richards, C. S. (1979). Assessment of heterosocial skills in male college students: Empirical development of a behavioral role-playing test. *Behavior Modification, 3*(3), 337–354.

Piaget, J. (1962). *Plays, dreams and imitation in childhood.* (G. Gattegno & F.M. Hodgson, Trans.). New York: W. W. Norton. (Original work published 1945).

Pickett, J. P. (Ed.). (2000). American *Heritage Dictionary of the English Language* (4th ed.). Boston: Houghton Mifflin Company.

Santrock, J. W. (1983). *Life-span development.* Madison, WI: Brown and Benchmark.

Sarbin, T. R., & Allen, V. L. (1968). Increasing participation in a natural group setting: A preliminary report. *Psychological Record, 18,* 1–7.

Sattler, J. (1988). *Assessment of children: Revised and updated third edition.* San Diego, CA: Jerome Sattler, Publisher, Inc.

Schwebel, M. (1953). Role-playing in counselor-training. *Personnel & Guidance Journal, 32,* 196–201.

Shakespeare, W. (1598/1988). As you like it. In A.L. Rowse (Ed.). *The annotated Shakespeare*, pp. 334–389.

Simon, T., & Smith, P. K. (1985) Play and problem solving: A paradigm questioned. *Merrill-Palmer Quarterly, 31*(3), 265–277.

Singer, D. G., & Singer, J. L. (1990). *The house of make-believe: Children's play and the developing imagination.* Cambridge, MA: Harvard University Press.

Stanislavski, C. (1987) *Building a character* (E. R. Hapgood, Trans.). New York: Theatre Arts Books. (Original Work published in 1949.)

Stanton, H., Back, K. W., & Litwak, E. (1956). Role-playing in survey research. *American Journal of Sociology, 62,* 172–176.

Swan, G. E., & MacDonald, M. L. (1978). Behavior therapy in practice: A national survey of behavior therapists. *Behavior Therapy, 9,* 799–807.

Swink, D. F., & Buchanan, D. R. (1984). The effects of sociodramatic goal-oriented role-play and non-goal-oriented role-play on locus of control. *Journal of Clinical Psychology, 40*(5), 1178–1183.

Van Hasselt, V. B., Hersen, M., & Bellack, A. S. (1981). The validity of role-play tests for assessing social skills in children. *Behavior Therapy. 12*(2), 202–216.

Watkins, C. E., Campbell, V. L., Nieberding, R., & Hallmark, R. (1995). Contemporary practice of psychological assessment by clinical psychologists. *Professional Psychology: Research & Practice, 26,* 54–60.

Westby, C. E. (1991). A scale for assessing children's pretend play. In C. E. Schaeffer, K. Gitlin, & A. Sandgrund (Eds.). *Play diagnosis and assessment* (pp. 131–161). New York: John Wiley & Sons.

Williamson, D. (1983). Criterion-related validity of a role-play social skills test for children. *Behavior Therapy, 14*(4), 466–481.

Biographical Statement

Ted Rubenstein, MFA, RDT, PsyD, received his BA from Indiana University in Psychology and Theatre, his MFA from the DePaul Theatre School, and his PsyD from the Chicago School of Professional Psychology. Dr. Rubenstein is the Vice-President of Expressive Arts Therapy for the Music Institute of Chicago and the Clinical Director of the Institute for Therapy through the Arts, a program of the Music Institute of Chicago. He is a drama therapist and is the Central Regional Representative for the National Association of Drama Therapy. Dr. Rubenstein is a faculty member of DePaul University and adjunct faculty member of the Chicago School of Professional Psychology. Dr. Rubenstein is a stage director, with most recent productions of *Fiddler on the Roof* and *Guys and Dolls.* His play, *Afterimage,* was produced in May of 2004 and is being remounted in September, 2005. Dr. Rubenstein was an ensemble member of the Eclipse Theatre in Chicago and the Raven Theatre also of Chicago.

Ted Rubenstein, PsyD
Clinical Director
Institute for Therapy through the Arts
6160 N. Cicero #122
Chicago, IL 60646

Chapter 25

DRAMATHERAPY AND REFUGEE YOUTH

YASMINE RANA

That the fist too was once the palm of an open hand and fingers.

Yehuda Amichai

THE ROLE OF THE PSYCHOSOCIAL SUPPORT SYSTEM

As youth who have survived the violence and instability of a humanitarian emergency, such as war, experience the transition from conflict to a period of reconciliation, providers, such as clinicians and other members of the psychosocial support system, are called to aid the young people who have been living in adverse environments. Often times, this post-war period is as unstable and unsafe as the time during the actual conflict. The need for a support system to remain in the area is as vital following a war as it is throughout the war. These children experiencing the humanitarian emergency have been removed from their routines and natural environments, either by force or by circumstance. They find themselves dependent on traumatized adults in the forms of their parents, siblings, and other adult members of their communities. These means of support most likely have shared traumatic experiences with their children, and are unable to provide the stability and consistency needed for a sense of security and a path toward social development (Jensen, 1996).

A strong external support system would help supplement what the youth have lost. Personal losses would most likely include familiar support that had provided the most basic, yet most imperative, survival elements such as healthcare, food, shelter, and clothing. The conflict has ridden the children of their lines of support and stability. As a result of

this absence of leadership and security, caretakers entering the post-war community as psychosocial supporters are called to recreate what has been stagnated and lost in the children's lives.

The purpose of this chapter is to provide background information, along with applicable techniques when working with this population. As a drama therapist with experiences in Bosnia and The Republic of Georgia, I have witnessed the effects of trauma on youth who have survived war and have seen the benefits of a creative therapeutic process.

Loss

The reconciliation period identifies the need refugee and returning children have for stable adult role models. Their previous models may have been traumatized, and have found themselves unable to provide basic needs and emotional comfort. These adult figures may have been killed, injured, or psychologically traumatized to the extent of an inability to serve in the parental role. If the adults are living their own personal trauma, this may exceed their capability to take on their children's emotional needs. Witnessing a parent's trauma may lead to the perpetuation of the child's own trauma (Mandalakas, Olness, & Torjesen, 1999).

As part of the reconciliation process, children in presently stable environments should be able to cite people in their social atoms who provide safety, direction, boundaries, education, and healthcare. Children who have experienced a humanitarian emergency often lack those human resources. After surviving the emergency, children may develop a sense of mistrust toward the adults and organizational systems that once signified complete consistency and security. This is most apparent in the community. What was in the past has now been lost.

In addition to homes and families being lost to violence, schools may no longer be in session following the emergency. Local educators are now unable to provide the familiar environment children experienced most of the day. Their routines have been disrupted, along with their education. The playful structure has been dismantled, as chaos and disarray have taken its place. For older children, there may be a lack of fearing the unknown as they perhaps have seen the very worst of humanity. Their definition of trouble may have been changed to alter their new identities as refugees or displaced people (Rana, 2001). For children who are older siblings, their roles may be changed from children to parental children, as they gain the responsibility caring for younger siblings. This care could range from emotional support, to housing and healthcare, a tremendous burden for a traumatized young person. Without a stable adult, community support, and a routine to adhere to, returning and refugee children may fall deeper into their trauma (Rana, 2001). Their mistrust of adults could also deepen and allow for an emotional closure to any adult offering assistance.

Providing Support

Although youth living through war may have lost the familiar and communal support who provided their playful structure and most basic needs, new caretakers in the roles of teachers, clinicians, and other members of the psychosocial support system have the ability to recreate a stable and nurturing environment that would enhance and cultivate the children's self-awareness, self-esteem, and social development. This may be accomplished through a basic human connection made between youth and caregiver. After entering a post-war setting and developing a needs assessment, the psychosocial support system can rebuild the children's environment with structure, as educational settings can be created in any space (Mandalakas, Olness, & Torjesen, 1999). Implementation of a creative arts therapy program, particularly the modality of dramatherapy, which will be discussed throughout this chapter, as an alternative educational methodology, would provide the children with the forum to express their trauma, loss, anxiety, and hope for the future. Engaging the children in drama, art, music,

and play will invoke thoughts and feelings that had been suppressed. Interpersonal and self-expression skills would then be given the opportunity to develop. These skills and emotions had most likely been present in the children, but had been stagnated during the conflict. Creating a daily routine comprised of creative and therapeutic activities led by a well-trained staff would provide the children with the sense of familiarity that had been lost (Rana, 2001).

Setting Goals

Once a psychosocial therapeutic team comprised of teachers, creative arts therapists, and other mental health workers has been assembled, a setting would need to be designated to provide the environment to pursue this therapeutic work. The selection of the most appropriate team of support staff would encompass assembling those whose qualities relate to professional skills and emotional nurturing.

> Even in the complex humanitarian emergency setting, resilience can be promoted in children. Any person or staff providing services can attempt to connect each child to a trusting, loving older person. Any person working with children can praise their accomplishments, show love and empathy, and encourage their hope and confidence. And any person, especially in educational settings, can help children master skills. (Mandalakas, Olness, & Torjesen, 1999, p. 81)

Several nongovernmental agencies have understood the importance of developing sound programs in aiding children of conflict. These programs have been designed to meet physical, social, educational, and emotional needs. The United Methodist Committee on Relief (UMCOR) has been one example of an organization that has participated in the designing and implementing of such a program. UMCOR has established Youth Houses in conflicted areas and have remained in operation following the conflict which caused for their establishment. The mission of the Youth Houses is to provide local, returning, and refugee children with educational, psychosocial, and recreational support in a safe and nurturing environment. The Sarajevo Youth House, established in 1995, has been one example of the psychosocial support system utilizing the creative arts modalities to reach vulnerable youth, through music, the visual arts, and drama. Another example is UMCOR's Tbilisi Youth House in the Republic of Georgia, which staffs local and volunteer psychologists, social workers, and other mental health workers who include dramatherapy and other creative arts therapies in their practices. A dramatherapy group allows the youth of humanitarian emergencies to take center stage and express themselves. Dramatherapy practiced within a group would provide the clients with situations to rebuild trust, as collaborative activities are often applied (Winn, 1994).

It enables children to tell their stories in safe, alternative ways such as distancing and mask making. The setting of goals should be accomplished as a group effort between supporters and youth, as the young people involved should be given the opportunity to reclaim power in their own journey toward self-expression and self-confidence. This process may be expressed in the children's own language with a local staff, or with the help of translation if the support staff is not from the area of conflict. These goals should include ideals that would better their own sense of self and their sense of those around them. Any proposed and agreed upon goal may also acknowledge the present political state that led them to this moment, and therefore include ideals related to ways of exploring peaceful resolution.

Primary goals for a dramatherapy group with this population focuses on development of self-esteem and self-awareness. Refugee youth need to regain their sense of self within a safe space to express their traumatic experiences. Once that safe space has been designated, the group could focus on development of interpersonal skills and establishment of a better sense of boundary setting. Once the goals of the group have been proposed and unanimously agreed upon, the creative and therapeutic process may begin to develop.

Dramatherapy Techniques

At the Tbilisi Youth House in the Republic of Georgia, a country faced with political strife, I gave a dramatherapy workshop to staff psychologists and social workers who were eager to explore alternative creative and therapeutic techniques. The Tbilisi Youth House had a large population of teenagers willing to participate in a drama group. These young people had experienced the conflict within their country firsthand and were seeking peaceful, creative means of self-expression and interaction. Here are some commonly used dramatherapy techniques that were shared and later applied with this population.

1. *The Magic Box*: a widely-used dramatherapy technique allowing participants to cite the emotions they wish to discard at the beginning of a session, and the emotions they wish to take with them at the closing of a session.
2. *Playback Theatre*: this utilizes interpersonal conflicts to role-play scenarios allowing participants to alter the outcomes.
3. *Human Sculptures*: a nonverbal technique used to illustrate one's emotions and one's social atom.
4. *Storytelling*: a method of ritual used to "act out" basic moral and ethical dilemmas using well-known tales with application to one's personal experiences.
5. *A Ten-Minute Play*: a forum to build a community and interact with its members incorporating improvisational methods.
6. *Sound and Motion*: a playful technique of mirroring and transforming a sound and motion to match one's present emotional climate.

These widely-used practices provide a creative, self-expressive, and enjoyable experience, while focusing on specific therapeutic goals. Several of the collaborative activities call for diverse situations and outcomes to be role-played. This experience would allow the clients to explore peaceful solutions to emotionally challenging issues. While practicing these techniques within their own peer group who have formulated a shared existence in a violent war-torn country, the youth within the dramatherapy group will see each other and their group leaders as support. Group leaders, psychologists, and social workers may explore group sessions for parents or any other adult family members to solidify and enhance the progress being made in the youth group. This exploration of the possibility for any remaining family members to participate would indeed be beneficial for the client, but this would be dependent on the client's family status.

CONCLUSION

Despite the loss of security and family, a child of a humanitarian emergency may have suffered, the applications of dramatherapy under the leadership of a nurturing support staff can help reclaim the youth's self-awareness and self-expression in a creative, expressive manner. A dramatherapy group provides the youth the opportunity to rebuild the trust that was lost during the conflict, by interacting with their peers and adult role models. By working together, the members of the group are rebuilding a community and a sense of belonging.

REFERENCES

Jenson, S.B. (1996). Frontlines of mental health under war conditions: The example of former Yugoslavia. In *Helping the children: A practical handbook for complex humanitarian emergencies*. Mandalakas, A., Torjesen, K., Olness, K. (Eds.). Kenyon, MN: Health Frontiers.

Mandalakas, A., Olness, K, & Torjesen, K. (1999). *Helping the children: A practical handbook for complex humanitarian emergencies*. Health Frontiers.

Rana, Y. (2001; October). Frontlines of mental health under war conditions: The case example of the former Yugoslavia. Paper presented at New York University's International Trauma Studies Program in New York City.

Winn, L. (1994). *Post-traumatic stress disorder and dramatherapy: Treatment and risk reduction*. London: Jessica Kingsley Publishers.

Biographical Statement

Yasmine Rana, MFA, MAT, RDT, is a Registered Drama Therapist who has worked in Sarajevo, Bosnia-Herzegovina, and Tbilisi, The Republic of Georgia, as a dramatherapist. Yasmine is also a playwright with productions in New York, Los Angeles, England, and Greece. Many of her plays reflect her experiences as a dramatherapist in areas of conflict.

Chapter 26

PSYCHODRAMA STILL GROWING AND EVOLVING AFTER ALL THESE YEARS

Karen Carnabucci

INTRODUCTION

Psychodrama originated in 1921 by the European-born physician, Jacob L. Moreno, who is the modern forerunner of all creative arts therapies as we know them today. This multidimensional method (Blatner, 2000) is also an effective way to build community, which is powerful for both healing and educating others. Its triadic system is also an important avenue to develop creativity and spontaneity in daily life.

In psychodrama – literally the psyche in action – people enact relevant events in their lives in a safe environment with a method based on psychological, relational, and theatrical principles. The enactment may involve not only exploring the history but also the psychological dimensions that are not typically addressed in the conventional dramatic process. Such dimensions may include: Unspoken thoughts and feelings, encounters with those not present, portrayals of fantasies of another's perspective, dreams, and imagining future possibilities and choices (Blatner, 2000).

Psychodrama is not drama therapy – which is a separate and distinct creative arts discipline. It does not refer to current events, movies, television, or theatrical productions that are psychologically intense, as the media often suggests. Group leaders, facilitators, and therapists who use role-play are not necessarily using psychodrama, although psychodramatic theory and practice certainly are the root of modern role-play.

Origins of Psychodrama

A convergence of observations in Vienna, Austria, in the early 1900s contributed to Moreno's philosophy (Fox, 1987; Hare & Hare, 1996; Marineau, 1989). As he strolled through the parks of Vienna, he watched children at play, improvising situations about their own lives and finding emotional resolution. Also on these walks, he noticed police officers arresting prostitutes in the city's red-light district. He organized an informal group where the women could talk about their problems. They gradually moved from discussing their problems with the police to more personal issues, providing emotional support to each other.

Moreno was at odds with the ideas of his elder contemporary Sigmund Freud, who had developed the only organized treatment of mental problems in modern times. He disagreed with Freud's emphasis on pathology and verbal exploration of issues while the analyst remained a blank slate to hold the patient's projections and transference. Moreno saw that humans occupy and move in space, not just talk, and take roles in relationships with others rather than stay in isolation. He postulated that improvisation in a group setting could help people discover their inner truths, express emotions, and experiment with new behaviors (Fox, 1987).

Moreno designed a three-tiered stage as a space for action to take place and collected a group of people from which issues could emerge. He also identified the protagonist as the person who enacts his or her inner drama with the help of a leader, called a director. Group members are called auxiliaries when they play roles in the enactment with the guidance of the director. They also may not play roles but rather staying in the group, serving as witnesses to the action (Blatner, 2000; Dayton, 1994). He also developed sociodrama, a similar group process that explored the dynamics of groups or subgroups rather than personal issues.

After immigrating to the United States, Moreno established Beacon Hospital, an alternative hospital with a therapeutic theater, in Beacon, N.Y., in the late 1930s. Shortly after, he met Zerka Toeman, a European-born woman who was seeking help for her psychotic sister. At a time when psychiatric medications had not yet been developed, psychodrama provided a measure of relief. Zerka would become Moreno's assistant, then his collaborator, and finally, his wife. Since Moreno's death in 1974, she has traveled the world to continue to demonstrate and teach this method.

The Method of Role Theory

Psychodrama is a complex method with a distinct philosophy and theory that interlocks role theory, spontaneity, creativity, and catharsis (Blatner, 1998, 2000; Fox, 1987). The centerpiece, role theory, involves working to expand or strengthen certain desired roles and to reduce the dominance of others that are maladaptive. Moreno's role theory was applied, rather than academic or theoretical, and he cited (Fox, 1987; Moreno, 1960) three main categories of roles:

- Roles that are particular to the person's individual functioning on a basic level, which we call somatic: such as eater, sleeper, defecator, etc., that we all have in common with each other as human beings.
- Roles that are social in nature, which inform how we relate to other people in our social networks, which might include wife, daughter, student, mother, sister, friend, employee, neighbor – and so forth.
- Roles that are psychodramatic – roles within the self that are based on characters in the imagination, memories, and dreams. These roles may be cooperative or conflicting in daily life or at stressful times. Examples of interior roles may include the self who is angry, the self who is sad, the observing ego, the self who can contain strong feelings, etc.

Sociometry

Because roles function in the context of relationships, Moreno devised a second field, which he called sociometry. Sociometry refers to the measurement of social relationships through a variety of choice-making activities within a group (Moreno, 1960). The activities make invisible relationships visible by recognizing "tele," the energetic connection between people. By noting relationship preferences, choices, similarities, and differences, both the director and the group members can understand the dynamics that contribute to the interactions in the group (Dayton, 1994). Moreno considered sociometry the basis of his work with psychodrama as detailed in his seminal volume, *Who shall survive?* (1953 & 1993) and actually saw psychodrama as secondary, providing repair to distorted relationships.

Warm-up, Action, and Sharing

When setting up a simple vignette – or a full-length drama with multiple scenes – it is helpful to warm up the participants with an activity that engages them to move into the action phase with greater readiness. A good warm-up will pay attention to sociometric measurements – noticing who's in the group and allowing people to mingle and share about these connections – is also important to the warm-up of the group process. A good warm-up will support group trust, spontaneity, the emergence of a theme, and ultimately a protagonist for a drama. A director may use a traditional warm-up activity such as a spectrogram, locogram, or hands-on choice – or may spontaneously devise an activity to suit the special needs of the group. There is no limit to the kinds of warm-ups; for beginners who need help with warm-up activities, The Warm Up Box is a useful resource as is The Warm Up Book (Hollander, 1978). Hollander (1969) also elaborated on Moreno's classic elements of warm-up, action, and sharing. He developed a design that he called the Hollander Psychodramatic Curve to represent the flow of an effective group process. Borrowing the shape that represents a bell curve, Hollander illustrated how each of the three segments of warm-up, action, and sharing contributed to an effective and complete psychodramatic session. The rising curve on the left represented the warm-up phase, which contributes to group cohesion, trust in the director and each other, and readiness. The high point is representative of the action phase of the session, when a specific protagonist enacts a personal issue that is facilitated by the director with the support of auxiliary actors. Finally, the declining curve on the right represents integration and refers to the sharing that should take place as auxiliaries return to their own selves after playing roles and group members comment on their personal past experiences in relating to content of the protagonist's drama.

The sharing is vitally important, not only for returning the protagonist into the group but also for the cognitive integration that occurs within the participants as they share verbally. Group members are instructed to offer words, memories, and observations to their experience on stage or as witnesses. People's thoughts and analysis about the protagonist's psychological dynamics are not permitted (Blatner, 1988; 2000).

Role Reversal

During the enactment, the director may opt for a number of techniques (Blatner, 1998) to deepen an understanding of a role, practice new behaviors, or integrate a lost or neglected part of self. Role reversal – stepping into the shoes of another and speaking, moving, and thinking from his or her perspective – is the most common tool of psychodrama. When a protagonist role reverses with another, it is a way of transcending the habitual limitations of egocentricity. Role reversal is indicated when it is appropriate for the protagonist to empathize with another person's experience or viewpoint. Role reversal is also helpful in setting up a scene and warming up the protagonist as he or she shows the auxiliary how to play the role most effectively.

If the goal is to primarily rehearse or refine a role, such has how to behave during a job interview, how to ask someone for a date, or how to say no to an activity that is not healthy, he or she will be involved in role training. When a person brings a fair amount of spontaneity to the role, he or she is showing role creativity. Other techniques, such as soliloquy, doubling, the mirror, the interview, empty chair, and future projection, may be interspersed throughout the drama as the director decides that a specific technique is therapeutically indicated to expand a role, develop empathy, gain insight, provide catharsis, or concretize a goal or plan.

It is a common misconception that a psychodrama must be highly dramatic: That the protagonist should lose control, yell, scream, sob, and beat pillows for effective healing work. Although release of feelings in a safe setting can be valuable, true catharsis is integration of internal dissonance. A new awareness can be an extremely important

intellectual catharsis, and effective work can take place with sharing an inner struggle in a monodrama or a simple role reversal (Blattner, 2000).

Standards and Complexity

It is also important to note that psychodrama is more than a nontraditional kind of therapy, and the exercises are not mere techniques. Psychodrama is a complex method that is adaptable to health, education, theater, business, and worship settings. The American Board of Examiners in Psychodrama, Sociometry and Group Psychotherapy has designated two standards of proficiency: The certified practitioner (CP) and the trainer, educator, and practitioner (TEP) that show the meeting of rigorous standards for practice and training respectively.

Parts of the psychodramatic method have been adapted by Fritz Perls in his Gestalt therapy, including the "empty chair" technique originated by Moreno; with family therapist Virginia Satir incorporating the action sociogram, calling it sculpting; and Eric Berne identifying the ego states of parent, adult, and child in the development of Transactional Analysis (Blatner, 1988). In the 1960s and later, many psychotherapists began using a combination of these ideas and others, sometimes using the catch-all name "experiential therapy."

Innovations as Psychodrama Evolves

Through the years, psychodrama has been evolving and growing, often in quite exciting ways. In therapeutic circles, some practitioners and trainers have enthusiastically integrated the psychoanalytical perspective with psychodrama while others have chosen to incorporate various creative arts therapies, including art, poetry, puppetry, sandplay, dance and movement, and music. Practitioners have also adapted the method for individual sessions as well as educational programs and personal growth programs. The newly revised edition of *Handbook of Psychotherapy and Behavior Change* (Elliott, Greenberg, & Lietaer, 2003) has named experiential psychotherapy as the treatment of choice for survivors of trauma, with the premise that traditional talk therapy, which addresses the cognitive left brain, cannot fully access the trauma memories and feelings that are locked in the creative right brain.

Yet another derivative is Playback Theatre (Salas, 1994; Salas & Swallow, 1994; Fox, 1999), developed by Jonathan Fox, which uses psychodramatic principles to enhance community building and storytelling. Individual troupes have further adapted Playback for semitherapeutic purposes on single themes such as bereavement. John Bergman has combined drama therapy with elements of Playback Theatre, theatre improvisation, and psychodrama in his development of Geese Theatre (Baim, Brookes, & Mountford, 2002; Bergman & Hewish, 2003) in working with offenders, particularly those who are incarcerated for serious crimes. With his expertise as a music therapist and a researcher studying the music of healers of indigenous cultures, Joseph Moreno, the nephew of J.L. Moreno and a respected music therapist in his own right, has integrated psychodrama with music therapy (1999) to illustrate how creative arts therapies can work synergistically.

Among the specific modifications happening in the field is the development of the Therapeutic Spiral Model by Hudgins (2002) for the treatment of survivors of trauma. This model is spreading throughout the United States and internationally and is slowly building its own body of research that shows the efficacy of its main action intervention, the Containing Double, for Post-Traumatic Stress Disorder and Dissociative Disorders.

Another recently developed model is the Interactive-Behavioral Model of Group Psychotherapy, named and advanced by Tomasulo (1992, 1999) for people with mental retardation and chronic psychiatric disabilities. Gong Shu (2004) has combined traditional Chinese medicine with psychodrama and the creative arts therapies, based on her cross-cultural work in Asia and her own heritage and knowledge of the Eastern culture. A particularly growing nonpsychotherapeutic derivative of psychodrama is Bibliodrama, developed by Pitzele (1995, 1998), and other adaptations that address psychospiritual issues, including Souldrama created by Miller (2002).

CONCLUSION

Several trainers have made efforts to compile innovations in psychodrama around the world since Moreno's death (Gershoni, 2003; Holmes, Karp, & Watson, 1994; Hudgins & Kellermann, 2000). There is every reason to believe that psychodrama will continue to evolve and flourish in the twenty-first century as practitioners continue to experiment with new ideas and document their innovations and practices in their work with new populations and current research.

GLOSSARY OF TERMS

Doubling. The protagonist is joined by an auxiliary, either a trained co-leader or a group member, whose role is to present the protagonist's feelings and thoughts. This role has been adapted for specific interventions by other trainers, including the Containing Double and Body Double (Hudgins, 2002) and the Cognitive Double (Kipper, 2002).

Empty chair. An empty chair representing the position or role of another person or a part of self that is central to the dramatic vignette.

Future projection. A specific scene in the future is enacted, often as a wished-for dream, an exaggeration, or as an exploration or rehearsal of an upcoming event.

Interview. The director interviews the protagonist in another role, attempting to learn more information about the person, situation, or relationship.

Mirror. Protagonist steps out of the drama to observe his or her role played by an auxiliary to gain a wider perspective of the issue or problem.

Monodrama. Protagonist plays all the parts in the enactment, often self-directed.

Soliloquy. Protagonist shares with the group inner thoughts and feelings that would normally not be expressed.

REFERENCES

Baim, C., Brookes, S., & Mountford, A. (Eds.). (2002). *The Geese Theatre handbook: Drama with offenders and people at risk.* Winchester, England: Waterside Press.

Bergman, J. & Hewish, S. (2003). *Challenging experience: An experiential approach to the treatment of serious offenders.* Oklahoma City: Woods N Barnes.

Blatner, A. (1988). *Acting-in: Practical application of psychodramatic methods.* (2nd ed.). New York: Springer Publishing Co.

Blatner, A. (1998). *Foundations of psychodrama: History, theory and practice.* (4th ed.). New York: Springer Publishing Co.

Dayton, T. (1994). *The drama within: Psychodrama and experiential therapy.* Deerfield Beach, FL: Health Communications.

Dayton, T. (2005). *The living stage: A step-by-step guide to psychodrama, sociometry and experiential group therapy.* Deerfield Beach, FL: Health Communications.

Elliott, R., Greenberg, L. S. & Lietaer, G.. (2003). Research on experiential psychotherapies. In M. Lambert, A. Bergin, & S. Garfield (Eds.). *Handbook of psychotherapy and behavior change* (5th ed.), New York: Wiley.

Fox, J. (Ed.). (1987). *The essential Moreno: Writings on psychodrama, group method and spontaneity.* New York: Springer Publishing Co.

Fox, J. (Ed.). (1999). *Gathering voices: Essays on playback theatre.* New Paltz, NY: Tusitala.

Fox, J. (Ed.). (1987). *The essential Moreno: Writings on psychodrama, group method and spontaneity.* New York: Springer Publishing Co.

Gershoni, J. (Ed.). (2003) *Psychodrama in the 21st century.* New York: Springer Publishing Co.

Gong, S. (2004). *Yi shu: the art of living with change – Integrating traditional Chinese medicine, psychodrama and the creative arts.* St. Louis, MO: F.E. Robbins & Sons Press.

Hare, P., & Hare, J. R. (1996). *J. L. Moreno.* London: Sage.

Hollander, C.E. (1969). *A process for psychodrama training: The Hollander Psychodrama Curve.* Denver, CO: Snow Lion Press.

Hollander, C. E. (1978). *The warm-up box.* Littleton, CO: Hollander Institute for Human Development and Family Growth.

Holmes, P., Karp, M. & Watson, M. (Eds.). (1994). *Psychodrama since Moreno: Innovations in theory and practice.* London & New York: Tavistock/Routledge.

Hudgins, M. K. (2000). The therapeutic spiral model: Treating PTSD in action. In P. F. Kellermann & M. K. Hudgins, (Eds.). *Psychodrama with trauma survivors: Acting out your pain.* London & Philadelphia: Jessica Kingsley.

Hudgins, M. K. (2002). *Experiential treatment of PTSD: The therapeutic spiral model.* New York: Springer.

Kellermann, P. F. & Hudgins, M. K. (2000). *Psychodrama with trauma survivors: Acting out your pain.* London & Philadelphia: Jessica Kingsley.

Kipper, D.A. (2002). The cognitive double: Integrating cognitive and action techniques. *Journal of Group Psychotherapy, Psychodrama & Sociometry, 55,* 93–106.

Marineau, R. E. (1989). *Jacob Levy Moreno: 1889–1974.* London & New York: Tavistock/Routledge.

Miller, C. (2002). *Souldrama: A journey into the heart of God.* (2nd ed.). Spring Lake Heights, NJ: Spring Lake Heights Counseling Center.

Moreno, J.L. (1960). *The sociometry reader.* Glencoe, IL: The Free Press.

Moreno, J.L. (1953/1993). *Who shall survive?* (3rd ed.). Princeton, NJ: American Society of Group Psychotherapy and Psychodrama.

Moreno, J. (1999). *Acting your inner music: Music therapy and psychodrama.* St. Louis, MO: MMB Publications.

Pitzele, P. (1998). *Scripture windows: Toward a practice of bibliodrama.* Los Angeles: Torah Aura.

Pitzele, P. (1995). *Our fathers' wells.* San Francisco: Harper.

Sachnoff, E.A.. (1996). *The warm up book.* Chicago: The Oasis Psychodrama Training Institute.

Salas, J. (1994). *Improvising real life: Personal story in playback theater.* Dubuque, Iowa: Kendall/Hunt.

Salas, J. & Swallow, J. (1994). *Tracing our roots: Finding our place.* Videotape. McLean, VA: American Society of Group Psychotherapy and Psychodrama.

Razza, N. J. & Tomasulo, D. J. (2004). *Healing trauma: The power of group treatment for people with intellectual disabilities.* Washington, DC: American Psychological Association.

Tomasulo, D. J. (1992). *Group counseling for people with developmental disabilities.* (Video and training manual). New York: Young Adult Institute.

Tomasulo, D. J. (1999). Group therapy for people with mental retardation: The interactive-behavioral therapy approach. In D. Wiener, (Ed.). *Beyond talk therapy: Using movement and expressive techniques in clinical practice.* Washington, DC: American Psychological Association.

Biographical Statement

Karen Carnabucci, MSS, LCSW, TEP, is a licensed clinical social worker and a nationally board-certified trainer, educator, and practitioner in psychodrama, sociometry ,and group psychotherapy. She practices and teaches psychodrama and the use of the creative arts in psychotherapy, education, and personal growth, and has developed ethics practice-building workshops for helping professionals using action methods. Her consulting, training, and psychotherapy practice is based in Racine, Wisconsin. She may be reached at karen @companionsin healing.com or www.companions inhealing.com.

Chapter 27

POETRY, THE HEALING PEN

Mari Alschuler

INTRODUCTION

Poetry therapy (PT) refers to the intentional use of poetry and other literature to assist people with therapeutic and personal growth goals. Poetry therapy "has a pluralistic base that has evolved through the exploration and evaluation of the therapeutic aspects of the language arts in various helping and educational capacities" (Mazza, 1994, p. 121). Poetry therapists may utilize poems, song lyrics, short stories, fairy tales and myths, novels, journals, essays, memoirs, autobiographies, plays, and films as their tools.

Bibliotherapy, journal therapy, and biblio-poetry therapy are related terms used interchangeably with poetry therapy. The term "bibliotherapy" is derived from the Greek for book (*biblion*) and healing (*oepatteid*). . . . The term was coined in 1916 by Samuel McChord Crothers (Palmer, Biller, Rancourt, & Teets, 1997).

Poetry therapy has historical roots dating back to ancient times. The Greeks placed Apollo on Mount Olympus as the god of music, poetry, and the healing arts. Apollo's son, Asclepius, was the god of healing, and the ancestor of modern medicine (Perakis, 2000). William Carlos Williams, one of America's greatest poets, was a physician.

The nine muses represented nine aspects of the creative arts, including lyric and epic poetry, and theatrical representations of tragedies (Gorelick, 1987). Aristotle first proposed the effects of *katharsis* (catharsis) "or purgation of the feelings of pity and fear latent in the spectator of a tragic drama. He pointed out that it is the release of these emotions which brings pleasure to the spectators" (Abrams, 1994, p. 64). Gorelick asserts that these ancient tragedies caused audience members to "vicariously experience two roles – the sufferer-victim and the observer-helper. If the theatre experience were personally and deeply felt, it would carry over to personal life beyond the theatrical space" (Abrams, 1994, p. 40). As in drama therapy and psychodrama, in poetry therapy the expression of thoughts and emotions through ventilation leads to healing and recovery.

Aspects of Poetry Therapy

Like dance/movement therapy and music therapy, PT utilizes the natural rhythm of language and sound to access deeper aspects of the self. Talerico (1986) writes about the link between the creative process and therapy as the encouragement of the expression of feelings, confidence through risk-taking, communication with the unconscious, development of new insights, resolution of conflict, reduction of anxiety, and rechanneling of psychic energy for problem-solving purposes (as cited in Alschuler, 1995). Rossiter (1992) writes that some of the commonalities among the creative arts therapies are "(1) the use of creative processes and products to facilitate personal growth and solve problems; (2) intrinsic positivity; (3) indirectness; and (4) breadth of appeal and applicability" (p. 228). Poetry therapists often employ related modalities (drawing a response to a poem, writing to music, moving to a poem) in the practice of poetry therapy.

Application of PT

PT can occur in nearly any setting for a variety of client populations. It is generally provided on a group basis but can also be used with individuals, couples, families, and companies. An environment conducive to fostering trust, self-esteem, and safety is the first goal in developing a PT group. Reiter (1997), in a report originally submitted to NCATA for testimony on Capitol Hill, outlines the specific goals of PT as follows:

a. to improve the capacity to respond to vivid images and concepts, and the feelings aroused by them;
b. to enhance self-understanding and accuracy in self-perception;
c. to increase awareness of interpersonal relationships;
d. to heighten reality orientation;
e. to develop creativity, self-expression, and greater self-esteem;
f. to encourage positive thinking and creative problem-solving;
g. to strengthen communication, particularly listening and speaking skills;
h. to integrate the different aspects of the self for psychological wholeness;
i. to ventilate overpowering emotions and release tension;
j. to find new meaning through new ideas, insights, and/or information; and
k. to help participants experience the liberating and nourishing qualities of beauty (pp. 170–171).

PT is most commonly employed in three techniques that can be used alone or in combination with one another. The first is the use of pre-existing literature in the session. The second is providing writing exercises for clients to complete during or in between sessions. The third is the group poem, or collaborative writing, done with a therapy group, couple, or family (Golden, 2000). When a poetry therapist asks group members to write in response to a poem, "there is an increase in self-awareness, group interaction, and self-esteem" (p. 130). Mazza (1994) points out that collaborative poems advance group cohesion and reflect the group's developmental stage. Mazza also adds an additional technique – dyadic poems – for use in couples counseling, to assess the relationship.

Lerner (1993) speaks about the simultaneous internal processes that may occur within the person exposed to poetry within a PT session. He writes that a poem:

may often evoke images which are processed in the individual's framework of personal dynamics. Thus, a poem may enable a person to feel, while imaging and thinking about what is felt. Head and heart are combined with the realistic possibility of enhancing one's own self-esteem. . . . Potentially a poem contains the ingredients of an appropriate and effective interpretation and can often get at the core of a person's emotional difficulties" (p. 52).

Historical Development of PT

PT as an organized treatment or adjunctive treatment modality had its foundation in the early psychiatric hospital movement of the late 1800s (Abrams, 1994). Benjamin Rush, the "father" of contemporary psychiatry in the U.S., utilized poetry in the psychiatric wards of the Pennsylvania Hospital. The inpatients began to publish an internal newsletter containing their poems and artwork (Gorelick, 1987; Reiter, 1997). Although this newsletter eventually ceased operation, psychiatric and recovery programs worldwide frequently publish their clients' writings (often accompanied by their artwork), and there is a national movement in the U.S. to showcase writing by people with mental illness, addiction, domestic violence, and other issues. For instance, ARIA (Awareness of Rape and Incest through Art) in New York City puts on an annual night to heal that promotes the poetry, art, dance, drama, and music of sexual abuse and rape survivors (ARIA, 2005).

In 1969, leaders of the poetry therapy movement created an organization, the American Association for Poetry Therapy, later named the National Association for Poetry Therapy (NAPT). NAPT created two training avenues: Certified Poetry Therapists (CPT), for bachelor-level paraprofessionals to work with developmental populations, and Registered Poetry Therapists (RPT), for mental health professionals holding at least a master's degree, to work with clinical populations. All trainees are supervised by accredited Mentor/Supervisors (M/S). The National Federation of Bibliopoetry Therapy, a separate credentialing arm of NAPT, oversees the professional credentialing and supervised training of poetry therapists. NAPT is a member of NCATA, the National Creative Arts Therapies Association. The website for NAPT and its related branches is http://www.poetrytherapy.org.

While the field is relatively young in comparison to its sister expressive arts modalities, PT has also found a voice on Capitol Hill through our collaboration with NCATA. Dr. Sherry Reiter (1997), a past president of both NAPT and the Federation, presented poetry therapy to legislators in the hopes of obtaining federal recognition of poetry therapy as a professional expressive therapy. Local NAPT members continue to work at the state level to attain professional recognition by third-party payers and insurance carriers.

The pioneers of PT – Jack Leedy, Arthur Lerner, Gil Schloss, Molly Harrower, Arleen McCarty Hynes, and Mary Hynes-Berry – wrote the first textbooks in the field. A recent addition to the field is an excellent textbook by Nicholas Mazza, *Poetry therapy: Interface of the arts and psychology*. These books (see bibliography) remain standard texts; they are required reading for people seeking credentialing as a poetry therapist.

Harrower (1972) declared that poetry is "therapy and is part and parcel of normal development. People have struggled to cope with their inevitable inner turmoil. One way of so coping has been the ballad, the song, or the poem. Once crystallized into words, all-engulfing feelings become manageable, and once challenged into explicitness, the burden of the incommunicable becomes less heavy. The very act of creating is a self-sustaining experience, and in the poetic moment the self becomes both the ministering 'therapist' and the comforted 'patient'" (p. 3). Parallels may be drawn to the two roles of vicarious observer in Gorelick's version of responses to Greek tragedies.

One of the earliest proponents of PT, Dr. Jack Leedy, theorized an "isoprinciple" – a concept he borrowed from music therapy. The isoprinciple is used prescriptively as the guiding idea behind poetry selection. He suggested that poetry therapists "select literature which is similar to client moods, but contains an element of hope" (Golden, 2000, p. 129). Leedy (1985) felt that by selecting poems "that are close in feeling to the mood of the patient . . . the poem becomes symbolically an understanding of someone with whom they can share their feelings" (p. 82). By providing universalization of common concerns and issues among group members, participants would feel heard, understood, and accepted.

According to Schloss (1976), Dr. Arthur Lerner favored "an approach which could be called an interpersonal poetry dialogue" (p. 15). In this model, group members can bring in their own or outside published works, read a piece related to current group themes or issues, and hold a discussion. The topic may be changed or altered by group participants, or by the poetry therapist. Lerner himself believed that therapists need to understand poetry and "its potential to invoke, evoke, and provoke feelings at various levels of experience," and that poetry therapists must "be versed in therapy as well as in poetry" (1991a, pp. 235–236). He uses a wonderful simile in describing the effects of a carefully selected poem on a PT session: "A poem appropriately used in a therapy session is like a pebble dropped in a pool of water. It makes waves. In this instance the waves are the emotional and intellectual reactions elicited and the potential for interpretation" (1994, p. 30).

Schloss (1976) was a member of the Institute for Sociotherapy in the 1970s. He developed psychopoetry there, and employed aspects of psychodramatic principles and techniques with "an emphasis upon spontaneity . . . [as]events emerge from the action occurring at the moment in the group" (p. 15). Thus, different poetry therapists – including the pioneers of the field – may have different slants to their practices. The heterogeneity of the field allows practitioners to study the variety of proponents and to develop their own styles and methodologies. Other writers, past and present, continue to write and publish articles in the scholarly journal, *Journal of Poetry Therapy*, first published in 1987. NAPT members also receive and may publish in its internal newsletter, the *Museletter*.

Hynes and Hynes-Berry (1994) contributed to the field by integrating previous theoretical and practical work outlined by authors mentioned above. Their interactive bibliotherapy can be defined as a "therapeutic modality in which guided discussion of literature, other media material and/or creative writing by the participant or group is used to achieve prescribed therapeutic goals" (in Rossiter and Brown, 1988, p. 158). The major aspect of their interactive bibliotherapeutic approach is that the best choices of literature will have universal as well as positive themes. Hynes and Hynes-Berry outline four steps in the bibliotherapeutic process for a participant: (1) catching one's attention in the reading (recognition); (2) looking at the issues and the personal response or feeling about the issues presented in the poem (examination); (3) deepening the level of understanding by assimilating any

Smart

More notes on Process

new feelings or ideas that emerge during the discussion of the reading (juxtaposition); and (4) evaluating the insights and integrating them into one's own inner self (self-application). "The whole process culminates in a new, deeply personal meaning that will inform future attitudes and actions" (p. 43). In their interactive model, Hynes and Hynes-Berry focus on the interrelationship between the client, the therapist, and the selected poem or other literature. They posit a triad between the poet (the poem's author or speaker), the reader/listener/client, and the therapist (Lerner, 1995). The emphasis in interactive bibliotherapy is on the client's emotional response.

Choosing the right poem is based on an understanding of both the PT group's goals and the current phase of the group process (Golden, 2000). Lerner (1992) reports that the most effective literature for PT has themes, metaphors, and similes that are within the "client's frame of experiential reference" (p. 161). Hynes and Hynes-Berry (1994) also delineated four thematic (universal experience or emotion; powerful; comprehensible; positive) and four stylistic (compelling rhythm; striking, concrete imagery; simple, clear, precise language and vocabulary; succinct and of a manageable length) dimensions in selecting appropriate material for use in a PT session.

Literacy Issues

One of the main considerations in the choice of expressive modality is literacy level. Unlike other creative arts therapies, poetry and journal therapy rely on the ability to read and write. PT allows people to "express what they may be unable to say in any other way" (Reiter, 1997, p. 172). Low literacy levels do not need to be barriers to the use of PT, however. Using a tape recorder, "scribing" for an illiterate client, or assigning a peer to act as a writing surrogate for the client are all techniques that encourage the expression of language in all its forms. Clients who are not able to communicate in the therapist's language may also benefit from a peer transcribing their words, in addition to translating aloud to the group. Deaf or hard-of-hearing clients may also benefit from PT by utilizing signers to translate ASL.

PT Group

There is a world of difference between a PT group and a poetry writing group: The difference

between the process of self-exploration, and the creation of a work of art to be performed or published; critique or feedback is employed. It is the significant difference between *process* and *product.* Mazza (1994) writes that the aim of PT is not to educate the client about poetry, "but to facilitate his exploration of the feelings and associations evoked" by the poem (p. 2). Mazza reminds us that poetry writing and PT are two distinct endeavors. A poetry therapist utilizes an external stimulus – the poem – to which clients will respond. In this manner, poems help to provoke an individual to "understand and express his emotions, problems, and concerns. Regardless of a poem's value as a work of art, the more a poem stimulates an individual to respond, the more potential it has in aiding the therapeutic process" (p. 2). Indeed, poetry chosen for use in a PT session need not be selected based on literary merit, says Reiter (1997), but rather "as a tool for awareness and self-discovery" (p. 173).

Instructions given to clients to write in response to a poem or other text, a theme, or a topic, very often include the following: Do not worry about grammar, spelling, and punctuation; it does not have to rhyme; use any language in which you feel comfortable writing. This is in stark contrast to creative writing groups, where the desired outcome may be publication. In PT, the desired outcomes include achieving therapeutic goals through self-expression. Reiter (1997) states that group members who use writing-in-session to "externalize feelings through writing . . . gives participants a sense of mastery and . . . allows individuals to view their feelings from a different perspective" (p. 173). Poetry's "honesty helps people to explore difficult issues. When participants hear a group member . . . speak from the heart, they become more willing to do so themselves" (p. 173).

Therefore, before setting out to lead a PT group, education and supervision are required. Lerner (1992) acknowledges that different group members "will have diverse intellectual as well as emotional reactions to poems read or shared in a group session," as will, of course, those of the poetry therapist (p. 163). Having the ability to empathize with clients allows the poetry therapist to make relatively accurate assessments of mood, theme, and literacy level, the hallmarks of an effective poetry therapist. Pies (1993) warns about the difficulty inherent in predicting a client's "reac-

[handwritten: Therapist emotional differentiation]

tions to a particular poem, text, or illustration, even when the therapist feels that the work in question is likely to be helpful" (p. 145).

In addition to training, "two types of attitudes" should be activated and maintained, according to Abrams (1994): "First, an inner-directed self-awareness and openness is necessary in order to monitor internal reactions to the patient. . . . The second . . . is that of emotional separateness. . . . [The therapist] is then more able to see himself as a separate person while maintaining empathy for the patient's experience. . . . Thus, the poetry therapist must not only trigger insights with poems about the patient's internal conflict but must also be able to maintain a positive, active relationship without being manipulated or overwhelmed by the patient's disturbed feelings. . . . Empathic separateness permits and facilitates the nonjudgmental neutrality necessary for effective therapeutic interventions" (p. 70).

Healing and PT

Recent research conducted with people diagnosed with rheumatoid arthritis and asthma concluded there were considerable clinical differences in the autoimmune functioning of patients who wrote about traumatic events in their pasts, as compared to patients who wrote about insignificant events (Pennebaker, 1990; Silverman, 1997). Pennebaker (1990) began his approach by wondering why there is a worldwide urge to tell their stories. This inner urge to create a narrative assists in problem solving and conflict resolution, according to Mazza (1999), who asserts that "stories are central to our functioning. We create stories about all of our experiences" (p. 22). Pennebaker's main discovery indicates that "actively holding back or inhibiting our thoughts and feelings can be hard work," undermining our physiological defenses and affecting "immune function, the action of the heart and vascular systems, and even the biochemical workings of the brain and nervous systems" (p. 2). Perhaps Aristotle (and later, Freud) was right all along: ventilation, or catharsis, through language – the written or the spoken word – has ultimate healing benefits.

Another of Pennebaker's findings is that the need for completion (the same theory underpinning Gestalt psychology and Gestalt therapy) drives one to search for meaning and solutions to one's problems. He found that simply writing about his problems helped him to solve them. Further, writing about upsetting or traumatic events led to a new understanding of the emotional events themselves. "When people write about major upheavals, they begin to organize and understand them. . . . Once people can distill complex experiences into more understandable packages, they can begin to move beyond the trauma" (p. 185). Problems that had seemed overwhelming became more circumscribed and manageable after putting them on paper.

Robinson and Mowbray (1985) also highlight the problem-solving nature of poetry writing in the context of PT: "The poet's motives are conscious and deliberate, his productions the result of a skillful use of his tools to express rather than to conceal. He uses fantasy to elicit meaning in a fresh context; he distorts in order to clarify; he symbolizes in an effort to illuminate. To translate feelings into a verbal unit suggests an awareness of self. To probe for insights requires experimentation with language and economy of words. To give form to thought represents a maturity of effort, a growth-producing experience compatible with therapeutic aims" (p. 20). Pennebaker concluded that one reason "that writing about traumas can be so beneficial is that it is a powerful tool to discover meaning. Writing promotes self-understanding" (p. 93).

Other research projects to date have also evaluated the efficacy of poetry and journal writing with abused women (Palmer et al., 1997), addicts (Rossiter & Brown, 1988), formerly homeless, mentally ill adults (Alschuler, 1995), and other populations. Since the 1970s, research has supported bibliotherapy as having a positive effect on areas such as assertiveness, self-concept, personal growth, coping with loss, and emotional adjustment (Palmer et al., 1997). Through a PT group, members make connections with others and "individuals come to realize the lessening of aloneness in their own lives" (Silverman, 1997, p. 51). More research is needed to reveal the physiological, as well as the psychological, benefits of writing or journaling (Mazza, 1999).

If writing and responding to others' writing is curative in and of itself, then PT contains strong elements toward achievement of therapeutic aims. Perakis (2000) writes that poetry "is capable of inducing a state of wholeness, something that incorporates magic, illusion, obliqueness, and obscurity. It expresses primal energies and patterns in a form not yet altered by the intellect; a state of

[handwritten: Not meaning but Hope]

[handwritten: I don't agree w/ this and it's Gestalt!]

[handwritten: or, the relational component of being witnessed is the key]

→ Shakespeare

wholeness that is borne of primitive bodily senses" (p. 228).

Ritual, myth, and religion are steeped in poetry, rhythm, and rhyme (Silverman, 1997). Human desires to connect with the universal can be seen in poetry, drama, and religion, all of which "evolved from a common ritual whose purpose it was to annul the participant's consciousness of separate personality, exalting him to union with his group and its God" (Morrison, 1985, p. 212). Poetry is the stream by which particular individuals may be released into "the healing ambience of the universal. To one suffering from a sense of alienation, the awareness that another's steps have preceded him on the same lonesome road is comforting. . . . Poets expressing their deepest fears, insecurities, and anxieties give voice to what we feel deepest within ourselves," states Morrison (p. 213). Kempler (2003) writes that the use of poetry in therapy "not only allows for expression of deep-seated symbolic material, but also for the development of a truly personal voice which can be used to communicate . . . with others for further therapeutic gain" (p. 219). We live our life in symbols according to Ansell (1994). Since the arts allow humans to transcend "the experience witnessed by the mind" people are able to press "deeper into states of feeling not immediately accessible to consciousness," he asserts (p. 20).

Poetry as a change agent is a significant avenue for personal growth and healing. By creating their own writing in a PT session, clients are enabled simultaneously to begin to relinquish their own therapy through mastery; clients are encouraged toward independence, not fostered to depend on the therapist. By developing the ability to form meaning on their own, clients are enabled to become more self-sufficient and independent. Schloss (1976) acknowledges the transformative power of poetry to heal: "Sometimes writing a poem may have seemed the only means of dissipating loneliness, depression, or despair. Sometimes in finding the right words to express their feelings, they gained a sense of accomplishment. Often they have experienced a transformation of personal pain into aesthetic pleasure" (p. 1). Silverman (1997) speaks about this issue in highlighting the progressive nature of PT: "The creation of symbolic images is a means of becoming independent ultimately of therapeutic help; and poetry therapy then is a mirror that the patient makes to find her

or his own self reflection" (p. 50). Metaphor, simile, and imagery can all be helpful for reframing clients' situations, to "bypass defenses and help promote change" (Palmer et al., 1997, p. 5) while clients re-evaluate their thoughts and feelings through personal meaning and association.

"Our first rhythm was our heartbeat, and the cadences of poems' meters and rhymes hearken back to earlier times – childhood nursery rhymes, parents reading aloud to us, even to our mother's heartbeat while we were *in utero*" (Schloss, 1976, p. 9). The expressive arts allow people to attempt to make "sense out of no sense or nonsense" and to create order from chaos (Lerner, 1991b, p. 113). Poetry "makes arrangement out of derangement, harmony out of disharmony," adds Heninger (1994, p. 57). Rossiter (1992) believes that merely engaging in creative expression can have curative results. Sharing creative activities with others further enhances the experience and the clients' "self-exploration and understanding" (p. 229).

Psychotherapeutic metaphors, so frequently found in and associated with poetry, are "designed to parallel the client's experience so that the client, at an unconscious level, derives meaning from the metaphor which will enable the client to solve the problem" (Morgan, 1988, p. 170). The language of poetry and poetic devices, such as metaphor, simile, personification, and rhyme, consists of "symbols proving illumination and extending awareness" to the reader (Perakis, 2000, p. 228). As part of the therapeutic session, observation and utilization of a client's metaphors may reveal additional layers to the client's material, and can indicate supplemental areas for future sessions. The use of a poem in a PT session can help significant therapeutic material fly under the radar of resistance. Rossiter (1992) claims that the indirect suggestions made through the creative writing activity during a poetry therapy session cause participants to be "more willing to explore rather than resist," to feel less threatened, "to be more self-reflective and self-revealing" (p. 231).

Imagery in poetry embodies "the concrete representation of a person's perception of his or her inner and outer world experience" (Lorenz, 1998, p. 78). Because the client locates the metaphor in the poem – outside of her or himself – the origination point of the metaphor or image may make the client "less resistant to the suggestions or directives contained within the metaphor." Metaphors can

hmm..' self witnessing like : IFS.

looking 4 culture

I wonder if pre-mature babies, or children of mothers w/ irregular heartbeats also "illustrate a point, suggest a solution, increase motivation, [or] redefine or reframe a problem" (Morgan, 1988, p. 170). In a PT session, then, metaphor and simile become the "mediums of communication" (Lerner, 1995, p. 48). It is less important to analyze the poem itself than the responses to the poem. Literal interpretation does not belong in a poetry therapy group.

Poetry in and of itself may have a "healing influence," according to Silverman (1997). He writes that "reading and thinking about poetry is a healing power; and the writing of poems in itself provides deep insight into problems of the individual, in the process objectifying them in ways unexplainable but cathartic. For the written word is a powerful tool as image or metaphor; and the language of poetry is the utter language of the preconscious and the subconscious" (p. 49). Poetry and therapy both involve latent materials "including dreams, daydreams, and fantasies. Both employ the defense mechanisms of condensation, sublimation, displacement, and symbolization" (Robinson & Mowbray, 1985, p. 20). Chase (1988) calls the therapeutic uncovering of latent material through poetry therapy the protective veil of metaphor. She adds that poetry "offers the protection of a veil, a metaphor, to dare tell the truth" (p. 90). Emily Dickinson further emphasized the necessity of revealing one's inner self by telling the truth; yet, "tell it slant." It is that veil or camouflage "that allows the writer (and reader) to ventilate unacceptable, emotionally laden ideas and unconscious conflicts . . . to circumvent the usual repressive barriers and come to the surface" (Heninger, 1994, p. 57). Reiter (1997) adds that poetry's multiple layers of meaning and "its ability to conceal as well as reveal [give] participants the freedom to express themselves without being judged" (p. 173).

Lerner (1991a) relates the ingredients of poetry – metaphor, imagery, simile, and other poetic devices – to the personal responses that may lead to reshaping or changing human behavior. He observed that poetry therapists are "constantly in the process of going from poem to person and person to poem, with all the potential interpretations inherent in the experience" (p. 236). By including the person, the poem, and the therapist in the triadic PT experience, then, the observing ego can utilize the contents of the poem as well as the poetic session in order to examine and organize them (Heninger, 1994). The ability to use symbolic language is "an essential characteristic of poetic communication," according to Stainbrook (1994, p. 1).

Types of PT

Developmental PT, provided by Certified Poetry Therapists, reaches out to people of all ages who are coping with life transitions, stages of life, and environmental stressors. For example, a CPT may work with people going through divorce, adolescents dealing with parental separation or death, couples dealing with infertility, children whose parents are incarcerated, elderly nursing home residents, the terminally ill, and people recovering from war and other traumas. Normal life transitions, such as childhood, adolescence, early adulthood, midlife, and aging, are all relevant developmental periods for which a CPT might create therapeutic writing groups or sessions. These types of developmental PT groups can be found in schools, libraries, nursing homes, hospices, community centers, and counseling centers. CPTs often come from all walks of life, but typically include educators, librarians, and mental health or healthcare paraprofessionals.

Clinical PT is provided by mental health professionals who are RPTs, such as social workers, mental health counselors, pastoral counselors, marriage and family therapists, psychiatric nurses, psychiatrists, and psychologists. A variety of poetry therapists have written about the wide array of uses of PT with various clinical populations (see Abrams, 1994; Alschuler, 1995; Alschuler, 2000; Chase, 1988; Gillespie, 2001; Heninger, 1994; Morrison, 1985; Rossiter & Brown, 1988): substance abusers and alcoholics, the mentally ill, prisoners, people with eating disorders, or emotionally disturbed children and adolescents. Some RPTs provide PT in private practice; others do so in hospitals, nursing homes, outpatient clinics, inpatient units, or residential treatment programs.

PT with Special Populations

An early proponent of PT in the field of drug addiction, Schechter (1985) discovered that prevalent symptoms of addicts were "depression, loneliness, withdrawal, morbid suspicion and disorientation from drug abuse" (p. 289). She helped members increase their attention spans, concern for self and others, and help build honest and concrete revelations. Relating back to Alschuler's work (2000) leading PT groups in a

have a harder time w/ rhythm?

drug treatment program with both residential and outpatient units, Gillespie (2001) details his use of collaborative poetry in a drug and alcohol treatment program with clients dually diagnosed with both addiction and mental illness. He makes three main points, as an introduction to the groups he was beginning, which focus on the practical uses of poetry:

1. Writing poetry can be a practical way to organize and process personal experiences;
2. Writing poetry provides an opportunity to develop insight into oneself and others; and
3. Writing poetry can be public as well as private (p. 84).

On the psychiatric ward, clinicians may utilize the written word as a window into the patient's thoughts and concerns. Chase (1988) observes the commonalities between the use of language of mentally ill patients in an inpatient setting, and that of poets themselves: "inventing words, alliterating, rhyming, punning, free associating, and using condensed language" (pp. 89–90). She describes the "job of the poet in the hospital is to offer patients a chance to discover and make heard their writing voice, their writing style. Thus, they have the chance to use language to make contact with others, all the while maintaining their individual stance. The pleasure of this contact," she adds, "has eluded many of these people" (p. 90). Alschuler (1995) reports that the use of structured writing exercises, including the use of formal verse forms such as sonnets, list poems, or sestinas, assisted disorganized schizophrenic clients to contain their psychoses during and in between PT groups. She states that "formal poetry is a safe container for overwhelming emotions, psychotic thoughts or delusions, big or scary memories, or traumatic situations or decisions" (p. 73). Psychiatric patients burdened by stigma and poor self-esteem may find solace and acceptance within the borders of a PT group, according to Bjorklund (1999), who states that PT groups have "the potential to foster self-expression and promote peer interaction, thereby reducing stigma and enhancing traditional group treatment modalities" (p. 211).

PT may be a subtle way to introduce difficult themes or issues into a therapy group or session. It may be experienced as "less confrontational and less threatening than other therapies" (Reiter, 1997, p. 173) and may be appealing to certain clients who may be less willing to attend other forms of therapy. One of the differences between PT and the other creative arts therapies is in the medium of language. Kempler (2003) observes that although other arts promote creative expression of conscious and unconscious materials, they do not allow the client to blend these insights and expressions into the language of the therapeutic endeavor because they are not language based. Clients who are provided with other expressive arts therapies "are essentially still left fumbling for the words that allow them to share these meanings with the therapist and thus receive the benefits of an empathic witness. . . . [Language] is built-in to the art and so only needs to be shifted from an *intra*-personal to an *inter*-personal dialogue" (p. 219).

Ospina-Kammerer (1999) asserts that clients "who otherwise have difficulties expressing themselves find through poetry a way to describe in their own words their emotional pain and suffering" (p. 170). Clients diagnosed with 'alexithymia' – "a disturbance in affective and symbolic function" which overlaps various diagnostic criteria (Krystal, 1988, p. 242) – may benefit from poetry therapy. Alexithymic clients tend to react somatically ("It hurts") rather than emotionally; many cannot identify internal feeling states at all, or cannot differentiate between feeling states ("Am I tired, sad, or hungry?"). This leads to a paucity of speech and facial expression. Krystal (1988) points out that "only when one experiences the cognitive aspect of an emotion – the meaning of the affect and some indication of the 'story behind it' – and simultaneously has the expressive reaction and an adequate capacity for reflective self-awareness [sic], can one observe that one is experiencing a 'feeling' and identify it" (p. 243). Alexithymic clients may respond to the external stimulus of poetry as an avenue for first identifying, and then experiencing emotions more based in reality than in somaticism.

CONCLUSION

The full extent of the usefulness of poetry therapy has yet to be explored. Poetry therapy has its roots in both medicine and literature. Through the intentional use of poetry and other forms of literature, trained poetry therapists are able to reach beneath clients' resistance and assist them in achieving therapeutic or developmental goals, thus achieving a sense of mastery and increased independence, leading to personal growth and healing.

REFERENCES

ARIA. (2005). Awareness of Rape and Incest through Art. Retrieved on June 6, 2005 from http://www.ariany.org/

Abrams, A.S. (1994). Poetry therapy in the psychiatric hospital. In A. Lerner (Ed.). *Poetry in the therapeutic experience.* (2nd ed.). (pp. 64–72). St. Louis: MMB Music.

Alschuler, M. (1995). Finding our way home: Poetry therapy in a supportive single room occupancy residence. *Journal of Poetry Therapy, 9*(2), 63–78.

___ (2000). Healing from addictions through poetry therapy. *Journal of Poetry Therapy, 13*(3), 165–17

Ansell, C. (1994). Psychoanalysis and poetry. In A. Lerner (Ed.). *Poetry in the therapeutic experience.* (2nd ed.). (pp. 12–23). St. Louis: MMB Music.

Bjorklund, R. W. (1999). Exploring diagnostic identity of psychiatric patients throughpoetry therapy. *Journal of Poetry Therapy, 12*(4), 211-217.

Chase, K. (1988). A poet's job on the ward. *Journal of Poetry Therapy, 2*(2), 89–92.

Gillespie, C. (2001). Recovery poetry 101: The use of collaborative poetry in a dual-diagnosis drug and alcohol treatment program. *Journal of Poetry Therapy, 15*(2), 83–92.

Golden, K.M. (2000). The use of collaborative writing to enhance cohesion in poetry therapy groups. *Journal of Poetry Therapy, 13*(3), 125–137.

Gorelick. K. (1987). Greek tragedy and ancient healing: Poems as theatre and Asclepian temple in miniature. *Journal of Poetry Therapy, 1*(1), 38–43.

Harrower, M. (1972). *The therapy of poetry.* Springfield, IL: Charles C Thomas, Publisher, Ltd.

Heninger, O.E. (1994). Poetry therapy in private practice: An odyssey into the healing power of poetry. In A. Lerner (Ed.). *Poetry in the therapeutic experience.* (2nd ed.). (pp. 57–63). St. Louis: MMB Music.

Hynes, A., and Hynes-Berry, M. (1994). *Biblio/poetry therapy: The interactive process: A handbook.* St. Cloud, MN: North Star Press.

Kempler, N.Z. (2003). Finding our voice through poetry and psychotherapy. *Journal of Poetry Therapy, 16*(4), 217–220.

Krystal, H. (1988). *Integration & self-healing: Affect, trauma, alexithymia.* Hillsdale, NJ: The Analytic Press, Inc.

Leedy, J.J. (Ed.). (1985). *Poetry as healer: Mending the troubled mind.* New York: Vanguard Press.

Lerner, A. (Ed.). (1994). *Poetry in the therapeutic experience.* (2nd ed.). St. Louis: MMB Music, Inc.

—— (1991a). Poetry therapy corner. *Journal of Poetry Therapy, 4*(4), 235–237.

—— (1991b). Poetry therapy corner. *Journal of Poetry Therapy, 5*(2), 113–115.

—— (1992). Poetry therapy corner. *Journal of Poetry Therapy, 5*(3), 161–163.

—— (1993). Poetry therapy corner. *Journal of Poetry Therapy, 7*(1), 51–54.

—— (1994). Poetry therapy corner. *Journal of Poetry Therapy, 8*(1), 29–33.

—— (1995). Poetry therapy corner. *Journal of Poetry Therapy, 9*(1), 47–49.

Lorenz, D. (1998). The "healing process" of a developmental creative poetry therapy as reflected by the written poems (product analysis). *Journal of Poetry Therapy, 12*(2), 77–83.

Mazza, N. (1999). *Poetry therapy: Interface of the arts and psychology.* Boca Raton, FL: CRC Press.

Mazza, N. (1994). Poetry therapy: Toward a research agenda for the 1990s. *Journal of Poetry Therapy, 7*(3), 121–136.

Morgan, L.B. (1988). Metaphoric communication and the psychotherapeutic process. *Journal of Poetry Therapy, 1*(3), 169–181.

Morrison, M.R. (1985). Poetry therapy with disturbed adolescents. In J.J. Leedy (Ed.). *Poetry as healer: Mending the troubled mind.* (pp. 212–227). New York: Vanguard Press.

Ospina-Kammerer, V. (1999). Poetry therapy within a therapist's practice model. *Journal of Poetry Therapy, 12*(3), 169–175.

Palmer, B.C., Biller, D.L., Rancourt, R.E., & Teets, K.A. (1997). Interactive bibliotherapy: An effective method for healing and empowering emotionally-abused women. *Journal of Poetry Therapy, 11*(1), 3–15.

Pennebaker, J.W. (1990). *Opening up: The healing power of expressing emotions.* New York: Guilford Press.

Perakis, C. R. (2000). Poetry or medicine. *Journal of Poetry Therapy, 13*(4), 225–229.

Pies, R. (1993). Adverse reaction to poetry therapy: A case report. *Journal of Poetry Therapy, 5*(3), 143–147.

Reiter, S. (1997). Poetry therapy: Testimony on Capitol Hill. *Journal of Poetry Therapy, 10*(3), 169–178.

Robinson, S.S,. & Mowbray, J.K. (1985). Why Poetry? In J.J. Leedy (Ed.). *Poetry as healer: Mending the troubled mind.* (pp. 17–27). New York: Vanguard Press.

Rossiter, C., & Brown, R. (1988). An evaluation of interactive bibliotherapy in a clinical setting. *Journal of Poetry Therapy, 1*(3), 157–168.

Rossiter, C. (1992). Commonalities among the creative arts therapies as a basis for research collaboration. *Journal of Poetry Therapy, 5*(4), 227–235.

Schechter, R.L. (1985). Poetry: A therapeutic tool in the treatment of drug abuse. In J.J. Leedy (Ed.). *Poetry as healer: Mending the troubled mind.* (pp. 287–293). New York: Vanguard Press.

Schloss. G.A. (1976). *Psychopoetry.* New York: Grosset & Dunlap.

Silverman, H.L. (1997). The meaning of poetry therapy as part and science: Its essence, religious quality, and spiritual values. *Journal of Poetry Therapy, 11*(1), 49–52.

Stainbrook, E. (1994). Poetry and behavior in the psychotherapeutic experience. In A. Lerner (Ed.). *Poetry in the therapeutic experience.* (2nd ed.). (pp. 1–11). St. Louis: MMB Music.

Talerico, C.J. (1986). The expressive arts and creativity as a form of therapeutic experience in the field of mental health. *The Journal of Creative Behavior, 20,* 229–247.

Biographical Statement

Mari Alschuler, LCSW, RPT, M/S, is a Licensed Clinical Social Worker, Registered Poetry Therapist, and Mentor/Supervisor with the National Association for Poetry Therapy. She is the Quality Assurance Coordinator of a major mental health clinic in Miami, Florida and the author of several professional journal articles, a book of poems, *The Nightmare of Falling Teeth* (Pudding House Press, 1998), and teaches creative writing and composition as an Adjunct Professor at Broward Community College. She holds a BA in Semiotics from Brown University, an MFA in Poetry from Columbia University, and master's degrees in psychology (Teachers College/Columbia University) and social work (Fordham University).

Chapter 28

THE THERAPEUTIC VALUE OF POETRY

Norma Leedy

INTRODUCTION

Poetry therapy is a creative art modality used therapeutically and/or as a productive emotional outlet with patients and clients. It encourages reflection on moods, feelings, and ideas and the positive release of intense emotions. The methods, techniques, and tools are based on the individual's and group's capabilities, interests, and needs. Esthetics and accuracy of ability to write in correct form are not important aspects of the poetry and are not emphasized. Poetry can be read, heard, memorized, written, dictated, and recorded. Approaches may vary from one individual or group therapy session to the next. Looking at art, listening to music, and handling various objects may encourage poetic responses. Stimulation of the five senses is used to influence creativity and expression, which exist in all people.

One of the founders of poetry therapy was Dr. Jack Leedy, a psychiatrist in New York City. He developed the idea of using poetry and verbal expression to address emotions and experiences. He was dedicated to utilizing the natural resources of poetry for healing. Dr. Leedy expanded the scope of the use of poetry and used it in treating drug addicts, residents in correctional settings, the deaf, and disturbed that indicated that poetry therapy contributes to the art of peace.

Using Dr. Leedy's ideas, I have worked with various populations in my role as a Registered Poetry Therapist. I have developed techniques of using poetry therapy that were unique for each of these populations: the elderly in nursing homes and elementary school children. In addition, I have worked with (mentally retarded and emotionally disturbed) adults in a day treatment setting. This chapter will focus primarily on my work with this latter population. As part of the daily program activities, poetry therapy sessions were offered to interested program participants. Two major poetry therapy groups evolved and several individual Poetry Therapy sessions were established. Giving an example of these sessions will highlight the techniques used with this population.

Monday Poetry Therapy Group

This group consisted of 6–7 participants. They had diagnoses of being developmentally delayed, and, in addition, had a psychiatric disability. The following is an example of a typical Poetry Therapy session:

> Today we will speak about dreams and formulate a group poem with lines from all of you who wish to participate. Would someone like to tell us about a dream they remember or may imagine?

In this session, someone spoke about a dream involved with a scene that included a garden with growing mushrooms. This idea was elaborated upon and a poem was formulated. The lines offered by group members included children in this garden, fairies that would grant wishes, and other similar thoughts. The emphasis was on the fact that we may live in prose but we can dream in poetry. One participant suggested that the wish he made was "to have a girlfriend who was happy and beautiful" and this was followed by a line from another that although the fairies heard the wishes, they were not really their friends or would they really grant them a wish. A discussion then followed about expectations of friendship and trusting of others, which revealed some very basic problem areas for this group.

John, an active member of this group, revealed his great difficulty in trusting others. John had been placed in an institution from early childhood. Although he had some positive reactions from staff, as his personality reflected quick verbal responses and a sense of humor, he was often disappointed in promises that had been made to him by staff, and not fulfilled. His final thoughts in the dream poem were that even though the fairies may hear him they were not really his friends. He made a statement to the group that the only real trust he has is for himself. Throughout his life, he stated, he was forced to rely on staff; he showed that he now accepted that staff promises could not always be trusted and he must take responsibility for his own actions and reactions. This was a major step forward in his progress toward moving on to a less restrictive environment, e.g., a workshop setting.

Many members of that group spoke of similar feelings and of their loses, regrets, and jealousies. At one point closure was achieved when all agreed to sharing those feelings that others had and then reassured each other of the members of the groups feelings of friendship and caring for each other. In his discussion concerning Poetry Therapy groups, Gillipsie stated: "Although not my actual intention our work also helped to create a social bond between participants, a bond that carried on to their lives outside of the work shop" (Gillipsie, 2003).

Tuesday Poetry Therapy Group

This group consisted of members who did have the ability to read and write. Participants wrote their individual poetic reactions to the image or images shown. The responses were then shared with the group and suggested additions or subtractions were sometimes made. Some participants chose to have their poems displayed on the Poetry Therapy Room's bulletin board. Copies were offered to the individuals in the group if they wished to have them.

In some sessions, a person would read the poem they had written to the group. There was usually a lot of laughter and all would exit the group meeting appearing happy and positive in their affect. Observations were often made by staff that there were seldom any negative outbursts in the members of the poetry group following the weekly session. The following are some of the benefits that

were observed and documented regarding these poetry therapy groups, after six months.

- Improved self-esteem *Benefits*
- Increased receptive and expressive language abilities
- Acceptable methods for appropriate expression of emotion
- Increased variety of leisure activities
- Increased socialization abilities and an awareness of self and others
- A new view of life with new perspectives

Group Poetry Therapy Techniques and Methods

The actual techniques and methods used in poetry therapy sessions are varied. Some of the techniques that were used when leading both individual and group poetry therapy sessions in a day treatment center for an extremely mentally challenged population are as follows:

Each session is offered on a specific day and time and is voluntarily attended by the participants in the day program. The group consisted of six to eight adults. The session usually started with relaxation techniques of stretching and deep breathing, often with soft music playing so that all could be in a relaxed creative state. In the words of Dr. Jack Leedy, the following was a consideration when choosing poetry to be used in a session.

With some patients, poems that are more regular in their rhythmic scheme have proved more helpful than poems with less conventional patterns. Poems with regular rhythms, those that most nearly approximate the beat of the human heart, affect many patients deeply. This is to say that some masterpieces of poetry may not be therapeutic, whereas mediocre poems, never included in anthologies, may be extremely helpful or right for a patient, and may be his bridge to reality. (Leedy, 1985)

One method used was to show a painting, photograph, or print and pose the question: "What do you see in this work and what does it make you think of?" Everyone in the group is encouraged to respond. In groups where the members did not have writing ability, each one's words were recorded or written down in a poetry format by the poetry therapist. Groups whose members did have the ability to write, wrote their individual poetic reactions to the image shown.

Another typical session of a poetry therapy group meeting was as follows: A poem was read to the group and/or copies were distributed and people read the poem aloud, if they wished. We then interpreted the poem's meaning and a discussion took place as to how the individuals related to this poem. People sometimes voluntarily memorized the poem and then, with encouragement, read or recited it in moments of extreme stress (anger, grief, insomnia, etc.).

An example of a famous poem that had been memorized by a participant was William Wordsworth's *Daffodils*. George, a participant, who was known to have frequent outbursts and loss of control, would recite this entire poem from memory, when prompted, whenever he was emotionally upset, depressed, or agitated. This would impress his audience (staff and peers) greatly. It served to replace his negative emotions with a positive action and immediately calm him. Barbara Kreisberg, MS, CTRS, CPT, and Charles Rossiter, PhD, CPT, stated, "The poem is seen as a memory that has made such an impact on the writer, that its recall becomes a comfort and a pleasure whenever the writer feels sad and lonely."

The group discussion revealed John's difficulty in trusting others. Throughout his life he was forced to rely on staff. He had been placed in an institution from early childhood. Although he had some positive reactions from staff, as his personality reflected his quick wit and sense of humor, he was often disappointed in promises that had been made to him by staff. His final sentence in his dream poem, "The fairies hear him but they are not his friends!" was the summation of his belief and acceptance that staff promises could not always be trusted. He made the statement to the group that "I can really only trust myself and I must take responsibility for my own actions." This was a major step forward in his progress toward moving on to a less restrictive environment, e.g., a workshop.

In Charles Gillispie's article on poetry therapy techniques which were applied to a recreation adult education group for the mentally ill stated: "Many members of that group followed this poem by a group discussion, which triggered many feelings of loss, regret and jealousy." It was then brought to closure when all agreed to having had similar feelings and then reassured each other of their friendship and caring for fellow group members.

The benefits of being involved in a poetry therapy session (whether group or individual) are numerous. Writing, dictating, or recording poetry is available to all people regardless of intelligence, age, sex, or status. Poetry clarifies and expresses feelings that may have been previously denied or suppressed. It validates emotions and gives a sense of worth to one's existence.

Poetry was written in a session where sheets of writing paper were given out with printed stars decorating the corners of this blank paper. The instruction that were given to the group was to write whatever this paper stimulated them to write. This group was somewhat literate and able to read and write on about a second grade level. The results of this stimulus were very successful. Upon completion of the poetry therapy group, the members reflected positive attitudes about themselves. The poetry techniques used were a way of building self-esteem.

For another example, the "People Poem" was a tool used in poetry therapy groups. The method introduced was as follows: Each person was given the opportunity to be the "Star" of the people poem. The people poem was written by the group in a round-robin fashion, each person contributing a positive statement about the "Star." To inspire positive descriptions and encourage the right atmosphere the following poem was read at the beginning of this group activity:

I Know Something Good About You

Wouldn't this old world be better
If the folks we meet would say –
"I know something good about you!"
And treat us just that way?

Wouldn't it be fine and dandy?
If each handclasp, fond and true,
Carried with it this assurance –
"I know something good about you!"

Wouldn't life be lots more happy
If the good that's in us all
Were the only thing about us
That folks bothered to recall?

Wouldn't life be lots more happy
If we praised the good we see?
For there's such a lot of goodness
In the worst of you and me!

Wouldn't it be nice to practice
That fine way of thinking too?
You know something good about me!
I know something good about you!

–Louis C. Shimon, 1935

This poem encouraged the members to focus and construct a "People Poem." After many months all group participants had a completed "People Poem" about themselves. These were mounted on the bulletin board, and during each session, one person was selected to read or hear their poem. People Poems were sometimes formed by the use of the "Star's" name as a framework. A positive descriptive statement was made for each letter of that person's name.

Another technique used to stimulate creativity was "Silence." The poetry therapist told the group to sit silently and a timer was set for two minutes. Then each member of the group contributed a line on what was heard during that period of silence. It was amazing to the participants that each person heard something different, e.g., the sound of footsteps, water dripping, doors closing, etc. A unique poem was created from their auditory perceptions.

On a trip to a local Art Museum, the poetry therapy members brought sketching materials with them and the foundation of the next poetry therapy session was formulated. Walking through the sculpture gallery, each person chose a work of art they liked, and copied it or made a sketch of it to be brought back to program. These sketches were collected and presented back to them the next day. They were then asked to write, record, or dictate about this particular work describing it verbally and in poetry form. The responses were shared with the group and a poem was formed.

An approach of using one of the five senses is that of smell. "Smell Stimuli" is the use of odors for finding words for poetry. This method involves the awareness of smells in the environment. For example, during one poetry therapy session, the use of smell was initiated. The group was seated in a circle outdoors. They were instructed to close their eyes and use their nose. This worked particularly well in the fall when there were burning leaves, garbage waiting to be picked up on a hot day, or when there were outdoor cooking odors in the air. An indoor sense of smell activity used was where "smell cups" were brought to the group. In these "smell cups" were various herbs, spices, powdered chocolate,

ketchup, alcohol, vinegar, etc. This inspired words for poetry and memories. For a group that has difficulty in abstracting, it was surprising what concrete stimulation would bring forth.

One afternoon, during poetry therapy group, a strange smell drifted into the meeting area. One participant said it smelled like "wood burning," another said, "No, it smells like my Mom's kitchen," and others added their own ideas. We then wrote a poem about the smell that just happened to be there by chance. It turned out to be an interesting group poem and everyone contributed a line.

Another stimulating poetry group session was with a dance/movement therapist co-leading the group. A poem was read aloud and the participants interpreted the poem through dance and movement. When a group was co-led by a speech therapist, the participants were offered speech techniques to help them in their oral responses.

Individual Poetry Therapy

Individual poetry therapy sessions are particularly successful with clients who have great difficulty in venting or discussing their problems. A poem can trigger a thought, memory, or emotion. The poem is a method of focus that helps the client deal with issues that are "not his but the poem's." This has proven an excellent way to "deal with reality" when it is too painful to cope with directly.

The following are examples of participants who attended these individual poetry therapy sessions: Alice was a 43-year-old participant in our day treatment program. She had been diagnosed with a bipolar disorder as well as mental retardation. She would strike out at staff or other participants frequently, often to attain negative staff attention, or withdraw, refusing to get out of bed, or go to the day program. She was unable to read or write. When she began our program, a plan was developed, using behavior modification techniques to address her symptoms. One of her goals was for her to attend program regularly. As part of her behavior plan she was given the reinforcement opportunity to meet with a staff person of her choice at the end of the day. She chose to meet with the poetry therapist. At one of the sessions a poem was read to her. She reacted very positively to both the hearing of poetry of others and dictating her own poetry to the therapist. She came daily for her reward. She composed poems about every topic and experience she had both currently and in her past. She would express much of her hidden feelings and emotions. Her behavior in all areas improved greatly. She truly believed that once her feelings were out of her on paper they no longer would disturb her as suggested to her by the therapist. She has composed over 200 poems, which were typed and kept for her to hear and read to her again. She made vast improvement in many of her behavior goals and attended program regularly. It was interesting to note that not only did the poetry therapy sessions have a strong effect on her, but on her parents as well. Alice's parents, who were retired teachers, would meet regularly with her and staff to hear her progress reports. At a meeting, the poetry therapist read out loud, with Alice's permission, a poem that Alice had dictated during a reinforcement session. Her mother was shocked, and stated, "I would never have believed that Alice could create a poem. I know she dictated that poem because she refers to events that only she and I would know about." Her mother was so emotionally moved that she cried in joy. Alice was so pleased that after that, prior to every meeting with her mother, she would choose a specific poem in advance to be read at that meeting. Alice would then make the statement, with a big smile on her face, "That's the poem I want read because I know that poem will make my mother cry!" Alice expressed to the therapist that she had, at last, been successful in pleasing her mother.

Another success story of poetry therapy was demonstrated in Elliot, a man in his mid 30s. He was diagnosed with schizophrenia and developmental delays. He had spent most of his life in an institution and now lived in a residence. He was often aggressive and unmanageable in his behavior. Elliot functioned with low-level academic skills but exhibited an excellent memory. Elliot loved the creative arts, and was very excited by poetry therapy. He wrote many poems and deemed himself an "Assistant Poetry Therapist." The writing, reading, and reciting of poetry proved to be a major step in helping him to integrate with others. After many years in our treatment program he moved on to a workshop environment. These are just a couple examples of the use of individual poetry therapy in a day treatment setting. There are many other success stories in which participation in individual poetry therapy sessions played an important role in the growth and improvement of individuals attending our program.

Staff and Poetry Therapy

Poetry therapy was introduced to the staff of our day treatment center by the poetry therapist and outside consultants. Poetry therapy in our treatment center was used by staff to vent their own emotions and self-address coping with their frustrations and needs. Poetry techniques of many kinds were offered including the *isoprinciple* as formulated by Dr. Jack Leedy as follows.

The Isoprinciple

I like this concept

The isoprinciple, effective in music therapy, has proved important in the choice of poems for use in poetry therapy. As music that has the same feeling as the mood or mental tempo of the patient has proved a valuable tool, so poems that are close in feeling to the mood of the patient have been found helpful. Depressed patients, for example, are helped by poems sad and gloomy in tone, yet having lines or stanzas that reflect hope and optimism, especially toward their conclusion. By reading, studying, memorizing, reciting, or creating this kind of poem, depressed patients come to feel that they are not alone in their depression, that others are also depressed, that others have been depressed and recovered from their depression, and that no disgrace attaches to victims of extreme alterations of mood. For them, crying precipitated by a poem is often therapeutically helpful: the poem becomes symbolically an understanding someone with whom they can share their despair (Leedy, 1985). The following is an example of a poem written by a staff person after being criticized by her supervisor. She said she felt immediate relief after writing it, but wished to remain anonymous when sharing it.

> *So What!*
> *It's shitty to indulge in self-pity*
> *So what!*
> *To feel mad and then feel sad*
> *So what!*
> *I think and feel just as I like*
> *I'll tell all criticizers to take a hike.*
> *So what!*
> *Stay away from me if you don't want to hear me*
> *I'll keep my thoughts to myself but I'll let them be.*
> *It's my life that I'll live just as I wish*
> *That's What!*

To relieve the staff stress, poetry was used. They were encouraged to write poetry and the poems were collected for a staff publication. This helped the staff to feel supported and connected.

CONCLUSION

The use of poetry therapy with individuals, in groups, and with staff has enriched our experience in the day treatment center. Furthermore, the use of poetry in the written in creative form has proven to be a major therapeutic benefit by fostering the flowering of creativity in all people who avail themselves of this modality.

REFERENCES

Chavis, G. G. & Weisberger, L. L., (Eds.). (2003). *The healing fountain: Poetry therapy for life's journey.* St. Cloud, MN: North Star Press of St. Cloud.

Gillispie, C. (2003) Poetry therapy techniques applied to recreation/adult education group for the mentally ill. *Journal of Poetry Therapy 16*(2), 97–106.

Holliman, D. (2001). Human behavior and the social environment, self-disclosure, and poetry. *Journal of Poetry Therapy 15*(2), 99–105.

Kreisberg, B., & Gillispie, C. (2005). *More than meets the eye: Poetry of the visual arts.* Presentation NAPT's 25th annual conference, "Gateway to Wholeness: Poetry Therapy for the Individual, Family and Community," at St. Louis, Missouri.

Leedy, J. J. (1985). *Poetry as healer: Mending the troubled mind.* New York: The Vanguard Press.

Leedy, J.J. (1973). *Poetry the healer.* Philadelphia, Toronto: J.B. Lippincott Company.

Leedy, N. (1996). *Healing the healer: Poetry created by the staff of Carl Fenichel Day Treatment Center.* Brooklyn, NY: League Treatment Center.

Shimon, L. C. (1936). *The best loved poems of the American people.* New York, London, Toronto, Sydney, Auckland: Doubleday.

Biographical Statement

Norma Leedy, MS, RPT, M/S, has been a Registered Poetry Therapist since 1994, a Certified Poetry Therapist since 1969 and in 2004, a Mentor/Supervisor. In the 1960s, her husband, the late Jack J. Leedy, M.D., developed Poetry Therapy as a creative art modality, and founded the Association of Poetry Therapy, which later became the National Association for Poetry Therapy. For over twenty years, Ms. Leedy was a Developmental/Habilitation Specialist, Program Supervisor, and Poetry Therapist at the League Treatment Center, Carl Fenichel Community Services, Brooklyn, New York. As a member of the clinical team, she trained staff in the techniques of Poetry Therapy, devised behavioral approaches for the individual needs of program participants, and worked directly with adults dually-diagnosed with both moderate to severe cognitive impairment and psychiatric disabilities. She has organized and conducted Poetry Therapy groups in a variety of settings ranging from nursery schools to nursing homes, and sees clients in individual Poetry Therapy sessions. She has led workshops and/or assisted others at Poetry Therapy conferences at Brown University, The New England Library Association, Long Island University, University of Louisville, Bangor (Maine) Mental Health Clinic, Ohio State University, and elsewhere. She has also conducted Poetry Therapy groups in collaboration with practitioners in other fields, such as Dance-Movement Therapy, Speech Therapy, and Art Therapy. Ms. Leedy received her Master of Science degree in 1993 from Adelphi University, New York, New York.

Chapter 29

CREATIVE CONNECTIONS

Michael P. Hand

INTRODUCTION

According to Ambrose Bierce (1842–1914): "There is nothing new under the sun but there are lots of old things we don't know." When first stumbling across Bierce's quote sometime early in my teens, I remember being appalled and dismayed. All the great adventures I had imagined for my life – the discoveries and creations – seemed to whither like fruit in a sudden frost. If nothing could be new, then what wondrous thing could I contribute that would earn me fame, fortune, and the respect of all fans of Horatio Alger – I was a teenage boy, you will recall.

Somewhat later, likely as a defense against the loss of all my dreams and unborn plans, I considered Bierce's quote again. After more careful consideration, I was not so sure that he was correct. This thought alone was enough to cause me giddy exhilaration. It was the first time I dared consider that someone quoted in a book might actually be wrong. And, even if he were right, there may have been things that, though not new, were unknown. Unknown. The word enticed me with images of great explorers and innovators: Marie Curie . . . Watson and Crick . . . Jonas Salk . . . . I also considered that discovering something unknown was, perhaps, almost as good as discovering something new. I was reborn.

My world had changed. I had experienced what I later came to know as a "paradigm shift" or a "reframe." Whatever the name, something important had occurred: I had gone from destroyed to renewed, and the difference was both how I thought about the experience, and that I dared to consider that a different way of thinking about

something I had previously accepted as incontestable truth. And, finally, I discovered that there was something very powerful – powerfully good or powerfully bad – in an idea. But what, you might wonder, does any of this have to do with innovations in therapy? The answer lies in the story itself.

Parables, Proverbs, and Personal Portraits

The story about my reaction to the quote by Ambrose Bierce is a rather sneaky demonstration of a technique I use and, as Bierce's quote asserts, is not uniquely new. Rather, the technique is inspired by Milton Erickson (c.f., Erickson, Hershman, & Secter, 1989; Erickson & Rossi, 1976, 1981, 1989; Erickson, Rossi, & Rossi, 1979; Rossi, 1980), a psychiatrist, master hypnotherapist, and psychotherapist. During the course of conducting therapy, Erickson would tell stories which were seemingly irrelevant. Some of these stories would involve other clients. Some would be about his family. Some, similar to the one I told here, were about himself.

A review of the story told here will hopefully clarify what I believe to be its critical elements and therapeutic value. Firstly, it cites Ambrose Bierce who, though he may not be all that well-known to most, it is likely apparent to the listener that he was someone of note; someone whose thoughts and words are worthy of serious consideration. With this subtle and likely subliminal point made, the listener is more likely to accept what is said with less resistance and give it more credence.

While the use of a notable authority is helpful, I have found that it is not absolutely necessary to achieve the desired impact. A story attributed to the storyteller's grandmother, father, a former teacher, or mentor is sufficient to impart the impression of a homily of time-tested truth. The choice between a recognized authority or homey wisdom is much a matter of personal choice, though the therapist's insights about the particular client (discussed in more detail later) may tip the scale one direction or the other.

The second notable element of the story is that it contains a short, easily remembered, perhaps "catchy" quote or saying (more on this later). If the quote or saying is well-known, so much the better. A familiar bit of wisdom is more easily accepted as a reminder of something already known rather than a new idea or concept that requires convincing. The use of little sayings, whether as described here in a story, or an encapsulated bit of "truth" that the therapist attributes to him- or herself, can then easily become a short-cut reminder of the underlying point later as the need or occasion arises.

A third element to the story is that there is an initial element of adversity. In the sample story, the main character (me, in this case) was initially dismayed by my newly gained belief that the prospects for an exciting, noteworthy life had been diminished. This element of dynamic tension helps capture the listener's attention and there is a natural tendency to sympathize with this wounded character, to identify with the feeling of loss and frustration. This identification sets the stage for the next element in the story: overcoming the adversity.

The primary character in this particular story overcomes the adversity posed by the thought that there is nothing new to be achieved by two means. First, he dares to reject the negative idea, therefore feeling empowered. Second, he accepts a more positive idea, which changes his perspective from one of preclusion to one of possibility. These two senses, empowerment and possibility, are elements that have been identified by many as important to emotional well-being. Snyder (1994) sees these as being critical to the formation and maintenance of hope. Seligman (1998) identifies this sense of personal ability as key to optimism. Rotter (1990; 1966; 1954) considers a sense of internal control as a determinant of decreased anxiety and depression. The present author's own recent research (Hand, 2003) supports the importance of optimism, hope, and internal sense of control – individually and in combination – as being key to effectively dealing with life adversity. Moreover, the more recent of this author's research highlights that the experience of life adversity can be *beneficial* to the development of resilience.

The last element in the sample story is that the adversity, feeling that nothing new and important was left to be accomplished, was overcome through a change in the way I thought about both what was possible, and my ability to achieve it. This shift in personal paradigm, or "reframing," allowed me to recapture hope, optimism, and a personal sense of control over my future. And, with this change in my thinking, my emotional state changed from one bordering on despair to one of elation. This change subtly demonstrates to the listener that how he or she thinks about things determines feelings about those things. Said differently, changes in thoughts and perceptions change our experience of ourselves, others, and the world in which we live.

In review, the simple story used here as an introduction provides an example of what I have found to be a powerful technique for facilitating therapeutic change. Four story elements that I find valuable include: (1) being attributable to either a person of note who is held in high regard, or couched as a personal anecdote; (2) entailing a catchy quote or saying that is easily remembered and encapsulates the meaning of the story; (3) possessing an element of adversity or tension to help capture the client's interest; and (4) the resolution of the adversity or tension through the "hero" gaining a new perspective and insight into the problem, thereby discovering a possible path to success.

As Bierce suggested, this technique of facilitating knowledge and insight is not new. Stories, fables, parables, and myths have been used for similar purposes throughout the ages, from Homer's *Iliad* and *Odyssey*, to Socrates' "questions," to the Grimm Brothers' *Fairy Tales*. If there is a difference between the type of story presented here and those of its precursors, it is that the present story is more closely tailored to the specific "needs" of its audience, making a particular point at a particular time. While much more might be said about the use of stories and parables as therapeutic tools, time might be better spent discussing a second, closely related technique.

Michael's Maddening Maxims

I have accumulated, over considerable time, a set of "truisms" that I have found to be useful in helping clients gain a particular insight, and do so in a way that is both easily understood and easily remembered. As it turns out, many of these little truths are frustrating in that they highlight something about life that we all wish were not so – hence the client-ascribed "maddening" label. These little sayings are so often frustrating that I generally tell clients they will likely feel a strong urge to slap me, though I encourage restraint. I also tell them that the maddening maxims will get stuck in their heads like a Muzak rendition of McCartney's *Maybe I'm Amazed*.

Now, having endured my rather sneaky approach to the story technique, the reader may be suspicious of my "true" motives for making such a comment to a client, even before he or she even hears the maxim. Though not one to encourage cynicism, such mistrust of my motives would be warranted. Again borrowing from the precepts of Milton Erickson, my intent is to diffuse resistance to what I am about to say through the use of humor and by promoting focus on what is to come, and to provide a suggestion that they will not be able to forget the upcoming truth, even if they wanted to. Like the old trick of asking someone not to think of the word "hippopotamus" for the next five minutes, the more they try *not* to think of the word, the more they *are* thinking of the word. As anecdotal proof that this actually works, I have had many former clients tell me, years later, that they periodically recalled one or more of these maxims and found themselves smiling at the truth of my prediction. So, without further ado, I list my top five maddening maxims.

1. *If you want something to be different, you must do some thing differently.* While somewhat lower on the maddening scale, this saying gets at a central issue that I have found true for most clients: wanting to have things change without changing anything. It often seems to me that clients come to therapy after having tried many different times to solve whatever problematic issue is in their lives. However, they have been attempting the same, unsuccessful solution over and over, with the same unsatisfying result. It is as if they think, "surely this has to work. If only I try it one more time. . . ." The client then comes to therapy wanting the therapist to tell them how to make this tried-and-untrue strategy work. The maxim attempts to disabuse the

client of this notion. It also opens the door to experimentation. That is, I go on to make the point that, like a chemist or a cook, if you change the ingredients, you change the outcome. So, if the cake is coming out flat and tasteless. . . .

2. *In virtually every aspect of life, there is an easier way and a harder way . . . and the harder way is always the better way.* Similar to my observations regarding clients wanting change without changing, I have found that clients also often have been avoiding the more difficult solution(s) to their issues. It is not that they are lazy, only fearful of the discomfort they see as inherent in the more difficult, sometimes painful, solutions. I generally expand upon this maxim by highlighting a few endeavors that demonstrate its truth. Working out in the gym seems a good example. If you work out with the wimpy weights, not much happens. However, the more difficult path of straining against the heavier weights builds strength. I often challenge the client to come up with a scenario that contradicts the maxim, and have yet to be presented with one that holds up under scrutiny.

The value to this maxim, as I see it, is that it highlights both the efforts that the client has been making to resolve their issue, and the one(s) avoided. This opens the door to exploring those avoided solutions, why they are perceived (often *mis*perceived) as so difficult, and their fantasy of what would happen if they actually let themselves do the harder thing. As true with all the maxims, this can serve as a method for reframing, a mechanism for opening the exploration to the client's self-concept, belief systems, and attribution style, and a catchy reminder.

3. *Strong timber does not grow with ease, the stronger the wind, the stronger the trees.* This saying is not my own, but "borrowed" from something I read many years ago, but cannot remember the source. This maxim is closely related to the previous one, but different in a subtle yet important way. While the previous saying's focus was on "doing the harder thing," this one is more about the *value* of adversity. I often find that clients (and most others) consider the experience of adversity

as universally and unequivocally negative. However, as this saying highlights, there is a tempering – strengthening – that comes from successfully overcoming adversity. Many researchers (e.g., Frankl, 1984; Hand, 2003; Maddi, 1999; Siebert, 1996) have explored this "truth" in much more detail than is possible to review in this chapter. Suffice it here to say that some exposure to adversity in life has been found to have a beneficial effect upon the development and sustenance of resilience. These and other researchers have explored many variables which appear to have either positive or negative mitigating effect on this relationship, but it seems that having too little experience with adversity may as bad – or worse – than having too much.

Does this mean that clients should actively seek out adversity in their lives? While many seem to do exactly that, such a practice is not recommended. Rather, the therapist might find ways, as I to do with my little aphorism, to help reframe the client's view of their adversities, perhaps even finding some value from the experience. Another truism, admittedly not my own, may say it best: whatever doesn't kill us makes us stronger.

4. *There are few places in life more painful than straddling a fence.* The intent of this hopefully humorous observation is to encourage *movement.* I have often found that clients come, finally, to therapy because they are stuck between options for whatever problems they face. Should I go or should I stay? Which is more painful, keeping things the way they are or changing? Will I be happier/unhappier doing this, or doing that? Often, the imagined consequence of either choice is so dire that the only "safe" choice is to do nothing at all. The fact that they are now in therapy tells me that this safe path is no longer working. Their hope – conscious or not – is to have me help find a way to not only make the old system work but, even less likely, make it comfortable.

The use of this analogy also allows for a discussion of the "splinters" that might be acquired from straddling life's fences. The splinters would be the long-lasting, often-

painful impacts of indecisiveness and inaction, such as garnered mistrust, missed opportunities, and, even more important, misattribution regarding who it is that has the right and responsibility to make decisions. Doing nothing is really, at its core, a rather passive-aggressive means for forcing someone else to make a decision. Worse, it encourages others to make decisions which may not be in the client's best interests. In this regard, I often "ban" clients from using the phrases: "I don't know," I don't care," and "whatever you want." I have heard later from former clients that eliminating these from their vocabulary was the most life-altering skill acquired during their therapy. More than mere vocabulary change, the client's focus on these phrases entails – requires – a shift in mindset which is counter to codependency, and promotive of personal empowerment.

5. *Feelings are one thing, behavior is another.* This is a hard concept for many to accept. There are really two points associated with this saying: we have control over both our feelings and our behavior regarding them. Many seem to have adopted the belief that feelings just happen, and that they have no possible control over them. So, for instance, if someone says something mean, they *must* feel hurt, sad, angry, or some other emotion. The extension of this concept of uncontrollable feelings is unavoidable behavior. Feeling angry, for example, requires that they slam doors, get drunk, pout, eat, or other such responses.

So long as the client subscribes to the idea that emotions are automatic, provoking knee-jerk responses, there is a sense of loss of personal control. Many (e.g., Rotter, 1990, 1966, 1954; Rotter, Chance, & Phares, 1972) have described the relationship between perceived control and general psychological well-being, and others have determined a strong relationship between perceived control and other psychological resilience factors such as learned helplessness/hopelessness (Peterson, Maier, & Seligman, 1993; Seligman, 1998); optimism (Seligman, 1998; Taylor et al., 2000); and resilience itself (Chorpita & Barlow, 1998; Hart, Hoffman, Edelstein, & Keller, 1997).

Given this relationship between a sense of personal control and good psychological health, it seems to me important to emphasize and reinforce it whenever possible. When clients can see – and accept – that they do have control over their feelings, they have taken a rather large step toward personal empowerment. Suddenly, as the schoolyard chant affirms, while sticks and stones might break one's bones, words need no longer hurt.

The second part of the saying addresses behavior. Just as with feelings, subscription to the idea that one's behavior is beyond control is disempowering, and the opposite is empowering. In addition, owning one's behavior as voluntary has important, if maddening, implications. Firstly, this means that lashing out at someone whenever we are upset, tired, or ill is neither unavoidable nor a birthright. Secondly, acknowledgement of responsibility over our behavior, regardless of feelings, undercuts many of the excuses we give ourselves *not* to do those things we know we really need to do, or do the things we really should not. For example, I often hear from patients that they do things because not doing them makes them feel so uncomfortable, and doing whatever it is makes them feel less so. Smoking is a good example. So is binging and purging, drinking or taking drugs, gambling, washing one's hands a hundred times a day, and many other "compulsive" behaviors.

While I fully appreciate that some parts of these behaviors may well have some biochemical bases, there still remains the fact that giving in to these urges is ultimately voluntary. Giving in to such urges is often defended by the contention that the underlying sensations and emotions demand the behavior with no possibility of resistance. Thus, with the simple "reminder" that both emotions and behavior are under control – or can be – the therapist can help the client alter their frame of reference for themselves and others in such a way that is empowering and enhancing of resilience.

While there are a number of other rather idiosyncratic approaches and techniques I employ in working with clients, I believe that those presented here provide sufficient examples to allow for their own experimentation. I am not alone, of course, in considering therapy to be a melding of art and science. It should be apparent that I have provided only my own artistic predilections here. The reader is encouraged to adapt, revise, and otherwise amend these techniques to fit their own tastes and meet their own and their clients' needs.

While therapy certainly warrants the utmost professionalism and genuineness, I believe there is ample room, and often good therapeutic reason, for levity. A part of my approach as described is meant to demystify the process and dissipate some of the natural uneasiness that clients experience entering into therapy. I have received frequent positive feedback from clients that this approach is helpful, and I am confident that similar efforts will garner the same for others.

In conclusion, I often tell clients that they might try doing/thinking/behaving in some way differently, saying: "What have you got to lose? If it doesn't work for you, you can always go back to how you were before." I suggest the same for the reader. In any case, there is nothing magical in the specific suggestions made here. Rather, the magic is found in the application of creative efforts – whatever they may be – to make it easier for the client to understand, remember, and apply the insights encountered during therapy. The quality of the connection between client and therapist is arguably the most important element in successful therapy, and perhaps the most difficult to teach. Just as in learning to paint, there is technique and . . . something more. The something more is the artist's connection with the viewer through communication of an idea in a unique and evocative way. The same is true of therapy.

REFERENCES

Chorpita, B. F., & Barlow, D. H. (1998). The development of anxiety: The role of control in early environment. *Psychological Bulletin, 124*(1), 3–21.

Erickson, M., Hershman, S., & Secter, I. (1989). *The practical application of medical and dental hypnosis* (3rd ed.). New York: Brunner/Mazel.

Erickson, M., & Rossi, E. (1989). *The February man: Evolving consciousness and identity in hypnotherapy.* New York: Brunner/Mazel.

Erickson, M., Rossi, E. (1981). *Experiencing hypnosis: Therapeutic approaches to altered state.* New York: Irvington.

Erickson, M., Rossi, E. (1979). *Hypnotherapy: An exploratory casebook.* New York: Irvington.

Erickson, M. H., Rossi, E. L., & Rossi, S. I. (1976). *Hypnotic realities: The induction of clinical hypnosis and forms of indirect suggest.* New York: Irvington.

Hand, M.P. (2003). Psychological Resilience: The Influence of Positive and Negative Life Events upon

Optimism, Hope, and Perceived Locus of Control. Unpublished doctoral dissertation. Walden University, Minneapolis, MN.

Hart, D., Hofmann, V., Edelstein, W., & Keller, M. (1997). The relation of childhood personality types to adolescent behavior and development: A longitudinal study of Icelandic children. *Developmental Psychology, 33*(2), 195–205.

Maddi, S.R. (1999). The personality construct of hardiness: Effects on experiencing, coping, and strain. *Counseling Psychology Journal: Practice and Research, 51*(2), 83–94.

Peterson, C., Maier, S. F., & Seligman, M. E. P. (1993). *Learned helplessness: A theory for the age of personal control.* New York: Oxford University Press.

Rossi, E. L. (Ed.). (1980). *The collected papers of Milton H. Erickson on hypnosis: Vol. 4. Innovative hypnotherapy.* New York: Irvington.

Rotter, J. B. (1990). Internal versus external control of reinforcement: A case history of a variable. *American Psychologist, 45*(4), 489–493.

Rotter, J. B. (1966). Generalized expectancies for internal versus external control of reinforcement. *Psychological Monographs, 81*(1), Whole No. 609.

Rotter, J. B. (1954). *Social learning theory and clinical psychology.* Englewood Cliffs, NJ: Prentice Hall.

Rotter, J. B., Chance, J. E., & Phares, E. J. (Eds.). (1972). *Social learning theory of personality.* New York: Holt, Rinehart and Winston.

Seligman, M. E. P. (1998). *Learned optimism: How to change your mind and your life.* New York: Pocket Books.

Snyder, C. R. (1994). *The psychology of hope: You can get there from here.* New York: The Free Press.

Taylor, S. E., Kemeny, M. E., Bower, J. E., Gruenewald, T. L., & Reed, G. M. (2000). Psychological resources, positive illusions, and health. *American Psychologist, 55*(1), 99–109.

Biographical Statement

Dr. Michael P. Hand began his career as a psychotherapist while a sophomore undergraduate when hired as a psychological technician by one of his professors in 1970. Since then, he has worked in both private practice and numerous private and public agencies. His experience encompasses a wide range of clients, including children and adolescents, families, couples, and adult individuals of all ages in inpatient and outpatient settings. In addition to general clinical practice, he has extensive experience treating those with substance abuse and addictions, eating disorders, chronic and acute medical conditions, posttrauma stress disorders, developmentally impaired, and the chronically mentally ill. His specialties are posttrauma stress and its concomitant severe anxiety and depression disorders, and behavioral medicine. He also lectures and conducts workshops on psychological resilience and is in the process of writing a book on the topic.

Chapter 30

ETHICAL DELIVERY OF CREATIVE THERAPEUTIC APPROACHES

KRISTIN LARSON

INTRODUCTION

The inclusion of creative techniques in the counseling process can strengthen the therapeutic alliance, deepen understanding, and hasten insight. These contributions can be powerfully constructive, but require special consideration in order to protect the well-being, freedom of choice, and dignity of the participants (Levick, 1995; Miller, 2003). Ethical practices are the foundation of effective therapy. Providers of creative therapies are faced with a myriad of ethical decisions, including the fundamental question of whether to treat a client, and more complex questions of what modality to use and what to do with the client's creation. While many of these questions are easily answered, practitioners inevitably experience ethical dilemmas that require referral to relevant ethical codes, consultation with colleagues, and long consideration of what is in the best interest of the client. It is when we are working with populations that have personally experienced trauma, emotional pain, and distrust that we are reminded that only the highest level of ethical practice will do. The purpose of this chapter is to emphasize knowledge and practice of ethical standards in the unique circumstances of implementing creative modalities in the therapeutic process, and to review the specific ethical guidelines that are unique to the provision of creative modalities, but avoiding those guidelines that are common to all therapy modalities.

Ethical Guidelines

It does not take long in the field of therapy to be faced with a difficult decision regarding the best interest of your client. The first formal guidelines for ethical decision-making in researching and treating humans was created in response to the Nuremburg trial, which exposed biomedical experiments conducted on unwilling prisoners of war in Germany during World War II (Sieber, 1992). These formal guidelines, named the Nuremburg code, emphasized the need to obtain informed consent from clients (Sieber, 1992) and set the standard for all subsequent ethical guidelines.

Currently, most therapists refer to the American Psychological Association's *Ethical principles of psychologists and code of conduct* most recently published in 2002, or the American Counseling Association's *Code of Ethics and Standards of Practice* (1995) for guidelines related to the provision of therapeutic services. There are also associations whose ethical guidelines recognize the unique questions faced by therapists using creative modalities, that provide guidance in the decision-making process based on the experiences of professionals, including the American Art Therapy Association (2003), American Dance Therapy Association (1966), American Music Therapy Association (2003), Association for Play Therapy (2000), National Association for Music Therapy (1987), and National Association for Poetry Therapy (National Fair Access Coalition on Testing, 2000). While organizational codes of ethics are mandatory for their membership, they are often considered the standard of treatment by state governing boards and professionals practicing in related fields. Interestingly, the American Counseling Association's guidelines state that therapists are to actively participate in relevant local, state, and national organizations, such as those previously mentioned, in order to foster professional development and improvement of skills (ACA, 1995).

Professional Competence

Ethical guidelines require that therapists provide only those techniques with which they are competent, based on education, training, supervision, and credentialing (if applicable) through a professional organization (AATA, 1999; ACA, 1995; APA, 2000). While a therapy provider may spend their free time painting with water colors and believe that it would make an effective creative modality in their therapy practice, it would be unethical for this individual to incorporate this modality in their practice without the experience required by the ethical guidelines. While developing the necessary skills to provide professional creative modalities, a therapist is directed to get supervision and inform their clients of their developmental status and provide the client with the supervisor's name (ACA, 1995; APA, 2002).

While creative therapies are by nature more freeform and less structured than traditional talk therapies, it is still necessary to provide treatment plans, set goals, and keep records in compliance with professional regulations (AATA, 1999; ACA, 1995; APA, 2000). In addition, therapists should inform the client of their expertise, training, and credentials prior to providing services. This can be accomplished verbally or through an informed consent form.

Informed Consent

The purpose of the informed consent form is to provide the client with all relevant information regarding the nature of the counseling process in order to make an informed decision regarding participation. When offering a creative modality, the informed consent must include (a) a description of the modality; (b) the purpose and goals of the modality; (c) the risks involved in the modality, including emotional upset; (d) the benefits of the modality; and (e) the alternatives to the modality (ACA, 1995). Therapists who provide creative modalities often have strong beliefs in the value of their specific technique and professional investment that comes from years of education and experience. Recognizing this natural bias toward their technique of choice, it is the therapist's ultimate responsibility to respect the client's freedom to choose based on an informed decision.

Informed consent also protects the provider by documenting the client's agreement for services.

This is particularly important with some non-traditional therapies such as the use of touch during dance and movement therapy (Willis, 1987). Although most ethical guidelines do not require written consent by the client (only verbal consent), it is in the best interest of the therapist to have the client's signature on the informed consent form. Be sure to obtain an informed consent signature for each new modality (art, dance, play, etc.) introduced to the therapeutic process. See the Appendix for a sample informed consent form.

Client Safety

Some creative therapies have the unique quality of being physically active (Levick, 1995). Therefore, special attention must be paid to the client's physical safety. The AATA (1999) includes in its Standards of Practice guidelines related to safety and toxicity when using art supplies in therapy. Movement and dance therapies also require awareness of the possible physical limitations of the clients and the impact of the therapy on their physical health (American Dance Therapy Association, 1966).

Confidentiality

Confidentiality refers to the client's right to privacy for all information related to their counseling process. This privacy includes the basic fact that they are participating in therapy. Confidentiality has been breached when the product of a creative modality is intentionally or unintentionally displayed (ACA, 1995). A drying table for sculptures in view of other clients or sharing a client's poetry violates confidentiality even if the anonymity is provided by withholding the client's name.

According to the AATA Standards of Practice (Malchiodi, 2003), all artistic creations must be considered to be confidential communications, just as verbal communications in therapy are. Clients must be advised of the limitations of confidentiality and that these limitations also extend to their art. Artistic creations are often created with the expectation of display (Malchiodi, 1998) and yet display of art that is produced as a part of the therapeutic process is not always appropriate or desired. The right to privacy can be waived by the client (ACA, 1995) by express *written* consent (AATA, 1999) and often will be waived by a client eager to share their healing; yet, it is still vital that the therapist choose based on the best interest of the client.

Consider that the uniqueness of a client's art may be difficult to disguise even if the name is removed. It is always a risk that someone could recognize the artistic style and destroy the attempt at anonymity (Malchiodi, 1998). In addition, children are commonly asked to draw a picture of their family which often contains recognizable details. The therapist must consider the ramifications of display or, in the case of parental abuse, allowing the child to take the expression home (Malchiodi, 1998). It is also an important consideration that a child or adult may alter the content of their art, knowing that their work may be on display. Any public display or dissemination of the product of a client's therapy should be accompanied by written consent by the client, including (a) the purpose of the display; (b) the time and place of the display; (c) the date of termination of the display; and (d) the fate of the product after the display. In the case of art produced by children, you must get permission from both the parent or guardian and the child (Malchiodi, 1998) to display the art. Malchiodi (1998) describes an exhibit in a residential treatment center that featured children's art from their therapeutic art class. Many of the expressions were emotionally sensitive and revealing; yet, the staff felt it was appropriate in order to call attention to the center's programs. In addition, some of the children who created the art were interviewed on local television, further compromising their confidentiality.

Consistent with this responsibility, therapists must arrange for secure storage of their client's creations, as in the case of children's confidential expressions or unfinished pieces (Malchiodi, 2003). If artwork is to be treated as part of an ongoing record of therapy, then the rule of keeping documentation for seven years in secure storage must apply (Hammond & Gantt, 1998). A large room or closet with a secure lock would qualify if it can accommodate the largest piece of artwork likely to be produced.

Drama therapy provides a challenge to the maintenance of confidentiality, as it is most often conducted in a group setting. Group members will often endorse an oath to maintain confidentiality (Moreno, 1962); yet, the therapist has little control over group member's behavior outside of the therapeutic setting. In this case, the therapist's responsibilities lie in explaining and reviewing the policy regarding confidentiality, describing the limitations of the policy, and immediately addressing any breaches in confidentiality that come to their awareness.

Ownership

It is common practice in art therapy to consider the client the owner of their artistic creation (Malchiodi, 2003), although this issue is complex and still under debate. Art therapists are expected to maintain detailed progress notes describing the artistic creations, and often make photographic or digital copies of the creation when necessary. Hammond and Gantt (1998) state that the practice of photographing client art is not only time consuming and expensive, but also may violate confidentiality. They believe that artwork should be summarized, in the same way a traditional therapist would summarize a conversation. Additionally, Hammond and Gantt (1998) encourage therapists to obtain written consent before photographing any client's artistic expression. If the artistic expression indicates harm to self or others, or some form of abuse, it is then treated as similarly to medical records, and retained for record-keeping purposes (Malchiodi, 2003). Lastly, it can be considered a violation of ownership for a therapist to write notes directly on a work of art (Malchiodi, 2003).

Use of Creative Modalities for Assessment

While the use of art, dance, and poetry is often for therapeutic purposes, some creative techniques are also used for assessment. Clients must be made aware of this distinction and also be informed of the assessment purpose of any creative modality implemented in therapy. In other words, a client who participates in drawing during therapy, for the purpose of expressing anger, must be informed if the drawing is used for assessment. Assessments include projective and objective tests, naturalistic observations, and participation in the artistic modality (Bruscia, 1988).

The use of projective or subjective procedures, such as the Draw-A-Person Test (DAP), is controversial due to limited reliability and validity evidence (Brooke, 2004; Malchiodi, 2003). While the use of drawings for the assessment of brain damage is well supported in the scientific literature, the use of art in assessment of emotional states, personality, or history of sexual abuse has little scientific support (Brooke, 2004). If a therapist chooses to use projective drawing for assessment, they must be knowledgeable regarding the most recent research in this area, recognize their limitations, and use them in conjunction with other more objective measures (Brooke, 2004; Malchiodi, 2003). Bruscia (1988) identified seven standards for assessment using art therapies: (a) have clearly defined objectives; (b) be conducted by a qualified therapist; (c) offer unique clinical advantages; (d) employ effective methods of data collection; (e) produce reliable data; (f) lead to valid conclusions; and (g) adhere to ethical standards (p. 5).

In addition, the client has the right to know (a) the results of the assessment; (b) any interpretations made based on the assessment; and (c) the basis for the therapist's conclusions and recommendations (ACA, 1995). The guidelines go on to say that therapists should only use those creative modalities in assessment for which they have been trained (ACA, 1995; Bruscia, 1988). It is required that this training include, if applicable, the related reliability, validity, error of measurement, and the standardization of assessment techniques.

Diversity

Creative therapies are rich with meaning, which contributes to their impact and effectiveness. Yet, the meaning is unique for each client, forming from their diverse life experiences. As a result, consideration of a client's culture, gender, ethnicity, sexual orientation, and religion is crucial when choosing a modality and interpreting the results (AATA, 1999).

It is an ethical standard that therapists are educated regarding diversity and oppression (AATA, 1999), particularly for the diverse populations that they are most likely to treat. When necessary, seek supervision from colleagues from the culture or those who have experience working with the specific diverse characteristic (AATA, 1999; APA, 2003). These guidelines will assist the therapist in choosing appropriate mediums and avoid overlooking pathways to healing (Brown, 2001). For example, a poetry therapist may encourage a client of Puerto Rican descent to refer to traditional folk tales for inspiration. A music therapist might want to avoid traditional Christmas music when working with a Jewish client (Clair, 1994). A dance therapist can draw from many cultural traditions of dance and might even consider introducing these to clients of differing ethnic backgrounds. At the same time, do not assume that someone with a physical disability

would not be interested in dance or movement therapy. A drama therapist has a unique ability to give a voice to the pain experienced by oppressed people. In addition, drama and play therapy can facilitate the reenactment of a traditional or ethnic approach to the resolution of an issue.

Multiple Therapists

A unique aspect of providing creative therapies is that the professional often receives referrals from other therapists who see the need for alternative treatments. This can be a wonderful opportunity to work in concert with colleagues and see amazing gains in the client's goals. This circumstance can also create conflicting therapies if there is a lack of communication and coordination between therapists or if the client initiated the contact and the primary therapist did not know that they have sought alternative treatment. When treating a client who is receiving services from another therapist, require that the client inform the primary therapist in order to continue treatment, and seek contact with the other therapist to obtain agreement to continue and coordinate services (AATA, 1999; ACA, 1995).

Bartering for Services

Therapists are generally discouraged from receiving goods from their clients in payment for services (ACA, 1995). Creative therapy seems to be a ripe circumstance for this dilemma. It is possible to imagine a client creating paintings in the course of therapy, and then offering them to the therapist in place of payment. This process has the potential to change the nature of the counseling relationship, create conflicts, and develop untoward expectations, in addition to putting the client at risk for exploitation (ACA, 1995). Unless there is no alternative to bartering, therapists must engage in the unpleasant task of politely refusing the client's offer.

Professional Development

It is best practice for therapists to continue their education in their creative modality in order to stay current regarding their field (AATA, 1999; ACA, 1995; APA, 2002). This education can come in the form of conferences, training, and continuing education programs. At the least, therapists should regularly consult with other professionals within and outside their place of business in order to monitor their effectiveness (ACA, 1995), and limit the effects of burnout. In addition, technology provides the opportunity to connect with a national or international community of therapists in the creative modalities. Several professional organizations maintain bulletin boards and "listserves" to facilitate communication among their members including the American Dance Therapy Association: http://www.adta.org/listserv.html; The International Networking Group of Art Therapists: http://www.emporia.edu/ingat/; and National Association for Drama Therapy: http://www.nadt.org/.

Resolution of Ethical Dilemmas

The issues related to the provision of therapy can be complex and often require the development of judgment that goes beyond compliance with ethical standards. Because of the complexity of human nature, relationships, and the creative experience, ethical dilemmas are not uncommon in therapy. When faced with an ethical dilemma, therapists should first consult the appropriate guidelines. Ethical codes are the culmination of decades of professional experience with dilemmas, and lessons learned through others' mistakes.

While ethical guidelines represent the standard for treatment, they are still only guidelines, and therefore require wisdom and consideration by the therapist (Larson, in press). Because of the enormous span of therapies, techniques, and issues, authors of the various ethical guidelines have chosen a general, if not vague, approach (Sieber, 1994), providing minimal guidance in the decision-making process. Do not expect to see explicit directives in the use of any specific technique. Therefore, practitioners of creative therapies must interpret the guidelines and use wisdom in applying them to specific dilemmas, such as the rights of parents to see a child's drawings or where to keep a sculpture a client has given a therapist as a gift. Imagine yourself in the place of the most vulnerable client that could be involved in this situation. Take a "worse case scenario" view and follow it to its conclusion in order to anticipate any ethical violations (i.e., What if my receptionist compliments my client on their painting of "betrayal" after seeing it in my office?) (Larson, in press).

Clearly, not every dilemma will be addressed within a code of ethics. If the course of action continues to be unclear, therapists are encouraged to seek consultation with colleagues who are knowledgeable

about ethics (ACA, 1995) or seek out members of a local professional organization. Therapists early in their careers can be misled by the vagueness of ethical codes and overlook some obscure risk to the well-being of the client. The more feedback you obtain, the greater the chance you have of identifying all of the potential ethical concerns. As a last resort, therapists may contact a state board of ethics with their ethical questions. It is always wise to document these consultations in the chance that the therapist's actions are questioned.

CONCLUSION

The use of creative modalities in therapy contributes to the quality and value of the field of therapy as a whole. It also provides clients with effective alternatives in their search for healing. Familiarity with ethical guidelines is essential to the practice of creative therapies, ensuring quality services that the public can trust.

Each therapist who provides creative techniques is called upon to be detailed, conscientious, and sometimes imaginative when providing ethical services. While creative modalities may, at times, require more diligence to ethical complexities than the traditional modalities, the results are rewarding. Consider sharing your unique experiences with ethical dilemmas with your colleagues in person and in publication, contributing to others' professional growth and to the body of knowledge related to the ethical practice of therapy (Larson, in press).

REFERENCES

American Art Therapy Association (2003). Ethical principles for art therapists. Retrieved September 10, 2004 from http://www.arttherapy.org/aboutarttherapy/ethicsfinal2003.pdf

American Counseling Association. (1995). *Code of ethics and standards of practice.* Alexandria, VA: Author.

American Dance Therapy Association. (1966). *ADTA code of ethical practice.* Columbia, MD: Author.

American Music Therapy Association (2003). *AMTA code of ethics.* Retrieved August 30, 2004 from http://www.musictherapy.org/ethics.html

American Psychological Association (2002). Ethical principles of psychologists and code of conduct. *American Psychologist, 57*(12), 1060–1073.

Association for Play Therapy (2000). Recommended play therapy practice guidelines. Retrieved September 7th, 2004 from http://www.a4pt.org/forms/guidelines.pdf.

Brooke, S.L. (2004). *Tools of the trade: A therapist's guide to art therapy assessments.* (2nd ed.). Springfield, IL: Charles C Thomas, Publisher, Ltd.

Brown, J. (2001). Towards a culturally centered music therapy practice. *Canadian Journal of Music Therapy, 8*(1), 11–24.

Bruscia, K. (1988). Standards for clinical assessment in the arts therapies. *The Arts in Psychotherapy, 15,* 5–10.

Clair, A. A. (1994). Ethics and values in music therapy for persons who are elderly. *Activities, Adaptation & Aging, 18*(3-4) 27–46.

Hammond, L. C. & Gantt, L. (1998). Using art in counseling: Ethical considerations. *Journal of Counseling and Development, 76*(3), 271–276.

Larson, K. (in press). Research ethics and the use of human subjects. In S. Lapan (Ed.), *An introduction to research.* Hillsdale, NJ: Lawrence Erlbaum.

Levick, M. F. (1995). The identity of the creative arts therapist: Guided by ethics. *The Arts in Psychotherapy, 22*(4), 283–295.

Malchiodi, C. A. (1998). *Understanding children's drawings.* New York: The Guilford Press.

Malchiodi, C. A. (2003). *Handbook of art therapy.* New York: The Guilford Press.

Miller, C. (2003). Ethical guidelines in research. In J. C. Thomas and H. Hersen (Eds.). *Understanding research in clinical and counseling psychology.* (pp. 271–293).

Moreno, J. L. (1962). *Code of ethics for group psychotherapy and psychodrama.* Oxford, England: Beacon House.

The National Association for Music Therapy (1987). *Code of Ethics.* Silver Spring, MD: Author.

National Fair Access Coalition on Testing (2000). *NAPT code of ethics.* Retrieved July 1, 2004 from http://www.fairaccess.org/naptE.htm

Sieber, J. E. (1992). *Planning ethically responsible research: A guide for students and internal review boards.* Newbury Park, CA: Sage Publications.

Willis, C. (1987). Legal and ethical issues of touch in dance/movement therapy. *American Journal of Dance Therapy, 10,* 41–53.

Biographical Statement

Kristin Larson, Ed.D., Licensed Clinical Psychologist, is a full-time Visiting Assistant Professor at Monmouth College and a Licensed Clinical Psychologist in Illinois. Her doctorate is in Counseling Psychology. Dr. Larson has been in clinical practice and trained counselors for 10 years, with her research focusing primarily in the area of ethics in research and practice.

APPENDIX

Sample Informed Consent Form

Artsy B. Therapist
1234 Dance Lane
Play, Alabama 12345

Qualifications

M.A. in Counseling and Guidance, University of Arizona 1991
M.A. in Drama and Art Therapy from Concordia University 1996
Member: American Art Therapy Association, since 1997
Certification: Licensed Professional Counselor, Illinois #12345
Private practice since 1991

Counseling Relationship

The purpose and goals of the counseling relationship shall be established collaboratively and reviewed periodically. Understand that the goals of counseling cannot be guaranteed. It is unethical for counselors to have dual relationships with their clients, therefore our contact will be limited to counseling sessions or emergency contact. In order to protect your confidentiality, I will allow you to initiate contact in any other setting.

Services

I am qualified to provide general counseling. I also have training in specific techniques including art therapy. The techniques used in therapy will be suggested by the therapist, determined collaboratively, and will depend on the presenting concern.

Art therapy utilizes art media, the creative process, and the client's reaction to the process and product to pursue counseling goals. The media used in art therapy can include paint, clay, paper, canvas, glue, pens, crayons, and a multitude of other materials.

The format can include painting, drawing, sculpting, and collage. The goals of art therapy include, but are not limited to, emotional catharsis, facilitating memories, developing self-awareness, and reducing anxiety.

Confidentiality

All disclosures within the counseling setting will be kept confidential and will only be released with a written consent or where required by law. Confidentiality includes the fact that you are obtaining services at this facility. Documentation of the counseling sessions will be kept in the form of a client file. These files are stored in a secure location and kept for 7 years following the termination of therapy, as required by law. Legal requirements for disclosure include any indication of harm to yourself or others, indication of neglect or abuse of a child, elderly, or disabled person, or a court order or subpoena. Insurance company or third-party payment requests will be documented and made available to the client. When possible, you will be notified of any legal requirement disclosure. Any artistic expressions that you produce are not intended for public display. Any type of public display must be agreed upon by both therapist and client, and client consent must be in writing.

Risks and Benefits

There are risks and benefits associated with any type of counseling services. Generally, the potential risks in therapy are related to experiencing strong emotions, remembering unpleasant memories, and changing the nature of significant relationships.

Art therapy is very effective in facilitating emotional expression and processing of memories which may be uncomfortable. Very strong emotions may be experienced during the process of creating art or while discussing the implications of the art. Be aware also that you may come in contact with a variety of art mediums. Please inform the therapist of you have any sensitivities or allergies. If you are not comfortable participating in creative or artistic techniques in pursuit of your counseling goals, alternative techniques will be offered.

Fees

You are responsible for payment for each session at the time of service. You are responsible for the full amount, regardless of insurance or third-party payment. Sessions are schedules for 50 minutes or 90 minutes. Please refer to the fee schedule for standard and sliding-scale fees. If necessary, please cancel 24 hours in advance of your appointment or you will be charged a fee.

Participation in these counseling services is completely voluntary. You have the right to refuse counseling or any particular technique at any time.

I have read this informed consent form and clarified any questions I amy have.

_____   _____
Client Signature   Date

I have discussed this informed consent form with the client and offered to clarify any questions

_____   _____
Therapist Signature   Date

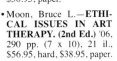